TEACHER'S PLANNING GUIDE

Project-Based Inquiry Science™

ENERGY

NSF

IT's ABOUT TIME®

HERFF JONES EDUCATION DIVISION

84 Business Park Drive, Armonk, NY 10504
Phone (914) 273-2233 Fax (914) 273-2227
www.its-about-time.com

Program Components

Student Edition	Durable Equipment Kit
Teacher's Planning Guide	Consumable Equipment Kit
Teacher's Resources Guide	

Project-Based Inquiry Science™ (PBIS) ©Copyright 2010: Georgia Tech Research Corporation.
Licensed exclusively to It's About Time, Herff Jones Education Division.

Printed and bound in the United States of America.

ISBN 978-1-58591-637-5
1 2 3 4 5 13 12 11 10 09

This project was supported, in part, by the **National Science Foundation** under grant nos. 0137807, 0527341, and 0639978.
Opinions expressed are those of the authors and not necessarily those of the National Science Foundation.

eliciting and steering discussion and collaboration among the students. At the completion of a project, students publicly exhibit what they have learned along with their solutions to the specific challenge. Personal reflection to help students learn from the experience is embedded in student activities, as are opportunities for assessment.

The curriculum will provide three years of piloted project-based inquiry materials for middle-school science. Individual curriculum units have been defined that cover the scope of the national content and process standards for the middle-school grades. Each Unit focuses on helping students acquire qualitative understanding of targeted science principles and move toward quantitative understanding, is infused with technology, and provides a foundation in reasoning skills, science content, and science process that will ready them for more advanced science. The curriculum as a whole introduces students to a wide range of investigative approaches in science (e.g., experimentation, modeling) and is designed to help them develop scientific reasoning skills that span those investigative approaches.

Technology can be used in project-based inquiry to make available to students some of the same kinds of tools and aids used by scientists in the field. These range from pencil-and-paper tools for organized data recording, collection, and management to software tools for analysis, simulation, modeling, and other tasks. Such infusion provides a platform for providing prompts, hints, examples, and other kinds of aids to students as they are engaging in scientific reasoning. The learning technologies and tools that are integrated into the curriculum offer essential scaffolding to students as they are developing their scientific reasoning skills, and are seamlessly infused into the overall completion of project activities and investigations.

Standards-Based Development

Development of each curriculum Unit begins by identifying the specific relevant national standards to be addressed. Each Unit has been designed to cover a specific portion of the national standards. This phase of development also includes an analysis of curriculum requirements across multiple states. Our intent is to deliver a product that will provide coverage of the content deemed essential on the widest practical scope and that will be easily adaptable to the needs of teachers across the country.

Once the appropriate standards have been identified, the development team works to define specific learning goals built from those standards, and takes into account conceptions and misunderstandings common among middle-school students. An orienting design challenge or driving question for investigation is chosen that motivates achieving those learning goals, and the team then sequences activities and the presentation of specific concepts so that students can construct an accurate understanding of the subject matter.

Inquiry-Based Design

The individual curriculum Units present two types of projects: engineering-design challenges and driving-question investigations. Design-challenge Units begin by presenting students with a scenario and problem and challenging them to design a device or plan that will solve the problem. Driving-question investigations begin by presenting students with a complex question with real-world implications. Students are challenged to develop answers to the questions. The scenario and problem in the design Units and the driving question in the investigation Units are carefully selected to lead the students into investigation of specific science concepts, and the solution processes are carefully structured to require use of specific scientific reasoning skills.

Pedagogical Rationale

Research shows that individual project-based learning units promote excitement and deep learning of the targeted concepts. However, achieving deep, flexible, transferable learning of cross-disciplinary content (e.g., the notion of a model, time scale, variable, experiment) and science practice requires a learning environment that consistently, persistently, and pervasively encourages the use of such content and practices over an extended period of time. By developing project-based inquiry materials that cover the spectrum of middle-school science content in a coherent framework, we provide this extended exposure to the type of learning environment most likely to produce competent scientific thinkers who are well grounded in their understanding of both basic science concepts and the standards and practices of science in general.

Evidence of Effectiveness

There is compelling evidence showing that a project-based inquiry approach meets this goal. Working at Georgia Tech, the University of Michigan, and Northwestern University, we have developed, piloted, and/or field-tested many individual project-based units. Our evaluation evidence shows that these materials engage students well and are manageable by teachers, and that students learn both content and process skills. In every summative evaluation, student performance on post-tests improved significantly from pretest performance (Krajcik, et al., 2000; Holbrook, et al., 2001; Gray et. al. 2001). For example, in the second year in a project-based classroom in Detroit, the average student at post-test scored at about the 95th percentile of the pre-test distribution. Further, we have repeatedly documented significant gains in content knowledge relative to other inquiry-based (but not project-based) instructional methods. In one set of results, performance by a project-based class

in Atlanta doubled on the content test while the matched comparison class (with an excellent teacher) experienced only a 20% gain (significance $p < .001$). Other comparisons have shown more modest differences, but project-based students consistently perform better than their comparisons. Most exciting about the Atlanta results is that results from performance assessments show that, within comparable student populations, project-based students score higher on all categories of problem-solving and analysis and are more sophisticated at science practice and managing a collaborative scientific investigation. Indeed, the performance of average-ability project-based students is often statistically indistinguishable from or better than performance of comparison honors students learning in an inquiry-oriented but not project-based classroom. The Chicago group also has documented significant change in process skills in project-based classrooms. Students become more effective in constructing and critiquing scientific arguments (Sandoval, 1998) and in constructing scientific explanations using discipline-specific knowledge, such as evolutionary explanations for animal behavior (Smith & Reiser, 1998).

Researchers at Northwestern have also investigated the changes in classroom practices that are elicited by project-based units. Analyses of the artifacts students produce indicate that students are engaging in ambitious learning practices, requiring weighing and synthesizing many results from complex analyses of data, and constructing scientific arguments that require synthesizing results from multiple complex analyses of data (Edelson et al, 1998; Reiser et al, 2001). Students are engaged in planning, performing, monitoring and revising their investigations, and reporting on their investigation processes as well as their results (Loh et al, 1998). In general, the classrooms engaging in project-based activities reveal substantial moves toward a scientific discourse community in which students focus on arguing from evidence, critiquing ideas, and conjecturing, rather than simply reporting on what they have read or been told (Tabak & Reiser, 1997).

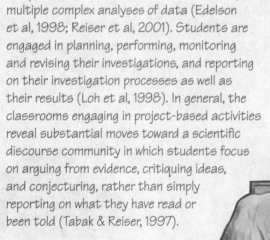

Introducing PBIS

What Do Scientists Do?

1) Scientists...address big challenges and big questions.

Students will find many different kinds of *Big Challenges* and *Questions* in *PBIS* Units. Some ask them to think about why something is a certain way. Some ask them to think about what causes something to change. Some challenge them to design a solution to a problem. Most are about things that can and do happen in the real world.

Understand the Big Challenge or Question

As students get started with each Unit, they will do activities that help them understand the *Big Question* or *Challenge* for that Unit. They will think about what they already know that might help them, and they will identify some of the new things they will need to learn.

Project Board

The *Project Board* helps you and your students keep track of their learning. For each challenge or question, they will use a *Project Board* to keep track of what they know, what they need to learn, and what they are learning. As they learn and gather evidence, they will record that on the *Project Board*. After they have answered each small question or challenge, they will return to the *Project Board* to record how what they have learned helps them answer the *Big Question* or *Challenge*.

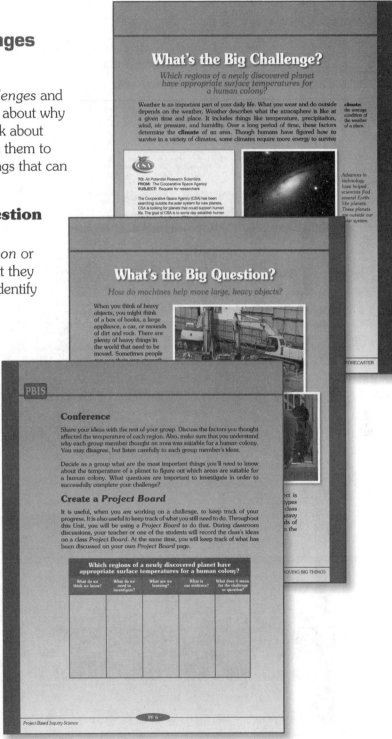

Learning Set 1

How Do Flowing Water and Land Interact in a Community?

The big question for this unit is *How does water quality affect the ecology of a community?* So far you have considered what you already know about what water quality is. Now you may be wondering where the water you use comes from. If you live in a city or town, the water you use may come from a river. You would want to know the quality of the water you are using. To do so, it is important to know how the water gets into the river. You also need to know what happens to the water as the river flows across the land.

You may have seen rivers or other water bodies near your home, your school, or in your city. Think about the river closest to where you live. Consider from where the water in the river comes. If you have traveled along the river, think about what the land around the river looks like. Try to figure out what human activities occur in the area. Speculate as to whether these activities affect the quality of water in the river.

To answer the big question, you need to break it down into smaller questions. In this *Learning Set*, you will investigate two smaller questions. As you will discover, these questions are very closely related and very hard to separate. The smaller questions are *How does water affect the land as it moves through the community?* and *How does land use affect water as it moves through a...*

Address the Big Challenge

How Do Scientists Work Together to Solve Problems?

You began this unit with the question, *how do scientists work together to solve problems?* You did several small challenges. As you worked on those challenges you learned about how scientists solve problems. You will now watch a video about real-life designers. You will see what the people in the video are doing that is like what you have been doing. Then you will think about all the different things you have been doing during this unit. Lastly, you will write about what you have learned about doing science and being a scientist.

Watch

IDEO Video

The video you will watch follows a group of designers at IDEO. IDEO is an innovation and design firm. In the video, they face the challenge of designing and building a new kind of shopping cart. These designers are doing many of the same things that you did. They also use other practices that you did not use. As you watch the video, record the interesting things you see.

After watching the video, answer the questions on the next page. You might want to look at them before you watch the video. Answering these questions should help you answer the big question of this unit: *How do scientists work together to solve problems?*

100

Learning Sets

Each Unit is composed of a group of *Learning Sets*, one for each of the smaller questions that needs to be answered to address the *Big Question* or *Challenge*. In each *Learning Set*, students will investigate and read to find answers to the *Learning Set's* question. They will also have a chance to share the results of their investigations with their classmates and work together to make sense of what they are learning. As students come to understand answers to the questions on the *Project Board*, you will record those answers and the evidence they collected. At the end of each *Learning Set*, they will apply their knowledge to the *Big Question* or *Challenge*.

Answer the Big Question/ Address the Big Challenge

At the end of each Unit, students will put everything they have learned together to tackle the *Big Question* or *Challenge*.

2) Scientists...address smaller questions and challenges.

What Students Do in a Learning Set

Understanding the Question or Challenge

At the start of each *Learning Set*, students will usually do activities that will help them understand the *Learning Set's* question or challenge and recognize what they already know that can help them answer the question or achieve the challenge. Usually, they will visit the *Project Board* after these activities and record on it the even smaller questions that they need to investigate to answer a *Learning Set's* question.

Investigate/Explore

There are many different kinds of investigations students might do to find answers to questions. In the *Learning Sets,* they might

- design and run experiments;
- design and run simulations;
- design and build models;
- examine large sets of data.

Don't worry if your students haven't done these things before. The text will provide them with lots of help in designing their investigations and in analyzing their data.

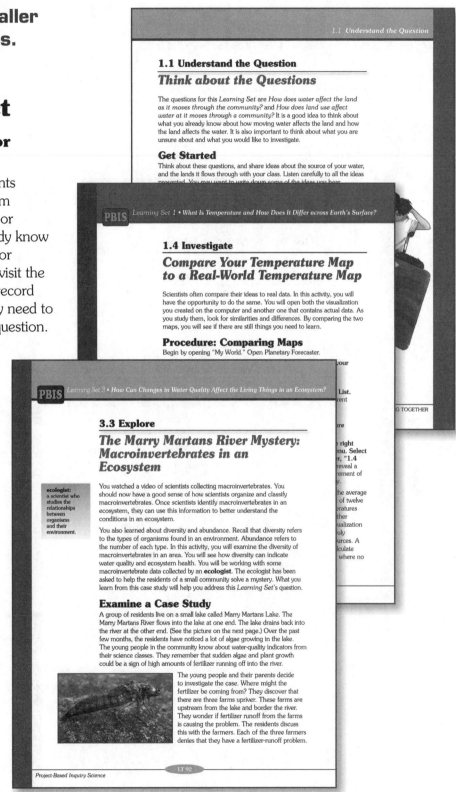

1.1 Understand the Question
Think about the Questions

The questions for this *Learning Set* are *How does water affect the land as it moves through the community?* and *How does land use affect water at it moves through a community?* It is a good idea to think about what you already know about how moving water affects the land and how the land affects the water. It is also important to think about what you are unsure about and what you would like to investigate.

Get Started
Think about these questions, and share ideas about the source of your water, and the lands it flows through with your class. Listen carefully to all the ideas presented. You may want to write down some of the ideas you hear.

Learning Set 1 • What Is Temperature and How Does It Differ across Earth's Surface?

1.4 Investigate
Compare Your Temperature Map to a Real-World Temperature Map

Scientists often compare their ideas to real data. In this activity, you will have the opportunity to do the same. You will open both the visualization you created on the computer and another one that contains actual data. As you study them, look for similarities and differences. By comparing the two maps, you will see if there are still things you need to learn.

Procedure: Comparing Maps
Begin by opening "My World." Open Planetary Forecaster.

Learning Set 3 • How Can Changes in Water Quality Affect the Living Things in an Ecosystem?

3.3 Explore
The Marry Martans River Mystery: Macroinvertebrates in an Ecosystem

ecologist: a scientist who studies the relationships between organisms and their environment.

You watched a video of scientists collecting macroinvertebrates. You should now have a good sense of how scientists organize and classify macroinvertebrates. Once scientists identify macroinvertebrates in an ecosystem, they can use this information to better understand the conditions in an ecosystem.

You also learned about diversity and abundance. Recall that diversity refers to the types of organisms found in an environment. Abundance refers to the number of each type. In this activity, you will examine the diversity of macroinvertebrates in an area. You will see how diversity can indicate water quality and ecosystem health. You will be working with some macroinvertebrate data collected by an **ecologist**. The ecologist has been asked to help the residents of a small community solve a mystery. What you learn from this case study will help you address this *Learning Set's* question.

Examine a Case Study
A group of residents live on a small lake called Marry Martans Lake. The Marry Martans River flows into the lake at one end. The lake drains back into the river at the other end. (See the picture on the next page.) Over the past few months, the residents have noticed a lot of algae growing in the lake. The young people in the community know about water-quality indicators from their science classes. They remember that sudden algae and plant growth could be a sign of high amounts of fertilizer running off into the river.

The young people and their parents decide to investigate the case. Where might the fertilizer be coming from? They discover that there are three farms upriver. These farms are upstream from the lake and border the river. They wonder if fertilizer runoff from the farms is causing the problem. The residents discuss this with the farmers. Each of the three farmers denies that they have a fertilizer-runoff problem.

LT 92

Project-Based Inquiry Science

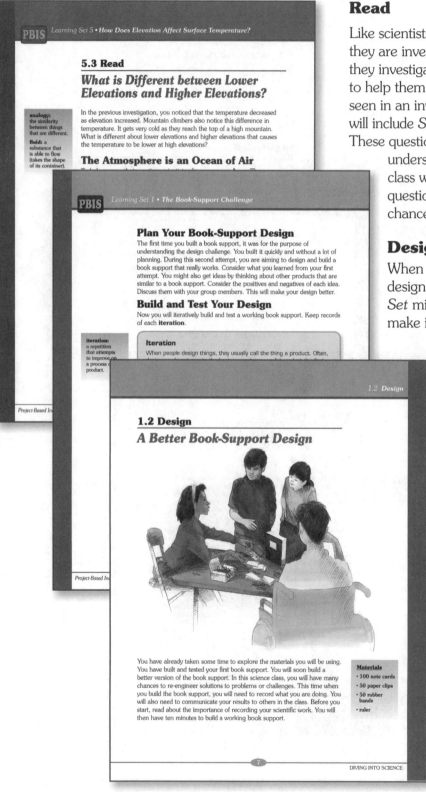

Read

Like scientists, students will also read about the science they are investigating. They will read a little bit before they investigate, but most of the reading they do will be to help them understand what they have experienced or seen in an investigation. Each time they read, the text will include *Stop and Think* questions after the reading. These questions will help students gauge how well they understand what they have read. Usually, the class will discuss the answers to *Stop and Think* questions before going on so that everybody has a chance to make sense of the reading.

Design and Build

When the *Big Challenge* for a Unit asks them to design something, the challenge in a *Learning Set* might also ask them to design something and make it work. Often students will design a part of the thing they will design and build for the *Big Challenge*. When a *Learning Set* challenges students to design and build something, they will do several things:

- identify what questions they need to answer to be successful

- investigate to find answers to those questions

- use those answers to plan a good design solution

- build and test their design

Because designs don't always work the way one wants them to, students will usually do a design challenge more than once. Each time through, they will test their design. If their design doesn't work as well as they would like, they will determine why it is not working and identify other things they need to investigate to make it work better. Then, they will learn those things and try again.

Explain and Recommend

A big part of what scientists do is explain, or try to make sense of why things happen the way they do. An explanation describes why something is the way it is or behaves the way it does. An explanation is a statement one makes built from claims (what you think you know), evidence (from an investigation) that supports the claim, and science knowledge. As they learn, scientists get better at explaining. You will see that students get better, too, as they work through the *Learning Sets*.

A recommendation is a special kind of claim—one where you advise somebody about what to do. Students will make recommendations and support them with evidence, science knowledge, and explanations.

3.5 Explain
Create an Explanation

After scientists get results from an investigation, they try to make a claim. They base their claim on what their evidence shows. They also use what they already know to make their claim. They explain why their claim is valid. The purpose of a science explanation is to help others understand the following:

* what was learned from a set of investigations
* why the scientists reached this conclusion

Later, other scientists will use these explanations to help them explain other phenomena. The explanations will also help them predict what will happen in other situations.

You will do the same thing now. Your claim will be the trend you found in your experiment. You will use data you collected and science knowledge you have read to create a good explanation. This will help you decide whether your claim is valid. You will be reporting the results of the investigation to your classmates. With a good explanation that matches your claim, you can convince them that your claim is valid.

Because your understanding of the science of forces is not complete, you may not be able to fully explain your results. But you will use what you have read to come up with your best explanation. Scientists finding out about new things do the same thing. When they only partly understand something, it is impossible for them to form a "perfect" explanation. They do the best they can based on what they understand. As they learn more, they make their explanations better. This is what you will do now and what you will be doing throughout PBIS. You will explain your results the best you can based

---

4.3 Explain and Recommend
Explanations and Recommendations about Parachutes

As you did after your whirligig experiments, you will spend some time now explaining your results. You will also try to come up with recommendations. Remember that explanations include your claims, the evidence for your claims, and the science you know that can help you understand the claim. A recommendation is a statement about what someone should do. The best recommendations also have evidence, science, and an explanation associated with them. In the *Whirligig Challenge*, you created explanations and recommendations separately from each other. This time you will work on both at the same time.

Create and Share Your Recommendation and Explanation

Work with your group. Use the hints on the *Create Your Explanation* pages to make your first attempt at explaining your results. You'll read about parachute science later. After that, you will probably want to revise your explanations. Right now, use the science you learned during the *Whirligig Challenge* for your first attempt.

Write your recommendation. It should be about designing a slow-falling parachute. Remember that it should be written so that it will help someone else. They should be able to apply what you have learned about the effects of your variable. If you are having trouble, review the example in *Learning Set 3*.

Create Your Explanation

Name: _____ Date: _____

Use this page to explain the lesson of your recent investigations.

Write a brief summary of the results from your investigation. You will use this summary to help you write your Explanation.

Claim – a statement of what you understand or a conclusion that you have reached from an investigation or a set of investigations.

Evidence – data collected during investigations and trends in that data.

Science knowledge – knowledge about how things work. You may have learned this through reading, talking to an expert, discussion, or other experiences.

Write your Explanation using the **Claim**, **Evidence** and **Science knowledge**.

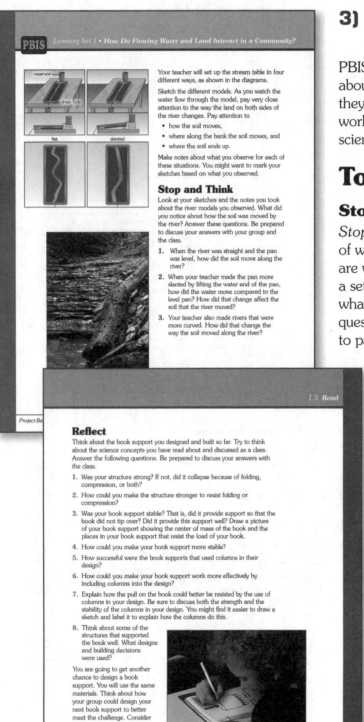

3) Scientists...reflect in many different ways.

PBIS provides guidance to help students think about what they are doing and to recognize what they are learning. Doing this often as they are working will help students be successful student scientists.

Tools for Making Sense

Stop and Think

Stop and Think sections help students make sens of what they have been doing in the section they are working on. *Stop and Think* sections include a set of questions to help students understand what they have just read or done. Sometimes the questions will remind them of something they nee to pay more attention to. Sometimes they will hel students connect what they have just read to things they already know. When there is a *Stop and Think* in the text, students will work individually or with a partner to answer the questions, and then the whole class will discuss the answers.

Reflect

Reflect sections help students connect wha they have just done with other things they have read or done earlier in the Unit (or in another Unit). When there is a *Reflect* in the text, students will work individually or with a partner or small group to answer the questions. Then, the whole class will discus the answers. You may want to ask students to answer *Reflect* questions for homework

Analyze Your Data

Whenever students have to analyze data, the text will provide hints about how to do that and what to look for.

Mess About

"Messing about" is a term that comes from design. It means exploring the materials to be used for designing or building something or examining something that works like what is to be designed. Messing about helps students discover new ideas—and it can be a lot of fun. The text will usually give them ideas about things to notice as they are messing about.

What's the Point?

At the end of each *Learning Set*, students will find a summary, called *What's the Point?*, of the important information from the *Learning Set*. These summaries can help students remember how what they did and learned is connected to the *Big Question* or *Challenge* they are working on.

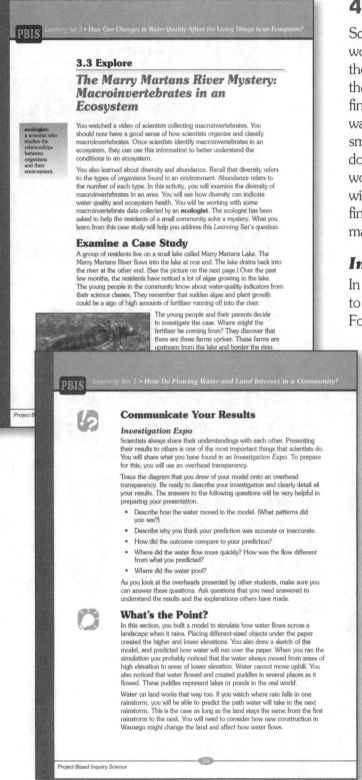

4) Scientists...collaborate.

Scientists never do all their work alone. They work with other scientists (collaborate) and share their knowledge. *PBIS* helps students by giving them lots of opportunities for sharing their findings, ideas, and discoveries with others (the way scientists do). Students will work together in small groups to investigate, design, explain, and do other science activities. Sometimes they will work in pairs to figure out things together. They will also have lots of opportunities to share their findings with the rest of their classmates and make sense together of what they are learning.

Investigation Expo

In an *Investigation Expo*, small groups report to the class about an investigation they've done. For each *Investigation Expo*, students will make a poster detailing what they were trying to learn from their investigation, what they did, their data, and their interpretation of the data. The text gives them hints about what to present and what to look for in other groups' presentations. *Investigation Expos* are always followed by discussions about the investigations and about how to do science well. You may want to ask students to write a lab report following an investigation.

Plan Briefing/Solution Briefing/ Idea Briefing

Briefings are presentations of work in progress. They give students a chance to get advice from their classmates that can help them move forward. During a *Plan Briefing*, students present their plans to the class. They might be plans for an experiment for solving a problem or achieving a challenge. During a *Solution Briefing*, students present their solutions in progress and ask the class to help them make their solutions better. During an *Idea Briefing*, students present their ideas, including their evidence in support of their plans, solutions, or ideas. Often, they will prepare posters to help them make their presentation. Briefings are almost always followed by discussions of their investigations and how they will move forward.

Solution Showcase

Solution Showcases usually happen near the end of a Unit. During a *Solution Showcase*, students show their classmates their finished products—either their answer to a question or solution to a challenge. Students will also tell the class why they think it is a good answer or solution, what evidence and science they used to get to their solution, and what they tried along the way before getting to their answers or solutions. Sometimes a *Solution Showcase* is followed by a competition. It is almost always followed by a discussion comparing and contrasting the different answers and solutions groups have come up with. You may want to ask students to write a report or paper following a *Solution Showcase*.

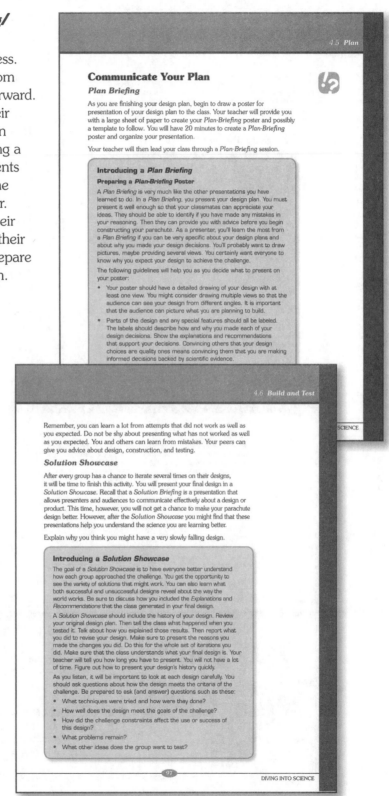

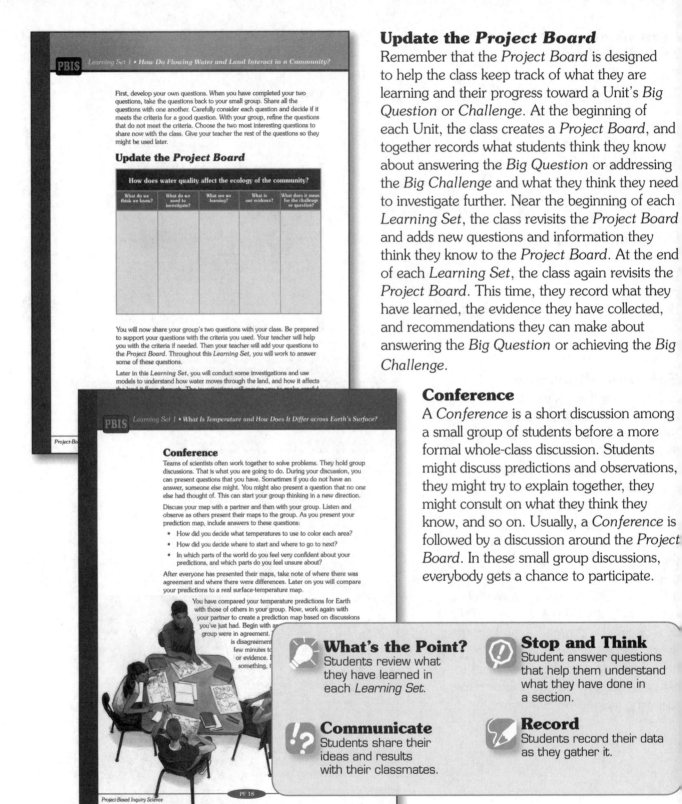

Update the *Project Board*

Remember that the *Project Board* is designed to help the class keep track of what they are learning and their progress toward a Unit's *Big Question* or *Challenge*. At the beginning of each Unit, the class creates a *Project Board*, and together records what students think they know about answering the *Big Question* or addressing the *Big Challenge* and what they think they need to investigate further. Near the beginning of each *Learning Set*, the class revisits the *Project Board* and adds new questions and information they think they know to the *Project Board*. At the end of each *Learning Set*, the class again revisits the *Project Board*. This time, they record what they have learned, the evidence they have collected, and recommendations they can make about answering the *Big Question* or achieving the *Big Challenge*.

Conference

A *Conference* is a short discussion among a small group of students before a more formal whole-class discussion. Students might discuss predictions and observations, they might try to explain together, they might consult on what they think they know, and so on. Usually, a *Conference* is followed by a discussion around the *Project Board*. In these small group discussions, everybody gets a chance to participate.

What's the Point?
Students review what they have learned in each *Learning Set*.

Stop and Think
Student answer questions that help them understand what they have done in a section.

Communicate
Students share their ideas and results with their classmates.

Record
Students record their data as they gather it.

NOTES

NOTES

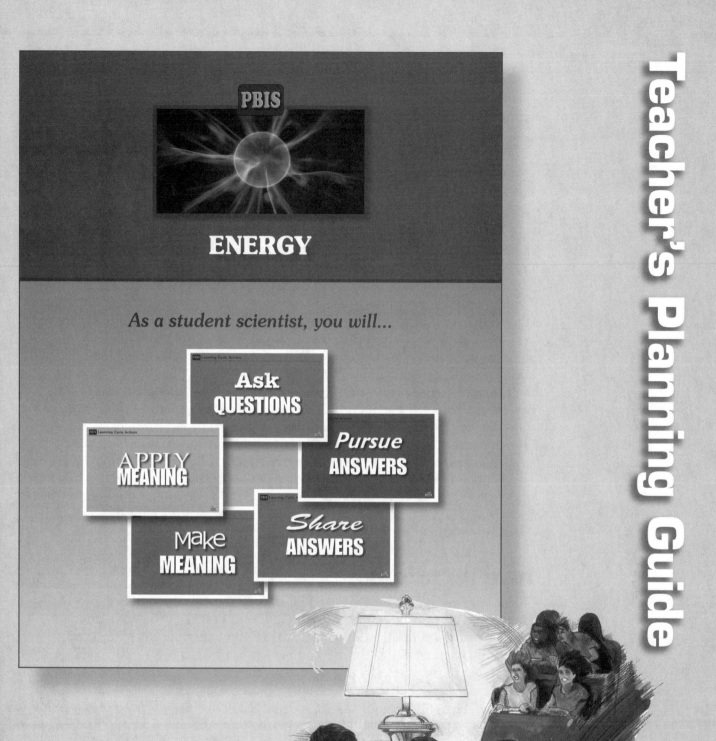

PBIS

ENERGY

As a student scientist, you will...

Ask QUESTIONS

APPLY MEANING

Pursue ANSWERS

Make MEANING

Share ANSWERS

ENERGY

Content

In *Energy,* students focus on the *Big Challenge: Design a Rube Goldberg machine to turn off a light.* After being presented with a basic description of energy, students are given opportunities to examine examples of energy in order to identify evidence of energy and changes in energy. As they learn to look for changes in matter as indicators, they are introduced to different forms of energy individually. Each time they consider a new form of energy, students have an opportunity to look for examples in a Rube Goldberg design and then apply the concepts to their own design. Throughout the Unit, students collaborate as they run investigations and construct explanations and make recommendations. They work iteratively to plan designs and revise their designs. In *Learning Set 1,* students examine a radiometer along with household objects for evidence of energy. In *Learning Set 2,* students begin to differentiate between kinetic and potential energy. In *Learning Set 3,* students are introduced to examples of chemical and thermal energy. In *Learning Set 4,* students explore sound and light energy. In *Learning Set 5,* students investigate electrical and magnetic energy. In *Learning Set 6,* students tie concepts together to consider changes in energy. Between *Learning Sets* and at the end of the Unit, students use what they are learning to propose a design for a device that will turn off a light.

Investigations

Students investigate types of energy and evidence by which they can be identified as they address the *Big Challenge* and make recommendations for improving their initial designs for a machine that will turn off a light. In *Learning Set 1,* students observe the motion of a radiometer under different conditions to discover how energy causes the device to move. They go on to examine changes that occur in familiar objects, such as pop-up toasters. These demonstrations and investigations are performed for the purpose of observing indicators of the existence of energy. In *Learning Set 2,* students observe changes that occur in various objects, including wind-up toys, Newton's cradle, and bouncy balls as a means of comparing amounts of kinetic energy. They go on to develop ways to quantify amounts of kinetic energy, and conduct similar investigations involving gravitational and elastic potential energy. In *Learning Set 3,* students examine some of the objects they have already observed, this time looking for indicators of chemical and thermal energy. Students then investigate changes in energy associated with a hand warmer and water at different temperatures. They go on to complete several chemical reactions and investigate factors that affect chemical reactions. In *Learning Set 4,* students examine objects that involve either sound or light energy in varied explorations.

74 class periods

A class period is considered to be one 40 to 50 minute class.

They investigate the transfer of sound energy from their voices, the motion of mechanical waves, factors that affect the intensity of light energy, and the wave nature of light. In *Learning Set 5,* students build a simple circuit and an electromagnet. They manipulate their circuits to control the operation of a bulb and discover the uses of a switch. They then construct a galvanometer, investigate batteries with different voltages, compare series and parallel circuits, and construct a battery or generator. In *Learning Set 6,* students investigate changes in energy through a variety of situations and examine energy conservation.

Nature of Science

As students learn about the challenge, they are exposed to the work of previous scientists. They see that while scientists work with the information available to develop the best possible theories, they modify their ideas as new information becomes available. In *Learning Set 2,* students are introduced to the work of Galileo. From this, they come to understand changes in gravitational potential energy so they can apply the concept to their own investigations. In *Learning Set 4,* students learn about the discoveries of Sir Isaac Newton to recognize that white light can be separated into colors by a prism. In *Learning Set 5,* students are introduced to the work of Thales, George Bose, and Benjamin Franklin. Through this they discover the process through which these scientists learned about electrical energy. They go on to find out about how Hans Oersted discovered the relationship between electricity and magnetism, and what Thomas Edison and George Westinghouse believed about the transmission of electrical energy.

Students engage in making claims and supporting those claims with evidence through the Unit. They repeatedly propose a design, support elements of their design, and provide the best explanations for the use of energy in their designs. They use what they analyze from Rube Goldberg designs and what they discover through investigations to add steps to their designs. This gives them experience using the same process as real scientists. Performing investigations with their groups and sharing their findings with the class, students learn that it is effective to collaborate and share their knowledge with the scientific community. While engaging in the social practices of scientists, students realize the value of sharing and building on each others' ideas as well as assigning credit to others as appropriate.

Artifacts

Throughout the Unit, students use a *Project Board* to keep track of what they are learning, the evidence they are collecting, questions they need to investigate, and recommendations for addressing the challenge. The *Project Board* helps them keep track of progress toward addressing the *Big Challenge.*

Students use a variety of charts and graphs in this Unit to keep track of and to analyze their data. In *Learning Set 2*, students graph data to identify trends in changes that occur to gravitational potential energy as different factors are changed. In *Learning Set 3*, students use Temperature-Time line graphs and bar graphs to analyze changes in temperature among samples of water. They also complete a chart comparing amounts of thermal energy between familiar objects. In *Learning Set 4*, students work together to complete a chart exploring factors that affect sound. They go on to use a chart along with a graph to relate the intensity of light to different sources. In *Learning Set 5*, students use a chart to summarize information about electricity for an *Investigation Expo*. In *Learning Set 6*, students graph data representing energy transformations in bouncing balls and rolling marbles.

Targeted Concepts, Skills, and Nature of Science	Section
Criteria and constraints are important in determining effective scientific procedures and answering scientific questions.	LS 1, ABC
Scientists must keep accurate and descriptive records of what they do so they can share their work with others and consider what they did, why they did it, and what they want to do next.	LS 1, LS 2, LS 4
Scientists often work together and then share their findings. Sharing findings makes new information available and helps scientists refine their ideas and build on others' ideas. When another person's or group's idea is used, credit needs to be given.	LS 1, LS 3, LS 4, LS 5, LS 6, ABC
Studying the work of different scientists provides understanding of scientific inquiry and reminds students that science is a human endeavor.	LS 2, LS 4, LS 5, LS 6
Scientists make claims (conclusions) based on evidence (trends in data) from reliable investigations.	LS 2, LS 6
Scientific knowledge is developed through observations, recording and analysis of data, and development of explanations based on evidence.	LS 2, ABC
Energy is the ability to cause change or do work.	LS 1, LS 2, LS 4, LS 5, LS 6
Energy exists in different forms and can be changed from one form to another	LS 1, LS 2, LS 6
Energy is neither created nor destroyed in ordinary processes.	LS 2, LS 6
Kinetic energy is associated with the motion of an object.	LS 1, LS 2, LS 6

Targeted Concepts, Skills, and Nature of Science	Section
Potential energy is stored energy associated with position or condition.	LS 1, LS 2, LS 3, LS 6
Visible light is a small band within the electromagnetic spectrum, which is energy that travels in the form of waves.	LS 1
Electrical energy is the flow of charges through a circuit.	LS1
Sound is the transfer of energy as longitudinal waves that cannot travel through a vacuum.	LS 1, LS 4
Thermal energy is the energy of the particles of matter.	LS 1, LS 3
Heat is the transfer of thermal energy from a substance at a higher temperature to a substance at a lower temperature.	LS 1, LS 3
The addition or removal of heat may result in a temperature change in a system.	LS3
Energy is absorbed or released during a chemical reaction.	LS3
Every substance can be described by its specific heat.	LS3
Large bodies of water moderate nearby climates.	LS3
Heat is transferred by conduction, convection, and radiation.	LS3
The Sun is a source of heat energy.	LS3
Solar energy is a renewable energy resource.	LS3
Geothermal energy is a renewable energy resource from Earth.	LS3
During a chemical change, the original substances are changed into new substances with different properties.	LS3
Visible light is a small band within the electromagnetic spectrum, which is energy that travels in the form of waves.	LS4
The ear is the human organ that detects sound.	LS4
Mechanical waves can be described as longitudinal waves or transverse waves.	LS4

Targeted Concepts, Skills, and Nature of Science	Section
The speed of sound depends on the medium through which it travels.	LS4
Waves involve a transfer of energy from one place to another.	LS4
Light can be described by a particle nature.	LS4
Light can be described by its intensity.	LS4
Light can be described by a wave nature.	LS4
White light is made up of different colors of light.	LS4
The electromagnetic spectrum arranges radiation in terms of frequency and wavelength.	LS4
Light travels at different speeds in different materials.	LS4
The eye is the human organ that detects light.	LS4
Light interacts with surfaces through reflection and refraction.	LS4
Electrical energy can flow through circuits.	LS5
Electrical energy is the flow of charges through a circuit.	LS5
Like electric charges exert a force of repulsion whereas unlike electric charges exert a force of attraction.	LS5
Electrical energy is used by appliances and equipment.	LS5
Like poles of a magnet repel whereas unlike poles attract.	LS5
An electric current flowing through a coil of wire can be used to produce an electromagnet.	LS5
A galvanometer is used to measure electric current.	LS5
Magnetic forces are exerted in the magnetic field around a magnet, with the forces being strongest near the poles.	LS5
Electricity gives rise to magnetism and magnetism gives rise to electricity.	LS5

Targeted Concepts, Skills, and Nature of Science	Section
An electric current flowing through a coil of wire can be used to produce an electromagnet.	LS5
The voltage of a battery determines the amount of electric current in a circuit.	LS5
Electric circuits can be wired in series or in parallel.	LS5
A battery converts stored chemical energy into electrical energy.	LS5
Conductors allow electric charges to flow through them easily whereas insulators limit the flow of charge through them.	LS5
The amount of current flowing through a circuit depends on voltage and resistance.	LS5
A generator transforms mechanical energy into electrical energy.	LS5
Electric current can be direct or alternating.	LS5
Some energy resources are renewable, such as wind energy, hydroelectric energy, solar energy, biomass energy, geothermal energy, and tidal energy whereas others are nonrenewable, such as fossil fuel energy and nuclear energy.	LS6
Nuclear reactions include fission during large nuclei are split apart, and fusion during which smaller nuclei are joined together.	LS6
During nuclear reactions, small amounts of mass are converted into large amounts of energy.	LS6

NOTES

....

....

....

....

ENERGY

Unit Materials List

Quantities for groups of 4-6 students.		
Unit Durable Group Items	**Section**	**Quantity**
Flashlight	1.1, 1.2, 2.6, 4.5, 4.5	1
Bouncy ball	1.2, 2.1, 2.6, 6.2, 6.3, 6.4	2
Windup toy, pkg. of 2	1.2, 2.1, 2.6	1
Steel ball, 1 in.	2.3, 2.5	1
Steel ball, ½ in.	2.3, 2.5, 6.2, 6.3, 6.4	2
Ruler with groove	2.5, 4.2, 4.5, 5.1	1
Glass ball	2.5	1
Marble	2.5	1
Reusable hand warmer	3.1	1
Thermometer	3.2	2
Beaker, 1000 mL	3.2	2
Stopwatch	1.1, 3.2, 3.5, 4.3	1
Plastic graduated cylinder, 100 mL	3.2, 3.5, 3.6	1
Film canister with cap	3.6	2
Magnet, small bar	5.1, 5.2	2
Nail, 12d	5.1, 5.2, 5.6	1
Battery Holder For D-Cell, stackable	5.1, 5.2, 5.3, 5.4, 5.5	2
Alligator clip leads	5.1, 5.2, 5.3, 5.4, 5.5, 5.6	5
Switch, SPST	5.1, 5.2, 5.3, 5.4, 5.5	1

Project-Based Inquiry Science

Quantities for groups of 4-6 students.

Unit Durable Group Items	Section	Quantity
Light bulb holder	5.1, 5.2, 5.3, 5.5	2
Compass	5.3, 5.4, 5.6	1

Quantities for 5 classes of 8 groups.

Unit Durable Classroom Items	Section	Quantity
Rube Goldberg Poster, Set of 8	Unit Intro, 1.BBC, 2.6, 4.1, 6, 6.4.2, 6.3, 6.BBC	1
Project Board, laminated	Unit Intro, 1.1, 1.2, 1.BBC, 2.1, 2.4, 2.5, 2.6, 2.BBC, 3.1, 3.4 3.5, 3.6, 3.BBC, 4.1, 4.2, 4.4, 4.5, 4.6, 4.BBC, 5.1, 5.2, 5.5, 5.6, 5.BBC, 6.1, 6.2, 6.3, 6.4, 6.6, 6.BBC	5
Project Board transparency	Unit Intro, 1.1, 1.2, 1.BBC, 2.1, 2.4, 2.5, 2.6, 2.BBC, 3.1, 3.4 3.5, 3.6, 3.BBC, 4.1, 4.2, 4.4, 4.5, 4.6, 4.BBC, 5.1, 5.2, 5.5, 5.6, 5.BBC, 6.1, 6.2, 6.3, 6.4, 6.6, 6.BBC	1
Physical Science Content DVD	Unit Intro, 2.2	1
Radiometer	1.1	1
Meterstick	1.1, 2.3, 3.6, 4.5, 6.2, 6.3	4
Yo-yo	1.2	2
Newton's cradle	1.2, 2.1, 2.6	1
Noise maker	1.2, 2.6	2
Spring Scale, 0-10N	1.2, 2.6	2

Quantities for 5 classes of 8 groups.		
Unit Durable Classroom Items	**Section**	**Quantity**
100g mass	1.2, 2.6	2
Pop-up toy	1.2, 2.6	2
Tuning Forks, Set of 4 (256, 320, 384, 512 hertz)	1.2, 2.6, 4.1, 4.2	2
Safety scissors	1.2, 2.6, 4.2	2
Weighing boat, pkg. of 25	2.5	1
Triple-beam balance	2.5, 3.2, 3.5	2
Rubber band, #64	2.6, 4.2, 5.2	1
Plastic Spoon	3.5	8
Funnel	3.5	1
Erlenmeyer Flask, 125 mL	3.5	4
Clear plastic cup, 10 oz	3.5	4
Wind-up tape measure	3.6	1
Colored filter paper	4.1	1
Light bulb socket with switch and 40-W bulb	4.1, 4.5	4
25-W bulb	4.1, 4.5	2
60-W frosted bulb	4.1, 4.5	2
Solar cell	4.1	2
Motor or propeller blade	4.1	2
Propeller blade, 5 in.	4.1	2
Cork stopper, # 3, pkg. of 100	4.2	1

Quantities for 5 classes of 8 groups.		
Unit Durable Classroom Items	**Section**	**Quantity**
Spool of thread	4.2	1
Coiled spring, heavy duty	4.3	2
Rope, 23 ft	4.3	2
Ball, 6 in.	4.5	1
Paper clips, pkg. of 100	5.1, 5.2	1
Nickel-plated magnet, ½ in.	5.6	8
Magnet wire, # 30, 300 ft	5.6	1
Galvanometer, 0-500 ma	5.6	1
Sand, 5 lb	6.2	1
Track	6.2, 6.3, 6.4	2
Track assembly	6.2, 6.3, 6.4	2
C-clamp	6.2, 6.3, 6.4	2

Quantities for groups of 4-6 students.		
Unit Consumable Group Items	**Section**	**Quantity**
Alkaline battery, D-cell	1.1, 1.2, 2.6, 4.5, 5.1, 5.2, 5.3, 5.4, 5.5	4
Mini light bulb	5.1, 5.2, 5.3, 5.5	3
Sandpaper, 220 grit	5.1, 5.2, 5.3, 5.4, 5.6	1
Resistor Ohm 15-10 Wt	5.4	2
Battery, 6-V, Heavy Duty	5.4	1

Quantities for groups of 4-6 students.		
Unit Consumable Classroom Items	**Section**	**Quantity**
Colored markers, Set of 8 colors	1.2, 2.5, 3.2, 3.6, 4.2, 6.3, 6.6	6
Restickable easel pad	2.5, 3.6, 4.2, 6.2, 6.6	5
Masking tape	2.3, 2.5, 2.6, 3.2, 3.6, 4.2, 4.5, 5.1, 5.2, 5.3, 5.6, 6.2, 6.3	2
Straws, pkg. of 100	3.2	1
Vinegar	3.5	2
Baking Soda	3.5	1
Balloon	3.5, 4.1	60
Salt	3.5	1
Effervescent antacid tablets, pkg. of 2	3.5, 3.6	85
Plastic wrap	4.2	1
Electrical tape	5.5	1
Magnet wire, #24, 60-ft roll	5.1, 5.2, 5.3, 5.4, 5.6	4
Graph paper	2.5, 3.2, 3.6, 6.2	4

Additional Items Needed Not Supplied	**Section**	**Quantity**
Pop-up toaster	1.2	1 per classroom
Piece of bread	1.2	1 per classroom
Piece of paper	1.2, 3.2, 4.2, 4.3	1 per group
Wooden rod for tuning forks	1.2, 4.1, 4.2	2 per classroom

Additional Items Needed Not Supplied	Section	Quantity
Access to large floor space	2.3, 4.3	1 per classroom
Paper cup	2.3, 2.5	2 per group or 2 per classroom if done as a demo
Erasable marker	2.3, 3.2, 4.5, 6.2	1 per group
Books	2.5, 6.2, 6.3, 6.4	6 per group
Extension and compression springs	2.6	4 each per classroom
Access to 3 bags of frozen water, 100 g each	3.2	4 per classroom
Access to warm water	3.2, 3.5, 3.6, 4.1, 4.6	1 L per group
Access to cold water	3.2	1600 mL per classroom
Roll of paper towels	3.2, 3.5, 3.6, 4.1, 4.6	1 per classroom
Dull stained pennies	3.5	50 per classroom
Steel screw	3.5	4 per classroom
Set of wind chimes with hollow tubes	4.1	2 per classroom
Grains of uncooked rice	4.2	5 per group
Small jar	4.2, 4.6	1 per group
Thin matching rubber bands	4.2	2 per group
Cans of different heights open at one end	4.2	4 per group
Poster board, with a 2 cm x 2 cm opening in the center	4.5	1 per group
Poster board, laminated, with a 2 cm x 2 cm grid	4.5	1 per group

Additional Items Needed Not Supplied	Section	Quantity
Stereo headphones	5.6	1 per group
Large lemons	5.6	2 per group
Galvanized nails	5.6	2 per group
Copper coins	5.6	2 per group
Plastic knife	5.6	1 per group
Open ended cardboard box, 8 cm x 3.5 cm	5.6	1 per group

NOTES

What's the Big Challenge?

Design a Rube Goldberg Machine to Turn Off a Light

◀ *2 class periods*

A class period is considered to be one 40 to 50 minute class.

Overview

Students are introduced to the *Big Challenge* of the Unit: *Design a Rube Goldberg machine to turn off a light*. They begin by considering the concept of energy in everyday examples. To better understand the *Big Challenge*, students are introduced to Rube Goldberg as a person and then investigate some of his designs using videos and diagrams. Students then have an opportunity to tie the concept of energy to the Rube Goldberg machines they investigated. Students identify criteria and constraints, develop questions about energy and work, and record what they think they know and what they need to find out on the *Project Board*.

Targeted Concepts, Skills, and Nature of Science	Performance Expectations
Criteria and constraints are important in determining effective scientific procedures and answering scientific questions.	Students identify the criteria and constraints of the *Big Challenge* and organize them into a table to refer to while working throughout the Unit.
Scientists must keep accurate and descriptive records of what they do so they can share their work with others and consider what they did, why they did it, and what they want to do next.	Students record their ideas and questions about the *Big Challenge* on the *Project Board*.
Scientists often work together and then share their findings. Sharing findings makes new information available and helps scientists refine their ideas and build on others' ideas. When another person's or group's idea is used, credit needs to be given.	Students share their individual ideas with their group and their group's ideas with the class as they consider how energy is related to Rube Goldberg machines and to everyday activities.

Materials	
1 per student	*Energy Types* page
	Rube Goldberg Videos page
	Rube Goldberg Sketch page
	Project Board page
1 per class	Class *Project Board*

Homework Options

Reflection

- **Science Content:** Name some devices you use every day to perform some task. *(Students might list devices as simple as a doorknob or as complex as a school bus.)*

- **Science Content:** How do the devices you use help you? *(Students might mention that they save time or they make a task easier to do.)*

NOTES

....

....

....

....

....

....

....

....

What's the Big Challenge?

Design a Rube Goldberg machine to turn off a light.

The word energy is used every day in many different ways. You have probably heard people say, *"I don't have the energy to clean my room," "Turn off the lights to save energy," "The energy from these batteries will make the flashlight light up,"* or *"People must conserve energy."* To what, exactly, are they referring? Every day you observe many different kinds of energy, and you probably do not even think about it. A few common examples are shown on the opposite page.

Look carefully at the picture. Do you think the soccer players have enough energy to play harder? Where does their energy come from? How can you know if the oven has enough energy to finish baking the cupcakes? Where does the oven's energy come from? Candles on a birthday cake produce both heat and light. Are heat and light energy? Where does this energy come from, and where does it go?

In this Unit, you will learn how to identify the presence of energy, and many different types of energy, and the ways energy is **transformed** from one type into another type of energy. Energy transformations are key to how work gets done. And that is the important word—*work*. You will be encountering this word many times in this Unit. Work and energy are closely related to one another.

transform: to convert from one form into another form.

Look at the *Big Challenge* in this science Unit: *Design a Rube Goldberg machine to turn off a light.* This project will be a lot of fun. You will give your imagination the freedom to be creative. You will not be able to design this machine right away. First, you will need to learn what energy is, what kinds of energy are in your world, and how one type of energy can be transformed into another type.

Welcome to Energy.
Enjoy your journey as a student scientist.

EN 3

ENERGY

What's the Big Challenge?

Design a Rube Goldberg machine to turn off a light.

5 min

Students are introduced to the Big Challenge.

META NOTES

Students unfamiliar with Rube Goldberg might begin asking about him right away. Assure them that they will have an opportunity to learn about him and his inventions later on in the Unit.

◯ Engage

Challenge students to make a list of words that have more than one meaning. Students should list homonyms, such as season, bowl, pound, and toll. Explain that, in science, words often have different meanings than they do in everyday conversation. Energy is an example of such a word.

*A class period is considered to be one 40 to 50 minute class.

Begin by eliciting students' ideas about what energy is and the different forms in which it exists. Allow students to share all ideas at this point, even if they are incorrect. You may want to keep a list that you can review later, after students have learned about energy.

"What do you think energy is? What are different forms of energy? When do you use energy?"

NOTES

Think About the *Big Challenge*
Design a Rube Goldberg machine to turn off a light.

Usually, when you turn off a light switch, you place a finger on the switch and use muscles to push down the switch. Your muscles use *energy* to do the *work* of pushing down a switch. You may not know exactly what the words energy and work mean. For now, if you think about energy as the ability to cause change and work as applying energy to objects, you will be able to get started understanding energy and achieving the challenge. By the end of this Unit, you will be able to give scientific definitions for these two words.

You will be learning more about energy and work as you address the *Big Challenge*. The *Big Challenge* in this Unit is to design a complex, multi-step machine that does the simple job of turning off a light. Designing this machine will allow you to use your imagination and creativity. If people think about how your machine will actually work, they may find it amusing or even laugh out loud. However, the task of designing the machine is serious. Your machine will use several types of energy to do the job of turning off a light. It will *transform* one kind of energy into another kind at each and every step.

Children playing on this merry-go-round provide the energy to power a water pump.

To prepare for addressing this challenge, you will first think about what you already know about energy. You cannot always see energy, but you can see the effects of energy transformations. Any time you observe a change in an object, you know that energy is being transformed.

A good example is a battery. A battery has stored energy, but you cannot see the energy in a battery. A "dead" battery looks exactly like a battery that is fully energized. Only by observing a change—a flashlight coming on, a toy car moving across the floor, or a car's engine starting up—can you know that the battery had stored energy, and that some of the energy has been used to perform a task.

EN 4

Project-Based Inquiry Science

Think About the Big Challenge

10 min

Students review examples of activities that involve energy.

△ Guide

Read through the student text as a class. Help students identify the various examples that are described. Point out that as they learn how energy is involved in different activities, they will gather the knowledge they need to complete the *Big Challenge*.

Your machine may use energy in unusual and funny ways. But around the world, people are designing and building machines that use energy in unusual ways to do serious work. One company in the Netherlands, *Enviu*, has designed a dance floor that uses dancers' energy to help power the amplifiers and disco lights. They use the term "sustainable dancing" to describe the conversion of fun into energy savings. Another example is using the energy of children at a playground to power a water pump. As the children use their energy to turn a merry-go-round, water is pumped up from a well for people in the village to use. In both examples, the energy that is normally lost in having fun is put to good use.

There are many types of energy. A machine often changes the available energy into a different form needed to perform a task. The merry-go-round water pump you read about transforms a child's energy into energy that can be used to pump water. In a flashlight, a battery's energy is transformed into the energy released by a light bulb. In a toy car, the energy in a battery is transformed into energy that makes the car start to move.

To succeed with this Unit's challenge, you will need to know

- how to identify and describe the effects of different types of energy,

- what affects how much energy an object has,

- how to store energy,

- how energy moves from one place to another,

- how to transform one type of energy into another type of energy, and

- how to control energy so it can do work.

Get Started

Meet Rube Goldberg. Rube Goldberg was a cartoonist who enjoyed drawing amusingly complex machines. Each machine included a series of complicated steps that combined together to achieve a simple task. In your challenge, the simple task is to turn off a light switch. Rube Goldberg's designs were only drawings and did not really carry out tasks. But they were imaginative and fun, and they amused millions of people. In the United States, machines like this are often called "Rube Goldberg machines."

EN 5

ENERGY

△ Guide

Lead students in a discussion about things that exist even though they cannot see them. Ask students to think of examples, such as air and music. Encourage them to recognize that they can observe these things in other ways. For example, they can breathe air or contain it in a balloon. They can hear music or feel its vibrations. In a similar way, they cannot see energy but they will learn to observe items that have energy, measure amounts of energy, and identify changes in energy.

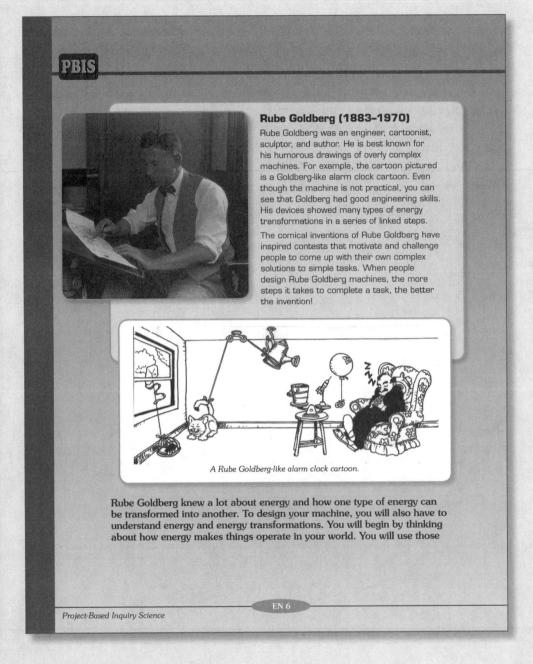

Rube Goldberg (1883–1970)

Rube Goldberg was an engineer, cartoonist, sculptor, and author. He is best known for his humorous drawings of overly complex machines. For example, the cartoon pictured is a Goldberg-like alarm clock cartoon. Even though the machine is not practical, you can see that Goldberg had good engineering skills. His devices showed many types of energy transformations in a series of linked steps.

The comical inventions of Rube Goldberg have inspired contests that motivate and challenge people to come up with their own complex solutions to simple tasks. When people design Rube Goldberg machines, the more steps it takes to complete a task, the better the invention!

A Rube Goldberg-like alarm clock cartoon.

Rube Goldberg knew a lot about energy and how one type of energy can be transformed into another. To design your machine, you will also have to understand energy and energy transformations. You will begin by thinking about how energy makes things operate in your world. You will use those

Project-Based Inquiry Science

EN 6

Get Started

15 min

Students learn who Rube Goldberg was and review several of his designs.

△ Guide

Have a student read about Rube Goldberg to the class. Then walk students through the Rube Goldberg alarm clock design so they gain an understanding of how his machines work.

"In this alarm clock design, the kite out the window is pulled by the wind. When the kite is pulled, it lifts the cage off the mouse. When the mouse is free, the cat chases the mouse. As the cat moves, the string on its tail tilts a watering can. The water can fills a bucket, causing it to become heavier. The can is sitting on a see-saw, so the see-saw gets weighed down. When the can goes down, the other end of the see-saw goes up. It pushes a dart into a balloon. When the balloon pops, it wakes up the man. "

NOTES

....

....

....

....

....

....

....

....

....

....

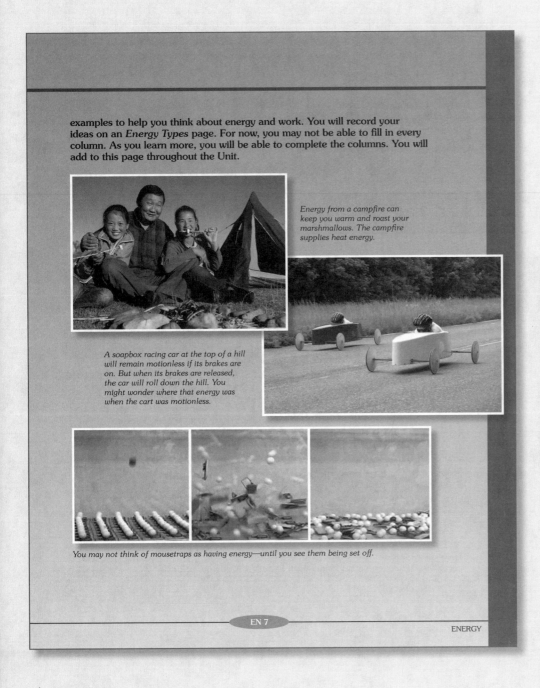

examples to help you think about energy and work. You will record your ideas on an *Energy Types* page. For now, you may not be able to fill in every column. As you learn more, you will be able to complete the columns. You will add to this page throughout the Unit.

Energy from a campfire can keep you warm and roast your marshmallows. The campfire supplies heat energy.

A soapbox racing car at the top of a hill will remain motionless if its brakes are on. But when its brakes are released, the car will roll down the hill. You might wonder where that energy was when the cart was motionless.

You may not think of mousetraps as having energy—until you see them being set off.

EN 7

ENERGY

META NOTES

Students may have difficulty finding a common thread among the three photos. It may help to describe each photo in terms of the change that is occurring. This will set students up to formulate a working definition of energy later on.

△ Guide

Discuss each photo shown in the student text. Allow volunteers to describe what the photos have in common. Help students recognize that some type of change occurs in each example. The marshmallows are cooked. The mousetrap pops. The soapbox racing car moves down the hill. Point out that each of these changes involves energy.

Conference

10 min

Students discuss examples that involve energy in their daily lives to develop initial definitions of energy and work.

META NOTES

Students can become hindered by the fact that they do not yet have formal definitions of energy or work. Encourage them to develop their own definitions based on experiences and observations. They will refine the definitions as they complete the Unit.

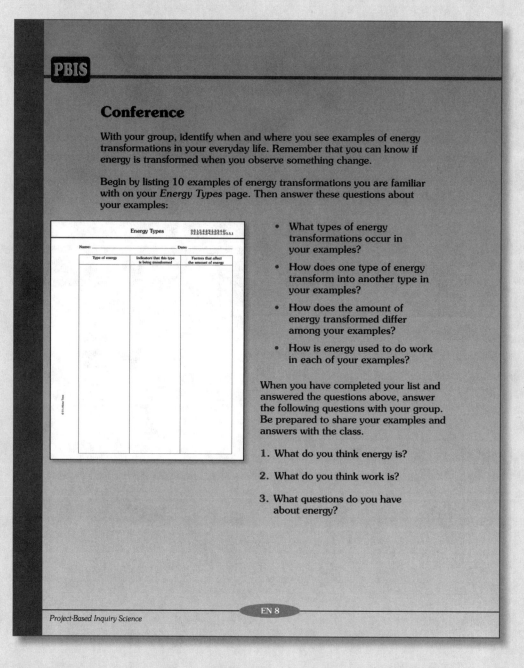

PBIS

Conference

With your group, identify when and where you see examples of energy transformations in your everyday life. Remember that you can know if energy is transformed when you observe something change.

Begin by listing 10 examples of energy transformations you are familiar with on your *Energy Types* page. Then answer these questions about your examples:

- What types of energy transformations occur in your examples?

- How does one type of energy transform into another type in your examples?

- How does the amount of energy transformed differ among your examples?

- How is energy used to do work in each of your examples?

When you have completed your list and answered the questions above, answer the following questions with your group. Be prepared to share your examples and answers with the class.

1. What do you think energy is?

2. What do you think work is?

3. What questions do you have about energy?

EN 8

Project-Based Inquiry Science

△ Guide

Ask groups to discuss the bulleted questions and then the numbered questions with their groups. Remind them to refer back to the examples on the previous pages to help them brainstorm ideas. They should record their answers on an *Energy Types* page.

If students are having difficulty answering the questions, give them ideas to initiate a discussion. For example, have them consider examples such as the following:

- objects that are moving and objects that can fall from some height

- lighting a match and blowing up an explosive

- pulling a child's wagon and pulling a car

Encourage students to formulate their own ideas about how energy is related to change.

META NOTES

The term *work* is introduced on this page. Point out to students that like energy, work is a term that has a very specific definition in science.

NOTES

Communicate

10 min

Groups share their ideas and explanations with the class.

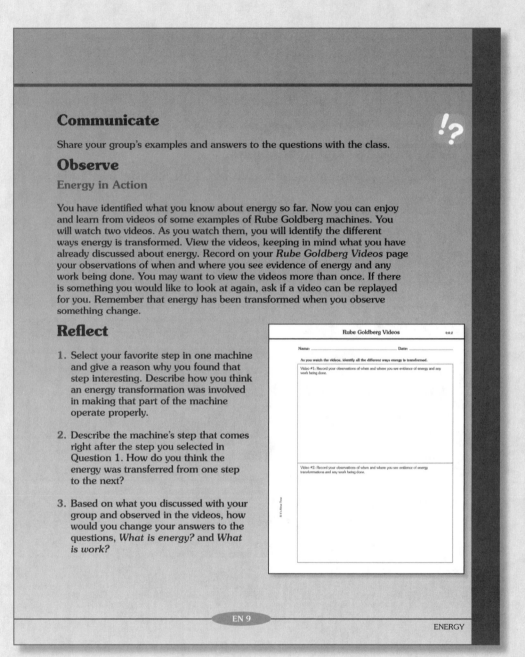

Communicate

Share your group's examples and answers to the questions with the class.

Observe

Energy in Action

You have identified what you know about energy so far. Now you can enjoy and learn from videos of some examples of Rube Goldberg machines. You will watch two videos. As you watch them, you will identify the different ways energy is transformed. View the videos, keeping in mind what you have already discussed about energy. Record on your *Rube Goldberg Videos* page your observations of when and where you see evidence of energy and any work being done. You may want to view the videos more than once. If there is something you would like to look at again, ask if a video can be replayed for you. Remember that energy has been transformed when you observe something change.

Reflect

1. Select your favorite step in one machine and give a reason why you found that step interesting. Describe how you think an energy transformation was involved in making that part of the machine operate properly.

2. Describe the machine's step that comes right after the step you selected in Question 1. How do you think the energy was transferred from one step to the next?

3. Based on what you discussed with your group and observed in the videos, how would you change your answers to the questions, *What is energy?* and *What is work?*

EN 9

ENERGY

△ **Guide**

Let each group present their examples. Record their answers on the board in a class list. Have students explain why they chose each example and how they think it involves energy.

Record a list of students' definitions of energy and work. Note any questions they have to add to the *Project Board* later.

⬡ Get Going

Distribute the *Rube Goldberg Videos* pages and tell students they are to record their observations on these. Show the videos showing examples of Rube Goldberg machines. Ask students to pay attention to the task performed by each machine and the steps involved in completing that task.

⬡ Get Going

Once students have seen the videos, have them answer the questions. Ask them to keep a record of their answers. It may help to begin the activity by describing a step in one machine that you found interesting.

NOTES

....

....

....

....

....

....

....

....

....

Observe: Energy in Action

5 min

Students watch videos showing Rube Goldberg machines and record their observations.

Reflect

10 min

Students analyze parts of the Rube Goldberg videos.

META NOTES

Students will encounter the terms *transfer* and *transform* throughout the Unit. Be aware of any confusion between the two terms. When energy is transferred, it passes from one object to another. When energy is transformed, it changes from one form to another.

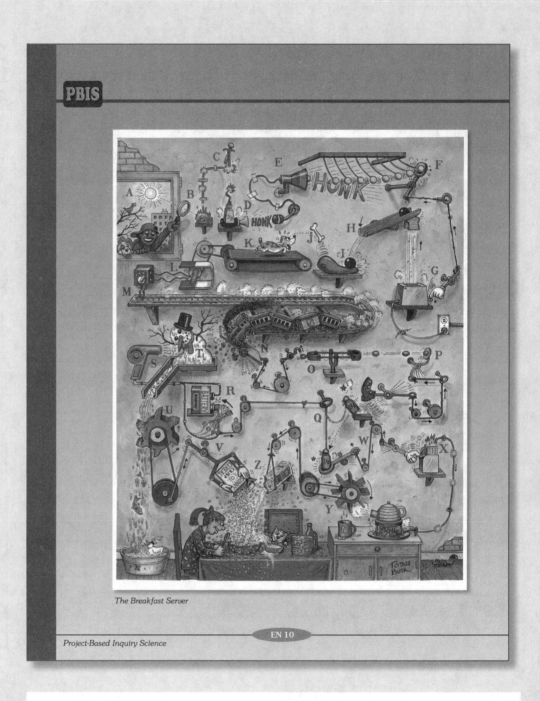

The Breakfast Server

EN 10

NOTES

The Trash-to-Stereo Server

NOTES

....

....

....

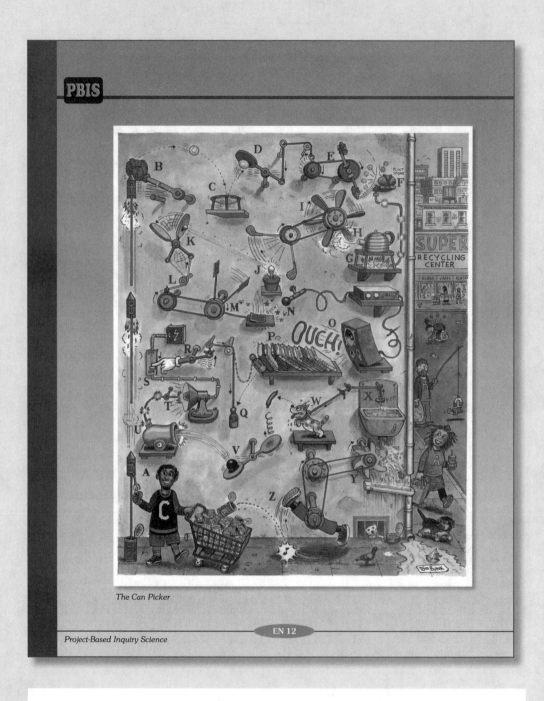

The Can Picker

EN 12

NOTES

The Orange Squeezer

NOTES

....

....

....

Explore

5 min

Students work in groups to review a diagram of a Rube Goldberg machine.

Explore

Your challenge for this Unit is to design your own machine that will turn off a light. To help you understand your goal and how you might accomplish it, each group will look at a different example of a Rube Goldberg machine designed by a professional cartoonist. These energy-transformation cartoons, shown on the previous pages, use many of the same concepts that you saw illustrated in the videos. Each machine performs what should be an easy task with a complicated series of steps. Your group will be assigned one of these four cartoons:

- *The Breakfast Server*
- *The Trash-to-Stereo Server*
- *The Can Picker*
- *The Orange Squeezer*

Each step in these machines has been labeled with a letter so that you can follow the actions taken by the machine. You will examine your machine and look for the change that occurs in each step. Then you will try to identify the type of energy transformation that is causing that change.

Procedure

1. Examine the machine your group was assigned. What is the purpose of the machine?

2. Identify what you can about how the machine carries out its task. Follow these instructions.

   a) List the changes that occur at each step in your machine on your *Energy-transformation Cartoon* page. For example, does an object go downhill from a higher point to a lower point? Does a fire start? Use as many *Energy-tranformation Cartoon* pages as you need.

   b) Identify what type of energy transformation occurs at each step. What type of energy is transformed into what other type?

   c) Wherever you can, identify how energy changes from one type to another within a step or between steps.

EN 14

Project-Based Inquiry Science

⬡ Get Going

Organize students as necessary so you have four groups. Assign one cartoon to each group. Remind students about the Rube Goldberg machines they have already seen. Challenge students to figure out how the machine they were assigned works.

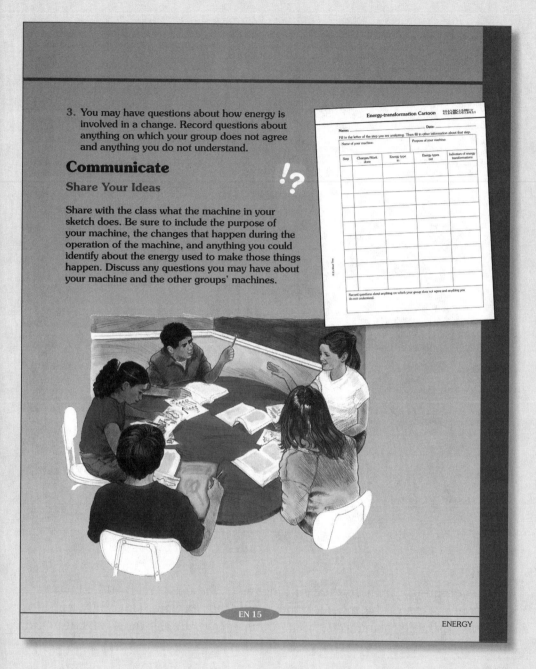

3. You may have questions about how energy is involved in a change. Record questions about anything on which your group does not agree and anything you do not understand.

Communicate

Share Your Ideas

Share with the class what the machine in your sketch does. Be sure to include the purpose of your machine, the changes that happen during the operation of the machine, and anything you could identify about the energy used to make those things happen. Discuss any questions you may have about your machine and the other groups' machines.

EN 15

ENERGY

Procedure

10 min

Students describe the steps involved in the Rube Goldberg machines they examined.

○ Get Going

Have students study the machine they were assigned. Tell them to start with the letter A and work their way through the diagram. Make sure students record their responses to each part of the procedure on their *Rube Goldberg Sketch* pages. Remind students that changes involve energy. This will help them to identify how energy is involved in the machine.

Communicate: Share Your Ideas

10 min

Students describe the machine they investigated to other groups in the class.

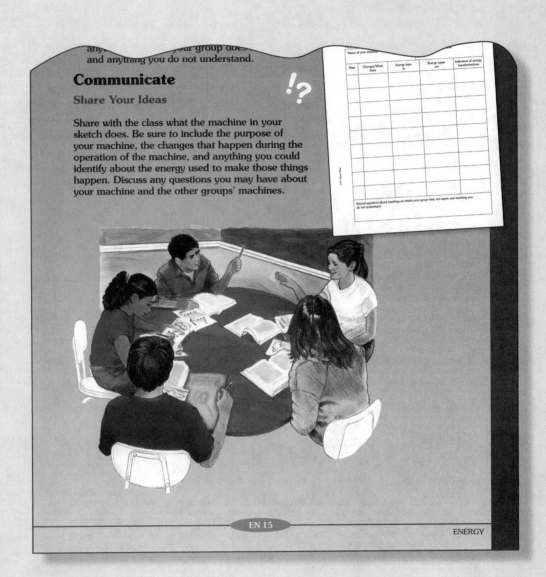

and anything you do not understand.

Communicate

Share Your Ideas

Share with the class what the machine in your sketch does. Be sure to include the purpose of your machine, the changes that happen during the operation of the machine, and anything you could identify about the energy used to make those things happen. Discuss any questions you may have about your machine and the other groups' machines.

EN 15

ENERGY

△ Guide

Allow each group to share their findings with the class. Ask students to identify any parts of the machine they could not explain. Have other groups suggest possible explanations. Invite other groups to ask questions. Remind students to be respectful to other groups.

NOTES

....

....

....

PBIS

Your Challenge

Your challenge is to design a machine to turn off a light. Your machine will include at least five steps and use at least three types of energy. You will design your machine and describe how and why each part of it operates properly. You will also describe the ways energy is transformed from one form to another.

You will not build your design. You will only draw it on paper. However, you must be able to convince your classmates that it would operate properly if built. That means each step must be believable, and the sequence of steps must be logical. Remember the cartoons and videos you have seen so far. Some of the steps in those machines seemed outrageous. But the steps combined in a way that completed a task.

Your machine should use materials commonly found in a home, a supermarket, or a hardware store. Even though you are not going to be building the machine, it should be designed to be safe enough to operate with a parent or teacher around to help. For example, it can use fire, but it should not use explosives.

Identify Criteria and Constraints

criteria (singular: criterion): conditions that must be satisfied to successfully achieve a challenge.

constraints: factors that limit how you can solve a problem.

Before you start, make sure you understand the **criteria** and **constraints** of your challenge. Criteria are conditions that must be satisfied to achieve the challenge. One criterion is that your machine must have at least five steps. Another criterion is that, in at least three of its steps, energy must be transformed from one form to another.

Constraints are factors that limit how to solve a problem. You will not build the machine, only design it and sketch it. However, one constraint is that each step must be logical and believable. Your classmates need to believe that it would operate properly if built. Another constraint is that the design must use easy-to-find materials. Another constraint is safety. Your design must be safe enough to operate with adult supervision.

Your Challenge
5 min

Students are introduced to the details of their challenge—draw a design for a machine to turn off a light.

△ Guide

Check that students understand the requirements of the challenge:

- machine must turn off a light
- must have at least five steps
- must use at least three forms of energy
- must be logical

- must use household items
- must be safe if built

Ask students to rewrite the requirements in their own words so they can refer back to the list as needed.

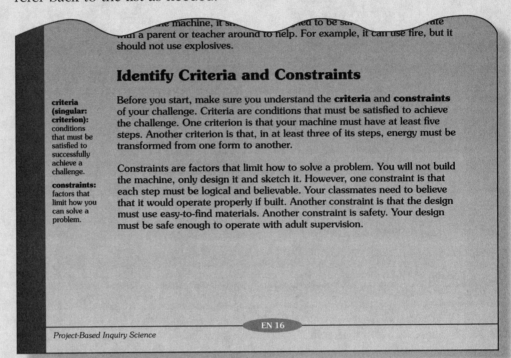

Identify Criteria and Constraints

10 min

Students list the criteria and constraints of the Big Challenge.

... machine, it s... ...ed to be sa... ...ate ...at a parent or teacher around to help. For example, it can use fire, but it should not use explosives.

Identify Criteria and Constraints

criteria (singular: criterion): conditions that must be satisfied to successfully achieve a challenge.

constraints: factors that limit how you can solve a problem.

Before you start, make sure you understand the **criteria** and **constraints** of your challenge. Criteria are conditions that must be satisfied to achieve the challenge. One criterion is that your machine must have at least five steps. Another criterion is that, in at least three of its steps, energy must be transformed from one form to another.

Constraints are factors that limit how to solve a problem. You will not build the machine, only design it and sketch it. However, one constraint is that each step must be logical and believable. Your classmates need to believe that it would operate properly if built. Another constraint is that the design must use easy-to-find materials. Another constraint is safety. Your design must be safe enough to operate with adult supervision.

EN 16

Project-Based Inquiry Science

○ Engage

Begin a discussion in which students imagine the features they would want their dream car to have if they could make it any way they wanted. Perhaps it would fly. Maybe it would use water instead of gasoline. Perhaps it would include a television, bed, and could even make food. Once they have their ideas, review the definition of criteria and constraints. Then, have students consider the different types of constraints they might face when making their dream car, such as cost, materials, fuel, time, labor, and so on. Help them to realize how criteria and constraints are related.

○ Get Going

Have students complete *Criteria and Constraints* for the machine they are going to design. Students may need to refer to the summary of requirements they wrote earlier.

Record the criteria and constraints in a table like the one shown below, so you can refer to them as you move through the Unit.

Design a Rube Goldberg machine to turn off a light	
Criteria	Constraints

Create a *Project Board*

It is useful to keep track of your progress when you are designing something. It is also useful to keep track of what you already know and what you still need to learn as you move through a challenge. Throughout this Unit, you will be using a *Project Board* to do this. During classroom discussions, the ideas from the class will be recorded on a class *Project Board*. At the same time, you will keep a record of what has been discussed on your own *Project Board* page.

Remember that a *Project Board* has space for answering five guiding questions:

- What do we think we know?
- What do we need to investigate?
- What are we learning?
- What is our evidence?
- What does it mean for the challenge or question?

EN 17

ENERGY

Create a *Project Board*

20 min

Students create a Project Board *and begin to record their ideas.*

⬡ Get Going

Tell the class that now that they have thought about the *Big Challenge,* and have identified some questions that need to be investigated, they are going to need a way to keep track of their progress.

Introduce students to the idea of a *Project Board* by having them read the selection in the text. Help students understand that the *Project Board* provides a way for the class to work together to plan and keep track of progress during a challenge.

To get started on this *Project Board,* you need to record the *Big Challenge* at the top of the *Project Board: Design a Rube Goldberg machine to turn off a light.*

Design a Rube Goldberg machine to turn off a light				
What do we think we know?	What do we need to investigate?	What are we learning?	What is our evidence?	What does it mean for the challenge or question?

What do we think we know?

In this column of the *Project Board* you will record what you think you know about energy, energy transformations, and work, and about completing the challenge. You have read about and discussed many ideas about energy in this introduction. You have also discussed many examples of Rube Goldberg machines. Record those ideas and thoughts in this column.

What do we need to investigate?

In this column, you will record what you need to know more about to complete the challenge. This column is designed to help you keep track of ideas that are debatable or unknown and need to be investigated. For example, you may disagree with members of your group about what energy is. This is something that needs to be investigated. You identified questions when you were watching the videos and examining the cartoon drawings of machines. Record those questions in this column.

Later in this Unit, you will return to the *Project Board.* For now, you and your classmates will fill in the first two columns.

Let students know that you will be keeping the class *Project Board* by recording ideas and questions throughout the Unit. Tell students that they should be keeping up their own *Project Board* to which they can refer as needed throughout the Unit. Begin the *Project Board* by writing the *Big Challenge* across the top.

△ Guide

Spend a few minutes discussing the first two columns of the *Project Board*. For the first column, make sure students know to include any ideas they have about energy. Caution them not to eliminate ideas because they think they might be incorrect or too simple. Tell students that this is simply a way to gather their ideas. They will continue to explore them throughout the Unit. Have students fill these into the *What do we think we know?* column.

In the second column, students should include any questions they have and any information they are unsure about. As in the first column, no question is a bad question. Point out to students that they only learn what they need to accomplish the *Big Challenge* by asking questions and then trying to answer them. Consider having students refer back to the bulleted list in the *Think About the Big Challenge* reading, if they are having difficulty. Also, ask students to recall any questions they had thought of and had not answered in the *Conference* segment earlier. Have students record these ideas in the *What do we need to investigate?* column. Explain that students will complete the other columns of the *Project Board* later in the Unit.

Teacher Reflection Questions

- What misconceptions about energy and work came up during the discussions? When during the Unit might you challenge these misconceptions?

- How could you tell if students were motivated by the challenge? What ideas do you have to continue to foster their motivation and the application of their ideas?

- What issues came up as the groups worked together? What can you do in the future to address these issues?

NOTES

....

....

....

NOTES

Project-Based Inquiry Science

LEARNING SET 1 INTRODUCTION

Learning Set 1

What Is Energy?

◄ *6 class periods*

A class period is considered to be one 40 to 50 minute class.

Students start to consider energy through observations of photographs and demonstrations to develop a definition of energy and to identify different forms of energy. They use their observations to recognize transformations in energy and think about how energy transformations may be involved in accomplishing the Big Challenge.

Overview

Students are introduced to the process of using indicators in science to learn about energy. They observe a Crookes radiometer to identify indicators that suggest energy is involved when light is shined on it. The demonstration is expanded by having students observe the radiometer as the light source is moved to different positions. Students are then introduced to examples of energy as it relates to the demonstration. They observe a pop-up toaster and other household objects as a means of identifying additional forms of energy. They add to their understanding and definition of energy by reading about the three types of energy. Then students apply this knowledge to investigate energy in a selection of objects. They share their analyses and make claims as best they can about the types of energy in their investigations. Students record their new science knowledge and questions they have on the *Project Board* and start to consider how what they have done may help them achieve the *Big Challenge*.

Targeted Concepts, Skills, and Nature of Science	Section
Criteria and constraints are important in determining effective scientific procedures and answering scientific questions.	1.1, 1.2
Scientists must keep accurate and descriptive records of what they do so they can share their work with others and consider what they did, why they did it, and what they want to do next.	1.1, 1.2
Scientists often work together and then share their findings. Sharing findings makes new information available and helps scientists refine their ideas and build on others' ideas. When another person's or group's idea is used, credit needs to be given.	1.2

Targeted Concepts, Skills, and Nature of Science	Section
Energy is the ability to cause change or do work.	1.1, 1.2
Energy exists in different forms and can be changed from one form to another.	1.1, 1.2
Kinetic energy is associated with the motion of an object.	1.1, 1.2
Potential energy is stored energy, associated with position or condition.	1.1, 1.2
Visible light is a small band within the electromagnetic spectrum that is energy traveling in the form of waves.	1.1
Electrical energy is the flow of charges through a circuit.	1.1
Sound is the transfer of energy as longitudinal waves that cannot travel through a vacuum.	1.2
Thermal energy is the energy of the particles of matter.	1.2
Heat is the transfer of thermal energy from a substance at a higher temperature to a substance at a lower temperature.	1.2

Students' Initial Conceptions and Capabilities	• Students usually think that energy is associated only, or primarily, with animate objects such as living things that need energy to live and be active (Solomon, 1983). • Some students associate energy with energy supply (Brook & Driver, 1984).

NOTES

....

....

....

....

....

Understanding for Teachers

Many students have misconceptions about energy because of the ways in which the term is used in everyday language. It is important to facilitate students' understanding as they are introduced to the various forms of energy. All of the related terms are not yet presented in this *Learning Set.* Instead, they are developed throughout the Unit. The goal is for students to steadily build the knowledge they need to understand the terms as they are introduced.

In this *Learning Set,* students are introduced to the idea that any moving object has kinetic energy. The spinning flags of a radiometer and the toast popping up out of a toaster have kinetic energy because they are in motion. Other objects have stored energy. Although the term is reserved at this point, stored energy is potential energy. Potential energy has the ability to cause change or do work. Elastic energy, which is the energy stored in a stretched rubber band or a compressed spring, is a type of potential energy.

In addition, energy can be described by its different forms. Almost any form of energy can change into any other form. No energy is produced or destroyed in the process. A change from one form of energy to another is known as an energy transformation.

The chart on the following page lists the forms of energy with their descriptions.

NOTES

....

....

....

....

....

....

....

....

Form of Energy	Description
radiant energy	This type of energy consists of waves made up of changing electric and magnetic fields. Also known as electromagnetic energy, this type of energy is believed to have a wave nature and a particle nature. Visible light is one form of radiation.
electrical energy	This type of energy is the energy of moving electric charges. All matter is made up of atoms, which are made up of smaller particles called electrons, protons, and neutrons. Protons and electrons carry electric charges. Charges can flow through a complete path known as a circuit.
chemical energy	This type of energy is stored in the bonds that hold matter together. When chemical bonds are broken, chemical energy is released.
mechanical energy	This type of energy has the ability to do work. It is the total of an object's kinetic and potential energy. Mechanical energy makes it possible for an object to apply a force on another object, causing it to move some distance.
sound energy	This type of energy is carried by the vibrations of matter. Sound travels as longitudinal waves, in which the direction the wave travels is parallel to the direction of vibration.
thermal energy	This type of energy is the energy associated with the particles of matter. These particles, which are in constant motion, have both kinetic and potential energy. Thermal energy is transferred as heat.
nuclear energy	This type of energy is the energy stored in the center, or nucleus, of an atom. This energy is released when nuclei are split apart or combined.

LEARNING SET 1 IMPLEMENTATION

Learning Set 1

What Is Energy?

In this *Learning Set,* you will answer the question, *What Is Energy?* You have already observed that energy is related to change. When anything changes, energy is transformed.

So far, you have analyzed an example of a Rube Goldberg machine. You have also generated a list of types of energy transformations. Just look around for lots of other examples of energy being transformed. Some examples are shown in the pictures below.

How do you think children are transforming energy when they play on a swing or play basketball? Where does that energy come from?

How do you think a Ferris wheel transforms energy? Where does that energy come from?

How do you think a sailboat transforms energy? Where does that energy come from?

ENERGY

Learning Set 1

What Is Energy?

5 min

Students are introduced to the question of the Learning Set: What Is Energy?

◯ **Engage**

Begin by pointing out that in order to build their own Rube Goldberg machines, students will need to know what energy is. Students began to consider energy in the *Unit Introduction*. Now use the photographs and captions on this page to begin a more detailed discussion about energy. Let students know they will learn the correct answers to the questions throughout in this *Learning Set*.

NOTES

SECTION 1.1 INTRODUCTION

1.1 Understand the Challenge

How Can You Identify Energy?

◀ **2 class periods**

A class period is
considered to be one
40 to 50 minute class.

Overview

Students discover that they cannot observe energy directly, and are
introduced to the need to identify indicators. They observe a flashlight
on a Crookes radiometer to look for indicators of energy and changes in
energy. Students analyze their observations, discuss their ideas, and develop
questions about energy. They begin to consider applying what they have
learned to the *Big Challenge* and record their ideas and questions on
the *Project Board* to refer to and build on as they progress through the
Learning Set.

Targeted Concepts, Skills, and Nature of Science	Performance Expectations
Scientists must keep accurate and descriptive records of what they do so they can share their work with others and consider what they did, why they did it, and what they want to do next.	Students record their observations describing the radiometer throughout the demonstration in which a flashlight is shined from different distances.
Energy is the ability to cause change or do work.	Students recognize that a change in the radiometer indicates the presence of energy.
Energy exists in different forms and can be changed from one form to another.	Students infer that light energy from a flashlight changes to mechanical energy, which causes the flags of a radiometer to move.
Kinetic energy is associated with the motion of an object.	Students recognize that the flags of a radiometer have kinetic energy when they are in motion.
Visible light is a small band within the electromagnetic spectrum that is energy traveling in the form of waves.	Students classify the light from the flashlight as light energy.

Targeted Concepts, Skills, and Nature of Science	Performance Expectations
Electrical energy is the flow of charges through a circuit.	Students classify the energy that causes the light to glow as electrical energy.
Potential energy is stored energy associated with position or condition.	Students classify the energy stored in the battery of the flashlight as chemical energy, which is a form of potential energy.

Materials	
1 per classroom	Radiometer Flashlight
1 per student	*Radiometer Observations* page *Project Board* page
1 per class	Class *Project Board*
Several per class (optional)	Batteries

Homework Options

Reflection

- **Science Process:** Why is it important to record your observations as they occur rather than at a later time? *(Students should recognize that if they do not record their observations as they make them, they might forget what they observed or they might record it differently than it occurred.)*

- **Science Content:** How might you identify that you are observing some form of energy in action? *(Students should recognize that they should look for some type of change to indicate a form of energy in action.)*

SECTION 1.1 IMPLEMENTATION

1.1 Understand the Challenge

How Can You Identify Energy?

In the *Introduction,* you observed real Rube Goldberg machines on video and then analyzed energy transformations in sketches of imaginary Rube Goldberg machines. You saw objects moving, falling, burning, and bubbling. When an object moves, falls, burns, or bubbles, it is changing. An object that gives off noise, light, or heat is also changing. All of these changes **indicate**, or show, that energy is being transformed.

indicate: to show.

indicators: observations that can tell you about the presence of some state or condition.

inference: a plausible conclusion or interpretation based on observations or evidence.

infer: to interpret from observations.

You can see the change in an icicle as it melts. Melting is an indicator. From observing the icicle, you can infer that energy must be added to solid ice to transform it to liquid water.

To design a machine that transforms energy, you need to be able to recognize when energy is being transformed and what type of energy is transformed into what other type. You will need to identify **indicators** that allow you to make an **inference** about the use of energy. An indicator is something you can observe and measure that tells you about the presence of something else. An inference is a plausible interpretation or conclusion based on observations or evidence. Once you know which indicators to look for, you will be able to **infer** when energy is being transformed.

Some indicators of energy transformations are difficult to observe. But you can experience many indicators of energy transformations with your five senses—touch, sight, hearing, taste, and smell. The simplest example is when you observe through sight that something has started to move. Energy is always being transformed when an object speeds up or slows down.

You can also see indicators of energy use when matter is changing form, such as when ice melts into water. Energy must be added to solid ice to transform it to liquid. When an object is burning, there may be several indicators to observe. You might see flames or smoke, and also smell smoke and hear the crackle and rush of the flames. All of these are indicators of energy transformations.

EN 20

Project-Based Inquiry Science

1.1 Understand the Challenge

How Can You Identify Energy?

10 min

Students are introduced to indicators that can be used to infer that energy occurs or is transformed.

○ **Engage**

Describe the following scenario to students:

> You see a puddle on the sidewalk early one morning. Later that day, the Sun is shining and the puddle is gone. What happened to the puddle?

Guide students to imagine some unlikely answers, such as a neighbor came and dried the puddle with a towel or a dog came along and drank the water in the puddle.

Then help students infer that the puddle evaporated in the sunlight. Explain that they did not observe the puddle disappear, they can figure out what most likely happened to the puddle based on past experiences and science knowledge. Let the students know this type of interpretation is an example of an inference.

△ Guide

Remind students that they cannot see energy like they can see trees, clouds, or bicycles. Instead, they have to act like detectives to infer the presence of energy using indicators. As in the case of the disappearing puddle, they can use what they know to interpret their observations. Use the photograph of a melting icicle as another example of how students can make an inference.

NOTES

1.1 Understand the Challenge

To practice identifying energy and indicators of energy transformation, you will participate in a class demonstration. You will use a simple device called a radiometer. A radiometer uses a sealed glass bulb similar to a light bulb. Inside the bulb is a spindle with four flags attached at its top. Under some conditions, the flags inside the radiometer start to turn. Because this is a change, you know that some kind of energy is being transformed. You will observe the radiometer to determine the type of energy that is transformed into the motion of the flags.

A Crookes radiometer.

Demonstration 1

Throughout the demonstration, carefully observe the radiometer. Focus your attention on the four flags at the top of the spindle inside the bulb. Record your observations on your *Radiometer Observations* page.

Observe

1. Your teacher will pass the radiometer from group to group. Watch the four flags at the top of the spindle for a few moments. What is happening to the flags? If the flags are still, how do you think they might move? Carefully turn it over and examine it. Can you figure out what might make the flags move or stop moving? Record your observations in the top chart of a *Radiometer Observations* page. If you have any ideas about what makes the flags move, record those in the *Causes* column. Make special note of anything that surprises you.

2. Observe the radiometer as it is placed on a table and a flashlight is held about 1 m from it. The light from the flashlight will shine on the radiometer for a full minute. Again, observe carefully and look for any changes in the radiometer that might be indicators of energy use. Record in the *Conditions* column the conditions of the demonstration. Record your observations of the radiometer in the *Observations* column.

Demonstration 1

10 min

Students observe a radiometer to practice identifying energy by using indicators.

META NOTES

The explanation for exactly why the vanes, or flags, of a Crookes radiometer spin has been the subject of much scientific debate since its invention. The current explanation is quite complex and is best avoided at this level. Avoid the temptation to oversimplify the operation of the radiometer. Students do not need to understand why the flags spin in order to recognize that an energy transformation is taking place.

○ Engage

Allow students to observe the radiometer when it is not in direct light. Ask them to think about how they can get the flags inside the glass to move. Students may suggest physical methods, such as shaking or twisting the glass. Have students record their predictions on their *Radiometer Observations* pages.

⬡ Get Going

Allow students to observe the radiometer. Caution students to be careful handling the glass. Place the radiometer on a desk that is not in direct light so students can observe the changes that occur when the flashlight is shined on it. Then shine a flashlight directly on the radiometer and have students record their observations.

NOTES

3. Observe as the flashlight is turned off. Observe the radiometer carefully. Record in the *Conditions* column that the light was turned off, and record your observations in the *Observations* column.

Analyze Your Data

1. What indicators of energy transformation did you record when you were passing the radiometer around? If you observed an indicator of energy transformation, what type of energy do you think was transformed into what other type of energy?

2. What indicators of energy transformation did you record when the flashlight was held 1 m from the radiometer? If you observed an indicator of energy transformation, what type of energy do you think was transformed into what other type of energy?

3. What happened when the flashlight was turned off? Does this confirm your thoughts in *Steps 1* and *2?* Why or why not? Record your reasoning in the *Causes* column of your table.

Analyze Your Data

5 min

Students think about the observations they made during the demonstration.

☐ Assess

Once students have observed the demonstration and recorded their observations, have them answer the questions with their groups. Let them know that they should refer to their *Radiometer Observations* pages to support their answers and update the *Causes* column as needed.

1. Students should have observed that the flags moved slightly when they picked up the radiometer. They might add pushing or pulling the radiometer to the *Causes* column.

2. Students should have observed that the flags moved when the flashlight was turned on. They might record the movement of the flags as an indicator of energy. They might add light to the *Causes* column.

3. Students should have observed that the flags stopped moving when the flashlight was turned off. They might conclude that some type of change is needed to keep the flags moving. Students might record that the light is energy that causes the flags to turn, citing how when the light was removed, the flags slowed down and came to a stop.

NOTES

Demonstration 2

Now that you have some ideas about indicators and sources of energy that caused the radiometer to turn, you will test your ideas. You will begin by predicting what will happen in several different situations. Then you will observe what actually happens in those situations. Record your predictions and observations in the second table of the *Radiometer Observations* page.

Predict

1. What do you think will happen if you turn on the flashlight and shine the light at the radiometer for 1 min from a distance of less than 1 m? Record your predictions in the first row of the table.

2. What do you think will happen if you turn on the flashlight and shine the light at the radiometer for 1 min from a distance of 2 m? Record your predictions in the second row of the table.

3. What do you think will happen if you shine the flashlight on the radiometer from 2 m away and then slowly move it closer to the radiometer? Record your predictions in the third row of the table.

Observe

Watch as your teacher performs the procedures described in the *Predict* section. First, observe the radiometer as the flashlight shines on it from up close for 1 min. Then observe the radiometer when the flashlight is held 2 m from the radiometer. Finally, repeat the procedure again, holding the flashlight 2 m away and slowly moving it toward the radiometer. Record your observations.

Analyze Your Data

1. What do you think is the source of energy for the motion of the flags in the radiometer?

2. Why do you think the radiometer reacts differently to a flashlight that is close to it than to a flashlight that is farther away?

3. Now think about the flashlight. What indicators do you have that energy is being transformed when the flashlight is turned on? What form of energy is being transformed to what other form of energy?

EN 23

ENERGY

Demonstration 2

5 min

Students identify how changes in the setup of the radiometer will affect their observations.

◯ Engage

Ask students if they have ever spun a merry-go-round at a playground. Describe a scenario in which a student pushes gently and the merry-go-round spins slowly. When the student pushes harder, the merry-go-round spins quickly. Now ask students to think again about the radiometer.

"The speed at which the flags of the radiometer spin can vary. What do you think is indicated if the flags spin quickly? If they spin slowly?"

Predict

5 min

Students consider varying the light shining on the radiometer and predict what will happen.

and obser... ...ne second table of the ... ...Observations page...

Predict

1. What do you think will happen if you turn on the flashlight and shine the light at the radiometer for 1 min from a distance of less than 1 m? Record your predictions in the first row of the table.

2. What do you think will happen if you turn on the flashlight and shine the light at the radiometer for 1 min from a distance of 2 m? Record your predictions in the second row of the table.

3. What do you think will happen if you shine the flashlight on the radiometer from 2 m away and then slowly move it closer to the radiometer? Record your predictions in the third row of the table.

Get Going

Ask students to predict how moving the flashlight different distances from the radiometer will affect what they observe. Have students record their predictions on the *Radiometer Observations* pages.

Observe

5 min

Students observe changes in the radiometer relative to changes in the distance to the flashlight.

Tabl... ...ur predictions in... ...the table.

Observe

Watch as your teacher performs the procedures described in the *Predict* section. First, observe the radiometer as the flashlight shines on it from up close for 1 min. Then observe the radiometer when the flashlight is held 2 m from the radiometer. Finally, repeat the procedure again, holding the flashlight 2 m away and slowly moving it toward the radiometer. Record your observations.

Get Going

Preform each experiment described in the student text by moving the flashlight accordingly for the class. Allow students time to observe the changes in the radiometer before moving on. Repeat as necessary. Make sure students record their observations on the second table of their *Radiometer Observations* pages.

Once the demonstration has been performed and students have recorded their observations, have them meet in their groups to answer the *Analyze Your Data* questions. Remind them that they may refer to their *Radiometer Observations* pages as needed. As groups discuss their answers, circulate the classroom and listen for the following:

your observations.

Analyze Your Data

1. What do you think is the source of energy for the motion of the flags in the radiometer?

2. Why do you think the radiometer reacts differently to a flashlight that is close to it than to a flashlight that is farther away?

3. Now think about the flashlight. What indicators do you have that energy is being transformed when the flashlight is turned on? What form of energy is being transformed to what other form of energy?

Analyze Your Data

5 min

Students think about the observations they made during the demonstration.

☐ **Assess**

1. Students should infer that the light is the source of energy for the motion of the flags.

2. Students may infer that energy spreads out as light from the flashlight travels across the room. Therefore, as the distance between the flashlight and the radiometer increases, more energy is spread out and less energy reaches the radiometer. The indicator they observed is the speed at which the flags spin. They spin faster when the flashlight is closer than when it is farther away.

3. Students should identify that when the flashlight is turned on, the light caused change to the radiometer, indicating that energy is being used. They may identify the flashlight's source of energy as its battery.

NOTES

....

....

....

Energy in the Crookes Radiometer

10 min

Students discover why the Crookes radiometer behaves as it does.

META NOTES

Be aware that there are different forms of energy: light energy, chemical energy, nuclear energy, and mechanical energy. There are also types of energy: kinetic and potential energy. Each form of energy can also be described as kinetic or potential. Chemical energy, for example, is potential energy stored in the bonds that hold matter together. The mechanical energy of a moving object is kinetic energy. At this point, students only need to know the terms they are introduced to in the student text.

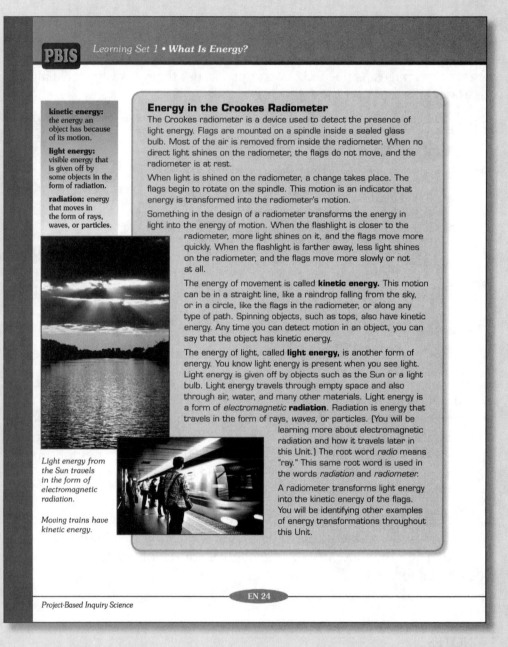

Learning Set 1 • What Is Energy?

kinetic energy: the energy an object has because of its motion.

light energy: visible energy that is given off by some objects in the form of radiation.

radiation: energy that moves in the form of rays, waves, or particles.

Energy in the Crookes Radiometer

The Crookes radiometer is a device used to detect the presence of light energy. Flags are mounted on a spindle inside a sealed glass bulb. Most of the air is removed from inside the radiometer. When no direct light shines on the radiometer, the flags do not move, and the radiometer is at rest.

When light is shined on the radiometer, a change takes place. The flags begin to rotate on the spindle. This motion is an indicator that energy is transformed into the radiometer's motion.

Something in the design of a radiometer transforms the energy in light into the energy of motion. When the flashlight is closer to the radiometer, more light shines on it, and the flags move more quickly. When the flashlight is farther away, less light shines on the radiometer, and the flags move more slowly or not at all.

The energy of movement is called **kinetic energy.** This motion can be in a straight line, like a raindrop falling from the sky, or in a circle, like the flags in the radiometer, or along any type of path. Spinning objects, such as tops, also have kinetic energy. Any time you can detect motion in an object, you can say that the object has kinetic energy.

The energy of light, called **light energy,** is another form of energy. You know light energy is present when you see light. Light energy is given off by objects such as the Sun or a light bulb. Light energy travels through empty space and also through air, water, and many other materials. Light energy is a form of *electromagnetic* **radiation**. Radiation is energy that travels in the form of rays, *waves*, or particles. (You will be learning more about electromagnetic radiation and how it travels later in this Unit.) The root word *radio* means "ray." This same root word is used in the words *radiation* and *radiometer*.

A radiometer transforms light energy into the kinetic energy of the flags. You will be identifying other examples of energy transformations throughout this Unit.

Light energy from the Sun travels in the form of electromagnetic radiation.

Moving trains have kinetic energy.

EN 24

Project-Based Inquiry Science

△ Guide

Read through the student text with the class, introducing the new terms to students. Build on their understanding by asking the class to brainstorm a list of examples of objects with kinetic energy. Help them recognize that any moving object has kinetic energy. Encourage students to be creative by listing less obvious examples, such as a falling raindrop or a satellite in space. Help students recognize that a radiometer converts the energy of radiation into mechanical energy that causes the flags to spin. When the flags are spinning, they have kinetic energy.

1.1 Understand the Challenge

Energy in a Flashlight

A flashlight also uses energy and transforms energy. It transforms energy stored in a battery into light energy. When a flashlight is turned on, the filament of the bulb begins to glow, and the flashlight **radiates** light. The change in the filament and the presence of light are both indicators that energy is being transformed. You can use your sense of sight to detect these indicators.

When you see a light bulb glowing, you can infer that the bulb is transforming energy. The filament of a bulb shines because *electricity* flows through the filament. Electricity is a form of **electrical energy** that flows between the negative and positive terminals of a battery. You cannot see the electrical energy, but you know that a light bulb needs electrical energy to glow.

In the case of a flashlight, the source of the electrical energy is the **chemical energy** stored within a battery. Chemical energy is energy that is stored until it is released by the reaction of chemicals in the battery. When the positive and negative terminals of a battery are connected by a wire, chemicals in the battery react to release energy to the wire.

When a flashlight is turned on, two energy transformations take place. First, chemical energy in the battery is transformed into electrical energy that travels through the filament wire. Then, the electrical energy traveling through the filament heats the filament and causes it to radiate light energy. The light energy given off by the flashlight is an indicator that chemical energy in the battery is transformed into electrical energy in the wire, which is transformed to the light given off by the flashlight.

radiate: give off energy.

electrical energy: the energy of moving electric charges.

chemical energy: energy stored in chemical bonds.

Chemical energy stored in batteries is transformed to light the light.

○ Engage

Ask students to think of devices in their homes that use electricity. Record their answers in a chart. In the first column, list suggested devices that plug into an electrical outlet. In the second column, list the suggested devices that use batteries. Help students realize that all of these devices transform electrical energy into some other form of energy. Once students have been introduced to the other forms of energy, you may want to return to the list so students can identify the transformations in each device.

Energy in a Flashlight

10 min

Students discover more forms of energy: electrical and chemical.

You may find it necessary to tell students that electricity can flow through certain materials. For example, electricity can flow through most metals, such as copper, but not through many nonmetals, such as rubber and plastic. A material through which electricity can flow is called a conductor. A material that does not allow electricity to flow through it is called an insulator. Electricity can flow through a closed loop of conductors, known as a circuit.

Students may be confused by electricity from an electrical outlet versus electricity from a battery. Electricity is electric current, or the flow of charged particles. Chemical changes inside a battery can cause charged particles to flow through a circuit. A flow of charged particles produced at a power plant can provide the electricity to an electrical outlet. Point out that no matter what the source, an electric current carries electrical energy.

△ Guide

Ask students why they need to eat food. Then point out that food contains stored chemical energy. The human body uses this energy for all of its life processes. Chemical energy is also stored in fuels, such as coal and gasoline. Guide students to understand that chemical energy is also stored inside a battery. This is true for all sizes of batteries. You may wish to display several batteries. When a battery is connected in a circuit, the chemical energy is transformed into electrical energy.

NOTES

....

....

....

....

....

....

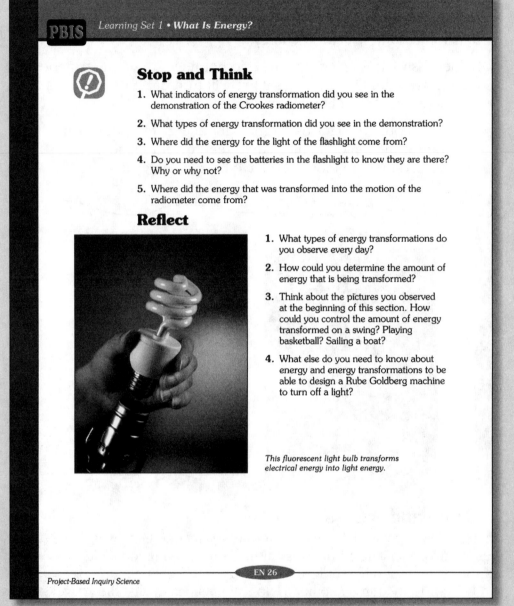

Stop and Think

1. What indicators of energy transformation did you see in the demonstration of the Crookes radiometer?

2. What types of energy transformation did you see in the demonstration?

3. Where did the energy for the light of the flashlight come from?

4. Do you need to see the batteries in the flashlight to know they are there? Why or why not?

5. Where did the energy that was transformed into the motion of the radiometer come from?

Reflect

1. What types of energy transformations do you observe every day?

2. How could you determine the amount of energy that is being transformed?

3. Think about the pictures you observed at the beginning of this section. How could you control the amount of energy transformed on a swing? Playing basketball? Sailing a boat?

4. What else do you need to know about energy and energy transformations to be able to design a Rube Goldberg machine to turn off a light?

This fluorescent light bulb transforms electrical energy into light energy.

Stop and Think

10 min

The class discusses the Stop and Think questions.

△ Guide and Assess

Lead a class discussion of the *Stop and Think* questions. Listen for the following in students' answers:

1. Students should discuss how the flags moving inside the radiometer, when exposed to light, were an indicator of energy.

2. Students should recognize that the moving flags had kinetic energy and the flashlight produced light energy.

3. Students should describe how the energy for the light of the flashlight came from the chemical energy in the battery, which was transformed into electrical energy.

4. Students should suggest that they do not need to see the batteries. If the batteries are there, the flashlight will turn on. If the batteries are not there, the flashlight will not turn on.

5. Students should recognize that the light energy from the flashlight was transformed into the mechanical energy of the radiometer's flags. This caused them to move and have kinetic energy.

Reflect

5 min

Students tie together all the ideas they have learned about energy so far and formulate questions they still need answered.

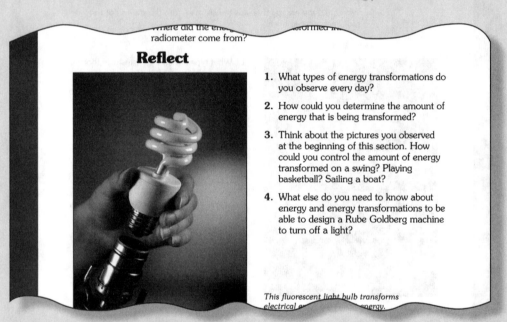

radiometer come from?

Reflect

1. What types of energy transformations do you observe every day?

2. How could you determine the amount of energy that is being transformed?

3. Think about the pictures you observed at the beginning of this section. How could you control the amount of energy transformed on a swing? Playing basketball? Sailing a boat?

4. What else do you need to know about energy and energy transformations to be able to design a Rube Goldberg machine to turn off a light?

This fluorescent light bulb transforms electrical e... ...energy.

△ Guide and Assess

Have students record their answers to the *Reflect* questions with their groups. Facilitate a brief class discussion checking for students' comprehension of different forms of energy, and how one form of energy can be transformed into another. Help students relate what they have learned to everyday situations, to the pictures they observed, and to the *Big Challenge*.

1. Students' answers will vary, but they should recognize many forms of electrical energy becoming light energy (room lights, radio, television, toaster) and sound energy (radio, television, CD player). They could mention wind energy becoming kinetic energy as it passes through a tree's leaves. Sporting events allow the

transformation of chemical energy in a player's body to the kinetic energy of a ball being hit, kicked, or dribbled. In turn, the kinetic energy of the ball can become potential energy as it is deformed. Or become sound energy when it hits a wall or floor.

2. This will vary widely as the type of energy transformed will vary. The intensity of a sound would be one indicator for the amount of energy being transformed from a radio or television.

3. Students may suggest that the energy transformed on a swing (chemical to kinetic) could be controlled by not pushing so hard, or pushing harder. In general, the amount of energy being transformed can be controlled by controlling the energy output. The wind energy transformed into kinetic energy in a sailboat is controlled by the size of the sail, or the angle of the sail to the wind direction.

4. Student answers will vary but they should understand that five transformations are required for their design. They may say that they need to know how to transform electrical energy from a battery to enough kinetic energy to turn off a light switch.

NOTES

....

....

....

....

....

....

....

....

ENERGY

Update the Project Board

5 min

Students add newly learned information to the Project Board.

Update the *Project Board*

In this section, you thought about types of energy transformations. You identified indicators of some types of energy transformations and some changes caused by the transformation of energy. Update the *Project Board* by adding ideas from your readings and the demonstrations in the *What do we think we know?* column. Be sure to add to the *Project Board* the ideas your class agreed on and areas you are not sure about. You may have questions about what energy is and the relationship between energy and motion. You may have ideas about investigations to help you find out more about energy and motion. Record your questions and ideas for investigations in the *What do we need to investigate?* column.

Design a Rube Goldberg machine to turn off a light				
What do we think we know?	What do we need to investigate?	What are we learning?	What is our evidence?	What does it mean for the challenge or question?

What's the Point?

By observing indicators, you can identify when energy is being transformed. An indicator is something you can observe and measure. You can experience many indicators with your senses—touch, sight, hearing, taste, and smell. The simplest example is seeing something start to move. You know an object has kinetic energy when it is moving, similar to the flags in the radiometer. When light energy enters a radiometer, it is transformed into the energy of motion, or kinetic energy. In a flashlight, when the flashlight is switched on, chemical energy is transformed into electrical energy, which is then transformed into light energy.

ENERGY

⬡ Get Going

Have students share ideas from the readings and demonstrations that they would like to add to the *Project Board*. Add the ideas to the *What do we think we know?* column. Then have students share any questions they have that will help them learn what they need to know to accomplish the *Big Challenge*. Record these questions in the *What do we need to investigate?* column.

△ Guide

Students might disagree about the content of the ideas or they might disagree about whether the idea is important for accomplishing the *Big Challenge*. Make sure they know that at this point, they do not need to agree. Explain that they are simply gathering their ideas based on readings and observations. They will use their questions to continue to investigate their ideas throughout the Unit.

Assessment Options

Targeted Concepts, Skills, and Nature of Science	How do I know if students got it?
Scientists must keep accurate and descriptive records of what they do so they can share their work with others and consider what they did, why they did it, and what they want to do next.	**ASK:** Why was it important to record your observations and share them with the class? **LISTEN:** Students should recognize that sharing information helps scientists and students confirm their ideas and identify sources of error. They may also have learned from others' observations and inferences, if another student noticed something that they did not.
Energy is the ability to cause change or do work.	**ASK:** What indicators suggested that energy was involved in the demonstrations? **LISTEN:** Students should understand that some type of change during the demonstrations was an indicator that energy was involved. Students may cite the spinning of the radiometer flags or the turning on of the flashlight.
Energy exists in different forms and can be changed from one form to another.	**ASK:** What indicators suggest that energy exists in different forms? **LISTEN:** Students should describe how the radiometer changed because the flags started to move. The flashlight changed because it produced light that was visible. They both had changes, even though they were different, suggesting that energy exists in different forms.

Targeted Concepts, Skills, and Nature of Science	How do I know if students got it?
Kinetic energy is associated with the motion of an object.	**ASK:** What type of indicator shows kinetic energy? **LISTEN:** Students should understand how anything that is moving has kinetic energy.
Visible light is a small band within the electromagnetic spectrum, that is energy traveling in the form of waves.	**ASK:** What type of energy does a flashlight produce? **LISTEN:** Students should answer that the flashlight produces visible light, which is a form of radiation.
Electrical energy is the flow of charges through a circuit.	**ASK:** How is electrical energy involved in the flashlight? **LISTEN:** Students should describe how electrical energy travels through the filament of the light bulb, causing it to glow.
Potential energy is stored energy associated with position or condition.	**ASK:** What type of energy is transformed into electrical energy in the flashlight? **LISTEN:** Students should understand that chemical energy stored in the battery is transformed into the electrical energy of the flashlight.

Teacher Reflection Questions

- What evidence do you have that students can recognize indicators of energy? What additional examples can you provide to make sure they understand this concept?

- How were you able to identify questions they still need to investigate for the *Project Board?* How can you help students with this as they progress through the *Learning Set?*

- How were you able to keep students engaged in the discussions in this section? What can you try next time?

1.2 Explore

What Types of Energy Transformations Occur in Your Everyday Life?

◀ *2 class periods*

A class period is considered to be one 40 to 50 minute class.

Overview

Students observe changes that take place in a pop-up toaster demonstration to introduce the three more forms of energy—elastic, sound, and thermal. In a group investigation, they use their new science knowledge to identify the forms of energy in other everyday objects. Students then take part in an *Investigation Expo* to share their findings, identify remaining questions, and update the *Project Board*.

Targeted Concepts, Skills, and Nature of Science	Performance Expectations
Scientists often work together and then share their findings. Sharing findings makes new information available and helps scientists refine their ideas and build on others' ideas. When another person's or group's idea is used, credit needs to be given.	After groups investigate and identify the forms of energy in several select objects, they share their findings in an *Investigation Expo* with the class. The rest of the class learns from the conclusions of other groups' work.
Sound is the transfer of energy as longitudinal waves that cannot travel through a vacuum.	Students discover that sound is a form of energy that moves in waves.
Thermal energy is the energy of the particles of matter.	Students identify thermal energy as a form of energy related to particles of matter.
Heat is the transfer of thermal energy from a substance at a higher temperature to a substance at a lower temperature.	Students discover that heat is thermal energy transferred from one object to another.

Materials	
1 per classroom	Pop-up toaster
	Slice of bread
	Small drum, or large bowl covered with plastic wrap secured by a rubber band
	Sand (may be substituted with sugar)
several per group	Tuning fork and wooden rod
	Scissors with a piece of paper
	Spring-powered toy
	Maracas
	Bouncy ball
	Flashlight
	Spring with mass
	Suction/pop-up toy
	Pendulum device
	Yo-yo
1 per student	*Energy Observations* page
	Energy Types page (filled in from the *Unit Introduction*)

Homework Options

Reflection

- **Science Content:** Do you think you can identify energy using indicators you cannot see? *(Students may realize that they can use their other senses, such as hearing and smelling, to identify some indicators of energy.)*

- **Nature of Science:** Why is it important to share your ideas with other students? *(Students should realize that they can build on each other's ideas.)*

SECTION 1.2 IMPLEMENTATION

1.2 Explore

What Types of Energy Transformations Occur in Your Everyday Life?

A kitchen is a great place to find different types of energy transformations and indicators of them. Many people use a pop-up toaster to make a warm slice of golden-brown toast to eat with their breakfast. How does a pop-up toaster transform energy to complete its task? What are the indicators of a toaster transforming energy? To prepare you to examine the energy transformed in other everyday devices, you will observe a toaster demonstration and discuss the energy transformations it shows. Then you will explore other devices you are familiar with and share with the class the many kinds of energy transformations and any indicators of them that you identify.

Many different energy transformations occur in a pop-up toaster.

Demonstration

As you observe the pop-up toaster, pay attention to all of the changes that are occurring. Every change is an indicator of energy transformation. Use as many of your senses as you can as you observe the toaster. You will not be close enough to touch or taste anything, but use your other senses. Make a list of all the changes you identify.

EN 28

Project-Based Inquiry Science

1.2 Explore

What Types of Energy Transformations Occur in Your Everyday Life?

10 min

Students start to consider the energy transformations in a pop-up toaster.

◯ **Engage**

Have students close their eyes. Ask them to listen to any sounds they might hear. Perhaps they hear a door closing in the hallway, students or teachers talking, or vehicles moving outside a window. Tell students that they have found another way to identify energy—by listening. Point out to students that they should use all of their senses to look for indicators of energy.

*A class period is considered to be one 40 to 50 minute class.

Demonstration

5 min

Students observe energy changes in a pop-up toaster.

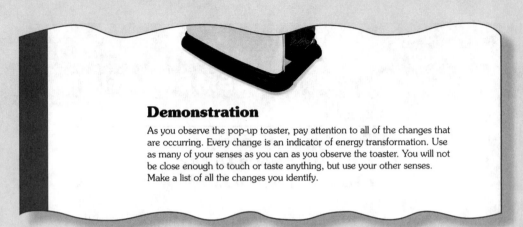

Demonstration

As you observe the pop-up toaster, pay attention to all of the changes that are occurring. Every change is an indicator of energy transformation. Use as many of your senses as you can as you observe the toaster. You will not be close enough to touch or taste anything, but use your other senses. Make a list of all the changes you identify.

△ Guide

Briefly review the operation of a pop-up toaster for students who may not be familiar with it. Then demonstrate how the toaster operates using a slice of bread. Ask students to use their senses, except for taste, to observe changes that took place.

TEACHER TALK

"What did you see? What did you hear? What did you smell? What do these observations indicate about energy?"

NOTES

....

....

....

....

....

....

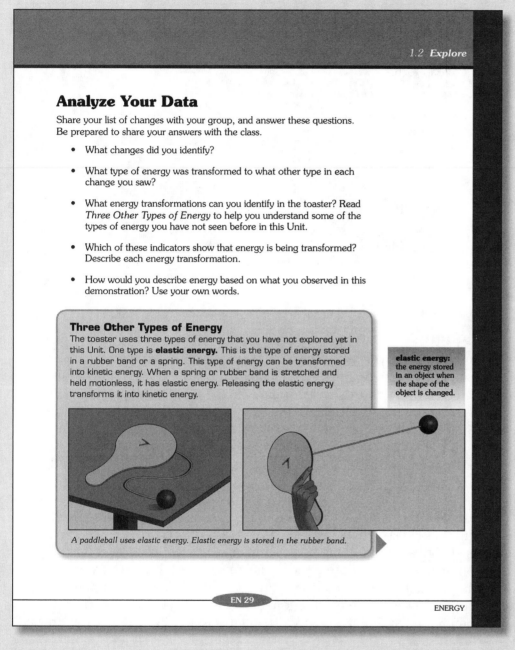

1.2 Explore

Analyze Your Data

Share your list of changes with your group, and answer these questions. Be prepared to share your answers with the class.

- What changes did you identify?

- What type of energy was transformed to what other type in each change you saw?

- What energy transformations can you identify in the toaster? Read *Three Other Types of Energy* to help you understand some of the types of energy you have not seen before in this Unit.

- Which of these indicators show that energy is being transformed? Describe each energy transformation.

- How would you describe energy based on what you observed in this demonstration? Use your own words.

Three Other Types of Energy

The toaster uses three types of energy that you have not explored yet in this Unit. One type is **elastic energy.** This is the type of energy stored in a rubber band or a spring. This type of energy can be transformed into kinetic energy. When a spring or rubber band is stretched and held motionless, it has elastic energy. Releasing the elastic energy transforms it into kinetic energy.

elastic energy:
the energy stored in an object when the shape of the object is changed.

A paddleball uses elastic energy. Elastic energy is stored in the rubber band.

EN 29

ENERGY

Analyze Your Data

5 min

Students identify the forms of energy they observed and the indicators they used to identify them.

△ Guide

Lead a discussion in which students share their ideas about the changes they observed. Help them recognize that the toast moved, the toaster made a sound, the bread produced a different smell, and the appearance of the bread changed. Direct students to read *Three Other Forms of Energy* to help them answer the questions.

Three Other Types of Energy

10 min

Students are introduced to definitions and examples of elastic, sound, and thermal energy.

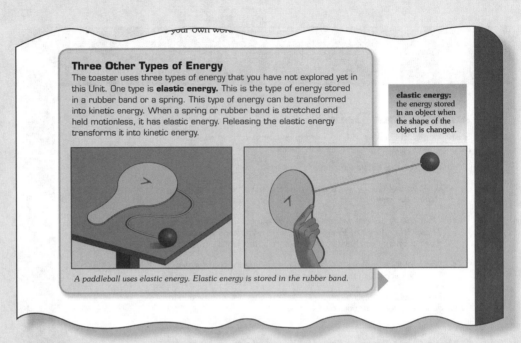

Three Other Types of Energy

The toaster uses three types of energy that you have not explored yet in this Unit. One type is **elastic energy.** This is the type of energy stored in a rubber band or a spring. This type of energy can be transformed into kinetic energy. When a spring or rubber band is stretched and held motionless, it has elastic energy. Releasing the elastic energy transforms it into kinetic energy.

elastic energy:
the energy stored in an object when the shape of the object is changed.

A paddleball uses elastic energy. Elastic energy is stored in the rubber band.

○ Engage

Introduce students to elastic energy by having them read the text. Then show students a coiled-spring toy. Gently stretch the toy and allow students to watch as the toy returns to its original shape. Explain that when you stretch the coil, you give it elastic energy. When you let go, that energy is transformed into the kinetic energy of the moving coil. Try stretching the coil to different distances so students can compare the movement of the coil back to its original position. Guide students to understand that the farther you stretch the coil, the greater is the amount of elastic energy you give it.

△ Guide

Point out to the class that elastic energy is stored energy when certain objects are stretched or compressed. When the object is allowed to return to its original form, the stored energy is transformed. Another example is pulling back an arrow in a bow. When the arrow is released, the stored energy is converted to the kinetic energy of the moving arrow. The compressed spring in some wristwatches is another example of an object that stores energy. As the spring is released, the stored energy is transformed into the kinetic energy of the moving hands of the watch.

META NOTES

The stored energy in elastic energy is *potential energy.* Keep this in mind as the class discusses their reading but do not introduce students to the term yet. They will learn this later in the Unit.

NOTES

....

Project-Based Inquiry Science

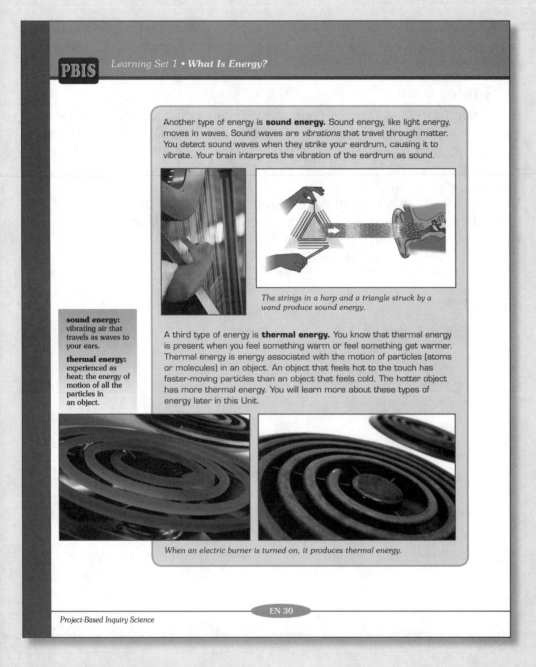

Another type of energy is **sound energy.** Sound energy, like light energy, moves in waves. Sound waves are *vibrations* that travel through matter. You detect sound waves when they strike your eardrum, causing it to vibrate. Your brain interprets the vibration of the eardrum as sound.

The strings in a harp and a triangle struck by a wand produce sound energy.

sound energy:
vibrating air that travels as waves to your ears.

thermal energy:
experienced as heat; the energy of motion of all the particles in an object.

A third type of energy is **thermal energy.** You know that thermal energy is present when you feel something warm or feel something get warmer. Thermal energy is energy associated with the motion of particles (atoms or molecules) in an object. An object that feels hot to the touch has faster-moving particles than an object that feels cold. The hotter object has more thermal energy. You will learn more about these types of energy later in this Unit.

When an electric burner is turned on, it produces thermal energy.

EN 30

Project-Based Inquiry Science

◯ Engage

When the class has been introduced to sound energy, enforce their understanding with a demonstration. Bring in a small drum or make a drum by stretching plastic wrap across a bowl and securing it with a large rubber band. Place sand or sugar on the drum head and gently tap the drum several times. Show students how the sand or sugar vibrates each time you hit the drum. If you continue, the sand or sugar granules will become arranged in rows. Explain that sound energy travels in waves produced when some form of matter vibrates back and forth. The sugar or sand granules bounce up and down as the sound wave passes them.

△ Guide

Introduce students to thermal energy using the student text and briefly explain that all matter is made up of smaller particles. Those particles are in constant motion. As a result, they have kinetic energy. They also have some stored energy. The total energy of the particles is thermal energy. Ask students what happens if they place an ice cube in a cup of hot tea. Students should answer that the ice cube melts. Explain to the class that thermal energy is transferred from a hotter substance, the tea, to a cooler substance, the ice cube. Describe the transfer of thermal energy as heat.

NOTES

....

....

....

....

....

....

....

....

....

....

1.2 Explore

What Types of Energy Play a Role in Everyday Devices, and What Are Their Indicators?

You have already begun to identify indicators of many different types of energy. As you complete this Unit, you will learn more about different types of energy. In this exploration, you will look for indicators of energy in everyday objects. Each group will explore and observe a different set of objects from the list of materials. After your exploration, you will report back to the class. Organize your observations on your *Energy Observations* page.

Procedure

1. List each object you have been given on your *Energy Observations* page.

2. Operate the object as it was intended to be used.

3. Record how the object operates and the energy indicators you observe. Record your observations about the types of energy present in the object. If you see a new form of energy, describe it as best you can. After you learn about more types of energy, you will return to this page.

Analyze Your Data

1. What changes did you observe that indicated the presence of a particular type of energy? List a change for each object you investigated. Record it in the *Observations* column.

2. If you observed changes that you were not able to link to a type of energy, describe them.

3. What indicators were similar among the objects you observed? Explain why you think the indicators were similar.

Materials
- tuning fork and wooden rod
- scissors with piece of paper
- spring-powered toy
- maracas
- bouncy ball
- flashlight
- spring with mass
- suction/pop-up toy
- Newton's cradle
- yo-yo

	Energy Observations		1.2.1/2.1.1
Name:		Date:	
Object	Observation of how the object works	Indicator	Type(s) of energy

EN 31

ENERGY

What Types of Energy Play a Role in Everyday Devices, and What Are Their Indicators?

15 min

Students prepare to observe household items for forms of energy.

⬡ **Get Going**

Have students meet with their groups and read the procedure. Ask them to get their *Energy Observations* pages ready to begin the investigation.

△ **Guide**

Allow students to manipulate the objects. Demonstrate the operation of objects if any students are unsure. Remind students to use their senses to observe any changes that occur and to record all of their observations.

Analyze Your Data

10 min

Students discuss their observations and answers to the questions.

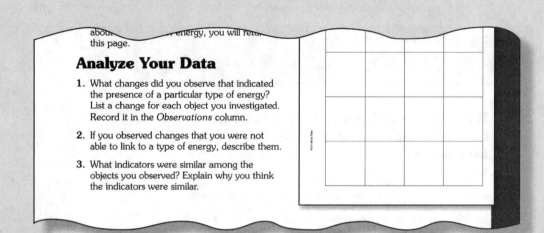

about ... energy, you will ret...
this page.

Analyze Your Data

1. What changes did you observe that indicated the presence of a particular type of energy? List a change for each object you investigated. Record it in the *Observations* column.

2. If you observed changes that you were not able to link to a type of energy, describe them.

3. What indicators were similar among the objects you observed? Explain why you think the indicators were similar.

△ Guide and Assess

Monitor group discussions. Make sure students are contributing to the discussion and taking notes. By the end of the discussion, they should be ready to present their answers to the class.

1. Students' answers will vary. For kinetic energy, some form of motion is the indicator. The maracas will make a sound, indicating sound energy, as will many of the other devices. Elastic potential energy will be indicated by a compressed spring or an extended spring. Chemical potential energy is indicated by the light from the flashlight.

2. Students' answers will vary. The pendulum may confuse students as it uses gravity, moving from potential energy at its highest point to kinetic energy at its lowest point.

3. Students should realize that all the spring toys fit into a common category, elastic energy. They may not realize that the bouncy ball also uses elastic energy. The tuning fork and maracas were similar in exhibiting sound energy. The pendulum and yo-yo are similar in exhibiting gravitational potential energy. The flashlight stands alone with chemical potential energy and light energy.

4. Students' answers will vary but should be similar to the answers above.

5. Students should understand that the most common form of energy indicator is motion. Motion is the indicator of kinetic energy.

4. How many types of energy were you able to identify in your objects? Describe each type of energy, including the indicator or indicators that allowed you to detect it.

5. What were the most common energy indicators you observed?

Communicate

Investigation Expo

Each group investigated a different set of objects. So that everyone in the class will experience each of the objects, you will present your objects to the class and describe how they operate. Before beginning, quickly make a small poster. It should include

- the information in your chart,

- your list of the forms of energy you identified and the indicators for each, and

- the most common indicators for your types of energy.

Do not worry if you do not know names of some of the types of energy you observed.

When it is your group's turn to present, take turns presenting different features of each object. Begin by demonstrating how your object operates. Then,

- identify the changes you observed and the indicators that allowed you to detect each type of energy,

- share your ideas with the class about the types of energy you saw in your objects, including any questions you have, and

- present the list of forms of energy and their indicators, and tell the class which indicators are most common for each form of energy.

As you are listening, note the different types of energy each group has identified and the indicators for each type. If you do not understand what a group is presenting, or if you disagree with their conclusions, ask questions. Remember to be respectful.

Project-Based Inquiry Science

Communicate
Investigation Expo
20 min

Students use an Investigation Expo *to share their ideas.*

⬡ Get Going

Ask groups to prepare their posters. Remind them to include the information on the bulleted list in their text. Allow each group to present their posters. Make sure students identify the forms of the energy they observed, either by naming them or describing them in their own words. Monitor to make sure that students are listening to the presentations of other groups. Tell students they can learn from what other students observed, but they do not always have to agree.

Reflect

5 min

Students revise their descriptions of energy.

After all of the groups have presented their results and shared their ideas, update your *Energy Types* page with all the energy types you learned about in this *Learning Set* and in the presentations. You can revise some of the information already recorded.

Reflect

At the beginning of this section, you wrote a description of energy based on what you observed in the demonstration of the pop-up toaster. How would you describe energy now that you have observed the operation of so many different objects?

Update the Project Board

As you read about different types of energy, you probably identified indicators for some of the types of energy you know about. Record what you have learned about indicators for each type of energy in the *What are we learning?* column. Record your evidence in the *What is our evidence?* column. Use the *What do we need to investigate?* column to record any new questions you have about energy and indicators.

Energy Types		
Name: _____		Date: _____
Type of energy	Indicators that this type is being transformed	Factors that affect the amount of energy

Design a Rube Goldberg machine to turn off a light				
What do we think we know?	What do we need to investigate?	What are we learning?	What is our evidence?	What does it mean for the challenge or question?

⬡ Get Going

Allow students to revise the descriptions of energy they wrote at the beginning of the section. Advise them to include information they have learned from the reading, the investigations of household items, and what they learned in the *Investigation Expo.*

◯ Get Going

Have a class discussion in which the class updates the *Project Board*. As students add to the *What do we think we know?* column, make sure they provide evidence to support their claims. Explain that evidence is the information they use to develop their ideas. It might be based on science knowledge they learned through reading or observations made during demonstrations or activities. Guide students to add evidence to support each idea to the *What is our evidence?* column of the *Project Board*.

Discuss any questions students still have about energy and any questions they need answers to in order to accomplish the *Big Challenge*. Add these questions to the *Project Board*.

Update the Project Board

15 min

Students add ideas, evidence, and questions to the Project Board.

META NOTES

If any of the questions students propose have simple yes or no answers, help them revise the questions to require substantive answers.

NOTES

What's the Point?

Changes are caused by the transformation of energy. Your senses, especially sight, are valuable in detecting indicators that show different types of energy transformations. The toaster and the objects you explored transformed electrical, kinetic, light, elastic, sound, chemical, and thermal energy. You identified indicators for each of these. Because energy is used everywhere, it is easy to observe many different energy indicators. Each type of energy is different from the others. What they all have in common is that they all are used to produce change.

A fire transforms chemical energy (contained in the fuel) into thermal energy.

NOTES

....

....

....

Assessment Options

Targeted Concepts, Skills, and Nature of Science	How do I know if students got it?
Scientists often work together and then share their findings. Sharing findings makes new information available and helps scientists refine their ideas and build on others' ideas. When another person's or group's idea is used, credit needs to be given.	**ASK:** What did you gain by listening to the ideas of others? **LISTEN:** Students may recall that they found out other students may have agreed with their ideas or they may have figured out something they were unsure about during their group discussion and the *Investigation Expo.*
Sound is the transfer of energy as longitudinal waves that cannot travel through a vacuum.	**ASK:** How is a sound produced? **LISTEN:** Students should recognize that air vibration produces a sound.
Thermal energy is the energy of the particles of matter.	**ASK:** What is the source of an object's thermal energy? **LISTEN:** Students should relate the motion of the particles of matter to thermal energy.
Heat is the transfer of thermal energy from a substance at a higher temperature to a substance at a lower temperature.	**ASK:** What is heat? **LISTEN:** Students should define heat as the transfer of thermal energy.

Teacher Reflection Questions

- What evidence do you have that students are developing a better understanding of energy?

- How were you able to determine if students could differentiate among different forms of energy?

- Did students have any difficulties making observations and keeping organized records of their observations? What might you do to help them develop better procedures next time?

NOTES

Back to the Big Challenge

Design a Rube Goldberg machine to turn off a light.

◀ *2 class periods*

A class period is considered to be one 40 to 50 minute class.

Overview

Students revisit the Rube Goldberg designs they investigated at the beginning of the Unit. They apply the science knowledge they have learned to interpret the designs and use this experience to plan their own Rube Goldberg machine that will turn off a light. They consider the specific details of the design and the energy transformations that take place. They share their ideas with the class before going on to learn about the importance of saving energy. Finally, they update the *Project Board* with the ideas they have learned and the questions they still need to have answered.

Targeted Concepts, Skills, and Nature of Science	Performance Expectations
Scientists often work together and then share their findings. Sharing findings makes new information available and helps scientists refine their ideas and build on others' ideas. When another person's or group's idea is used, credit needs to be given.	Students share their analyses of Rube Goldberg machines, share their designs, and share their ideas and questions to update the *Project Board*.

Materials	
1 per student	*Rube Goldberg Design* page *Project Board* page
1 per class	Class *Project Board*

Homework Options

Reflection

- **Science Content:** How is it possible for different students to have different designs to accomplish the same task? *(Students should recognize that there can be many different ways to perform the same task depending on the materials used and the types of energy involved.)*

- **Science Content:** What advantage is there to sharing possible designs? *(Students should suggest that students can learn from one another by sharing their designs.)*

NOTES

....

....

....

....

....

....

....

....

....

....

Learning Set 1

Back to the Big Challenge

Design a Rube Goldberg machine to turn off a light.

Your challenge is to design a machine that will turn off a light when light is no longer needed. To succeed at this task, you will use your creativity and imagination. In this *Learning Set*, you learned about some types of energy and about the indicators you can observe to know when energy is being transformed. Now you will examine your energy-transformation cartoon and apply what you have learned. You will identify the types of energy transformations in the cartoon and the indicators of each. Then you will use what you have learned about different types of energy and their indicators to begin designing your own Rube Goldberg machine.

Observe

During the introduction to this Unit, you examined an energy-transformation cartoon, and you identified many of the energy transformations in it. You have learned more about energy since then, and you can probably identify more types of energy than you could before. With your group, identify as many types of energy in the cartoon as you can. For each, identify the indicators that tell you what type of energy is being transformed to what other type. Record your ideas on an *Energy-transformation Cartoon* page.

EN 35

Learning Set 1

Back to the Big Challenge

5 min

Students begin the plan for their Rube Goldberg machine and investigate energy resources.

△ Guide

Tell students that they will be using what they have learned about energy to design their Rube Goldberg machine. Explain that before they come up with a plan, it will help to go back and review the designs they saw at the beginning of the Unit now that they have a better understanding of energy.

*A class period is considered to be one 40 to 50 minute class.

Observe

10 min

Students review the cartoons they saw at the beginning of the Unit.

transformed... w you will examine your energy-transformation cartoon and apply what you have learned. You will identify the types of energy transformations in the cartoon and the indicators of each. Then you will use what you have learned about different types of energy and their indicators to begin designing your own Rube Goldberg machine.

Observe

During the introduction to this Unit, you examined an energy-transformation cartoon, and you identified many of the energy transformations in it. You have learned more about energy since then, and you can probably identify more types of energy than you could before. With your group, identify as many types of energy in the cartoon as you can. For each, identify the indicators that tell you what type of energy is being transformed to what other type. Record your ideas on an *Energy-transformation Cartoon* page.

⬡ Get Going

Direct groups back to the Rube Goldberg design cartoons they investigated at the beginning of the Unit. Ask them to review their descriptions, which they wrote before they learned about energy. Ask students to consider all that they now know about energy and identity the forms of energy in the cartoons. Have them record their observations on the *Energy-transformation Cartoon* pages. Remind them to note the indicators they use to determine that energy is involved at each point in the design.

NOTES

....

....

....

....

....

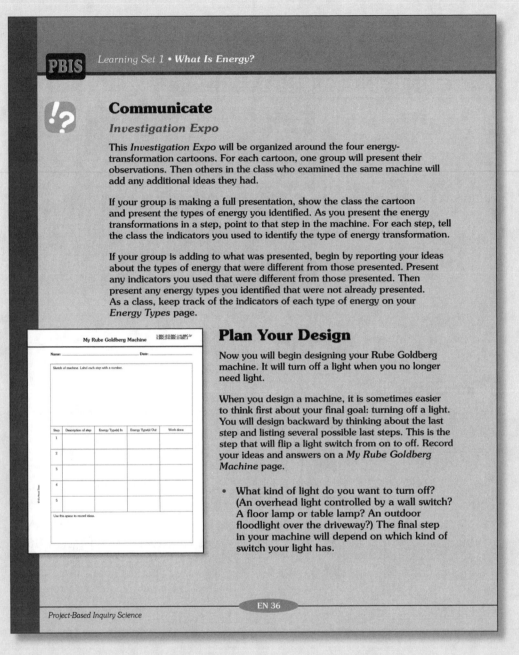

Communicate
Investigation Expo

This *Investigation Expo* will be organized around the four energy-transformation cartoons. For each cartoon, one group will present their observations. Then others in the class who examined the same machine will add any additional ideas they had.

If your group is making a full presentation, show the class the cartoon and present the types of energy you identified. As you present the energy transformations in a step, point to that step in the machine. For each step, tell the class the indicators you used to identify the type of energy transformation.

If your group is adding to what was presented, begin by reporting your ideas about the types of energy that were different from those presented. Present any indicators you used that were different from those presented. Then present any energy types you identified that were not already presented. As a class, keep track of the indicators of each type of energy on your *Energy Types* page.

Plan Your Design

Now you will begin designing your Rube Goldberg machine. It will turn off a light when you no longer need light.

When you design a machine, it is sometimes easier to think first about your final goal: turning off a light. You will design backward by thinking about the last step and listing several possible last steps. This is the step that will flip a light switch from on to off. Record your ideas and answers on a *My Rube Goldberg Machine* page.

- What kind of light do you want to turn off? (An overhead light controlled by a wall switch? A floor lamp or table lamp? An outdoor floodlight over the driveway?) The final step in your machine will depend on which kind of switch your light has.

Communicate Investigation Expo
15 min

Students share their ideas about the energy in the cartoons in an Investigation Expo.

△ Guide

Allow groups to present their observations of the Rube Goldberg cartoons. As groups present, they should show the cartoon and identify the forms of energy at each step. Others students in the class should share any additional ideas that they have as the cartoons are presented. Try to elicit ideas about forms of energy and indicators throughout the presentations. Remind students to point out examples involving energy, even if they are unsure about how to name the form of energy.

PBIS

Plan Your Design

15 min

Students will produce a preliminary design for a Rube Goldberg machine to turn off a light.

...types of energy ... ... from tho... ...

any indicators you used that were different from those presented. Then present any energy types you identified that were not already presented. As a class, keep track of the indicators of each type of energy on your *Energy Types* page.

My Rube Goldberg Machine				

Name: _____ Date: _____

Sketch of machine. Label each step with a number.

Step	Description of step	Energy Type(s) In	Energy Type(s) Out	Work done
1				
2				
3				
4				
5				

Use this space to record ideas.

Plan Your Design

Now you will begin designing your Rube Goldberg machine. It will turn off a light when you no longer need light.

When you design a machine, it is sometimes easier to think first about your final goal: turning off a light. You will design backward by thinking about the last step and listing several possible last steps. This is the step that will flip a light switch from on to off. Record your ideas and answers on a *My Rube Goldberg Machine* page.

- What kind of light do you want to turn off? (An overhead light controlled by a wall switch? A floor lamp or table lamp? An outdoor floodlight over the driveway?) The final step in your machine will depend on which kind of switch your light has.

⬡ Get Going

Let students know that they will now start to address the *Big Challenge*. Distribute the *Rube Goldberg Machine* pages and let students know they will start to record their designs on these. As students read the text, emphasize the instruction that they should plan the last step as their first step. Let students know that they should not produce one solution, but several for their group to consider and decide on.

Have students review the bulleted items before they start drawing. Ask them to think about each item carefully, and then use their decisions to plan their designs.

NOTES

_____

_____

_____

_____

_____

- Look for steps in the energy-transformation cartoons that you think would perform well as a final step for your machine. Select three possible final steps for your design. This will help you later if you decide you want to change your design because it does not look as if it will work.

- For each possible final step, list the kind of energy transformation needed to perform the task and what kind of energy the last step needs as an input.

- For each possible final step, think through how you might need to adapt the step in the energy-transformation cartoon.

Communicate

Plan Briefing

You will present the sketches of your ideas to the class in a *Plan Briefing*. The class will need to understand from your sketches how the last step of your design might operate. When it is your group's turn to present their ideas and answers to the questions, use your *My Rube Goldberg Machine* page as a guide. Present each of your design ideas, the type of energy transformation in each, and how you might provide energy for the last step. Show the class your sketches and describe your reasoning so that your classmates will understand your ideas.

As you listen to other groups, ask questions if you do not understand a group's ideas. Listen, too, for ideas that might help you meet your challenge.

Reflect

Earlier, you were introduced to the concepts of *energy* and *work*. You were told that energy does work, and you created descriptions of what you thought energy and work are. Now that you have experienced so many more examples of energy transformation, you probably have a better idea of what energy and work are. Look back at your old descriptions of energy and work, and answer these questions.

1. What is energy?

2. What is work?

3. What else do you need to know about energy, indicators, work, or energy transformations to successfully complete the challenge?

EN 37

ENERGY

Communicate
Plan Briefing

15 min

Students present their plans for a Rube Goldberg machine to the class.

△ Guide Presentations and Discussions

Have each group present their design sketches. Encourage them to describe the details of the design, including the forms of energy and their transformations. Make sure other students are listening carefully so they can not only provide the presenter with information, but also gather information they may need to improve their own designs.

Remind students not to become discouraged if you or other students point out shortcomings with their designs. Explain that the point of communicating their plans is to gather more information, identify problems, and make corrections. This will help them to better accomplish the *Big Challenge* in the end.

Reflect

5 min

Students think about additional information they still need to accomplish the Big Challenge.

As you listen to other groups, ask questions if you do not understand a group's ideas. Listen, too, for ideas that might help you meet your challenge.

Reflect

Earlier, you were introduced to the concepts of *energy* and *work*. You were told that energy does work, and you created descriptions of what you thought energy and work are. Now that you have experienced so many more examples of energy transformation, you probably have a better idea of what energy and work are. Look back at your old descriptions of energy and work, and answer these questions.

1. What is energy?

2. What is work?

3. What else do you need to know about energy, indicators, work, or energy transformations to successfully complete the challenge?

△ Guide and Assess

1. Student answers will vary but all new answers to this question should reflect their deeper understanding of energy based upon their experiences and discussions. In its essence, energy is the capacity to do something, and that something is work.

2. Student answers will vary but all new answers to this question should reflect their deeper understanding of work based upon their experiences and discussions. Fundamentally, work is doing something, using energy.

3. Student answers will vary.

△ Guide and Discuss

Have students use their designs to figure out what they still need to know in order to make their Rube Goldberg machine work. Discuss students' thoughts and questions. Many students have similar questions and may be able to work together to answer questions based on what they have already learned.

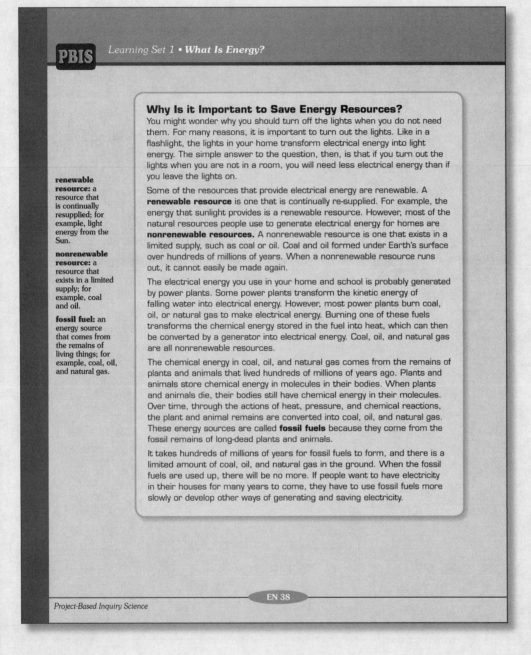

Why Is it Important to Save Energy Resources?

You might wonder why you should turn off the lights when you do not need them. For many reasons, it is important to turn out the lights. Like in a flashlight, the lights in your home transform electrical energy into light energy. The simple answer to the question, then, is that if you turn out the lights when you are not in a room, you will need less electrical energy than if you leave the lights on.

Some of the resources that provide electrical energy are renewable. A **renewable resource** is one that is continually re-supplied. For example, the energy that sunlight provides is a renewable resource. However, most of the natural resources people use to generate electrical energy for homes are **nonrenewable resources.** A nonrenewable resource is one that exists in a limited supply, such as coal or oil. Coal and oil formed under Earth's surface over hundreds of millions of years. When a nonrenewable resource runs out, it cannot easily be made again.

The electrical energy you use in your home and school is probably generated by power plants. Some power plants transform the kinetic energy of falling water into electrical energy. However, most power plants burn coal, oil, or natural gas to make electrical energy. Burning one of these fuels transforms the chemical energy stored in the fuel into heat, which can then be converted by a generator into electrical energy. Coal, oil, and natural gas are all nonrenewable resources.

The chemical energy in coal, oil, and natural gas comes from the remains of plants and animals that lived hundreds of millions of years ago. Plants and animals store chemical energy in molecules in their bodies. When plants and animals die, their bodies still have chemical energy in their molecules. Over time, through the actions of heat, pressure, and chemical reactions, the plant and animal remains are converted into coal, oil, and natural gas. These energy sources are called **fossil fuels** because they come from the fossil remains of long-dead plants and animals.

It takes hundreds of millions of years for fossil fuels to form, and there is a limited amount of coal, oil, and natural gas in the ground. When the fossil fuels are used up, there will be no more. If people want to have electricity in their houses for many years to come, they have to use fossil fuels more slowly or develop other ways of generating and saving electricity.

renewable resource: a resource that is continually resupplied; for example, light energy from the Sun.

nonrenewable resource: a resource that exists in a limited supply; for example, coal and oil.

fossil fuel: an energy source that comes from the remains of living things; for example, coal, oil, and natural gas.

Project-Based Inquiry Science

Why Is it Important to Save Energy?

10 min

Students are introduced to different types of energy resources.

META NOTES

Students may also know the term *inexhaustible resource*. An inexhaustible resource describes a source of energy that can never run out, such as solar energy and wind energy.

△ Guide

Explain to students that a natural resource used as a source of energy is often called an energy resource. You may wish to have students generate a table of renewable and nonrenewable energy resources such as the one on the following page.

Nonrenewable Energy Source	Renewable Energy Source
oil (fossil fuel)	solar
natural gas (fossil fuel)	wind
coal (fossil fuel)	geothermal
uranium (nuclear energy)	biomass
	hydropower
	tidal power

NOTES

....

....

....

....

....

....

....

....

....

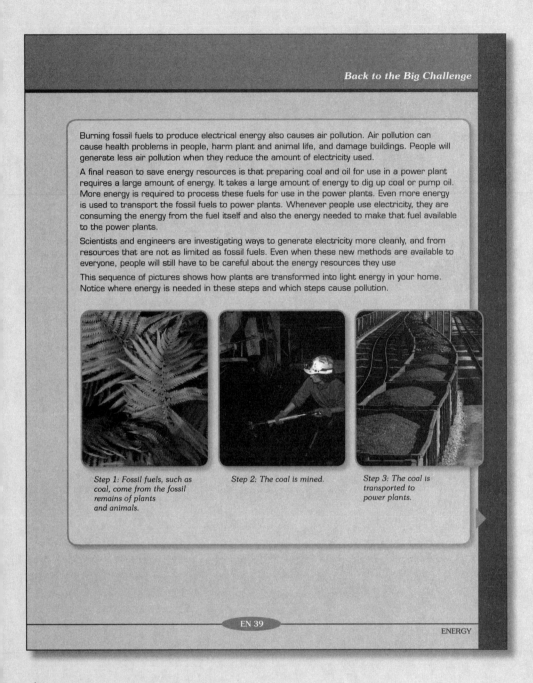

Burning fossil fuels to produce electrical energy also causes air pollution. Air pollution can cause health problems in people, harm plant and animal life, and damage buildings. People will generate less air pollution when they reduce the amount of electricity used.

A final reason to save energy resources is that preparing coal and oil for use in a power plant requires a large amount of energy. It takes a large amount of energy to dig up coal or pump oil. More energy is required to process these fuels for use in the power plants. Even more energy is used to transport the fossil fuels to power plants. Whenever people use electricity, they are consuming the energy from the fuel itself and also the energy needed to make that fuel available to the power plants.

Scientists and engineers are investigating ways to generate electricity more cleanly, and from resources that are not as limited as fossil fuels. Even when these new methods are available to everyone, people will still have to be careful about the energy resources they use

This sequence of pictures shows how plants are transformed into light energy in your home. Notice where energy is needed in these steps and which steps cause pollution.

Step 1: Fossil fuels, such as coal, come from the fossil remains of plants and animals.

Step 2: The coal is mined.

Step 3: The coal is transported to power plants.

EN 39

ENERGY

⚠ Guide and Discuss

Lead a discussion in which students discuss the importance of conserving nonrenewable resources. Encourage students to brainstorm ways that they can make changes in their own lives to reduce their use of energy in order to save natural resources.

Update the Project Board

10 min

Students add information to the Project Board.

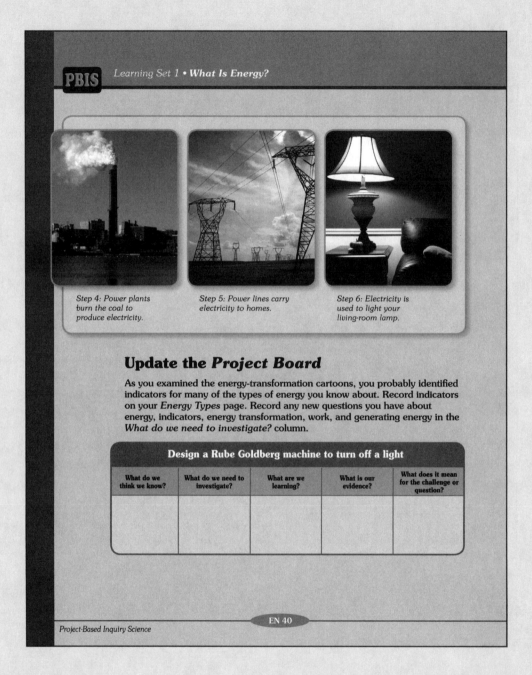

Step 4: Power plants burn the coal to produce electricity.

Step 5: Power lines carry electricity to homes.

Step 6: Electricity is used to light your living-room lamp.

Update the *Project Board*

As you examined the energy-transformation cartoons, you probably identified indicators for many of the types of energy you know about. Record indicators on your *Energy Types* page. Record any new questions you have about energy, indicators, energy transformation, work, and generating energy in the *What do we need to investigate?* column.

Design a Rube Goldberg machine to turn off a light				
What do we think we know?	What do we need to investigate?	What are we learning?	What is our evidence?	What does it mean for the challenge or question?

Project-Based Inquiry Science

EN 40

△ Guide

Ask students about any new ideas they developed as they reviewed the Rube Goldberg designs, planned their own design, and learned about saving energy. Add the ideas to the *Project Board*. Ask students what questions remain that they need answered. Add these to the *Project Board* as well.

Assessment Options

Targeted Concepts, Skills, and Nature of Science	How do I know if students got it?
Scientists often work together and then share their findings. Sharing findings makes new information available and helps scientists refine their ideas and build on others' ideas. When another person's or group's idea is used, credit needs to be given.	**ASK:** What did you learn by listening to the design plans of others? **LISTEN:** Students may suggest that they got ideas about how to improve upon their own designs during the *Investigation Expo* and *Plan Briefing*.

Teacher Reflection Questions

- What difficulties did students have in revising explanations they had already made? How might you encourage them in the future to make improvements to explanations and designs?

- What concerns did students have as they planned their Rube Goldberg designs? In what ways can you build their confidence as they work with their designs?

- How did you get students to contribute to the discussion of what to put on the *Project Board?* Are there other things you can do to encourage them?

NOTES

NOTES

LEARNING SET 2 INTRODUCTION

Learning Set 2

What Affects How Much Energy an Object Has?

◀ *12 class periods*

A class period is considered to be one 40 to 50 minute class.

Students investigate methods of measuring the amount of energy an object has. They learn to recognize kinetic energy and potential energy, as well as different types of potential energy. Students then apply what they learn about energy to design an experiment to measure how specific factors affect the amount of energy an object has.

Overview

Students begin by relating a change in some indicator to the amount of kinetic energy an object has. They consider the factors that determine the amount of energy. They learn how mass and speed affect kinetic energy. They then relate kinetic energy to mass and speed in common situations. They revisit the energy-transformation cartoons and analyze them again, this time in terms of work and kinetic energy. Students then use what they learned to decide whether mass or speed has the greater effect on kinetic energy. The topic of potential energy is then explored. Students are introduced to gravitational potential energy and elastic potential energy. The conservation of mechanical energy is introduced by showing students how transformations between kinetic and potential energy maintain a constant overall amount of energy in a system. Students then observe a demonstration that relates kinetic energy to the motion of an object that is falling due to the pull of gravity. Students use what they learn to design an experiment to test one factor that affects an object's potential energy. In their designs, students identify the independent and dependent variables. They perform their experiments, create graphs, and look for trends in their data. After developing an understanding of gravitational potential energy, students examine elastic potential energy more closely by identifying devices that store this type of energy.

Targeted Concepts, Skills, and Nature of Science	Section
Scientists often work together and then share their findings. Sharing findings makes new information available and helps scientists refine their ideas and build on others' ideas. When another person's or group's idea is used, credit needs to be given.	2.1, 2.2, 2.3, 2.5, 2.6

ENERGY

Targeted Concepts, Skills, and Nature of Science	Section
Energy is the ability to cause change or do work.	2.1, 2.2, 2.3, 2.4, 2.5, 2.6
Energy exists in different forms and can be changed from one form to another.	2.4, 2.5, 2.6
Energy is neither created nor destroyed in ordinary processes.	2.4
Kinetic energy is associated with the motion of an object.	2.1, 2.2, 2.3, 2.4, 2.5, 2.6
Potential energy is stored energy, associated with position or condition.	2.4, 2.5, 2.6
Studying the work of different scientists provides understanding of scientific inquiry and reminds students that science is a human endeavor.	2.5
Scientists make claims (conclusions) based on evidence (trends in data) from reliable investigations.	2.5
Scientific knowledge is developed through observations, recording and analysis of data, and development of explanations based on evidence.	2.5

Students' Initial Conceptions and Capabilities

- Students may believe that a moving object stops when its force is used up or that a moving object has its own force to keep it going without relating motion to changes in energy. (Abell and Lederman, 2007)

Understanding for Teachers

Kinetic energy is the energy of motion. The amount of kinetic energy is directly related to the mass of an object and the square of its velocity. Velocity is speed in a specific direction. If the direction is constant, speed can be used to determine kinetic energy.

$$KE = mv^2$$

The change in the kinetic energy of an object equals the work done on the object as described by the equation:

$$W = Fdcos\theta$$

W is the work done, F is the force exerted on the object, d is the displacement, and theta (θ) is the angle between the force and the displacement vector. If the force is exerted in the same direction as the object is displaced, the equation becomes:

$$W = Fd$$

For work to be done, the force exerted on an object must result in some displacement. A force is a push or pull. For example, a downward force results from Earth's gravitational field.

The work done on an object can also change its potential energy, or stored energy. For example, the work done to lift an object is stored as gravitational potential energy (G_{PE}). The amount of gravitational potential energy depends on the mass of the object, the acceleration due to gravity, and the height it is lifted.

$$G_{PE} = mgh$$

The work done to compress or stretch an object is stored as elastic potential energy (E_{PE}). The amount of elastic potential energy depends on the spring constant and the distance the spring is stretched.

$$E_{PE} = \frac{1}{2} kx^2$$

The sum total of an object's kinetic and potential energy is known as mechanical energy. The total amount of mechanical energy in a system is conserved. One form of energy can be transformed into the other, but energy is neither created nor destroyed in this process. Some energy, however, is transformed into thermal energy that is given off as heat.

NOTES

....

....

....

....

....

....

NOTES

LEARNING SET 2 IMPLEMENTATION

 Learning Set 2

What Affects How Much Energy an Object Has?

When you observed the radiometer, sometimes the flags moved faster. Sometimes they moved more slowly. And sometimes they did not move at all. You know that when an object is in motion, it has kinetic energy. However, you do not yet know what affects *how much* energy an object has or how its energy determines the amount of work that can be done.

In this *Learning Set,* you will explore some of the **factors** that affect how much energy objects have. A factor is a characteristic that you can measure. The factors that determine how much energy an object has are different for each type of energy. You will explore the factors that affect *kinetic energy,* *gravitational potential energy,* and *elastic potential energy.* You will also explore how objects can store energy and how work is used to change the amount of energy in an object. To design your best Rube Goldberg machine for turning off a light, you will need to know how to control factors that affect the amount of energy available at each step.

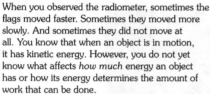

factor: a characteristic that can be measured.

EN 41

ENERGY

Learning Set 2

What Affects How Much Energy an Object Has?

5 min

Students extend their understanding of the concept of types of energy to think about the amount of energy an object has.

○ **Engage**

Ask students if they have ever gone bowling or watched someone else bowl. Then ask how the way in which the ball is thrown affects the number of pins that are knocked down.

TEACHER TALK

"What happens if you roll a bowling ball very slowly down a lane? *(It might knock down only one or two pins.)*
What happens if you throw the ball more forcefully? *(If the ball rolls to the same place, it will knock down more pins.)*
The difference has to do with the amount of energy the ball has. In this *Learning Set,* you are going to learn about factors that affect the amount of energy an object has and how you can measure differences in amounts of energy."

NOTES

2.1 Understand the Question

Think About What Affects How Much Energy an Object Has

◀ *1 class periods*

A class period is considered to be one 40 to 50 minute class.

Overview

Students observe three common toys to investigate kinetic energy. They look for indicators that they can use to compare amounts of energy. By manipulating the toys in different ways, students begin to recognize factors that affect the amount of energy each object has. Students then consider how they might be able to control the amount of kinetic energy of the objects in the machine they design to accomplish the *Big Challenge*.

Targeted Concepts, Skills, and Nature of Science	Performance Expectations
Scientists often work together and then share their findings. Sharing findings makes new information available and helps scientists refine their ideas and build on others' ideas. When another person's or group's idea is used, credit needs to be given.	Students share their ideas about energy in the toys they observe.
Energy is the ability to cause change or do work.	Students identify changes that occur in toys as indicators of energy.
Kinetic energy is associated with the motion of an object.	Students observe motion in windup toys, Newton's cradle, and bouncy balls to compare amounts of kinetic energy.

Materials	
1 per group	Windup toy Newton's cradle Bouncy ball

103

Materials	
1 per student	*Energy Observations* page *Project Board* page
1 per class	Class *Project Board*

Homework Options

Reflection

- **Science Content:** How can you identify energy if you cannot see it? *(Students should understand that they can identify indicators of energy, such as a change involving an object. It might be a change in motion, position, or shape.)*

- **Science Process:** What process can you use to compare changes in kinetic energy? *(Students should describe an organized method of changing one factor at a time to look for changes in the result, such as dropping a bouncy ball from different heights onto the same surface.)*

Preparation for 2.2

- **Science Process:** Kinetic energy is energy of motion. What indicators can you look for to decide if an object has more or less kinetic energy than another? *(This question is meant to engage students to think about finding a way to measure the "amount" of motion in order to measure the "amount" of kinetic energy.)*

SECTION 2.1 IMPLEMENTATION

2.1 Understand the Question

Think About What Affects How Much Energy an Object Has

The machine you design should have just the right amount of energy to turn off a light. If there is too much kinetic energy, the light switch might break. If there is not enough kinetic energy, the switch will not move. To design the last step, you will need to know how to control factors that affect the amount of kinetic energy available in each part of the machine. For some parts of your machine, you may want to know how to produce a lot of kinetic energy so an object will move quickly. For other parts, you may need to know how to slow or stop an object quickly and safely. In this section, you will begin to explore the factors that determine how much energy an object has.

Materials
- windup toy
- Newton's cradle
- bouncy ball

Use each toy as it was intended to be used. The ball should not be thrown hard; it should be thrown only at the floor, never at anybody or anything.

Get Started

Your group will explore three toys. Each toy has kinetic energy when it moves. Each toy gets energy from somewhere that allows it to move. Each toy performs differently depending on how much energy it has available. You will focus on three concepts as you operate each toy: the types of energy that play a role in its operation, the indicators of each type of energy, and the factors that affect how much energy it has.

2.1 Understand the Question

Think About What Affects How Much Energy an Object Has

10 min

Students consider factors that affect the amount of kinetic energy an object has.

○ Engage

Point out the photo of the snail windup toy and ask students how they can tell how much kinetic energy it contains. Give them the choices of none, a little, and a lot. Challenge them to identify the factors that control how much kinetic energy the toy snail contains. Then, wind up the toy as far as possible and release it. Have them judge how much kinetic energy it has, again using the terms, none, a little, a lot. Finally, wind up the toy only about one quarter of its full capacity and release it again. Help the students recognize that you are giving the energy to the toy snail when you wind it up. They should see that it is the work you do on the spring, as well as the capacity of the spring to store energy, that are factors in determining the amount of kinetic energy the toy initially has.

Get Started

10 min

Students manipulate three different toys to observe different amounts of kinetic energy.

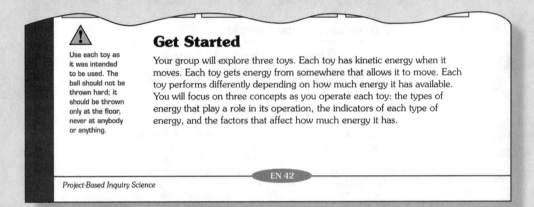

<!-- inset page image -->
⚠ Use each toy as it was intended to be used. The ball should not be thrown hard; it should be thrown only at the floor, never at anybody or anything.

Get Started

Your group will explore three toys. Each toy has kinetic energy when it moves. Each toy gets energy from somewhere that allows it to move. Each toy performs differently depending on how much energy it has available. You will focus on three concepts as you operate each toy: the types of energy that play a role in its operation, the indicators of each type of energy, and the factors that affect how much energy it has.

EN 42

Project-Based Inquiry Science

⬡ Get Going

Demonstrate how each toy should be used. Review the safety note as you do so. Prepare students for their explorations by pointing out what they should be looking at. Emphasize that they should focus on the following:

- the types of energy that play a role in its operation
- the indicators of each type of energy
- the factors that affect how much energy it has

△ Guide and Assess

As students make their observations, they should record their answers to the questions on their *Energy Observations* pages. Listen for the following in group discussions and offer any assistance if needed.

1. Students should recognize that each toy has kinetic energy when it displays some type of motion.

2. Students should relate the action they used to make the toy move to the amount of kinetic energy it has. For example, they can increase the kinetic energy by winding the toy longer, pulling the ball in Newton's cradle higher, and letting the ball bounce from a higher position.

3. Students should recognize that an increase in kinetic energy is observed as an increase in motion.

2.1 Understand the Question

In your group, examine each toy, one at a time.

Answer the following questions about each toy, and record your answers on your *Energy Observations* page.

1. How do you know the toy has kinetic energy? What indicators did you use?

2. How can you increase its kinetic energy?

3. How do you know when its kinetic energy has increased?

4. Where do you think the toy gets the energy that allows it to move?

5. What factors affect how the toy moves?

Communicate

Share Your Ideas

With your class, discuss the available energy of the toys you examined. Share your ideas about the types of energy in the toys and what indicators you observed. Also share your ideas about how you can control the amount of energy in each toy. It may be difficult to determine exactly where the energy came from, but think about it, and express it in your own words.

Energy Observations			1.2.1/2.1.1
Name:		Date:	
Object	Observation of how the object works	Indicator	Type(s) of energy

> **What Indicates That Kinetic Energy Is Present? What Affects How Much Kinetic Energy an Object Has?**
>
> You knew energy was present in all of the objects as you were playing with them because you could see the objects moving. Motion is an indicator of kinetic energy. You found ways to increase the motion of each of the toys. When you wound the windup toy tighter, it moved faster or for a longer time. When you pulled the steel ball higher before letting go of it, the ball on the opposite side also sprung up higher. When you dropped the ball from a higher position or threw it toward the ground with more force, it moved faster and bounced higher. When you saw more movement, you knew the objects had more energy in them.
>
> But what allowed each object to move? And why did it have more energy sometimes than at other times? You may have figured that out for some of the objects.

4. Students should conclude that they give the toy energy by what they do to start it in motion.

5. Students should relate the way they used the toys to the amount of energy. For example, they might drop the ball or they might throw it forcefully.

Communicate: Share Your Ideas

5 min

Students share their ideas and observations relating the motion of the toys to energy.

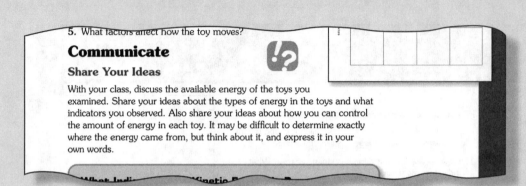

5. What factors affect how the toy moves?

Communicate

Share Your Ideas

With your class, discuss the available energy of the toys you examined. Share your ideas about the types of energy in the toys and what indicators you observed. Also share your ideas about how you can control the amount of energy in each toy. It may be difficult to determine exactly where the energy came from, but think about it, and express it in your own words.

△ Guide

Begin a brief discussion about the activity. Encourage students to share their ideas, even if they cannot describe every detail in terms of naming the energy form or source. Allow students to mention other examples of toys or objects as a means for expressing their thoughts.

NOTES

_____

_____

_____

_____

_____

_____

_____

_____

_____

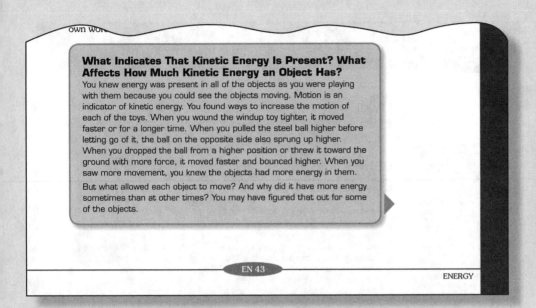

own wo...

What Indicates That Kinetic Energy Is Present? What Affects How Much Kinetic Energy an Object Has?

You knew energy was present in all of the objects as you were playing with them because you could see the objects moving. Motion is an indicator of kinetic energy. You found ways to increase the motion of each of the toys. When you wound the windup toy tighter, it moved faster or for a longer time. When you pulled the steel ball higher before letting go of it, the ball on the opposite side also sprung up higher. When you dropped the ball from a higher position or threw it toward the ground with more force, it moved faster and bounced higher. When you saw more movement, you knew the objects had more energy in them.

But what allowed each object to move? And why did it have more energy sometimes than at other times? You may have figured that out for some of the objects.

EN 43

ENERGY

What Indicates That Kinetic Energy Is Present? What Affects How Much Kinetic Energy an Object Has?

10 min

Students read about indicators and factors for kinetic energy.

△ **Guide**

Explain to students that each type of energy has indicators that it is present. Sometimes these are quite obvious, but sometimes the indicators are hard to see. Tell them also that each type of energy has factors which can be used to control the energy. Knowledge of factors will allow them to know how to make more of that type of energy or less.

Ask students to think of any examples of the energy types as they are introduced in the reading.

NOTES

....

....

....

....

....

....

Reflect

10 min

Students answer questions about the activity and think about any new questions they may have.

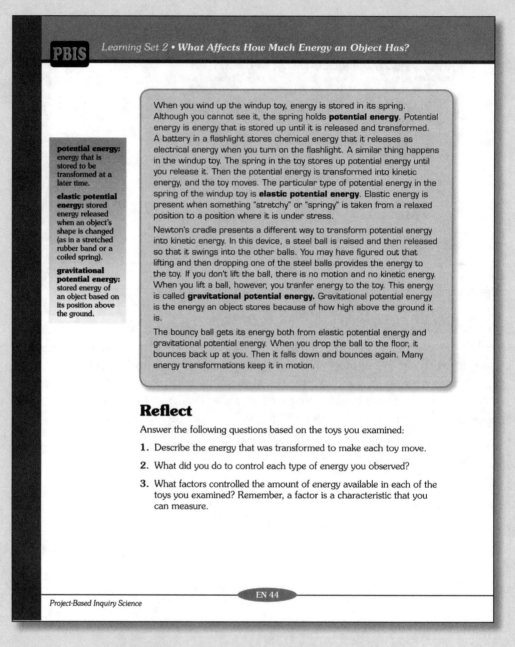

potential energy: energy that is stored to be transformed at a later time.

elastic potential energy: stored energy released when an object's shape is changed (as in a stretched rubber band or a coiled spring).

gravitational potential energy: stored energy of an object based on its position above the ground.

When you wind up the windup toy, energy is stored in its spring. Although you cannot see it, the spring holds **potential energy**. Potential energy is energy that is stored up until it is released and transformed. A battery in a flashlight stores chemical energy that it releases as electrical energy when you turn on the flashlight. A similar thing happens in the windup toy. The spring in the toy stores up potential energy until you release it. Then the potential energy is transformed into kinetic energy, and the toy moves. The particular type of potential energy in the spring of the windup toy is **elastic potential energy**. Elastic energy is present when something "stretchy" or "springy" is taken from a relaxed position to a position where it is under stress.

Newton's cradle presents a different way to transform potential energy into kinetic energy. In this device, a steel ball is raised and then released so that it swings into the other balls. You may have figured out that lifting and then dropping one of the steel balls provides the energy to the toy. If you don't lift the ball, there is no motion and no kinetic energy. When you lift a ball, however, you tranfer energy to the toy. This energy is called **gravitational potential energy.** Gravitational potential energy is the energy an object stores because of how high above the ground it is.

The bouncy ball gets its energy both from elastic potential energy and gravitational potential energy. When you drop the ball to the floor, it bounces back up at you. Then it falls down and bounces again. Many energy transformations keep it in motion.

Reflect

Answer the following questions based on the toys you examined:

1. Describe the energy that was transformed to make each toy move.

2. What did you do to control each type of energy you observed?

3. What factors controlled the amount of energy available in each of the toys you examined? Remember, a factor is a characteristic that you can measure.

Guide and Assess

Have students record their answers to the *Reflect* questions. If you find that students are having difficulty, demonstrate how each toy works one more time. Remind students that they are not expected to understand everything about energy at this time. Encourage them to provide the best possible answer with what they now know and then list questions they would still like to have answered.

1. Students should recognize that they put the energy into each toy in the form of potential energy. The windup toys stored elastic energy in a compressed spring which was transformed into kinetic energy. The bouncy ball was dropped from different heights which gave it various amounts of gravitational potential energy. As it fell, the gravitational potential energy changed to kinetic energy. When the ball struck the floor, the kinetic energy changed to elastic potential energy by deformation. Then the ball changed the elastic potential energy to kinetic energy upwards, converting the kinetic energy to gravitational potential energy. And over and over. Energy was also lost to sound and heat, but students may not know that yet. Finally, the Newton's cradle was given gravitational potential energy when a steel ball was lifted. Upon release, the stored energy became kinetic energy. A collision with the other steel balls moved the kinetic energy to the other balls (also sound and heat). Like the bouncy ball, this process continued until the balls became still.

2. Students should reply that they could vary the amount of energy in the Newton's cradle and the bouncy ball by adjusting the height to which they raised it. The energy of the windup toy was controlled by how tightly they wound (compressed) the spring.

3. Students should know that the gravitational potential energy of the bouncy ball was controlled by how high they could lift the ball above the floor before releasing it. The gravitational potential energy of the Newton's cradle was limited by the length of the string holding the first steel ball. The potential elastic energy put into the spring was limited by the characteristics of the spring. If wound too tightly, it could lose its elasticity.

NOTES

....

....

....

....

4. In each trial with a particular toy you examined, the toy could have had a different amount of kinetic energy. What indicators allowed you to compare the kinetic energy in different trials?

5. In the windup toy, the bouncy ball, and Newton's cradle, the motion eventually stopped. What did this tell you about the amount of kinetic energy in each toy?

6. What else do you need to know about kinetic and potential energy to control the motion in the machine you will design?

Update the *Project Board*

In this section, you thought about where the energy to move an object comes from. Update the *Project Board* by adding ideas to the *What do we think we know?* column. Add your ideas about how you would control the amount of energy available for motion. Also, record the factors you think determine the amount of kinetic energy. Be sure to add to the *Project Board* the ideas your group agreed on and ideas you are not sure about. You may have questions about how much a factor will control energy or how you can know how much kinetic energy or potenial energy an object has. Record your questions and ideas for investigations in the *What do we need to investigate?* column.

Design a Rube Goldberg machine to turn off a light				
What do we think we know?	What do we need to investigate?	What are we learning?	What is our evidence?	What does it mean for the challenge or question?

4. Students should understand that the height of the bounce of the bouncy ball is a measure of the kinetic energy it had when it hit the floor. The kinetic energy of the Newton's cradle steel balls can be measured by the distance traveled after being struck by the descending steel ball. The kinetic energy of the windup toy is more difficult to estimate, because the spring is constantly renewing the kinetic energy. They may say that the toy moved farther or moved faster. The total kinetic energy expended in each trial could be estimated by how long the toy runs.

5. Students should recognize that when any of the toys stopped moving, the kinetic energy was zero. How long it takes for the motion to stop would be a measure of how much initial kinetic energy the bouncy ball and Newton's cradle had. The windup toys will run until the potential elastic energy is exhausted.

6. Students' answers will vary. They may ask where the energy goes when the toy stops moving.

⬡ Get Going

As students discuss ideas to add to the *Project Board,* identify ideas about which they agree and disagree. Encourage students to use the term *factor* in their explanations of how the amount of kinetic energy an object has can vary.

Then ask students to share questions they still have from the previous *Learning Set* or that they have developed as a result of this activity. Add these questions to the *Project Board.*

Update the Project Board

5 min

Students add new ideas and questions to the Project Board.

NOTES

What's the Point?

Kinetic energy is the energy associated with motion. Motion can be started when an object's energy potential is released. The windup toy gets its kinetic energy from elastic potential energy in the toy's spring. The first ball in Newton's cradle gets its kinetic energy from the gravitational potential energy of the ball when it is raised. The bouncy ball has many different energy sources. You know that there is energy in motion and that stored energy can be transformed into kinetic energy to make something move. You know, too, that there are ways to control the amount of energy available for movement. You do not know, however, exactly what factors control movement and how to control those factors. In the rest of this *Learning Set,* you will be investigating how different types and amounts of potential energy affect the kinetic energy of an object.

Rides at the amusement park have kinetic energy and do work.

NOTES

....

....

....

Assessment Options

Targeted Concepts, Skills, and Nature of Science	How do I know if students got it?
Scientists often work together and then share their findings. Sharing findings makes new information available and helps scientists refine their ideas and build on others' ideas. When another person's or group's idea is used, credit needs to be given.	**ASK:** Why is it useful to share your ideas as a class? **LISTEN:** Students should recognize that they can learn from the ideas of other students by considering observations they might have overlooked.
Energy is the ability to cause change or do work.	**ASK:** How do you know you gave energy to each toy? **LISTEN:** Students should conclude that because the motion of the toy changed in some way, the energy must have been transferred to it.
Kinetic energy is associated with the motion of an object.	**ASK:** How is the amount of kinetic energy related to the motion of each toy? **LISTEN:** Students should recognize that each toy moved faster or farther when it had more kinetic energy than it did when it had less kinetic energy.

NOTES

....

....

....

....

Teacher Reflection Questions

- What evidence do you have that students are beginning to recognize what factors are and ways they can be measured? What specific examples can you point out to them?

- How do the ideas added to the *Project Board* build on what students learned in *Learning Set 1* observing household items? How can you help students tie the activities and demonstrations together?

- What did you do to encourage all students to share their ideas? What can you try next time to prevent some students from worrying that their ideas will be incorrect?

NOTES

....

....

....

....

....

....

....

....

....

....

....

SECTION 2.2 INTRODUCTION

2.2 Explore

What Factors Determine the Amount of Kinetic Energy of an Object?

◀ *2 class periods*

A class period is considered to be one 40 to 50 minute class.

Overview

Students consider familiar examples in which they can observe the results of different amounts of energy, such as making a dent in a car or getting hit by a ball. Once they begin to recognize factors that lead to different amounts of kinetic energy, as well as the different results they produce, students watch videos showing a cart running down a hill into a ball of clay. By observing changes in the clay, students recognize differences in kinetic energy and their causes. Then they read about PlayPump® and learn how this device depends on two specific factors—mass and speed.

Targeted Concepts, Skills, and Nature of Science	Performance Expectations
Scientists often work together and then share their findings. Sharing findings makes new information available and helps scientists refine their ideas and build on others' ideas. When another person's or group's idea is used, credit needs to be given.	Students communicate their ideas about the factors that affect the amount of kinetic energy an object has.
Energy is the ability to cause change or do work.	Students recognize changes in common objects, such as the metal of a car or a ball of clay, as indicators of energy.
Kinetic energy is associated with the motion of an object.	Students relate the kinetic energy of an object to its mass and speed.

117

Materials	
1 per student	*Cart-Clay Data Table* page
	Energy Types page (started in *Section 2.1*)
1 per class	Baseball and a plastic ball of similar size
	Ball of clay
	Cart-Clay video

Homework Options

Reflection

- **Science Content:** How is the mass and the speed of an object related to the amount of kinetic energy it has? *(Students should recognize that the amount of kinetic energy increases as the mass and speed increase.)*

- **Science Process:** Why is it important to change only one factor at a time when investigating the amount of kinetic energy in an object? *(Students should understand that if they change more than one factor at a time, they cannot be sure which factor was responsible for the results they observed.)*

Preparation for 2.3

- **Science Content:** What causes an object, such as a baseball or a cart on a hill, to move? *(This question is intended to engage students in thinking about what gives an object kinetic energy by setting an object into motion.)*

SECTION 2.2 IMPLEMENTATION

2.2 Explore

What Factors Determine the Amount of Kinetic Energy of an Object?

Imagine that a neighbor just bought a new car. Near where he parked it, four of your friends are playing catch with a ball. Two are using a baseball, and the other two are using a hollow plastic ball of the same size. The owner of the car hears a loud "THUNK!" when one of the balls hits the car.

You know that the baseball has caused the noise. Since the noise was loud, you know that the dent made by the ball is probably pretty big. But you may not know that the baseball had more kinetic energy than the plastic ball. In this section, you will identify some of the factors that affect how much kinetic energy an object has.

Conference

With your group, make a first attempt at identifying factors that determine how much kinetic energy an object has. Use the following scenarios and questions to help you.

The ball had kinetic energy before it struck the car.

1. Think about the situation above. What factors do you think would determine the size of the dent in the car?

EN 47

ENERGY

2.2 Explore

What Factors Determine the Amount of Kinetic Energy of an Object?

5 min

Students compare the effects of a moving baseball with that of a plastic ball.

○ Engage

Hold up a baseball and a plastic ball of similar size. Drop both balls on your desk from the same height. Ask students to listen for the sound each ball makes. Gently toss each ball to a student, one at a time. As a class, discuss how the baseball hits your hands with more force than the plastic ball, even though the balls are thrown at the same speed.

*A class period is considered to be one 40 to 50 minute class.

Conference

10 min

Students attempt to identify factors that determine the amount of kinetic energy an object has.

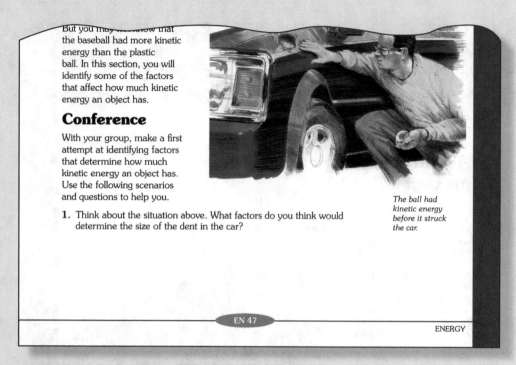

But you may ~~know that~~ the baseball had more kinetic energy than the plastic ball. In this section, you will identify some of the factors that affect how much kinetic energy an object has.

Conference

With your group, make a first attempt at identifying factors that determine how much kinetic energy an object has. Use the following scenarios and questions to help you.

1. Think about the situation above. What factors do you think would determine the size of the dent in the car?

The ball had kinetic energy before it struck the car.

EN 47

ENERGY

△ Guide

Have students look at the picture in the student text and share their answers to Question 1 with their groups. Guide them to share similar examples as a means of reaching their conclusions. Then read Question 2 and allow students to discuss their answers within their groups. Once students realize the relationship between the motion of and the nature of a ball to the damage it can cause, have students discuss Question 3. Accept all logical answers at this time.

1. Students should know that the mass of the ball would determine the size of the dent in the car. The baseball has more mass than the plastic ball. They might know that the speed of the ball when it hit the car would also be a factor.

2. Students should recognize that a plastic ball thrown by a child would not hurt them very much. A baseball thrown by a child might hurt a little. In the same way, the greater mass of the baseball compared to the plastic ball would cause greater injury and pain when thrown by a baseball player. The ball would fall to the ground after hitting them because its kinetic energy would be gone. Students should arrive at the conclusion that there are two factors at work here: the mass of the ball and its speed (velocity).

2. Imagine being hit by a ball. How would it feel to be hit by a plastic ball thrown by a child? What about a baseball thrown by a child? What about a plastic ball thrown by a baseball player? What about a baseball thrown by a baseball player? What do you think would happen to the ball, in each case, after it hit you? What factors determine how much the ball would hurt?

3. You know that when a faster-moving ball hits something, the result is different than when a slower-moving ball hits something. Using what you know about what happens when a ball hits something, what factors do you think you could measure to compare the kinetic energy in two different moving objects?

Communicate

Share Your Ideas

Discuss the answers to the *Conference* questions as a class. Make a class list of factors you think determine the amount of kinetic energy of a ball. Then discuss what you could measure to determine how much kinetic energy a moving object has.

Observe

What Affects a Cart's Kinetic Energy?

You will get a chance now to test your ideas about how different factors determine the amount of kinetic energy in an object. You are going to observe a set of videos showing a small cart running downhill into a ball of clay. Before each video, you will predict what will happen to the ball of clay.

---

3. Students should conclude that speed and mass are two important factors in determining kinetic energy and can be measured.

Communicate: Share Your Ideas

5 min

Groups share their ideas about energy with the class.

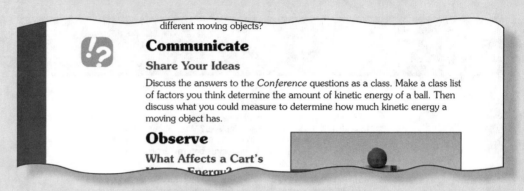

Communicate

Share Your Ideas

Discuss the answers to the *Conference* questions as a class. Make a class list of factors you think determine the amount of kinetic energy of a ball. Then discuss what you could measure to determine how much kinetic energy a moving object has.

Observe

What Affects a Cart's

⚠ Guide

Work with the class to develop a list of factors that determine the amount of kinetic energy. Then guide a discussion in which students brainstorm ways to measure the amount of kinetic energy a moving object has.

Observe: What Affects a Cart's Kinetic Energy?

10 min

Students are introduced to a video showing how a moving cart affects a ball of clay when hitting it.

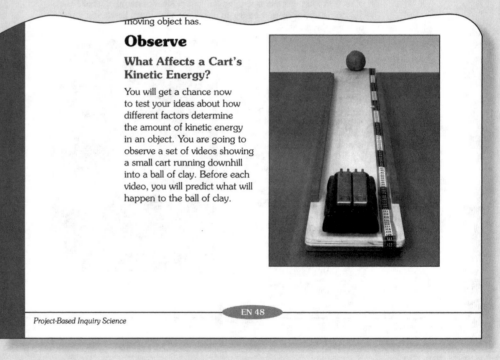

Observe

What Affects a Cart's Kinetic Energy?

You will get a chance now to test your ideas about how different factors determine the amount of kinetic energy in an object. You are going to observe a set of videos showing a small cart running downhill into a ball of clay. Before each video, you will predict what will happen to the ball of clay.

◯ Engage

Place a ball of clay on your desk or table. Punch the ball gently with your fist. Then punch it more forcefully. Allow students to observe the clay after each hit. Then point out the image of the cart. Ask volunteers to explain what will happen when the cart is released Students should recognize that the cart will deform the clay when it hits it, much as you deformed the clay when you punched it. Tell students that the way the clay is deformed depends on the motion of cart just as it depended on the motion of your fist.

2.2 Explore

Procedure

1. Begin by looking at the cart in its start position in the first video. This cart has a mass of 250 g (8.8 oz) and will be going 4 kph (2.4 mph) at the moment it hits the clay. Predict what will happen to the clay, and record your prediction in the *Predicted Smoosh* column on your *Cart-Clay Data* page.

2. Then watch the video, and observe what happens to the clay. Record the data from your observations in the *Actual Smoosh* column.

3. Now take a break from the videos. With your group, answer these three questions on your *Cart-Clay Data* page:

   a) What does the dent produced in the ball of clay mean?

   b) How do you think the dent in a ball of clay can be used to measure the kinetic energy of the cart?

   c) How do you think you might be able to change the kinetic energy of the cart?

4. Before going on, discuss your answers with the class.

5. Repeat *Steps 1* and *2* for the second and third videos. The mass and speed of the cart in each video is recorded in the *Cart-Clay Data* page.

Analyze Your Data

With your group, answer these questions:

1. Which cart had the most kinetic energy at the moment it hit the clay? Which cart had the least kinetic energy? How do you know?

2. Place the cart runs in order of least kinetic energy to most kinetic energy. What is your evidence for this order of the cart runs?

3. What factors do you think determined the cart's kinetic energy at the moment it hit the clay?

Cart–Clay Data Table 2.2.1

Name: .... Date: ....

Run #	Mass of cart and weight	Speed of cart	Predicted smoosh	Actual smoosh
1	250 g	4 km/hr		
Question 1	What does the dent produced in the ball of clay mean?			
Question 2	How do you think the dent in a ball of clay can be used to measure the kinetic energy of the cart?			
Question 3	How do you think you might be able to change the kinetic energy of the cart?			
2	750 g	4 km/hr		
3	250 g	12 km/hr		

Procedure
20 min

Students watch a series of three videos to identify factors that affect kinetic energy.

◯ Get Going

Make sure students record their predictions before showing the first video. Then, after watching the video, guide students to record their observations and answers to the three questions. Help students recognize that if the clay was changed in some way, energy was transferred to it from the cart. They should relate the amount of energy to the amount of change in the clay. Students may suggest that they can change the kinetic energy of the cart by pushing it harder, letting it roll down a steeper ramp, or adding mass to it.

Guide a discussion in which students share their answers. Use the following to assess students' understanding of the video:

3. a) Students should understand that the dent (smoosh) in the ball of clay is caused by the kinetic energy of the cart.

b) After seeing the first video, students should realize that the greater the kinetic energy of the cart, the greater the dent (smoosh) will be. In this way, it is a measure of the kinetic energy.

c) From the earlier discussions, student should know that they could change the speed (velocity) or mass of the cart to control its kinetic energy. This would be measured by producing larger or smaller dents.

Follow the same procedure to repeat Steps 1 and 2 for the two remaining videos. Remind students to record their predictions and observations, and to share their ideas respectfully.

Analyze Your Data

5 min

Students begin to interpret the observations they made about the videos.

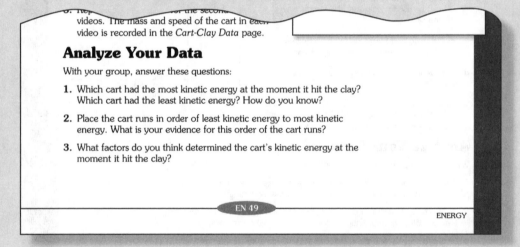

videos. The mass and speed of the cart in each video is recorded in the *Cart-Clay Data* page.

Analyze Your Data

With your group, answer these questions:

1. Which cart had the most kinetic energy at the moment it hit the clay? Which cart had the least kinetic energy? How do you know?

2. Place the cart runs in order of least kinetic energy to most kinetic energy. What is your evidence for this order of the cart runs?

3. What factors do you think determined the cart's kinetic energy at the moment it hit the clay?

EN 49

ENERGY

△ Guide

Have groups answer the questions and remind them to support their answers with evidence from the videos.

1. Students should state that the cart in the third video had the most kinetic energy at impact. They should also deduce that the cart in the first video had the least kinetic energy. Their statements are based on the size of the dent, or smoosh.

2. They should identify that the first video had the least kinetic energy, followed by the second video, and finish with the third video having the most kinetic energy. Their evidence is the size of the dent or smoosh.

3. Students should understand that the factors that determined the kinetic energy of the cart at impact were mass and speed (velocity).

Communicate

Share Your Ideas

Share your ideas about which cart had the most kinetic energy and which cart had the least kinetic energy at the moment of impact. Discuss what evidence you used to make the determination. Then make a class list of the factors that determined the kinetic energy of the carts in the videos.

Reflect

1. Choose a sport, such as football, softball, or track, and list three ways increased kinetic energy helps one team score or win over another team.

2. Which do you think is more important in determining the amount of kinetic energy: speed or mass? Or do you think they have about the same effect? Why do you think so?

3. How might knowing the speed and mass of objects in motion help you with your design challenge?

4. What ideas do you have about how to increase the speed or mass of an object?

5. You will be learning about many different forms of energy in this Unit. Now is a good time to use a new *Energy Types* page to summarize what you know about each type of energy, or you may edit the *Energy Types* page you began earlier. Record what you now know about kinetic energy—the indicators that tell you it is present, the factors that affect how much kinetic energy an object has, and examples you have seen of objects with kinetic energy.

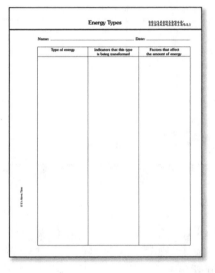

Communicate: Share Your Ideas

5 min

Students share their ideas based on their answers to the Analyze Your Data *questions.*

△ Guide and Assess

Listen to students' ideas about what they observed. Help students recognize that they can relate the amount of kinetic energy of each cart to the change they observed in the clay. Have students cite specific evidence from the videos. As students share and discuss ideas, make the class list of factors.

Reflect

5 min

Students apply what they have learned about kinetic energy to other moving objects.

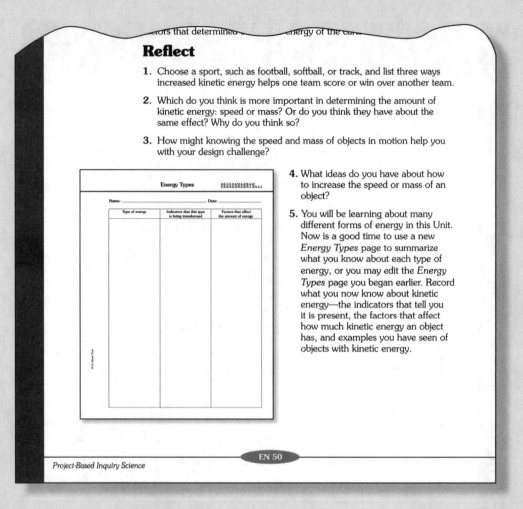

...tors that determined ...energy of the car...

Reflect

1. Choose a sport, such as football, softball, or track, and list three ways increased kinetic energy helps one team score or win over another team.

2. Which do you think is more important in determining the amount of kinetic energy: speed or mass? Or do you think they have about the same effect? Why do you think so?

3. How might knowing the speed and mass of objects in motion help you with your design challenge?

4. What ideas do you have about how to increase the speed or mass of an object?

5. You will be learning about many different forms of energy in this Unit. Now is a good time to use a new *Energy Types* page to summarize what you know about each type of energy, or you may edit the *Energy Types* page you began earlier. Record what you now know about kinetic energy—the indicators that tell you it is present, the factors that affect how much kinetic energy an object has, and examples you have seen of objects with kinetic energy.

Energy Types

Name: _____ Date: _____

Type of energy	Indicators that this type is being transformed	Factors that affect the amount of energy

EN 50

Project-Based Inquiry Science

△ Guide and Assess

Lead a discussion to consider each of the questions. Encourage students to develop their ideas using evidence they have observed and experiences they may have had. Accept all answers at this time as long as students provide a logical explanation.

1. Students' answers will vary widely. For a basketball example, they may suggest that a three-point shot has more kinetic energy than a two-point shot since it has a longer distance to travel. For football, students may suggest that a 40-yd field goal will need greater kinetic energy than a 20-yd field goal. In baseball, two suggestions that students will think of are the kinetic energy required for a home run versus the kinetic energy required for a single, or the greater kinetic energy of a fast ball to strike out a dangerous hitter. Golf, bowling, volleyball, softball, car racing—almost any sport can provide a rich resource for students' answers.

2. Many students will think that speed and mass have equal importance in determining the amount of kinetic energy. Some may look closely at the data generated from the three videos in which speed and mass were varied. Those students may recognize that tripling the speed caused more of a dent (smoosh) than tripling the mass.

3. Students should recognize from examining their Rube Goldberg design sketches that there are many instances where kinetic energy (motion) is used to accomplish a step. In their final Rube Goldberg designs, they may need to control speed and mass to affect a step toward turning off a light.

4. Students' thoughts on what they can do to increase the speed or mass of an object will vary. Students may use their sports examples from above and suggest that they can increase the mass and speed of the players on a football team by using bigger, faster players, or they may use another bat that increases the mass of a softball bat and use a stronger player so that the speed of the batter's arm is increased, or they may suggest increasing the speed of a volleyball player by having them run faster to bump the ball.

5. Students' work will vary but you should check to make certain they do a complete, thorough summary since this will be very useful for the rest of the Unit.

NOTES

....

....

....

....

....

....

....

The PlayPump® Story

10 min

Students read about a transformation of energy that provides people with clean drinking water.

META NOTES

Students may have questions about why clean water is not available to everyone. Explain that although more than 70 percent of Earth's surface is covered by water, only a very small portion of it is fresh water for people to drink. Much of that fresh water is located underground in porous rock forming an aquifer. As water moves to and through the aquifer, contaminants are filtered from it. A well is used to tap into an aquifer and bring the fresh water to the surface.

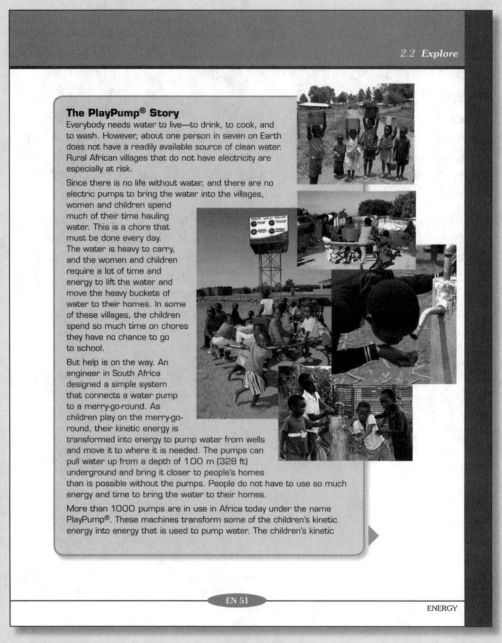

2.2 Explore

The PlayPump® Story

Everybody needs water to live—to drink, to cook, and to wash. However, about one person in seven on Earth does not have a readily available source of clean water. Rural African villages that do not have electricity are especially at risk.

Since there is no life without water, and there are no electric pumps to bring the water into the villages, women and children spend much of their time hauling water. This is a chore that must be done every day. The water is heavy to carry, and the women and children require a lot of time and energy to lift the water and move the heavy buckets of water to their homes. In some of these villages, the children spend so much time on chores they have no chance to go to school.

But help is on the way. An engineer in South Africa designed a simple system that connects a water pump to a merry-go-round. As children play on the merry-go-round, their kinetic energy is transformed into energy to pump water from wells and move it to where it is needed. The pumps can pull water up from a depth of 100 m (328 ft) underground and bring it closer to people's homes than is possible without the pumps. People do not have to use so much energy and time to bring the water to their homes.

More than 1000 pumps are in use in Africa today under the name PlayPump®. These machines transform some of the children's kinetic energy into energy that is used to pump water. The children's kinetic

EN 51

ENERGY

○ Engage

Ask students if they have every used a hand-cranked mixer or ice cream maker. If possible, have an example available to show. Explain how the crank on these devices is turned to mix ingredients together. Tell students that by using these devices, you change your energy into the kinetic energy of the spinning blades. Then have students look at the photographs. Discuss how these children use their energy to turn a device that does something far more important than making ice cream—it pumps clean drinking water to Earth's surface.

energy provides fun and accomplishes chores at the same time. Because they spend less time hauling and carrying water, they have time to play and to go to school. Women can use their saved time to earn money to help support the family.

Children have fun spinning on the PlayPump® merry-go-round. (1) Clean water is pumped (2) from a well (3) into a tank (4). A tap (5) makes it easy for adults and children to draw water. Excess water goes from the storage tank back down into the well (6).

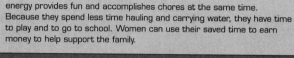
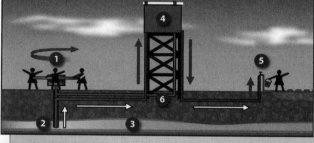

When you transfer kinetic energy to your bicycle, you cause it to move.

Two factors determine the amount of kinetic energy the children have: mass and speed. This means that when more children play on the merry-go-round, more water gets pumped. Also, the faster they spin the merry-go-round, the more water they pump. The kinetic energy of 25 singing, laughing children playing for 1 hour can pump about 1400 L (370 gal) of water to the surface.

The next time you are playing a sport, riding a bike, or running for exercise, think about how your kinetic energy could be transformed.

What's the Point?

Kinetic energy is the energy of motion. Mass and speed are factors that determine the amount of kinetic energy an object has. If you have two baseballs of the same mass thrown by a pitcher, the ball with the greater speed has more kinetic energy. If a softball and a baseball are thrown at the same speed, the softball will have the greater kinetic energy because it has a greater mass.

META NOTES

Students often need to be reminded of the relationship between liters and gallons. One gallon is about 3.8 liters.

△ Guide

Make sure students recognize mass and speed as the two factors that affect the amount of water that is pumped. As the mass of the children and the speed at which they move increases, more water is pumped from the well.

TEACHER TALK

"Suppose you sit on one end of a see-saw and two friends sit on the other. What will happen to you? Most likely, you'll be lifted up. How can you increase the mass on your end of the see-saw? You cannot increase your own mass, but you can have another friend join you. You and your friends each have mass. The more friends you put together, the more mass there is."

Assessment Options

Targeted Concepts, Skills, and Nature of Science	How do I know if students got it?
Scientists often work together and then share their findings. Sharing findings makes new information available and helps scientists refine their ideas and build on others' ideas. When another person's or group's idea is used, credit needs to be given.	**ASK:** What did you learn from the ideas other groups had after watching the videos? **LISTEN:** Students should mention at least one idea they did not learn until the groups shared their ideas.
Energy is the ability to cause change or do work.	**ASK:** How did you know that energy was transferred to the clay by the cart? **LISTEN:** Students should explain that the clay was changed when the cart hit it.
Kinetic energy is associated with the motion of an object.	**ASK:** What factors affected the kinetic energy of the cart in the videos? **LISTEN:** Students should recall that the mass and speed of the cart changed.

Teacher Reflection Questions

- What difficulties did students have with the concepts of mass and speed as they relate to kinetic energy? What can you do to make these concepts clear?

- How were you able to connect the reading about the PlayPump® to what students observed in the videos? What might you try next time to help students tie concepts together?

- How were you able to engage students in class discussions? What can you do to encourage students to participate?

NOTES

NOTES

SECTION 2.3 INTRODUCTION

2.3 Explore

How Does Work Increase or Decrease Kinetic Energy?

◀ **1 class period**

A class period is considered to be one 40 to 50 minute class.

Overview

Students are introduced to the concepts of work and force. They relate work to kinetic energy by completing an activity in which they roll marbles across a surface into paper cups. Students are challenged to identify indicators they can use to compare the amount of kinetic energy to the amount of work done. Returning to the energy-transformation cartoons they examined earlier in the Unit, students then get an opportunity to consider them again using what they learn about kinetic energy.

Targeted Concepts, Skills, and Nature of Science	Performance Expectations
Scientists often work together and then share their findings. Sharing findings makes new information available and helps scientists refine their ideas and build on others' ideas. When another person's or group's idea is used, credit needs to be given.	Students work together to explain the factors they changed and the results they observed to identify differences in kinetic energy.
Energy is the ability to cause change or do work.	Students recognize that energy is involved when a marble is used to move a paper cup.
Kinetic energy is associated with the motion of an object.	Students compare the movement of paper cups to the kinetic energy of the marbles that hit them.

NOTES

....

....

....

133

Materials	
1 per group	Small marble
	Large marble
	Tape
	Marker
2 per group	Paper cup

Homework Options

Reflection

- **Science Content:** How can you use an indicator to compare the kinetic energy of two marbles? *(Students should recognize that if each marble moves the cup a different distance, the distance the cup moves depends on the amount of kinetic energy the marble had.)*

- **Science Content:** How do you do work on a marble when you push it across a surface? *(Students should explain how they exert a force, or push, on the marble that causes it to move some distance in the same direction as the force.)*

NOTES

....

....

....

....

....

....

....

SECTION 2.3 IMPLEMENTATION

2.3 Explore

How Does Work Increase or Decrease Kinetic Energy?

When you saw the toys moving, you knew they had kinetic energy. Motion is an indicator of kinetic energy. You found ways to increase the motion of each of the toys. When you threw the bouncy ball toward the ground with more force, it moved faster and bounced higher. When you saw greater movement, you knew the ball had more kinetic energy.

One way to think about the kinetic energy of a moving object is to think about how much **work** you would have to do to stop the object. You do work when you apply a **force** through a distance to change the motion of an object. A force can be a push or a pull.

Imagine that you and several friends are at a fair. Someone is pushing a food cart. Suddenly, the person loses his grip and the cart keeps moving. The cart is moving at 2 m/s. You and your friends quickly go to help, bringing the cart to a stop. It takes a lot of work to stop the cart.

work: a way to increase (or decrease) an object's energy by using a force to change the object's motion or position.

force: a push or pull that acts on an object.

Now imagine that later that day you are playing in a baseball game. You are the catcher on the team. The pitcher throws you a ball at 30 m/s, and you catch it. The ball stings your hand, but you have no trouble stopping it with your glove. It did not take much work to stop the ball. Which do you think had more kinetic energy, the fastball or the food cart? Why? You may not be able to answer these questions now. The activity you will do will help you better answer these questions.

EN 53

ENERGY

2.3 Explore

How Does Work Increase or Decrease Kinetic Energy?

10 min

Students are introduced to the concepts of work and force as they relate to energy.

○ Engage

Ask a volunteer to push a book or other small object across a desk. Then ask the same volunteer to push as hard as he or she can against the wall. Encourage the volunteer to push on the wall with all of his or her might. Challenge the class to decide the situation in which the volunteer did more work. Students may be tempted to suggest that the volunteer did more work pushing against the wall.

*A class period is considered to be one 40 to 50 minute class.

Point out that despite all the effort, and perhaps even some perspiration, the student did not do any work at all pushing against the wall. The reason is that work is done only when a force causes an object to move some distance. If the object does not move, work is not done, even though a force was exerted.

△ Guide

Make sure that students recognize examples of forces. Ask students to brainstorm a list of everyday forces, such as lifting books, throwing a ball, pulling open the refrigerator door, and pushing a shopping cart. As a class, think about the examples of forces and objects that move as a result of the force. Point out that work is done when a force causes an object to move some distance in the direction of the force.

NOTES

Observing Kinetic Energy and Work

To help you understand the relationship between work and kinetic energy, you will observe the difference in kinetic energy between two objects and the difference in the amount of work that is done. If your classroom is large, you will be able to do this activity with your group. If there is not room for that, your teacher will set it up as a demonstration. Make sure you can see the cups move.

Procedure

Materials
- 1 small marble
- 1 large marble
- 2 paper cups
- tape
- marker

1. On the floor, place two strips of tape. The strips should be about 1 m apart. Label one strip *finish line* and the other strip *starting line*.

2. Place the two paper cups on their sides along the finish line as shown in the diagram. Both cups should face toward the starting line. Add a third strip of tape about half a meter behind the starting line.

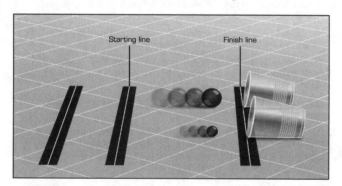

Starting line   Finish line

3. One student should take the two marbles and sit or kneel behind the starting line. With one marble in each hand, place the marbles on the third strip of tape. Slide the marbles along the floor and release them at the starting line so they each roll into a paper cup. The marbles should be released right at the starting line at the same time and reach the finish line (and the cups) at the same time. It may take several trials to get the aim and timing correct. You may find it easier to have each marble rolled by a different student. Measure and record how far each cup moves.

Project-Based Inquiry Science

Observing Kinetic Energy and Work

15 min

Students participate in an activity to compare the kinetic energy of two objects.

META NOTES

Discuss the variables in the activity. The changed variable is the mass (size) of the marble. The distance the cup moves is measured as a result. All other variables must be held constant, including the way in which the marbles are rolled.

⬡ Get Going

Read through the procedure with students to make sure they understand how to set up the strips of tape and the cups. Make sure students find a suitable location for the activity. The floor must be smooth, without seams or grout. Once they have set up the materials, let students practice rolling the marbles before they begin making observations and measurements.

4. Repeat *Step 3* until you have at least three trials where both marbles reach the cups at the same time.

5. Look across your trials. Compare the movement of the paper cup hit by the small marble to the movement of the cup hit by the large marble.

Reflect

Discuss with your group the answers to these questions. Be prepared to share your answers with the class.

1. When the marbles enter the paper cups, are the marbles traveling at the same speed? How do you know?

2. When the marbles enter the paper cups, do you think the marbles have the same amount of kinetic energy or different amounts of kinetic energy? Why?

3. Do you think one of the marbles does more work on the paper cup? How do you know?

4. Do you think one hand (or student) does more work on a marble to bring it from rest to the starting line? How do you know?

5. The marbles do work on the paper cups by pushing them away from the finish line. Do you think the paper cups also do work on the marbles? How do you know?

6. Which do you think takes more work to stop, a fast-moving baseball or a slow-moving car? Why?

7. Return to the energy-transformation cartoon you analyzed earlier in the Unit. Choose a step that involves kinetic energy. Describe how this step uses kinetic energy to do work. Then describe how work was done to input kinetic energy into the step.

Communicate

As a class, discuss the answers to the first six questions above. Then take turns sharing your analyses of the relationship between work and kinetic energy for a step in the energy-transformation cartoons.

ENERGY

△ Guide and Assess

Reflect

10 min

Students share answers to questions about the marble activity.

Before beginning, ask students to define force and work in their own words. Once you are convinced that students grasp the concepts, ask students to discuss the questions among their groups. Remind students to make their best attempts at answering the questions. Tell them that it is okay if they are unsure about some questions or parts of questions.

Once students have answered the questions, refer them back to the energy-transformation cartoon they examined earlier. Ask each group to describe one step in the cartoon in terms of kinetic energy.

1. Students may simply state that the two marbles looked like they were going the same speed. Ask them for better evidence. They should say that the marbles were released at the same time, covered the same distance, and struck the cup at the same time.

2. Students should know that the two marbles had different amounts of kinetic energy because the one cup was moved farther than the other. The larger marble did more work on the cup, moving it a greater distance.

3. Students should state that the larger marble did more work than the smaller marble because it moved the cup farther.

4. Students should reply that one hand (with the large marble) does more work than the other hand because it is moving a greater mass through the same distance.

5. Students may not understand at first that the cup does work on the marble. Try to get them to understand that if no opposing force was exerted on the marble, it would roll forever. The correct response should be that the cup does exert a force on the marble because it eventually stops the marble.

6. Students should understand that more work is done in stopping a slow-moving car than in stopping a fast-moving baseball. Work has two components—force (energy) and distance. The kinetic energy of the car is far greater than that of a baseball because it has a greater mass.

7. Students' answers will vary depending on the step selected from the cartoon. Make sure their answers mention the force (energy) applied to an object and the distance the object was moved.

△ Guide

Listen as students share their answers. Clarify any misconceptions, but allow students to express their ideas. Once the questions are reviewed, let each group present its analysis of its cartoon.

Communicate

5 min

Groups share their answers to the Reflect *questions and then relate them to the energy-transformation cartoons.*

How Does Work Affect Kinetic Energy?

5 min

Students read about the relationship of work and energy.

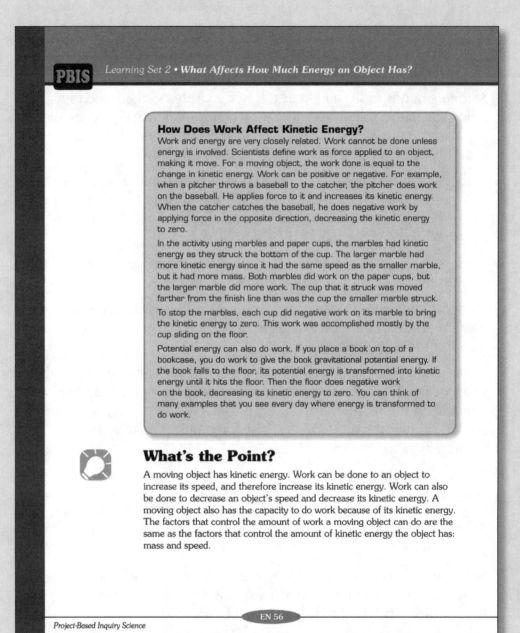

How Does Work Affect Kinetic Energy?

Work and energy are very closely related. Work cannot be done unless energy is involved. Scientists define work as force applied to an object, making it move. For a moving object, the work done is equal to the change in kinetic energy. Work can be positive or negative. For example, when a pitcher throws a baseball to the catcher, the pitcher does work on the baseball. He applies force to it and increases its kinetic energy. When the catcher catches the baseball, he does negative work by applying force in the opposite direction, decreasing the kinetic energy to zero.

In the activity using marbles and paper cups, the marbles had kinetic energy as they struck the bottom of the cup. The larger marble had more kinetic energy since it had the same speed as the smaller marble, but it had more mass. Both marbles did work on the paper cups, but the larger marble did more work. The cup that it struck was moved farther from the finish line than was the cup the smaller marble struck.

To stop the marbles, each cup did negative work on its marble to bring the kinetic energy to zero. This work was accomplished mostly by the cup sliding on the floor.

Potential energy can also do work. If you place a book on top of a bookcase, you do work to give the book gravitational potential energy. If the book falls to the floor, its potential energy is transformed into kinetic energy until it hits the floor. Then the floor does negative work on the book, decreasing its kinetic energy to zero. You can think of many examples that you see every day where energy is transformed to do work.

What's the Point?

A moving object has kinetic energy. Work can be done to an object to increase its speed, and therefore increase its kinetic energy. Work can also be done to decrease an object's speed and decrease its kinetic energy. A moving object also has the capacity to do work because of its kinetic energy. The factors that control the amount of work a moving object can do are the same as the factors that control the amount of kinetic energy the object has: mass and speed.

○ Engage

Ask the students, "In a baseball game, who does more work on each pitched ball, the pitcher or the catcher?" Draw the class into a discussion of the kinetic energy of the ball and where it goes.

Assessment Options

Targeted Concepts, Skills, and Nature of Science	How do I know if students got it?
Scientists often work together and then share their findings. Sharing findings makes new information available and helps scientists refine their ideas and build on others' ideas. When another person's or group's idea is used, credit needs to be given.	**ASK:** How was it helpful to work together as a group to conduct the activity? **LISTEN:** Students should recognize that, like scientists, they worked together to complete different parts of the activity and confirmed each other's observations.
Energy is the ability to cause change or do work.	**ASK:** How do you know work was done by the marbles on the cups? **LISTEN:** Students should explain that each marble exerted a force on a cup, causing the cup to move some distance.
Kinetic energy is associated with the motion of an object.	**ASK:** What factor affected the kinetic energy of the marbles? **LISTEN:** Students should recognize that the marbles had the same speed (velocity), but a different mass and, therefore, a different amount of kinetic energy.

Teacher Reflection Questions

- What difficulties did students have understanding the variable in the activity? How can you help them with this?

- How were you able to make sure that students could relate kinetic energy to work? What other examples could you provide to help them?

- How were you able to help students relate what they learned in this activity to the energy-transformation cartoons they examined earlier? What can you do to help students better tie concepts together?

NOTES

2.4 Read

How Does Work Increase Potential Energy?

◀ *1 class period*

A class period is considered to be one 40 to 50 minute class.

Overview

Students think about the toys they examined earlier. This time, they consider them in terms of potential energy. They read about two types of potential energy—elastic potential energy and gravitational potential energy. Through diagrams, they see that kinetic and potential energy can be transformed from one form to another, but they discover that energy is conserved in the process.

Targeted Concepts, Skills, and Nature of Science	Performance Expectations
Energy is the ability to cause change or do work.	Students recognize that energy is involved when an object changes form (by being stretched or compressed) or position (by being lifted or lowered).
Energy exists in different forms and can be changed from one form to another.	Students discover that kinetic energy and potential energy can be transformed into one another.
Energy is neither created nor destroyed in ordinary processes.	Students find out that the total amount of mechanical energy in a system is conserved.
Kinetic energy is associated with the motion of an object.	Students learn that the kinetic energy of an object increases as it falls.
Potential energy is stored energy, associated with position or condition.	Students learn that an object can store potential energy by being compressed, stretched, or lifted.

Materials	
1 per student	*Project Board* page
1 per class	Class *Project Board*

Homework Options

Reflection

- **Science Content:** How are the two types of potential energy similar, how are they different? *(Students should recognize that both types of potential energy are stored in an object. Elastic potential energy is related to an object's shape or condition and gravitational potential energy is related to an object's position.)*

Preparation for 2.5

- **Science Content:** What can you do to give an object elastic or gravitational potential energy? *(This question is intended to get students thinking that work must be done on an object to give it potential energy.)*

NOTES

....

....

....

....

....

....

....

SECTION 2.4 IMPLEMENTATION

◀ *1 class period**

2.4 Read

How Does Work Increase Potential Energy?

Think back to the windup toy and the Newton's cradle. How did you use work to increase the kinetic energy of each toy?

When you wound the windup toy, you did work to turn the key. But the work did not immediately become kinetic energy. The work was used to add potential energy to the toy. Only when you released the toy was the potential energy transformed into kinetic energy.

With the Newton's cradle, you did work when you pulled back the first steel ball. Then you held the ball in place before releasing it. At that moment, the toy had no kinetic energy because nothing was moving. The work you did (raising the ball) was stored as potential energy in the ball. When you released the ball, the potential energy was transformed into kinetic energy.

When you wind up a toy, the spring stores energy.

In both toys, you did work so that the object stored energy that could be transformed at a later time. What factors determine how much potential energy is stored in a toy? This is the question you will explore in this section.

How Is Elastic Potential Energy Stored?

When you wind up the windup toy, potential energy is stored in its spring. As you wind the spring tighter and tighter, the spring holds more potential energy. The kind of potential energy in the spring of a windup toy is elastic potential energy. Elastic potential energy is stored when something "stretchy" or "springy" is stretched or **compressed**. When you wind up the windup toy, you compress its spring. When you let go, the spring unwinds, and the toy moves.

compressed: squeezed or pressed together.

ENERGY

2.4 Read

How Does Work Increase Potential Energy?

5 min

Students review an activity they completed to look at it in terms of potential energy.

△ Guide

Remind students of the definition of potential energy. It is energy that is stored for later use. Then read through the student text with the class. Discuss the windup toy and Newton's cradle they explored earlier. Help students understand how potential energy is involved.

*A class period is considered to be one 40 to 50 minute class.

"What does it mean if a person is told that she or he "has potential"? Generally, it means they have the ability to accomplish something in the future. In science, potential energy is the ability to do work in the future."

How Is Elastic Potential Energy Stored?

10 min

Students are introduced to elastic potential energy through examples.

How Is Elastic Potential Energy Stored?
When you wind up the windup toy, potential energy is stored in its spring. As you wind the spring tighter and tighter, the spring holds more potential energy. The kind of potential energy in the spring of a windup toy is elastic potential energy. Elastic potential energy is stored when something "stretchy" or "springy" is stretched or **compressed**. When you wind up the windup toy, you compress its spring. When you let go, the spring unwinds, and the toy moves.

compressed: squeezed or pressed together.

△ Guide

Ask students to think about the windup toy they explored earlier in this *Learning Set*. Have them think about what they did. Explain that they exerted a force to turn the knob. Because they exerted a force that caused the knob to move some distance, they did work on it. As they did work, they transferred energy to the spring. Discuss how the energy was stored in the spring as elastic potential energy. Tell students that once the toy was let go, the potential energy was converted into kinetic energy.

NOTES

....

....

....

....

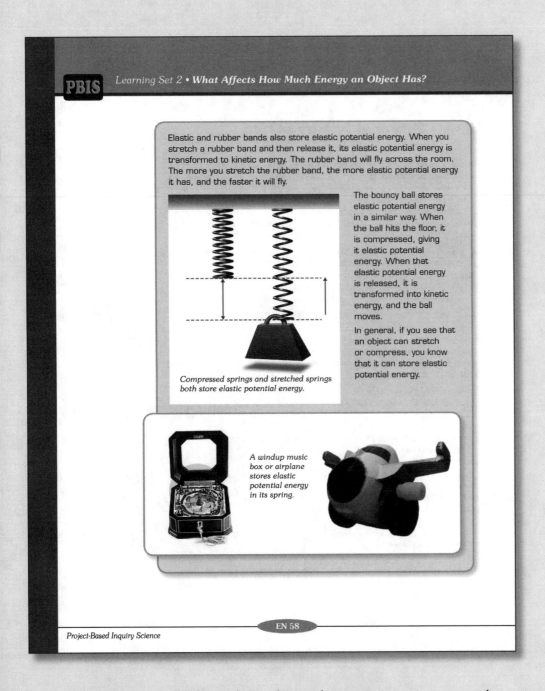

Elastic and rubber bands also store elastic potential energy. When you stretch a rubber band and then release it, its elastic potential energy is transformed to kinetic energy. The rubber band will fly across the room. The more you stretch the rubber band, the more elastic potential energy it has, and the faster it will fly.

The bouncy ball stores elastic potential energy in a similar way. When the ball hits the floor, it is compressed, giving it elastic potential energy. When that elastic potential energy is released, it is transformed into kinetic energy, and the ball moves.

In general, if you see that an object can stretch or compress, you know that it can store elastic potential energy.

Compressed springs and stretched springs both store elastic potential energy.

A windup music box or airplane stores elastic potential energy in its spring.

Use the diagram and photographs in the student text to review examples of objects that can store elastic potential energy. Ask students to share additional examples they might know.

How Is Potential Energy Stored Using Gravity?

10 min

Students are introduced to gravitational potential energy through examples.

How Is Potential Energy Stored Using Gravity?

Newton's cradle shows how **gravity** is used to store and transform potential energy. You have lived with gravity your whole life, yet for most people it remains a mysterious force. Part of the mystery is that gravity acts at a distance. When Earth pulls a steel ball toward the ground, there is nothing visible that connects the ball and the ground. Yet the indicators of gravity are familiar. Any time you see an object falling or see the effort it takes to lift a weight, you are seeing indicators of gravity.

By now you know that work is done when a force acts through a distance to change an object's motion or position. Sometimes you do work to overcome gravity. Just think back to the last time you climbed three flights of stairs. You did a lot of work to lift your body higher. As you did this work, you applied an upward force using the muscles in your legs.

When you lift the steel ball in Newton's cradle, you do work. This work is stored as potential energy in the ball. This type of potential energy is called gravitational potential energy—the energy an object stores because of its position above the ground. When you release the ball, its gravitational potential energy is transformed into kinetic energy, which is then transferred to the other balls.

You were able to control the amount of kinetic energy in the balls in the Newton's cradle by moving the steel ball higher or lower. If you lifted the ball higher, you did more work, so the ball stored more gravitational potential energy. This resulted in more kinetic energy when the released ball hit the other balls. When the greater amount of kinetic energy was transmitted through the other balls, the ball at the end of the line moved faster and higher.

> **gravity:** the force of attraction between any two masses. Near Earth's surface, gravity is the force that attracts objects toward the center of Earth.

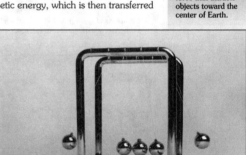

You can control the amount of kinetic energy in the Newton's cradle by moving the steel ball higher or lower.

EN 59

ENERGY

○ Engage

Ask students if they have seen photos of astronauts in space. Describe examples of objects floating in a spacecraft or astronauts lifting massive objects with ease. Explain that the force due to gravity in space is much less than it is on Earth. Tell students that because of this, the force required to move an object against gravity is less than it is on Earth.

△ Guide

Have a student lift an object in the classroom onto a desk or shelf. Guide the class to recognize that the student exerted an upward force to move the object in the upward position. Because the student exerted a force that caused the object to move some distance, the student did work on it. Explain that by doing work, the student transferred energy to the object. Tell students that even though the object does not appear to have energy as it sits on the desk or shelf, it does. Point out that the object has gravitational potential energy. If the object falls from its position, it can cause change to an object below it.

Once you have discussed gravitational potential energy, make sure students understand how they gave the ball gravitational potential energy when using Newton's cradle.

NOTES

Conservation of Mechanical Energy

10 min

Students define mechanical energy in terms of kinetic and potential energy.

META NOTES

The concept of a system can be difficult for students. It may be helpful to describe some examples, both scientific and nonscientific. Help them understand that the energy of individual objects in a system can change, but the total energy remains the same.

Conservation of Mechanical Energy

Think back to your experience with the bouncy ball. The ball can have kinetic energy from elastic potential energy and gravitational potential energy. When you lift the ball, you are doing work to increase its gravitational potential energy. When you then release the ball, gravitational energy is transformed into kinetic energy as the ball falls. When the ball hits the floor, the ball's shape changes as it flattens against the floor. The ball stops moving for an instant, so it no longer has kinetic energy. All of the ball's kinetic energy has been transformed into elastic potential energy. The ball then bounces upward, releasing its elastic potential energy, which is transformed back into kinetic energy, and so on. Many energy transformations keep the ball in motion.

Scientists often think about energy in terms of the total energy of a **system,** a collection of objects that interact. A system can have one object or many objects. If there are no forces that oppose motion, like friction or air resistance, and no energy is added to or removed from the system, then the **mechanical energy** of a system remains constant. Mechanical energy is the sum of the kinetic energy, gravitational potential energy, and elastic potential energy of a system. This concept is called the **conservation of mechanical energy.** Each time energy is transformed, all of the energy can be accounted for—none of the energy is lost.

system: a collection of objects that interact.

mechanical energy: the sum of the kinetic energy, gravitational potential energy, and elastic potential energy in a system.

conservation of mechanical energy: if there is no friction or air resistance, the mechanical energy of a system changes only if the system does work on something else or energy is added from outside the system.

When you release the ball, gravitational potential energy is transformed into kinetic energy as the ball falls.

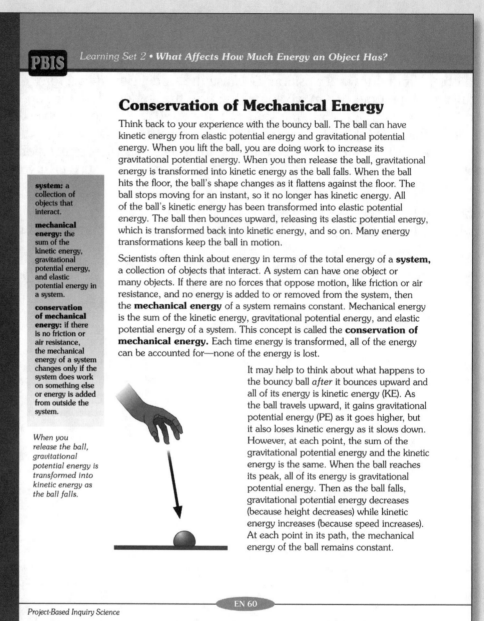

It may help to think about what happens to the bouncy ball *after* it bounces upward and all of its energy is kinetic energy (KE). As the ball travels upward, it gains gravitational potential energy (PE) as it goes higher, but it also loses kinetic energy as it slows down. However, at each point, the sum of the gravitational potential energy and the kinetic energy is the same. When the ball reaches its peak, all of its energy is gravitational potential energy. Then as the ball falls, gravitational potential energy decreases (because height decreases) while kinetic energy increases (because speed increases). At each point in its path, the mechanical energy of the ball remains constant.

△ Guide

Use the diagram to help students recognize that one form of energy can change into another, something they have been observing throughout the Unit. In the case of the bouncing ball, kinetic energy and potential energy are continuously transformed from one to the other.

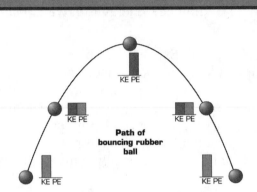

2.4 Read

Path of bouncing rubber ball

As the ball travels upward, it gains gravitational potential energy. What happens when the balls travels downward?

Reflect

Work with your group to answer these questions. Be prepared to share your answers with the class.

1. Think back to the step of the energy-transformation cartoon that you analyzed at the end of the last section. Was any potential energy stored or released during the step? Rewrite your description of the step from the last section if necessary, using what you have learned about gravitational and elastic potential energy.

2. How are potential energy and kinetic energy related?

3. What is the connection between work and energy?

Update the *Project Board*

You know a lot now about the relationships between potential energy and kinetic energy. Add what you know about the relationship between potential energy and kinetic energy to the *What are we learning?* column of the *Project Board*. Don't forget to add evidence to the *What is our evidence?* column. If you have new questions about potential energy, kinetic energy, or work, add them to the *What do we need to investigate?* column.

EN 61

ENERGY

META NOTES

Friction is a force that opposes motion. Some of the energy of a moving object is converted to thermal energy and transferred away from the object as heat. The energy is not destroyed, but it is said to be lost from the object. In these examples, friction is ignored.

Point to the ball at the bottom left of the diagram. Explain that as the ball leaves the ground, all of its energy is kinetic energy.

Then trace the path halfway to the highest point. Ask students what happens to the speed of the ball as it rises. *(Students should know that the speed decreases because the ball slows down.)* Use the bars to show that halfway up its path, the kinetic energy is equal to the potential energy. The kinetic energy has decreased because the ball has slowed down. The potential energy has increased because the height of the ball has increased.

PBIS

Show students that at the highest point, the ball stops moving for an instant. Ask students what must be true if the ball is not moving. *(Students should recognize that if there is no motion, the kinetic energy of the ball must be zero.)* At the highest point, all of the ball's energy is gravitational potential energy.

Trace the downward path of the ball. Explain that the opposite process occurs as the ball falls. Help students to understand that mechanical energy is the total kinetic and potential energy of an object or system. Even though kinetic energy can change into potential energy and potential energy can change into kinetic energy, the total amount of energy remains the same. The potential energy is transformed into kinetic energy. Use the heights of the bars to show that the total amount of energy remains the same throughout the ball's motion.

Reflect

5 min

Students relate their new understanding of mechanical energy to the energy-transformation cartoons.

Reflect

Work with your group to answer these questions. Be prepared to share your answers with the class.

1. Think back to the step of the energy-transformation cartoon that you analyzed at the end of the last section. Was any potential energy stored or released during the step? Rewrite your description of the step from the last section if necessary, using what you have learned about gravitational and elastic potential energy.

2. How are potential energy and kinetic energy related?

3. What is the connection between work and energy?

Update the Project Board

1. Students' answers and descriptions will vary depending on the step of the cartoon they analyzed. Each step does work, so whatever step in the cartoon they analyzed, potential energy was involved. However, it may be a form of potential energy they are unfamiliar with, such as chemical potential energy.

2. Students should understand that potential energy and kinetic energy have a reciprocal relationship. As one increases, the other decreases. The total mechanical energy remains the same.

3. Students should state that it takes energy (force) to do work. However, energy can be used without any work being done, if the object is not moved. Once an object is moving, it takes work to stop it.

3. What is the connection between work and energy?

Update the *Project Board*

You know a lot now about the relationships between potential energy and kinetic energy. Add what you know about the relationship between potential energy and kinetic energy to the *What are we learning?* column of the *Project Board*. Don't forget to add evidence to the *What is our evidence?* column. If you have new questions about potential energy, kinetic energy, or work, add them to the *What do we need to investigate?* column.

⬡ Get Going

Allow students to discuss what they think should be added to the *What are we learning?* and *What is our evidence?* columns of the *Project Board*. Add any new ideas to the *Project Board*.

Update the Project Board

5 min

Students add their ideas and questions to the Project Board.

NOTES

What's the Point?

Elastic potential energy is energy that is stored when an object, such as a spring, is stretched or compressed. When you release the spring, the potential energy is transformed into kinetic energy. Gravitational potential energy is energy that is stored by moving an object to a greater height above the ground. This energy is transformed into kinetic energy when the object is allowed to fall.

You can use work to add kinetic energy to a system or to increase potential energy in the system. Potential energy stored in any system can be released as kinetic energy. Kinetic energy can be transformed to do work or to increase potential energy. Sometimes energy is transferred without being transformed. This occurs when the balls in Newton's cradle transfer kinetic energy. Mechanical energy is the sum of the kinetic energy and potential energy in a system. The mechanical energy of a system remains constant if there is no friction or air resistance and no energy is added to or taken away from the system.

As a skydiver falls toward Earth, gravitional potential energy transforms into kinetic energy.

NOTES

....

....

....

Assessment Options

Targeted Concepts, Skills, and Nature of Science	How do I know if students got it?
Energy is the ability to cause change or do work.	**ASK:** How is kinetic energy different from potential energy? **LISTEN:** Students should explain that kinetic energy is energy of motion and potential energy is stored energy.
Energy exists in different forms and can be changed from one form to another.	**ASK:** What does it mean to say that mechanical energy is conserved? **LISTEN:** Students should recognize that energy is neither created nor destroyed when it is changed from one form to another.
Energy is neither created nor destroyed in ordinary processes.	**ASK:** What happens to the total mechanical energy of a ball as it falls? **LISTEN:** Students should describe how the ball's potential energy is changed into kinetic energy, but the total of potential and kinetic energy remains the same.
Kinetic energy is associated with the motion of an object.	**ASK:** What happens to an object when potential energy is converted into kinetic energy? **LISTEN:** Students should explain that the object begins to move or moves faster.
Potential energy is stored energy, associated with position or condition.	**ASK:** What are two types of potential energy? **LISTEN:** Students should list elastic potential energy and gravitational potential energy.

NOTES

....

Teacher Reflection Questions

- What difficulties did students have differentiating between the two forms of potential energy? What can you do to help them with these difficulties?

- What evidence do you have that students have a thorough understanding of the conservation of mechanical energy? How might you avoid any misconceptions with this topic?

- How were you able to keep students engaged in analyzing the cartoons? What might you try next time to help them build on prior knowledge?

NOTES

SECTION 2.5 INTRODUCTION

2.5 Investigate

How Are Gravity and Kinetic Energy Related?

◄ **4 class periods**

A class period is considered to be one 40 to 50 minute class.

Overview

Students begin the section by considering factors that affect the amount of gravitational potential energy an object has. They watch a demonstration in which a marble rolls down a track into a paper cup. From this variation of the marble activity they conducted earlier, students recognize that allowing the marble to roll downward from some height affects the amount of energy it has. Students use what they learn through observation to design an experiment to test for factors that affect an object's potential energy. In their design, students identify the independent and dependent variables as well as the controlled variables. They conduct their experiments, graph their data, and use their graphs to look for trends so they can make a claim about the relationship between the factor they investigated and the amount of gravitational potential energy. To share their findings, students hold an *Investigation Expo* in which they prepare posters summarizing their information. Students then read about Galileo's investigations with gravitational potential energy and they learn how gravitational potential energy is used to produce electricity in a hydroelectric power plant. Finally, students return to the energy-transformation cartoon they analyzed earlier to consider ways to change the amount of potential energy and relate this process to the *Big Challenge*.

Targeted Concepts, Skills, and Nature of Science	Performance Expectations
Scientists often work together and then share their findings. Sharing findings makes new information available and helps scientists refine their ideas and build on others' ideas. When another person's or group's idea is used, credit needs to be given.	Students revise their experimental designs based on the suggestions and questions of other students.

Targeted Concepts, Skills, and Nature of Science	Performance Expectations
Studying the work of different scientists provides understanding of scientific inquiry and reminds students that science is a human endeavor.	Students understand their experiments relative to the work of Galileo.
Scientific knowledge is developed through observations, recording and analysis of data, and development of explanations based on evidence.	Students design and conduct an experiment, graph their data, and identify trends in the data.
Scientists make claims (conclusions) based on evidence (trends in data) from reliable investigations.	Students state a claim based on the data they record during their experiment.
Energy is the ability to cause change or do work.	Students identify some change as the dependent variable in their experiments.
Energy exists in different forms and can be changed from one form to another.	Students use a change from potential energy to kinetic energy to design an experiment.
Kinetic energy is associated with the motion of an object.	Students recognize that a marble has kinetic energy as it rolls downhill.
Potential energy is stored energy, associated with position or condition.	Students recognize that a marble has potential energy when it is lifted to some height.

Materials	
several per group	Marbles of several different sizes
	Ball bearings of several different sizes
	Pieces of wood
	Books
1 per group	Ruler with a track in the middle
	Tape
	Triple-beam balance
	Paper cup

Materials	
1 per student	*Gravitational Potential Energy Planning Guide* page *Project Board* page Graph paper *Energy Types* page (filled in from *Section 2.2*)
1 per class (optional)	Toy pinwheel Basin tub or sink Water supply

Activity Setup and Preparation

Be ready to perform the demonstration before class by setting up the ramp assembly. Use books to adjust the height of the ramp and have the cup and marble ready.

Homework Options

Reflection

- **Science Content:** What are two ways to increase the gravitational potential energy of a marble? *(Students should recognize that they can use a marble with greater mass or lift the same marble to a greater height to increase the gravitational potential energy.)*

- **Science Process:** What were the independent and dependent variables in Galileo's experiment? *(Students should recognize that the mass of the balls was the independent variable and the time it took for them to reach the ground was the dependent variable.)*

Preparation for 2.6

- **Science Content:** How can you increase the potential energy that a toy with elasticity has? What are the factors controlling the amount of potential energy? *(This question is meant to help students begin thinking about the factors which control potential energy.)*

NOTES

SECTION 2.5 IMPLEMENTATION

2.5 Investigate

How Are Gravity and Kinetic Energy Related?

You know that if you drop a pencil, it will fall to the ground. You do not need to throw it toward the ground. You have already learned that when an object falls, gravitational potential energy is transformed into kinetic energy. In this section, you will investigate factors that determine how much gravitational potential energy an object has.

Demonstration

You will soon design an experiment to measure how different factors affect the amount of gravitational potential energy an object has. First, you will watch a marble roll down a track.

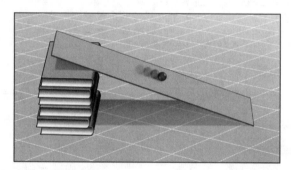

Watch as the marble rolls down the track.

One end of the track has been placed on a stack of books so that one end is higher than the other. To catch the marble, there is a paper cup at the bottom of the track. You cannot see the paper cup in the picture.

Observe carefully as the marble is released at the top of the track. Pay attention to the motion of the paper cup as the marble strikes it. What you observe in this demonstration will help you design your experiment.

EN 63

ENERGY

2.5 Investigate

How Are Gravity and Kinetic Energy Related?

5 min

Students prepare to investigate gravitational potential energy.

○ Engage

Push a pencil or some other object to the edge of your desk. Ask students what will happen if you push it farther. Students should predict that it will fall to the ground. Confirm their predictions and point out that they know that an object that can fall has gravitational potential energy. Then let them know that they will figure out how to measure different amounts of gravitational potential energy in this section.

*A class period is considered to be one 40 to 50 minute class.

Demonstration

5 min

Students watch a demonstration involving a marble rolling down a ramp.

gravitational _____ energy an object has.

Demonstration

You will soon design an experiment to measure how different factors affect the amount of gravitational potential energy an object has. First, you will watch a marble roll down a track.

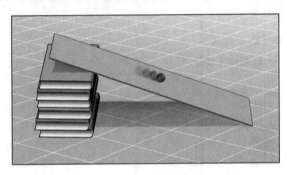

Watch as the marble rolls down the track.

One end of the track has been placed on a stack of books so that one end is higher than the other. To catch the marble, there is a paper cup at the bottom of the track. You cannot see the paper cup in the picture.

Observe carefully as the marble is released at the top of the track. Pay attention to the motion of the paper cup as the marble strikes it. What you observe in this demonstration will help you design your experiment.

EN 63

ENERGY

△ Guide

As students watch the demonstration, guide them to focus on the cup in their observations. Then allow the marble to roll down the track. Repeat the demonstration as needed to make sure all students have observed the marble shift the position of the cup.

NOTES

....

....

....

....

Stop and Think

Answer these questions with your group. Be prepared to discuss the answers with the class.

1. What type of energy does the marble have when it is placed at the top of the track? What indicators can you directly observe for this type of energy?

2. What types of energy does the marble have as it is rolling down the track? How do you know?

3. What do you think made the cup at the bottom of the track move?

4. How do you think you could change the amount of potential energy the marble has at the top of the track?

5. What do you think you can measure to know how a change affects the marble's potential energy?

Design an Experiment

Your class may now have some ideas about factors that can increase the potential energy of the marble at the top of the track. Each group will investigate the effects of one of these factors.

In your group, you will discuss and then design an experiment to investigate the effects of your factor on a marble's potential energy. You will begin by developing a question that your experiment will answer.

Then develop a procedure on which your group agrees. Record each step in the procedure in enough detail so that someone else could run your experiment. After you decide on your procedure, think about how trustworthy your data will be. If you think you can improve your data, revise your procedure.

When you are all in agreement that your procedure is the best you can develop, everyone in the group should record it on their *Gravitational Potential Energy Experiment Plan* page. Make sure you are prepared to share your experiment with others. Everyone in your class will need to know what makes your procedure a good one. The advice on the next page will help you design your experiment.

Materials

- marbles of several different sizes
- ball bearings of several different sizes
- ruler with a track in the middle
- pieces of wood to make tracks of different lengths
- tape
- stack of books
- triple-beam balance
- paper cup

Stop and Think

10 min

Students answer questions related to the Demonstration *with their groups.*

△ Guide and Assess

Have students meet in their groups and answer the *Stop and Think* questions. Listen to the group discussions. Make sure that students are using terms such as *kinetic energy, potential energy, gravitational energy,* and *indicator.* If you do not hear these terms being discussed, remind students of them to lead students in the right direction.

1. Students should respond that the marble has gravitational potential energy at the top of the track. The indicator for this is the position of the marble above the floor or table.

2. Students should realize that the marble has both kinetic energy and potential energy as it rolls down the track. They know this because of its motion (indicator) and its position above the floor or table (indicator).

3. Students will recognize that a force made the cup move and the force was the kinetic energy of the marble.

4. Most students will know that the amount of potential energy at the top of the track could be changed by raising the top of the track. They might not think of a second way to increase the potential energy available, but a heavier marble could be used.

5. Students may know that they could measure the height (indicator) of the marble above the floor to know that the potential energy changes. They should know that they can measure the kinetic energy at the bottom of the track by having the marble do work.

Design an Experiment

15 min

Students design an experiment to measure the amount of energy an object has.

META NOTES

Designing this kind of experiment can be challenging for students and they may struggle with it. Having them share and then revise their plans before they conduct the experiment will help them greatly with this activity.

- ball bearings of several different sizes
- ruler with a track in the middle
- pieces of wood to make tracks of different lengths
- tape
- stack of books
- triple-beam balance
- paper cup

What do you think you need to know how a the marble's potential energy?

Design an Experiment

Your class may now have some ideas about factors that can increase the potential energy of the marble at the top of the track. Each group will investigate the effects of one of these factors.

In your group, you will discuss and then design an experiment to investigate the effects of your factor on a marble's potential energy. You will begin by developing a question that your experiment will answer.

Then develop a procedure on which your group agrees. Record each step in the procedure in enough detail so that someone else could run your experiment. After you decide on your procedure, think about how trustworthy your data will be. If you think you can improve your data, revise your procedure.

When you are all in agreement that your procedure is the best you can develop, everyone in the group should record it on their *Gravitational Potential Energy Experiment Plan* page. Make sure you are prepared to share your experiment with others. Everyone in your class will need to know what makes your procedure a good one. The advice on the next page will help you design your experiment.

⬡ Get Going

Distribute the materials and let students know how much time they will have (10-15 min) before they present their designs to the class. Remind students that they must write clearly on their *Gravitational Potential Energy Planning Guide* pages so they can refer back to them and others can read them.

2.5 Investigate

Question

What question are you investigating and answering with this experiment? Your question will probably be in this form:

What is the effect of *[your factor]* on the potential energy of a marble at the top of a track?

Prediction

What do you think the answer is, and why do you think that?

Variable Identification

- What variable will you manipulate (change) in your experiment to test the effects on the potential energy of the marble? This is your **independent (manipulated) variable**.

- What conditions and procedures will you keep the same (hold constant or control) in your experiment? These are your **control variables.**

- How will you identify the effects of your variable? What will you measure? These are your **dependent (resulting) variables**.

- How many trials will you run for each value of the variable you manipulate?

Procedure and Data

Write detailed instructions for how to conduct the experiment. Include the following information:

- how you will set up the marble track

- how you will control other variables while changing only one variable at a time

- how you will measure your dependent (resulting) variable, the factor affected by changes in the independent (manipulated) variable

- how you will record the data, including the data table you will use

- how many trials you will complete for each value of your independent (manipulated) variable

control variables: conditions or procedures that are held constant.

independent (manipulated) variable: a factor that is changed to affect changes in the dependent (resulting) variable.

dependent (resulting) variable: a factor that is affected by changes in the independent (manipulated) variable.

ENERGY

Question
5 min

Students identify the factor they are investigating.

META NOTES

Every scientific investigation begins with a question that can be answered by using the scientific method. Point out to students that they are acting like scientists by formulating a scientific question. A possible answer to a scientific question is called a hypothesis. For scientists, a hypothesis is not a wild guess. It is based on research, experience, and prior investigations.

△ Guide

Work with the class to develop a list of possible factors that can affect the potential energy of the marble. The list should include the mass of the marble and the height to which it is lifted. If possible, allow groups to select one factor to investigate. If this is not practical, assign a factor to each group. Then have students write a question involving that factor. Remind students that a scientific question should not have a simple *yes* or *no* answer.

Prediction

5 min

Students pose a possible answer to the question they posed.

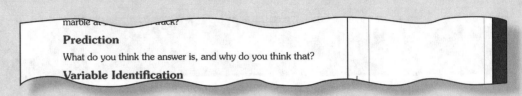

marble at ....track?

Prediction

What do you think the answer is, and why do you think that?

Variable Identification

△ Guide and Assess

Listen to students' predictions. Ask a volunteer from each group to explain how they developed their predictions based on the information they have learned so far in this Unit.

Variable Identification

5 min

Students identify the variables involved in their experiments.

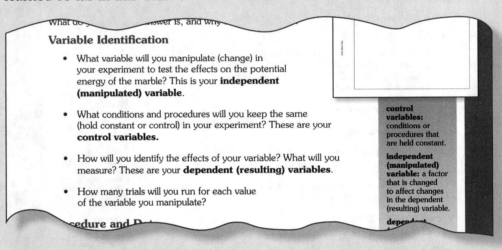

What do y..... .....swer is, and why

Variable Identification

- What variable will you manipulate (change) in your experiment to test the effects on the potential energy of the marble? This is your **independent (manipulated) variable**.

- What conditions and procedures will you keep the same (hold constant or control) in your experiment? These are your **control variables.**

- How will you identify the effects of your variable? What will you measure? These are your **dependent (resulting) variables**.

- How many trials will you run for each value of the variable you manipulate?

....cedure and D.....

control variables: conditions or procedures that are held constant.

independent (manipulated) variable: a factor that is changed to affect changes in the dependent (resulting) variable.

depend....

◇ Evaluate

Make sure students understand the different types of variables involved in a scientific investigation. Encourage students to listen to the ideas of other groups, because they may hear controlled variables that they had not considered. Clarify any misconceptions about the different types of variables.

NOTES

....

....

....

....

....

Procedure and Data

Write detailed instructions for how to conduct the experiment. Include the following information:

- how you will set up the marble track

- how you will control other variables while changing only one variable at a time

- how you will measure your dependent (resulting) variable, the factor affected by changes in the independent (manipulated) variable

- how you will record the data, including the data table you will use

- how many trials you will complete for each value of your independent (manipulated) variable

dependent (resulting) variable: a factor that is affected by changes in the independent (manipulated) variable.

Procedure and Data
10 min

Students record the detailed instructions of their experiments.

△ Guide

Ask students to complete the *Gravitational Potential Energy Planning Guide* page. Tell students to check that they have included the information listed next to each bullet in the list. Encourage students to include as many details as they can. Explain that a detailed procedure will make it easier for them to conduct their investigation and repeat it the same way for each trial.

NOTES

Communicate: Plan Briefing

15 min

Groups present their procedures to another group to discuss how they can be improved.

META NOTES

When groups begin to present their procedures, students might find it difficult to take over the discussion. If this happens, try modeling some questions for students. Once students become involved in the discussion, ask guiding questions to keep them on track.

Communicate

Plan Briefing

To help you check your experimental design, you will share it with another group. When it is your turn to present, first state the question you are answering. Then present the variable you will manipulate and what you will measure. Finally, share your procedure.

When you are listening to the other group's presentation, consider the following questions:

- How will their procedure help them answer their question?

- Is the other group controlling all of their variables except for the independent variable?

- Do they have a good way to measure the dependent variable?

- Do you think they are going to run enough trials?

- Do they have places on their data table to record the results of each trial? Do they have places to record the average of all the trials?

- Will they be recording their data in a way that will allow them to easily see how the value of their independent variable affects the value of their dependent variable?

Share your ideas about how you would revise the other group's plan.

Be sure to have your teacher check your plan before you conduct any experiment. You should conduct the experiment only as described in your procedure.

Revise Your Plan

With your group, decide if you want to revise your experimental plan based upon your discussion with the other group. Before you start your investigation, check to make sure each member of your group understands the procedure.

Run Your Experiment

Run the experiment, carefully following your recorded procedure. As you carry out your experiment, remember to record your results and any additional notes that will help you understand your results. When you are done running the experiment, you will graph and analyze your data and then report your results to the class.

EN 66

Project-Based Inquiry Science

△ Guide

Tell students what they are going to do and review the questions they should be thinking about. Decide how to pair the groups and have them begin. The goal of the task is to share their initial plans, get feedback for improvements, come to an agreement on overall procedure, and to think about what makes a procedure useful.

TEACHER TALK

"You are going to examine each other's plans so that you can help improve them. Listen closely, because there may be small problems with another group's plan, or with your own. As you listen, think if the procedure will work. If you don't think it will work, be ready to explain why.**"**

⬡ Get Going

Once groups have shared feedback, place students back into individual groups. Ask them to discuss the feedback they received so they can decide if they need to make changes to their plans. Check in on each group to make sure that all students agree to and understand the plan. If not, direct students to work together to come up with a final version that everyone accepts. Review the final plan for each group before they go on to conduct the experiment.

⬡ Get Going

Make sure students have everything they need to conduct their experiments. Have them begin their experiments. Remind them to record data. Try to make sure that all members of each group are participating in some way.

NOTES

....

....

....

....

....

....

Revise Your Plan

15 min

Students develop a final plan with their group.

Run Your Experiment

15 min

Students conduct the experiment they designed.

PBIS

Analyze Your Data

15 min

Students graph their data to look for trends.

Analyze Your Data

Finding Trends and Making Claims

You have collected data that may tell you how the gravitational potential energy of a marble affects its kinetic energy. You most likely measured the marble's kinetic energy by measuring the movement of the paper cup. It is now time to **interpret** those results. To interpret means to figure out what something means. Interpreting the results of an experiment means identifying what happens as a result of changing the independent (manipulated) variable.

For example, you may have used marbles of different masses. If so, you should look at how far the paper cup moved when you changed the mass of the marble. Ask yourself if the distance the cup moved increased or decreased as the mass of the marble increased.

You will do three things to interpret your results. First, you will graph your data. Second, you will try to identify a **trend** in the graph of your data. A trend is a pattern that you can see over several trials. For example, if the mass of the marbles was your independent variable, you might find that, as the mass increased, the distance the paper cup moved increased. Your trend would be, "As the mass of the marble increased, the distance the cup moved increased." Finally, you will decide what your trend shows about how potential energy affects kinetic energy.

Follow the steps below to graph your data, find a trend in your data, and interpret what the trends mean about how your variable affects gravitational potential energy.

> **interpret:** to find the meaning of something.
>
> **trend:** a pattern or a tendency you can see over a broad range of data.

1. Begin your data analysis by graphing the results. Make your own individual line graph. Be careful how you set up your graph, and make sure you label the x-axis and y-axis correctly. The x-axis should represent the variable you changed—your independent variable. The y-axis will represent the dependent variable, the variable you measured.

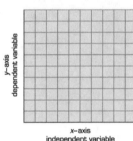

ENERGY

△ Guide

Make sure that all groups have recorded data from each trial of their experiment. As a class, review the terms *interpret, trend,* and *claim.* Then read through the steps for creating a graph of the data. Discuss how students must choose the intervals of the graph according to the data they have. For example, suppose their dependent variable was the distance the cup moved. If the distances they measured range from 1.5 cm to 2.5 cm, they may want to use an interval of 0.5 cm on the *y*-axis. Using a greater interval, such as 2 cm, would make it difficult to look for a trend.

⬡ Get Going

Once students are comfortable with the procedure for making a graph, ask them to graph their data. Walk around and assist any students who are struggling. Then challenge students to look for a trend in their data. It may help to draw some general examples on the board, such as a positive slope, a negative slope, and a slope of zero.

1. When the variable is height, that measurement should be the *x*-axis. The mass of the marble should be constant and the distance the cup moved will be the dependent variable. It should increase as height increases. When the students have selected mass as the variable, the mass measurements should be the *x*-axis. The beginning height of the marble should be held constant and the distance the cup moved should increase with height.

NOTES

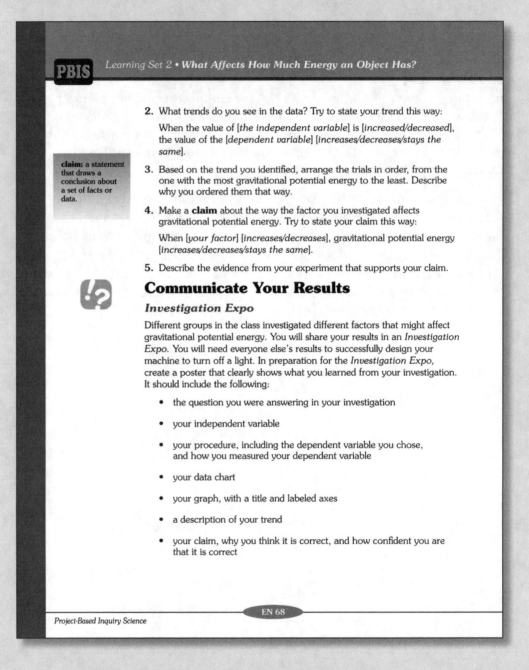

2. What trends do you see in the data? Try to state your trend this way:

When the value of [*the independent variable*] is [*increased/decreased*], the value of the [*dependent variable*] [*increases/decreases/stays the same*].

claim: a statement that draws a conclusion about a set of facts or data.

3. Based on the trend you identified, arrange the trials in order, from the one with the most gravitational potential energy to the least. Describe why you ordered them that way.

4. Make a **claim** about the way the factor you investigated affects gravitational potential energy. Try to state your claim this way:

When [*your factor*] [*increases/decreases*], gravitational potential energy [*increases/decreases/stays the same*].

5. Describe the evidence from your experiment that supports your claim.

Communicate Your Results

Investigation Expo

Different groups in the class investigated different factors that might affect gravitational potential energy. You will share your results in an *Investigation Expo.* You will need everyone else's results to successfully design your machine to turn off a light. In preparation for the *Investigation Expo,* create a poster that clearly shows what you learned from your investigation. It should include the following:

- the question you were answering in your investigation
- your independent variable
- your procedure, including the dependent variable you chose, and how you measured your dependent variable
- your data chart
- your graph, with a title and labeled axes
- a description of your trend
- your claim, why you think it is correct, and how confident you are that it is correct

EN 68

2. Students that chose to study the beginning height of the marble will state, *As the height of the marble increased, the distance the cup moved increased.* Students that chose to study the mass of the marble will state, *As the mass of the marble increased, the distance the cup moved increased.*

3. Students should notice that the trials are already placed in order by the process of graphing the data.

4. Student claims should be in the form of:
When height/mass increases, gravitational potential energy increases.

5. Students should use their graph to show the data that supports their claim. You might want to ask them to make a prediction for the distance the cup will move for a untested height/mass.

△ Guide and Assess

Have students create their posters. Make sure they include all of the bulleted items listed in the student text. Have groups display their posters around the classroom and then have students circulate to observe the other groups' posters. Select one group for each factor to present their posters to the class. Tell students to ask questions about the information they see and make notes of any claims with which they disagree. Emphasize that while doing this, they may learn something that will help them.

Communicate Your Results: Investigation Expo

15 min

Students share their results with the class using posters.

NOTES

You will begin this *Investigation Expo* by looking at all of the posters. Notice similarities and differences in the results and claims of groups that investigated the same factor. You will want to remember if you see different results or claims from groups that investigated the same question so that you can ask about that later. Make sure you understand why each group made their claim. Remember any claims with which you disagree, so you can ask later. You may want to record notes as you view the posters.

After you look at all the posters, one group assigned each factor will present. If your group presents, use your poster to help you organize your presentation. Remember that your classmates will want the following information:

- the question you were trying to answer in your investigation

- the procedure you used to answer the question, and your reasons for designing your procedure the way you did

- your results

- your graphs and the trends you identified

- your claim and how confident you are

As you listen to other groups present, decide if their results are trustworthy and whether you agree with their claims. Make sure you understand the claims. If there were groups with different results or claims, ask why.

As a class, make a list of the factors that affect how much gravitational potential energy an object has. You may also wish to make a list of factors that do not affect the amount of gravitational potential energy.

When all the factors have been presented, work as a class to make a cause-and-effect chart for each factor that shows how the factor affected the amount of gravitational potential energy.

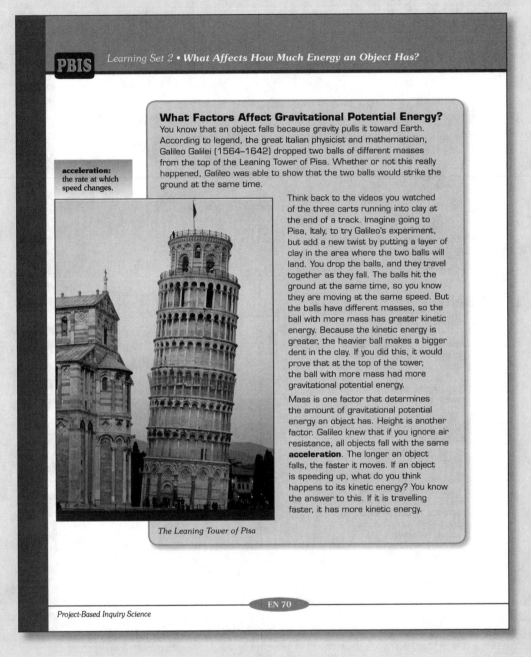

What Factors Affect Gravitational Potential Energy?

You know that an object falls because gravity pulls it toward Earth. According to legend, the great Italian physicist and mathematician, Galileo Galilei (1564–1642) dropped two balls of different masses from the top of the Leaning Tower of Pisa. Whether or not this really happened, Galileo was able to show that the two balls would strike the ground at the same time.

acceleration: the rate at which speed changes.

Think back to the videos you watched of the three carts running into clay at the end of a track. Imagine going to Pisa, Italy, to try Galileo's experiment, but add a new twist by putting a layer of clay in the area where the two balls will land. You drop the balls, and they travel together as they fall. The balls hit the ground at the same time, so you know they are moving at the same speed. But the balls have different masses, so the ball with more mass has greater kinetic energy. Because the kinetic energy is greater, the heavier ball makes a bigger dent in the clay. If you did this, it would prove that at the top of the tower, the ball with more mass had more gravitational potential energy.

Mass is one factor that determines the amount of gravitational potential energy an object has. Height is another factor. Galileo knew that if you ignore air resistance, all objects fall with the same **acceleration**. The longer an object falls, the faster it moves. If an object is speeding up, what do you think happens to its kinetic energy? You know the answer to this. If it is travelling faster, it has more kinetic energy.

The Leaning Tower of Pisa

What Factors Affect Gravitational Potential Energy?

10 min

Students read about examples of factors that affect gravitational potential energy.

META NOTES

Explain to students that air resistance is a type of friction, or a force that opposes motion. To help students understand air resistance, ask them to think about riding a bicycle. The more they expose themselves to air, the more they feel the air and are slowed down. If they tuck their bodies in tightly, they feel less air and move more quickly. Air resistance explains why a feather falls more slowly than a rock. In a vacuum, they would both fall at the same rate.

○ Engage

Describe an object with a relatively small mass, such as a golf ball, and an object with a greater mass, such as a bowling ball. Ask students which will land first if you dropped them from the same height at the same time. Students will most likely predict that the bowling ball will land first. You may surprise students by telling them that both balls will land at the same time. Then read through the information together. Identify the variables in Galileo's experiment and relate them to the experiments students conducted.

PBIS

2.5 Investigate

Because objects speed up, or accelerate, as they fall, they gain kinetic energy as they fall toward Earth. The mass of an object and its height above Earth's surface are the two most important factors controlling the amount of gravitational potential energy an object possesses.

In your experiments, you measured the kinetic energy of a marble at the bottom of the track by seeing how much work the marble did as it moved a cup. All of the ball's energy at the bottom of the track is kinetic energy. All of its energy at the top of the track is gravitational potential energy. According to conservation of mechanical energy, the kinetic energy at the bottom of the track must equal the gravitational potential energy the marble had at the top of the track. That is why you can use kinetic energy to indirectly measure gravitational potential energy.

Reflect

1. Return to the energy-transformation cartoon machine you analyzed earlier in the Unit. Find three objects that could have their potential energy changed. How would you increase it? How would you decrease it?

2. Why might it be important when designing your machine to turn off a light to know how much gravitational potential energy an object has?

3. Update your *Energy Types* page with what you now know about gravitational potential energy—its indicators and factors that affect the amount of energy.

Energy Types		
Name:		Date:
Type of energy	Indicators that this type is being transformed	Factors that affect the amount of energy

ENERGY

△ Guide

Explain that acceleration occurs whenever an object speeds up, slows down, or changes direction. Tell students that an object accelerates when it has an overall, or *net force*, acting on it. A falling object experiences downward acceleration because it is pulled by Earth's gravity. The object speeds up as it falls. Help students understand that because a falling object speeds up, the longer an object falls, the faster it moves.

☐ Assess

As students answer the questions, monitor their progress and check to see what difficulties they are having. Make sure they understand that they may need to understand how to control the amount of gravitational potential energy so they can use it to turn off a light for the *Big Challenge*.

1. Students' answers will vary depending on their cartoon. In all cases they should respond that gravitational potential energy can be increased by increasing the mass of an object or by raising it higher from the floor. It can be decreased by decreasing the mass or starting its motion closer to the floor.

2. Students should respond that one of the steps in their Rube Goldberg machine may need to do more work in which they would need to increase the gravitational potential energy of an object.

3. Students should update their *Energy Types* page with their new knowledge of gravitational potential energy.

Reflect

5 min

Students answer questions to relate what they read to what they have observed.

NOTES

....

....

....

....

....

....

....

....

Hydroelectric Power Plants

10 min

Students read about a use of gravitational potential energy to produce electricity.

META NOTES

In a hydroelectric power plant, the gravitational potential energy of the water in the dam is transformed into kinetic energy of the moving water. The moving water pushes the blades of the turbine. When the turbine turns, it operates a generator that produces electricity. In this way, the mechanical energy of the moving blades is converted to electrical energy. When a person uses electricity, that electrical energy is transformed into another form of energy. It may be useful to have students draw a flow chart to identify the energy transformations.

Hydroelectric Power Plants

About seven percent of electrical energy in the United States is generated by hydroelectric power plants. Hydroelectric power is a renewable form of energy, and it causes very little pollution. The gravitational potential energy of falling water is the source of this energy. A dam is built, usually on a river. The dam provides a way to control water as the water falls to the base of the dam through a penstock, or tunnel. The kinetic energy from the falling water turns turbines, which are used to generate electricity. Transmission lines then carry the electrical energy to homes and businesses.

A hydroelectric dam provides a way to control water that can be used to produce electricity.

The actual source of hydroelectric energy is the Sun. After water leaves the dam, the water in the river usually ends up in a lake or ocean. Energy from sunlight causes the water to slowly evaporate. The evaporated water can rise in Earth's atmosphere, collect in clouds, and then fall back to Earth as rain or snow. This water forms streams that eventually return water to the top of the dam, where it again can be used to generate electric energy.

The cycle of evaporation, precipitation, and collection of water is part of the water cycle. In many ways, thinking about the movement of water is a good way to think about conserving a quantity, because water can be accounted for at each step in the cycle. Overall, no water is lost in the cycle. It is simply converted to a different form. If you think about it, the water cycle is a pretty good example of a Rube Goldberg machine!

A hydroelectric dam creates a reservoir of water from a river and feeds the water through a pipe called a penstock. The kinetic energy of water falling through the penstock turns turbines. The turbines operate a generator that then generates electricity, which is carried away on power lines. The water is then returned to the river.

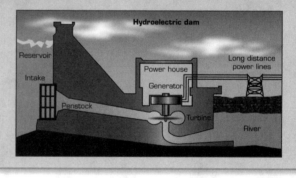

Hydroelectric dam

Reservoir

Intake

Penstock

Power house

Generator

Turbine

Long distance power lines

River

◯ Engage

If possible, obtain a toy pinwheel. Over a sink or basin tub, pour water on the pinwheel to make it move. Explain to students that the falling water turns the pinwheel much like water falling over a dam turns a turbine.

△ Guide

Walk students through the diagram of the hydroelectric dam. Make sure they understand how the falling water turns the turbine. Describe how the turbine operates a generator, which produces electricity. The electricity is then transported to where it is needed through wires.

Work with students to draw the water cycle on the board. The water cycle should begin with a large body of water, such as a lake. Solar energy evaporates water from the lake and the water vapor rises, forming clouds. The clouds release water in the form of rain in the mountains where it forms streams and rivers, finally running into a dam where it can be used to generate electricity. The energy transfers are: solar energy to gravitational potential energy (height above level ground), gravitational potential energy to kinetic energy (water running downhill and down through the turbine). Discuss its role in the generation of electricity at hydroelectric power plants. Have students conduct additional research if necessary.

NOTES

....
....
....
....
....
....
....
....
....

Update the Project Board

10 min

Students add new information from the section to the Project Board.

Update the *Project Board*

You have investigated a type of energy that you do not usually see and may have taken for granted—gravitational potential energy. To design a machine that will help you do the everyday task of turning off a light, you will need to know how the amount of this type of energy can be controlled. You will need to know how to increase or decrease gravitational potential energy, depending on the needs of your Rube Goldberg machine. Record what you know about gravitational potential energy in the *What are we learning?* column. Do not forget to record your evidence.

Design a Rube Goldberg machine to turn off a light				
What do we think we know?	What do we need to investigate?	What are we learning?	What is our evidence?	What does it mean for the challenge or question?

What's the Point?

Objects that have mass have gravitational potential energy because of Earth's gravity. A good indicator that an object has gravitational potential energy is its height above Earth's surface. The two main factors that affect how much gravitational potential energy an object has are its height above Earth's surface and its mass. The higher above Earth's surface an object is, the more gravitational potential energy it has. The more massive an object is, the more gravitational potential energy it has.

Because mechanical energy in a system is constant, and because there is very little friction between a marble and a ramp, you can indirectly measure the gravitational potential energy of a marble at the top of a track by measuring its kinetic energy at the bottom of the track.

ENERGY

△ Guide

Lead a discussion, guiding students to summarize the factors they investigated, the indicators they used, and the evidence they considered. Record any appropriate information on the *Project Board*. Ask students if they know something they would like to investigate further or any new questions they might have. Record this information, as well.

Assessment Options

Targeted Concepts, Skills, and Nature of Science	How do I know if students got it?
Scientists often work together and then share their findings. Sharing findings makes new information available and helps scientists refine their ideas and build on others' ideas. When another person's or group's idea is used, credit needs to be given.	**ASK:** How did you revise your experimental design based on the suggestions of other students? **LISTEN:** Students should describe the revisions they made to their design and identify the feedback that supported these changes. Or, they should explain why they did not revise their experimental design based on the feedback they received.
Studying the work of different scientists provides understanding of scientific inquiry and reminds students that science is a human endeavor.	**ASK:** What question did Galileo answer with his experiment at the Leaning Tower of Pisa? **LISTEN:** Students should describe how Galileo showed that all objects fall to the ground at the same rate regardless of mass.
Scientific knowledge is developed through observations, recording and analysis of data, and development of explanations based on evidence.	**ASK:** Why was it important to conduct more than one trial of your experiment? **LISTEN:** Students should understand that multiple trials helps to avoid errors in data that may result from mistakes made during one trial.
Scientists make claims (conclusions) based on evidence (trends in data) from reliable investigations.	**ASK:** What claim did you make based on trends in your data? **LISTEN:** Students should describe how the height (or mass) of the marble at the start of each trial was related to the gravitational potential energy.

Targeted Concepts, Skills, and Nature of Science	How do I know if students got it?
Energy is the ability to cause change or do work.	**ASK:** What change did you use as an indicator of energy in your experiment? **LISTEN:** Students should identify the dependent variable in their experiment, such as the displacement of a cup as the indicator of their experiment.
Energy exists in different forms and can be changed from one form to another.	**ASK:** How do you know that energy was transformed in your experiment? **LISTEN:** Students should explain that the marble began to move from rest, indicating that potential energy was converted to kinetic energy.
Kinetic energy is associated with the motion of an object.	**ASK:** How do you know if the kinetic energy of the marble increased during the experiment? **LISTEN:** Students should answer that the amount of work done by the marble increased during the experiment, indicating that the amount of kinetic energy must have increased.
Potential energy is stored energy, associated with position or condition.	**ASK:** How did you give the marble in your experiment gravitational potential energy? **LISTEN:** Students should answer that they did work on the marble to lift it some height, increasing the gravitational potential energy.

Teacher Reflection Questions

- What misconceptions did students have about falling objects? What can you do to address these misconceptions?

- How were you able to connect what students learned about gravitational potential energy to the *Big Challenge?* What might you try in the future?

- How were you able to make sure that all students participated in the experiment? What changes might you make in the future to involve all students?

2.6 Explore

How Does Elastic Potential Energy Affect Kinetic Energy?

◀ *2 class periods*

A class period is considered to be one 40 to 50 minute class.

Overview

Students review the concept of elastic potential energy. This time, they relate it to the amount of kinetic energy to which it can be converted. They consider several everyday objects that can store elastic potential energy. Following the introduction, students classify a group of objects according to whether or not they use elastic potential energy. Students return to the energy-transformation cartoons they examined earlier to consider it in terms of elastic potential energy. They read about properties of matter that cause some materials to store elastic potential energy whereas others do not.

Targeted Concepts, Skills, and Nature of Science	Performance Expectations
Scientists often work together and then share their findings. Sharing findings makes new information available and helps scientists refine their ideas and build on others' ideas. When another person's or group's idea is used, credit needs to be given.	Students discuss their classification scheme for objects that use elastic potential energy.
Energy is the ability to cause change or do work.	Students identify changes in objects that indicate energy.
Energy exists in different forms and can be changed from one form to another.	Students recognize that elastic potential energy can be changed into kinetic energy.
Kinetic energy is associated with the motion of an object.	Students consider how the amount of elastic potential energy is related to the amount of kinetic energy.
Potential energy is stored energy, associated with position or condition.	Students understand the properties of materials that enable them to store elastic potential energy.

Materials	
1 per group (each group will use several, but not one of each)	Compression spring Extension spring Rubber band Pop-up toy 50 g mass and spring 100 g mass and spring Windup toy Bouncy ball Marble Maraca Flashlight Newton's cradle Scissors Tuning fork Hand-crank generator
1 per student	*Elastic Energy Explorations* page *Energy Types* page (filled in from earlier in the *Learning Set*) *Project Board* page
1 per class	Class *Project Board*

Homework Options

Reflection

- **Science Content:** How is elastic potential energy related to kinetic energy? *(Students should recognize that elastic potential energy is changed into kinetic energy when certain objects work, such as a screen-door spring or a windup toy.)*

- **Science Process:** What evidence did you observe that suggests how to change the amount of elastic potential energy in an object? *(Students should mention ways to compress or stretch an object differently.)*

SECTION 2.6 IMPLEMENTATION

2.6 Explore

How Does Elastic Potential Energy Affect Kinetic Energy?

As you have learned, potential energy is stored energy and cannot be seen. When you put a marble at the top of a track, the marble has gravitational potential energy. This potential energy is a result of the marble's position. Elastic potential energy is also energy that results from an object's position. Think back to the pop-up toaster example. When you push down the toaster's lever, you compress a spring inside the toaster. It takes work to change the position of the lever and compress the spring. When the spring releases, the elastic potential energy is transformed into kinetic energy.

Materials
- compression spring
- extension spring
- rubber band
- pop-up toy
- 50-g mass and spring
- 100-g mass and spring
- windup toy
- bouncy ball
- marble
- maraca
- flashlight
- Newton's cradle
- scissors
- tuning fork
- hand-crank generator

Elastic potential energy can be a lot of fun!

The spring on a screen door can store elastic potential energy.

Many everyday things, including toys, containers, and clothing, transform elastic potential energy. Your group will explore a variety of objects that transform elastic potential energy. As you make your observations, think about the factors that determine how much elastic potential energy an object has.

EN 74

Project-Based Inquiry Science

2.6 Explore

How Does Elastic Potential Energy Affect Kinetic Energy?

5 min

Students consider examples of objects that can store elastic potential energy.

◯ Engage

Use the photograph of a screen door to show an example of a spring. Ask students to think of objects that contain springs. For example, they might suggest certain toys or they might know that some watches contain springs. If you still have the pop-up toaster available, show it to students to remind them of an example they already observed. Relate each example to elastic potential energy.

*A class period is considered to be one 40 to 50 minute class.

Explore Elastic Potential Energy

15 min

Students examine objects to determine if they use elastic potential energy.

Explore Elastic Potential Energy

Your group will explore several objects from the list of materials. Some of these objects transform elastic potential energy and some do not. You will begin your exploration by classifying the objects into two sets. Set 1 will include all of the objects that transform elastic potential energy in some way. Set 2 will include all of the objects that do not transform elastic potential energy. First, you will identify the indicators that determine in which set each item belongs. Then, you will further examine the items that transform elastic potential energy and identify the factors that affect how much elastic potential energy they have.

When the pole-vaulter's pole bends, it stores elastic potential energy. As the pole straightens, it transforms the elastic potential energy into kinetic energy, which does the work of sending the pole-vaulter over the bar.

Procedure

1. Explore the objects you have available, using them the way they are intended to be used. Identify which items transform elastic potential energy and which do not. Record your choices on your *Elastic Energy Explorations* page.

2. For each object, identify the indicators you used to decide whether or not it transforms elastic potential energy. Record the indicators in the *Indicators* column.

3. Continue to explore the items that you think transform elastic potential energy, and answer these questions:

   a) What do all of the objects in Set 1 have in common?

   b) How does this common property allow each object to store elastic potential energy?

   c) What factors affect how much elastic potential energy is stored? How do you know? How can you increase or decrease the amount of stored energy in each object? Record these factors on your *Elastic Energy Explorations* page.

EN 75

ENERGY

△ Guide

Distribute the materials to each group. Discuss what students will be doing and the criteria they will use to classify the objects into two groups. Remind students to have their *Elastic Energy Explorations* pages available to record their observations.

⬡ Get Going

Have students examine the objects to see how they work. If necessary, show students how specific items are used. Direct students to record their choices and indicators appropriately and to answer the questions listed.

△ Assess

Listen for the following in students' discussions of Question 3:

3. a) Students should know that all the items in Set 1 can transform elastic potential energy, even though they may look quite different. Set 1 may include a bouncy ball, a windup toy, a rubber band, or other items.

b) Students should respond that each item in Set 1 has a feature which can be stretched or compressed to store elastic potential energy.

c) Students should realize that the factors affecting how much elastic potential energy can be stored are unique to each item. The only factor that can be controlled is how much the spring, ball, or rubber band is distorted. Factors which cannot be controlled by the students are the size of the spring, ball, or rubber band. Or the type of alloy used in the spring, the type of rubber used in the ball or band.

NOTES

....

....

....

....

....

Communicate: Share Your Ideas

10 min

Students share their descriptions of an object that uses elastic potential energy.

4. Select one of the objects that transforms elastic potential energy. Prepare a description of how it operates. Make sure your list of indicators used to classify the object as having elastic potential energy is complete. Also, develop a good description of the factors that determine how much elastic potential energy it stores and how those factors can be changed. Be prepared to show the class your example and describe the factors.

The elastic potential energy in a golf ball transforms into kinetic energy when the golf club hits the ball.

Communicate

Share Your Ideas

When it is your group's turn to share your object, describe the object and what it does. Also, share the indicators you used to decide it transforms elastic potential energy and the factors that determine how much elastic potential energy is stored in it.

Listen carefully as each group presents. If the object presented is one you have investigated, compare their ideas to what you recorded on your *Elastic Potential Energy Explorations* page. If the object is different, add it to your page. Describe it well. Make sure you include the indicators and factors.

If you disagree with, or do not understand, a group's presentation, ask questions. Make sure you ask respectfully.

Reflect

1. Return to the energy-transformation cartoon machine you analyzed earlier in the Unit. Identify steps where elastic potential energy is used.

2. For each step, what indicators did you use to decide whether or not it transforms elastic potential energy?

3. For each step, how do you think you could increase the elastic potential energy? How do you think you could decrease it?

△ Guide

Make sure that each group selects one object to present. If possible, have each group select a different object. Ask students to pay attention to the details of how the object operates, what changes when the object operates, and what causes the object to operate.

◇ Evaluate

Listen to descriptions of the objects. Advise students to imagine describing the object to someone who has never seen it before. Make sure their descriptions are thorough and that they correctly identify the indicators they were able to use to recognize elastic potential energy.

△ Guide and Assess

Have students answer the *Reflect* questions with their groups. Encourage them to relate what they have observed about elastic potential energy to observations they made earlier in the Unit. Then determine if they are able to add this new knowledge to their ideas about how to design a machine to turn off a light.

1. Students' answers will vary with the steps selected.

2. Students' answers will vary with the steps selected. The students should see an object go from motionless to then having motion.

3. Students' answers will vary with the steps selected. The only form of control that the students might have is to wind a spring or rubber band more or less tightly.

Reflect

10 min

Students answer questions to relate the objects they observed to the Big Challenge.

NOTES

....

....

....

....

....

....

....

4. What would happen if you changed the elastic potential energy available in each step? What would still be successful? What would no longer be successful? What would operate differently?

5. Why might it be important to know how much elastic potential energy an object has when designing your machine to turn off a light?

Some materials, like rubber, readily return to their original shape after being deformed.

deformed: changed in shape because of an applied force.

elasticity: ability of a material to return to its original shape after it is deformed.

What Factors Affect Elastic Potential Energy?

Elastic potential energy is the energy stored in a springy material when the material is stretched, compressed, or otherwise **deformed**. When the material returns to its original shape, the potential energy is released, usually as kinetic energy. Many different materials, including rubber bands, trampolines, springs, and an archer's bow, can be deformed to store potential energy. The factors that determine the amount of elastic potential energy being stored include the type of material and the amount it is deformed. The more an object is deformed, the more stored energy it has.

Many sports use elastic materials in balls to provide the needed transformation of kinetic energy to potential energy and back to kinetic energy. These include golf balls, tennis balls, baseballs, basketballs, and footballs, as well as many others. In each case, the materials are selected for their **elasticity**.

Many of the objects you looked at use springs made of metal. You may never have thought you could stretch or compress metal. Because of its hardness and strength, metal is usually used to provide protection or structure. However, under certain conditions, a metal's elasticity can store elastic potential energy, as in a spring.

Pulling the bowstring compresses the bow. The more the archer compresses the bow, the farther the arrow will go.

ENERGY

4. Students' answers will vary with the steps selected. Students may suggest that if they used less elastic potential energy (by winding a rubber band less tightly), the step would not work. Listen for realistic ideas and answers.

5. Students might suggest that by controlling the amount of elastic potential energy an object has, the light can be turned off more reliably.

△ Guide

Describe to students that if you push your finger into a sponge, the sponge becomes momentarily deformed, but then returns to its original condition. Then describe how if you push your finger into a lump of clay, the clay remains deformed. Demonstrate as you describe the examples, if possible. Explain to students that some materials have greater elasticity than others. Those with greater elasticity can store more elastic potential energy than those with less elasticity.

What Factors Affect Elastic Potential Energy

10 min

Students read about elastic potential energy in terms of the particles of matter.

NOTES

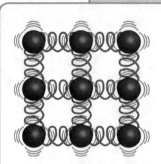 

This model of the atoms of a metal connected by imaginary springs shows what happens when the metal is deformed.

This coiled metal spring toy was invented in 1945 by a naval engineer while designing a part for battleships. Each toy is made from over 24 m (80 ft) of wire.

elastic limit: limit beyond which a deformed material does not return to its original shape.

To understand metal's elasticity, it is necessary to think about the atoms of metals. In metals, the atoms are usually evenly spaced, and they are held in place by forces of attraction. When you bend the metal, the atoms on one side stretch apart, while on the other side, the atoms are compressed together. When you release the metal, the forces tend to snap the atoms back in place. In fact, one way to model the atoms of a metal is to show them held together as if by springs.

When a metal spring is stretched, the distance between the atoms increases. When the spring is released, the atoms return to their original positions, and the spring returns to its original shape. When a spring is compressed, the distance between the atoms decreases. When the compressed spring is released, the atoms are pushed away from each other and return the spring to its original shape. It is possible to exceed a spring's **elastic limit** by stretching it too far. When this happens, the spring does not return to its original shape.

EN 78

NOTES

....

....

....

2.6 Explore

Springs are used to store elastic potential energy in many familiar objects, including screen doors, mattresses, and some light switches. The compression spring, extension spring, and masses with springs are some of the objects you examined that store elastic potential energy.

A basketball stores elastic potential energy.

Stop and Think

1. Describe how a coiled toy spring stretches and compresses when used as intended.

2. What do you think happens to the distance between atoms in a spring that exceeds its elastic limit?

3. Describe how a rubber ball is deformed when it bounces. Describe how a basketball is deformed when it bounces. What about a tennis ball? What about a baseball? Which kinds of balls do you think can store more elastic potential energy? Why?

4. Describe how a bow is deformed when it is used to shoot an arrow. Which part of the bow, the string or the wood, do you think stores more elastic potential energy? Why?

5. Suppose a car has a dent in it. Do you think there is elastic potential energy stored in that dent? Why or why not?

Reflect

Update your *Energy Types* page with what you now know about elastic potential energy. Revise your list of indicators. Add factors that affect how much elastic potential energy an object has.

Stop and Think

10 min

Students answer questions about elastic potential energy.

△ Guide and Assess

Have students work in their groups to answer the questions. As groups discuss the *Stop and Think* questions, visit each group to listen to their answers. Help students begin to differentiate among general types of materials in terms of the elastic potential energy they can store. When groups have had a chance to discuss the questions, lead a class discussion of their answers. Encourage students to comment on each other's ideas.

Listen for the following in students' answers to guide the discussion:

1. Students should describe how a coiled toy spring "walks" down a set of stairs by first stretching, then compressing, stretching and compressing.

2. Students should respond that when a spring exceeds its elastic limit, the distance between some of the atoms is increased beyond recovery and the change is permanent.

3. Students should describe how a moving ball begins in a spherical shape, with kinetic energy which is distorted when it hits a large object, such as the floor or a wall. It will momentarily be flat on one side, filled with potential energy. The elastic potential force in the ball will undo the distortion and it moves away from the large object with kinetic energy until it strikes another surface.

   Students should describe how a basketball is similar to the ball described above, except it is filled with air. When it strikes a surface, the ball is distorted and the air inside is compressed. Compressed air contains elastic potential energy and it pushes the wall of the basketball out again, giving it kinetic energy.

   Students should know that a tennis ball is filled with air (or nitrogen) and will behave like a basketball or football.

   Students should recall that a baseball is not hollow or made of rubber. It has an elastic core which stores the elastic potential energy when struck with a bat. The elastic potential energy returns the baseball to its original shape and the kinetic energy can take it hundreds of feet.

   Students may realize that golf ball can travel 300-400 yards and probably can store the most elastic potential energy, compared to the other balls, when struck.

4. Students should describe how when a bow is used to shoot an arrow, the ends of the bow are pulled back and closer together to store the elastic potential energy. The string stretches very little and most of the stored potential energy is in the bow, not the arrow. On the other hand, a child's toy bow and arrow usually uses an elastic band that stretches easily.

5. Students should reply that the dent in a car does not store elastic

Reflect

Update your *Energy Types* page with what you now
know about elastic potential energy. Revise your list of indicators. Add
factors that affect how much elastic potential energy an object has.

potential energy because it does not spring back into place. The
metal in the dent has been compressed beyond its elastic limit.

△ Guide

Allow students several minutes to add new information to the *Energy Types*
page. Remind students that like scientists, they will continue to add to their

NOTES

....

....

....

....

....

....

....

....

Reflect

5 min

*Students add what they
have learned to the
Energy Types page.*

META NOTES

It is important to remind
students that revising
earlier ideas does not
indicate a shortcoming
in their thinking. Instead,
it indicates an increase
in knowledge and
understanding based on
new observations and
evidence. This is the goal of
the process of science.

Update the Project Board

10 min

Students add new information to the Project Board.

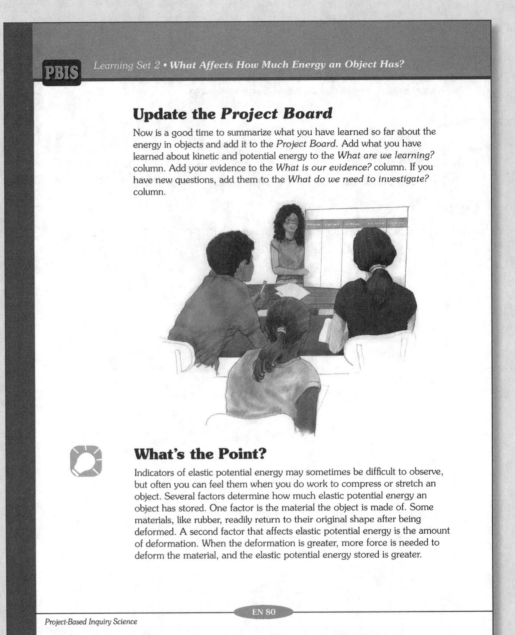

Update the *Project Board*

Now is a good time to summarize what you have learned so far about the energy in objects and add it to the *Project Board*. Add what you have learned about kinetic and potential energy to the *What are we learning?* column. Add your evidence to the *What is our evidence?* column. If you have new questions, add them to the *What do we need to investigate?* column.

What's the Point?

Indicators of elastic potential energy may sometimes be difficult to observe, but often you can feel them when you do work to compress or stretch an object. Several factors determine how much elastic potential energy an object has stored. One factor is the material the object is made of. Some materials, like rubber, readily return to their original shape after being deformed. A second factor that affects elastic potential energy is the amount of deformation. When the deformation is greater, more force is needed to deform the material, and the elastic potential energy stored is greater.

EN 80

Project-Based Inquiry Science

knowledge based on new observations. Explain that this might also include revising earlier ideas.

△ Guide

As a class, summarize any new information learned about types of potential energy. Make sure students support each example with evidence. Invite students to share any questions they still have or any new questions they have formulated. Add the information to the *Project Board* in the appropriate columns.

Assessment Options

Targeted Concepts, Skills, and Nature of Science	How do I know if students got it?
Scientists often work together and then share their findings. Sharing findings makes new information available and helps scientists refine their ideas and build on others' ideas. When another person's or group's idea is used, credit needs to be given.	**ASK:** What did you discover by listening to the ways that other students grouped objects according to elastic potential energy? **LISTEN:** Students may answer that other groupings supported their ideas or that they recognized that they needed to move a specific object into another group after listening to others.
Energy is the ability to cause change or do work.	**ASK:** How did you know that each object you observed used energy? **LISTEN:** Students should describe that they observed some type of change in the object.
Energy exists in different forms and can be changed from one form to another.	**ASK:** What type of energy change did you observe when you used the objects you classified? **LISTEN:** Students should describe how the object's stored elastic potential energy changed into kinetic energy of motion.
Kinetic energy is associated with the motion of an object.	**ASK:** In what way does the amount of kinetic energy in an object, such as a windup toy, depend on the amount of elastic potential energy? **LISTEN:** Students should suggest that the amount of elastic potential energy is directly related to the amount of kinetic energy so the greater the elastic potential energy is, the greater the motion of the object is.

Targeted Concepts, Skills, and Nature of Science	How do I know if students got it?
Potential energy is stored energy, associated with position or condition.	**ASK:** What is the elasticity of an object? **LISTEN:** Students should explain that elasticity is the ability of an object to store elastic potential energy.

Teacher Reflection Questions

- How did you help students determine whether an object uses elastic potential energy? Is there anything you would do differently next time?

- Did students have any difficulties differentiating between types of materials based on elasticity? What examples can you use to help them understand the differences?

- How were you able to get students to relate their conclusions about elastic potential energy to specific indicators they observed? What can you do to encourage this in the future?

Back to the Big Challenge

Design a Rube Goldberg Machine to Turn Off a Light

◀ *1 class period*

A class period is considered to be one 40 to 50 minute class.

Overview

Students revise their earlier descriptions of energy. As a class, they discuss what they have learned about energy. Students then use what they have learned to revise their design for the *Big Challenge.*

Targeted Concepts, Skills, and Nature of Science	Performance Expectations
Scientists often work together and then share their findings. Sharing findings makes new information available and helps scientists refine their ideas and build on others' ideas. When another person's or group's idea is used, credit needs to be given.	Students review their ideas as a class and make suggestions on how to improve them.
Scientific knowledge is developed through observations, recording and analysis of data, and development of explanations based on evidence.	Students use their observations and explanations to revise earlier descriptions of energy and their initial design plans for the *Big Challenge.*
Energy is the ability to cause change or do work.	Students recognize that energy is the ability to cause change or do work.
Energy exists in different forms and can be changed from one form to another.	Students understand that energy can change forms, but the total energy in a system is conserved.
Energy is neither created nor destroyed in ordinary processes.	Students recognize that no energy is destroyed as one form of energy is changed to another.
Kinetic energy is associated with the motion of an object.	Students relate the motion of an object to the amount of kinetic energy it has.

Targeted Concepts, Skills, and Nature of Science	Performance Expectations
Potential energy is stored energy, associated with position or condition.	Students relate the kinetic energy produced by an object to the amount of potential energy it has.

Materials	
1 per student	*My Rube Goldberg Machine Page*

Homework Options

Reflection

- **Science Content:** How can you increase the speed at which a marble rolls down a ramp? *(Students should suggest factors they have investigated, such as increasing the mass of the marble or increasing the height of the marble. They might even suggest using a compressed spring to shoot the marble down the ramp.)*

- **Science Process:** Why should you not consider it a failure if your initial experimental design does not work? *(Students should recognize that even when a design does not work or a predicted answer to a question proves to be incorrect, they have new knowledge by learning this information. They can use the new knowledge to make revisions that will lead to a more successful design or a correct answer.)*

Learning Set 2

Back to the Big Challenge

Design a Rube Goldberg machine to turn off a light.

The *Big Challenge* for this Unit is *Design a Rube Goldberg machine to turn off a light*. At the end of *Learning Set 1*, you began to think about what kind of light you want to turn off and what the last step of your design needs to do. Your last step almost certainly has some object that needs to move. You now know enough about the energy of objects to figure out how to give that object kinetic energy and how to control the amount of kinetic energy it will have. You will now continue to design backward to address the challenge. You will use what you know to make your last step more specific. You will identify what has to happen before the last step for the last step to operate successfully. But first, you will describe energy one more time.

Conference

You wrote a description of energy at the beginning of *Learning Set 1*, before you knew a lot about different kinds of energy. You described energy again after you thought about the different ways your energy-transformation cartoon transformed energy. Before moving on, you will once again describe energy. This time, you will use what you have learned about the energy of objects. You now know about several types of energy—kinetic energy, gravitational potential energy, and elastic potential energy. You know how to identify when each is present, and you know the factors that determine how much of each is present.

Revise your description of energy so it takes into account all the different things you now know about energy. Keep track of the changes you make in your description, and record why you are making the changes.

ENERGY

Learning Set 2

Back to the Big Challenge

5 min

Students revisit the goal of the Big Challenge *by summarizing what they have learned about energy.*

META NOTES

It is easy for students to lose track of the big picture as they focus on individual tasks along the way. Take this opportunity to refocus students' attention on the *Big Challenge*, but do so in terms of the information they have learned in the first two *Learning Sets*.

△ Guide

Review the *Big Challenge* once more. Point out that to accomplish the task, they will need to create some type of motion. Ask students to describe and define an object in motion. *(Students should recognize that the object has kinetic energy.)* Lead students to realize that they will use what they have learned about types of energy and changes in energy to make some object move.

Conference

10 min

Students discuss how to revise their earlier descriptions of energy.

Conference

But first... noe energy one mo...

You wrote a description of energy at the beginning of *Learning Set 1*, before you knew a lot about different kinds of energy. You described energy again after you thought about the different ways your energy-transformation cartoon transformed energy. Before moving on, you will once again describe energy. This time, you will use what you have learned about the energy of objects. You now know about several types of energy—kinetic energy, gravitational potential energy, and elastic potential energy. You know how to identify when each is present, and you know the factors that determine how much of each is present.

Revise your description of energy so it takes into account all the different things you now know about energy. Keep track of the changes you make in your description, and record why you are making the changes.

◇ Evaluate

In their groups, have students discuss what they have learned about energy. Listen to their ideas and clarify any misconceptions that may have developed. Tell students to review any notes they have made or pages they have completed to make sure they include everything they have learned. You may wish to suggest to students that they include a graphic organizer to relate the different kinds of energy they have explored.

NOTES

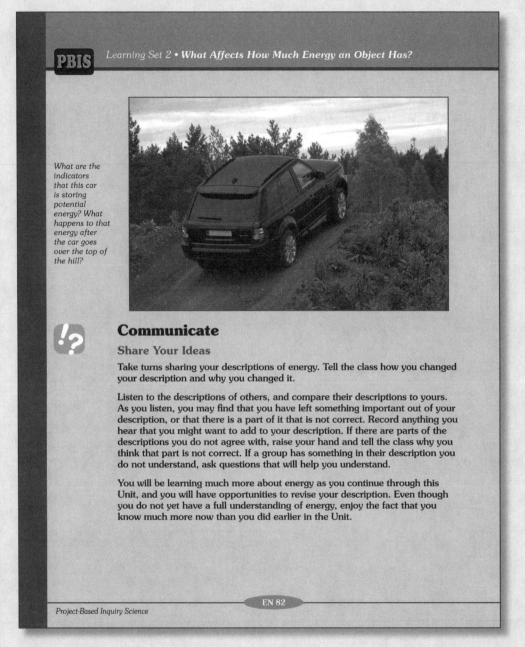

PBIS *Learning Set 2 • What Affects How Much Energy an Object Has?*

What are the indicators that this car is storing potential energy? What happens to that energy after the car goes over the top of the hill?

Communicate

Share Your Ideas

Take turns sharing your descriptions of energy. Tell the class how you changed your description and why you changed it.

Listen to the descriptions of others, and compare their descriptions to yours. As you listen, you may find that you have left something important out of your description, or that there is a part of it that is not correct. Record anything you hear that you might want to add to your description. If there are parts of the descriptions you do not agree with, raise your hand and tell the class why you think that part is not correct. If a group has something in their description you do not understand, ask questions that will help you understand.

You will be learning much more about energy as you continue through this Unit, and you will have opportunities to revise your description. Even though you do not yet have a full understanding of energy, enjoy the fact that you know much more now than you did earlier in the Unit.

Communicate: Share Your Ideas

10 min

Students share their revised descriptions of energy with the class.

⬡ **Get Going**

Allow students a certain amount of time (2-3 min each) to present their revised descriptions of energy to the class. Make sure that other students listen carefully and encourage them to take notes of ideas they did not include. Encourage students to ask questions and to point out errors in a respectful manner.

Revise Your Design

You developed three possible last steps for your design. Each of them probably has a moving part. Every movement involves kinetic energy. You know a lot now about how objects can get kinetic energy and how the amount of kinetic energy they have can be controlled. Now analyze each of your possible last steps. Use what you know about the factors that affect the amount of kinetic energy and potential energy, and how potential energy is transformed into kinetic energy. Your analysis should include three parts:

1. Identify how much kinetic energy your machine will need in its last step— a little, a lot, or a huge amount.

2. Identify how the moving part in your last step could get kinetic energy.

3. Identify how you might control the amount of kinetic energy of the moving part in your last step.

You may get some ideas about how to supply energy to your last step from the energy-transformation cartoons the class examined.

Sketch your ideas about how to supply energy to the last step of your design. Make sure to show the moving part that will turn off the light. Identify what type of energy you might transform to supply energy to your last step. Be prepared to present your ideas to the class, including any ideas about which you are still unsure. Update your *My Rube Goldberg Machine* page with all of your design revisions and ideas.

My Rube Goldberg Machine				
Name:			Date:	
Sketch of machine. Label each step with a number.				
Step	Description of step	Energy Type(s) In	Energy Type(s) Out	Work done
1				
2				
3				
4				
5				
Use this space to record ideas.				

Revise Your Design

10 min

Students revise their design for the Big Challenge.

⬡ Get Going

Read through the material about revising the design together. Give an example of changes students might make based on what they have learned. For example, a student might incorporate a spring into the design to take advantage of elastic potential energy. Remind students to consider how they will control the amount of energy they use based on the observations they have made.

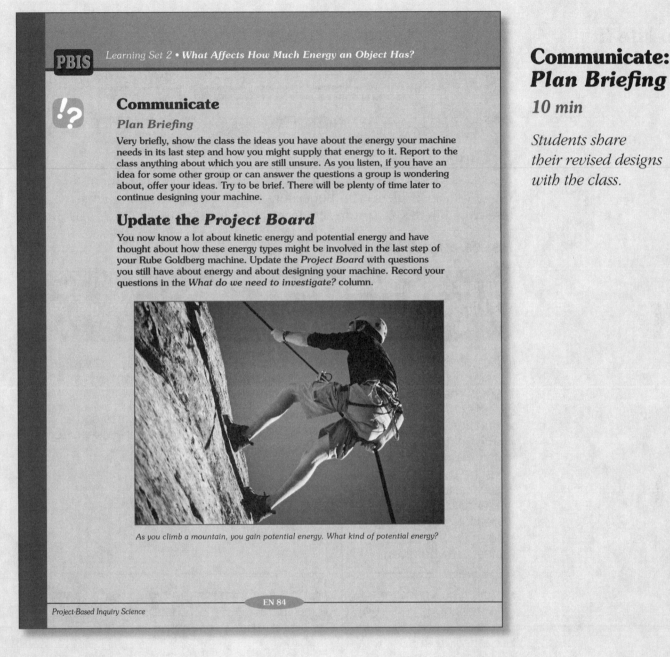

PBIS *Learning Set 2 • What Affects How Much Energy an Object Has?*

Communicate

Plan Briefing

Very briefly, show the class the ideas you have about the energy your machine needs in its last step and how you might supply that energy to it. Report to the class anything about which you are still unsure. As you listen, if you have an idea for some other group or can answer the questions a group is wondering about, offer your ideas. Try to be brief. There will be plenty of time later to continue designing your machine.

Update the *Project Board*

You now know a lot about kinetic energy and potential energy and have thought about how these energy types might be involved in the last step of your Rube Goldberg machine. Update the *Project Board* with questions you still have about energy and about designing your machine. Record your questions in the *What do we need to investigate?* column.

As you climb a mountain, you gain potential energy. What kind of potential energy?

EN 84

Project-Based Inquiry Science

Communicate: *Plan Briefing*

10 min

Students share their revised designs with the class.

○ Get Going

Have students briefly share their revised sketches with the class along with an explanation of why they made the changes they did. Remind students that they will have additional opportunities for revision so they do not need to be sure of every step at this point.

Update the Project Board

10 min

Students add new information to the Project Board.

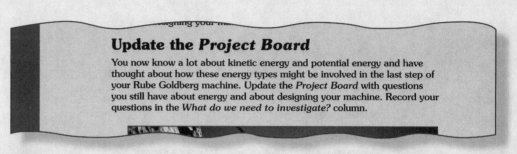

Update the *Project Board*

You now know a lot about kinetic energy and potential energy and have thought about how these energy types might be involved in the last step of your Rube Goldberg machine. Update the *Project Board* with questions you still have about energy and about designing your machine. Record your questions in the *What do we need to investigate?* column.

△ Guide

As a class, review the material on the *Project Board*. Invite students to suggest ideas, evidence, and questions to add based on what they have discovered in this *Learning Set*. Record the suggestions on the *Project Board*.

Assessment Options

Targeted Concepts, Skills, and Nature of Science	How do I know if students got it?
Scientists often work together and then share their findings. Sharing findings makes new information available and helps scientists refine their ideas and build on others' ideas. When another person's or group's idea is used, credit needs to be given.	**ASK:** What ideas about energy did you forget until you heard them from other students? **LISTEN:** Students should suggest some information they added to their description after listening to others.
Scientific knowledge is developed through observations, recording and analysis of data, and development of explanations based on evidence.	**ASK:** What information did you add to your description based on the demonstrations, activities, or experiments? **LISTEN:** Students should describe information they found out through direct observation.

Targeted Concepts, Skills, and Nature of Science	How do I know if students got it?
Energy is the ability to cause change or do work.	**ASK:** How would you define energy in your own words? **LISTEN:** Students should present a basic definition of energy as the ability to cause change or do work.
Energy exists in different forms and can be changed from one form to another.	**ASK:** What different forms of energy did you include in your design to accomplish the *Big Challenge?* **LISTEN:** Students should list the forms of energy, such as kinetic energy, gravitational potential energy, and elastic potential energy.
Energy is neither created nor destroyed in ordinary processes.	**ASK:** How is energy conserved in your design? **LISTEN:** Students might explain that one form of energy changes to another, but energy is not destroyed in the process.
Kinetic energy is associated with the motion of an object.	**ASK:** What parts of your design involve kinetic energy? **LISTEN:** Students should describe any moving parts of their design.
Potential energy is stored energy, associated with position or condition.	**ASK:** What parts of your design involve potential energy? **LISTEN:** Students should describe any parts of the design that involve lifting objects, falling objects, or compressing/stretching objects.

NOTES

....

....

Teacher Reflection Questions

- What difficulties did students have pulling all of the concepts together? How might you assist them with this process in the future?

- How were you able to keep students motivated while revising their descriptions of energy? What examples can you use to show them why this is important?

- How did you get students to contribute to the discussion of what to put on the *Project Board?* Are there other things you could do?

NOTES

_____

_____

_____

_____

_____

_____

_____

_____

_____

_____

_____

LEARNING SET 3 INTRODUCTION

Learning Set 3

What Are Thermal Energy and Chemical Energy?

◀ **15 class periods**

A class period is considered to be one 40 to 50 minute class.

Students learn the characteristics of thermal and kinetic energy through observations, investigations, and readings.

Overview

Students begin the section by identifying indicators of thermal energy and chemical energy in a pop-up toaster. They use hand warmers to investigate types of changes in energy. Students conduct experiments in which they manipulate the mass and temperature of water to measure amounts of thermal energy. Conducting a thought experiment, students consider kinetic energy and thermal energy to differentiate between the two quantities. They read about the quantities and how each is measured and compare examples in terms of thermal energy. Then students are presented with two identical samples of matter to consider in terms of specific heat. Students find out how specific heat affects the thermal energy and temperature of a sample, and how the specific heat of water moderates climates near large bodies of water. The three methods of heat transfer are described for students, and the renewable energy resources of solar energy and geothermal energy are discussed. Students identify chemical energy in four different types of changes and they conduct investigations to compare different amounts of chemical energy. They conclude the *Learning Set* by reading about the role of chemical energy in living systems.

Targeted Concepts, Skills, and Nature of Science	Section
Scientists often work together and then share their findings. Sharing findings makes new information available and helps scientists refine their ideas and build on others' ideas. When another person's or group's idea is used, credit needs to be given.	3.1, 3.2, 3.5, 3.6
Heat is the transfer of thermal energy from a substance at a higher temperature to a substance at a lower temperature.	3.1, 3.2, 3.3

Targeted Concepts, Skills, and Nature of Science	Section
The addition or removal of heat may result in a temperature change in a system.	3.1, 3.2, 3.3
Potential energy is stored energy, associated with position or condition.	3.1
Energy is absorbed or released during a chemical reaction.	3.1
Thermal energy is the energy of the particles of matter.	3.2, 3.3
The addition or removal of heat may result in a temperature change in a system.	3.3
Every substance can be described by its specific heat.	3.4
Large bodies of water moderate nearby climates.	3.4
Heat is transferred by conduction, convection, and radiation.	3.4
The Sun is a source of heat energy.	3.4
Solar energy is a renewable energy resource.	3.4
Geothermal energy is a renewable energy resource from Earth.	3.4
During a chemical change, the original substances are changed into new substances with different properties.	3.5, 3.6
Chemical energy is potential energy stored in the bonds that hold matter together.	3.5, 3.6
Some chemical changes absorb thermal energy and others release thermal energy.	3.5
Plants change the energy of sunlight into chemical energy during photosynthesis.	3.6
The cells of living things break down food during cell respiration to obtain energy.	3.6

Understanding for Teachers

Properties of Matter

Matter can be described by physical properties and chemical properties. Physical properties are those that can be observed and measured without changing the composition of the substance, such as boiling point, melting point, state of matter, mass, and density. A physical change is a change in the form or appearance of matter, but not its composition.

Chemical properties describe the ability of the substance to change into another substance, such as the ability to burn, tarnish, or rust. A chemical change is a change in the composition of a substance, otherwise known as a chemical reaction. During a chemical reaction, bonds between atoms are broken, atoms are rearranged, and new bonds are formed. Chemical energy is stored in the bonds that hold matter together. This energy is absorbed and released as bonds are broken and new bonds are formed.

Particles of matter, such as atoms and molecules, are in constant motion. The particles have kinetic energy, as well as some potential energy. The average kinetic energy of the molecules determines the temperature of the substance.

Thermal energy is transferred from a warmer substance to a cooler substance as heat. Heat can be transferred by conduction, convection, and radiation. A substance that gives up thermal energy becomes cooler whereas a substance that absorbs thermal energy becomes warmer.

NOTES

....

....

....

....

NOTES

LEARNING SET 3 IMPLEMENTATION

 Learning Set 3

What Are Thermal Energy and Chemical Energy?

Imagine biting into a warm stack of pancakes. The warmth of the pancakes easily melts a golden pat of butter. Before you even take a bite, the aroma tells you that this breakfast is going to be delicious. But, just minutes ago, these pancakes were a cool, runny blob of pale pancake batter. The unappealing batter was transformed into an appetizing treat for the eyes, nose, and mouth by thermal and chemical energy. Then thermal energy from the warm pancakes warmed the butter, causing it to melt.

Thermal energy and chemical energy are transformed in cooking to produce delicious results from raw ingredients.

The energy-transformation cartoons you examined all have examples of thermal energy and chemical energy. You might want to use thermal or chemical energy in the machine you are designing. In this *Learning Set*, you will explore these two types of energy and learn the indicators of each, the factors that affect how much energy is available, and how each type of energy is transformed to do work. As you are investigating them, notice how often the two types of energy are related to each other.

EN 85

ENERGY

Learning Set 3

What Are Thermal Energy and Chemical Energy?

5 min

Students are introduced to sections on thermal and chemical energy.

○ Engage

Use the photographs of the pancake batter and pancake stack to start a discussion about how heating or cooling foods can cause changes. Allow students to share other examples. Focus students by letting them know that they will be learning about the characteristics of thermal energy and chemical energy, which may be useful in accomplishing the *Big Challenge*.

NOTES

SECTION 3.1 INTRODUCTION

3.1 Understand the Question

Think About Thermal Energy and Chemical Energy

◀ *2 class periods*

A class period is considered to be one 40 to 50 minute class.

Overview

Students revisit their observations of the pop-up toaster from earlier to now consider it in terms of thermal energy, heat, and chemical changes. They share their thoughts on these energy types with the class, and together decide whether each of these are kinetic or potential energy. They apply their understanding of these concepts to consider the types of energy in another device—a hand warmer. In groups, students explore a hand warmer by examining it before and after it is activated. After making their observations and analyzing their results, students read about the operation of a chemical hand warmer in terms of exothermic and endothermic processes. They finish the section by returning to their energy-transformation cartoons and apply what they understand about thermal energy and chemical energy to answer questions about the cartoon. Then the class updates the *Project Board* with what they have learned and any questions that this introductory material has brought up.

Targeted Concepts, Skills, and Nature of Science	Performance Expectations
Scientists often work together and then share their findings. Sharing findings makes new information available and helps scientists refine their ideas and build on others' ideas. When another person's or group's idea is used, credit needs to be given.	Students share their ideas about what causes a hand warmer to give off heat.
Heat is the transfer of thermal energy from a substance at a higher temperature to a substance at a lower temperature.	Students recognize that heat is transferred from the warm hand warmer to cool hands.
The addition or removal of heat may result in a temperature change in a system.	Students learn that the temperature of a substance can rise as it absorbs heat.

Targeted Concepts, Skills, and Nature of Science	Performance Expectations
Potential energy is stored energy, associated with position or condition.	Students find that chemical energy, which is stored in the bonds that hold atoms together, can be released during a chemical change.
Energy is absorbed or released during a chemical reaction.	Students discover that energy is taken in during endothermic processes and released during exothermic processes.

Materials	
1 per group	Hand warmer
1 per student	*Project Board* page
1 per class	Class *Project Board*

Homework Options

Reflection

- **Science Content:** How is an endothermic process different from an exothermic process? *(Students should understand that an endothermic process absorbs heat and an exothermic process releases heat.)*

- **Science Process:** How can you compare the temperatures of substances using your sense of touch? *(Students should describe how they can feel two substances to decide which is warmer. The warmer substance has the higher temperature.)*

Preparation for 3.2

- **Science Process:** What indicators can you look for to decide if an object has more or less thermal energy than another? *(This question is meant to get students thinking about finding a way to measure the "amount" of thermal energy in terms of changes in heat and temperature.)*

SECTION 3.1 IMPLEMENTATION

3.1 Understand the Question

Think About Thermal Energy and Chemical Energy

You are already familiar with several types of energy. Some energy tranformations are easy to spot. For example, a child at the top of a playground slide has gravitational potential energy. The child has fun transforming this energy into kinetic energy. However, some types of energy are harder to see. The indicators are less visible. The factors may also be difficult to measure. As you explore thermal and chemical energy, pay attention to how their indicators and factors differ from those of other types of energy you have explored.

Get Started

Earlier in this Unit, you observed a pop-up toaster as it made a slice of toast. At that time, you made a list of all the kinds of energy you saw. Your list probably included transformations involving thermal energy and chemical energy, even if you did not yet have the names for them. You will return to that list now and review your observations of the operation of a toaster.

Thermal clothing helps keep thermal energy in so a person stays warm.

Look at your notes from the toaster demonstration and answer the following questions. Some will be easy to answer, and some might be difficult. If you do not know the answer to any of these questions now, you will by the end of this *Learning Set.*

- Thermal energy is experienced as *heat*. What happens in the toaster as a result of thermal energy? How do you know the toaster transforms thermal energy? What do you think might be an indicator of thermal energy?

- How can you tell how much thermal energy is present? What factors do you think would control how much thermal energy an object has?

- Chemical energy is energy that is related to *chemical changes.* What role do you think chemical energy plays in the toaster?

EN 86

Project-Based Inquiry Science

3.1 Understand the Question

Think About Thermal Energy and Chemical Energy

10 min

Students think about indicators of thermal and chemical energy.

○ **Engage**

Ask students to describe examples of changes in energy. Most likely, students will describe changes between kinetic and potential energy. If so, challenge them to give examples involving thermal and chemical energy. Most likely, they will find this difficult. Lead into a discussion about the need to find different indicators to detect these types of energy and different factors to control these types of energy.

Get Started

10 min

Students analyze a pop-up toaster in terms of thermal and chemical energy.

META NOTES

Students can have the misconception that thermal clothing, blankets, or insulation keep *cold* out. If the confusion arises, make sure students understand that *cold* is not a quantity. There is only thermal energy (heat) and the loss of thermal energy (cold). When they feel cold, it is because they are losing heat, or thermal energy. In this sense, *cold* is more of a direction, as an answer to the question, "Where is the heat going?"

types of energy you have explored.

Get Started

Earlier in this Unit, you observed a pop-up toaster as it made a slice of toast. At that time, you made a list of all the kinds of energy you saw. Your list probably included transformations involving thermal energy and chemical energy, even if you did not yet have the names for them. You will return to that list now and review your observations of the operation of a toaster.

Look at your notes from the toaster demonstration and answer the following questions. Some will be easy to answer, and some might be difficult. If you do not know the answer to any of these questions now, you will by the end of this *Learning Set*.

Thermal clothing helps keep thermal energy in so a person stays warm.

- Thermal energy is experienced as *heat*. What happens in the toaster as a result of thermal energy? How do you know the toaster transforms thermal energy? What do you think might be an indicator of thermal energy?

- How can you tell how much thermal energy is present? What factors do you think would control how much thermal energy an object has?

- Chemical energy is energy that is related to *chemical changes*. What role do you think chemical energy plays in the toaster?

EN 86

Project-Based Inquiry Science

△ Guide and Assess

Have students take out their notes from the pop-up toaster demonstration. Ask them to answer the questions listed in the student text. Tell students to use their notes, even though they may not have named the types of energy when they first made their observations.

- Students should recognize that the toaster heats up as the amount of thermal energy increases. Heat is an indicator of thermal energy.

- Students may suggest that the amount of thermal energy is related to how warm the toaster becomes or how dark the color of the toast becomes.

- Students should relate chemical energy to the changes they can observe in a piece of toast as it is heated in the toaster. The heat of the toaster makes chemical reactions happen. These reactions include the "browning" of toast and the formation of molecules that give the "toast smell."

- Do you think thermal energy is a type of potential energy or a type of kinetic energy?

- Do you think chemical energy is a type of potential energy or a type of kinetic energy?

Communicate

Share Your Ideas

Share your answers to the questions with the class. Discuss what roles thermal energy and chemical energy play in the toaster. Discuss whether each is kinetic or potential energy. Note any disagreements you have. Later, you will have a chance to put questions on the *Project Board* that you need to answer to settle your disagreements.

Explore

Skiers often use hand warmers when they are outside in cold weather. Hand warmers are small plastic pouches with a liquid in them. When you activate a hand warmer by snapping it, it gets warm without the use of batteries. You will be making some observations of a hand warmer. Observe the changes that happen, and look for indicators of thermal energy and chemical energy.

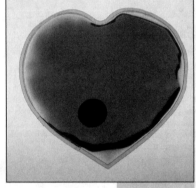

Materials
• **hand warmer**

Procedure

1. You will receive a hand warmer. Pass the hand warmer around your group. Handle it carefully so it is not activated before everybody in your group gets to examine it.

2. Make a drawing of the hand warmer, and record what you see and feel.

3. After everyone has examined it, activate the hand warmer by snapping it. Pay attention to the hand warmer from the time it is snapped. Record any changes you see, feel, or hear occurring inside the hand warmer.

4. Pass the hand warmer around again, and record other observations using your senses of sight and touch.

- Students may not realize it at this point, but they might suggest that thermal energy is kinetic energy because it is related to the motion of particles of matter.

- Students may correctly answer that chemical energy is potential energy stored in the bonds that hold atoms together.

Communicate: Share Your Ideas

10 min

Students share their answers to the questions about energy in the toaster.

---

of kinetic energy?

Communicate

Share Your Ideas

Share your answers to the questions with the class. Discuss what roles thermal energy and chemical energy play in the toaster. Discuss whether each is kinetic or potential energy. Note any disagreements you have. Later, you will have a chance to put questions on the *Project Board* that you need to answer to settle your disagreements.

Explore

△ Guide

Lead a class discussion in which students share their answers to the *Get Started* questions. Encourage students to describe their ideas even if they are unsure of their answers or the proper terms to use.

Explore

5 min

Students are introduced to an activity they will perform in which they determine the thermal and chemical energy in a hand warmer.

Explore

Skiers often use hand warmers when they are outside in cold weather. Hand warmers are small plastic pouches with a liquid in them. When you activate a hand warmer by snapping it, it gets warm without the use of batteries. You will be making some observations of a hand warmer. Observe the changes that happen, and look for indicators of thermal energy and chemical energy.

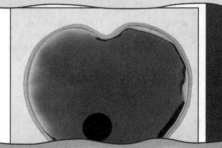

○ Engage

Ask students if they have ever used a hand warmer. Describe how a hand warmer might be used and a situation in which it might be useful.

TEACHER TALK

❝You will observe changes that occur when using a hand warmer. Remember how you looked for indicators of kinetic and potential energy? Now you will look for indicators that suggest that thermal or chemical energy are involved.❞

NOTES

....

....

....

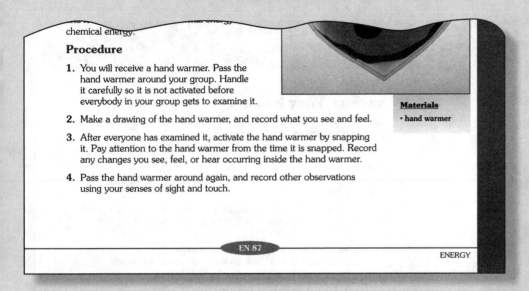

chemical energy.

Procedure

1. You will receive a hand warmer. Pass the hand warmer around your group. Handle it carefully so it is not activated before everybody in your group gets to examine it.

2. Make a drawing of the hand warmer, and record what you see and feel.

3. After everyone has examined it, activate the hand warmer by snapping it. Pay attention to the hand warmer from the time it is snapped. Record any changes you see, feel, or hear occurring inside the hand warmer.

4. Pass the hand warmer around again, and record other observations using your senses of sight and touch.

Materials
• hand warmer

EN 87

ENERGY

Procedure

10 min

Students observe a hand warmer before and after it is activated.

⬡ Get Going

Have students meet with their groups. Tell students to read through the procedure and make sure they understand the directions. Address any questions students may have. Then distribute a hand warmer to each group and let them begin. Remind students to record their observations.

NOTES

....

....

....

....

....

....

....

Analyze Your Results

10 min

Students answer questions to help analyze the results of their activity.

Analyze Your Results

After you have recorded all of your observations, discuss the following questions with members of your group.

1. What changes did you observe in the hand warmer after it was activated?

2. What do you think caused the change in temperature? Think about the events that occurred immediately after it was activated to help you justify your answer.

3. What types of energy can you identify in the hand warmer? What are the indicators of each type? Can you think of any factors that might affect the amount of energy?

4. Compare and contrast the operation of a hand warmer to the operation of a pop-up toaster. How are they alike? How are they different?

5. Can you think of other ways to generate these types of energy?

Communicate Your Results

Share Your Ideas

As a class, share your observations and ideas about the changes you observed in the hand warmer. Discuss the types of energy present in the hand warmer. Also, discuss their indicators, the factors that might affect how much energy is available, and other ways to generate thermal and chemical energy. Note any disagreements you have. Later, you will have a chance to put questions on the *Project Board* that will help you settle those disagreements.

heat: thermal energy that is transferred from one place to another.

exothermic: giving off heat because of a chemical change.

How Do Hand Warmers Work?

In the type of hand warmer you explored, a pouch contains water, a chemical called sodium acetate, and a small piece of metal. When the metal is bent, tiny pieces of the metal chip off. The metal chips are a perfect place for sodium acetate crystals to form. Before you know it, all of the sodium acetate has formed crystals. During this process, **heat** is given off. The heat is thermal energy that is transferred from inside the pouch to your hand. This is why you felt the *temperature* of the hand warmer rise. A process that gives off heat is called an **exothermic** process. The pouch also becomes harder as the liquid transforms into solid crystals.

△ **Guide**

Have groups discuss the questions. Remind students to provide evidence to support their answers. Walk around the room to listen to each group's discussion. Provide guidance as needed. Tell students to record their answers.

☐ Assess

As they share their ideas, the groups should come to agreement on the following answers:

1. Students may state that the filling of the hand warmer turned from a liquid to a solid and rose in temperature.

2. Students' answers will vary. It is unlikely they will know the chemistry involved. They may make a general statement, such as *Changing from a liquid to a solid made it give off heat.*

3. Students should identify heat as the indicator for thermal energy in the hand warmer. Although the reaction they observe is not a chemical reaction, it looks very much like a chemical reaction. Students might identify the amount of the substance in the plastic bag as a way to control the amount of energy released.

4. Students should suggest that the hand warmer and the toaster are similar because they both give off heat. They are different because the hand warmer uses a liquid in a plastic pouch and the process is reversible. The toaster does not use a liquid, does use electricity, has moving parts, and creates an irreversible change in the bread. The toaster cannot "untoast" a slice of bread.

5. Students should know that thermal energy can be generated in a variety of ways, such as burning paper and wood, heating a stove, or using the Sun. All of these can also generate chemical reactions.

△ Guide

Have groups take turns sharing their ideas and observations of their hand warmer. Let them know that they may use their answers to the *Analyze Your Data* questions to help summarize the information they share. Remind students to be specific in their comparisons of the hand warmer to the pop-up toaster. Encourage the class to be creative when thinking of other ways to generate these types of energy. Remind students that they do not have to agree with each other at this point. They are gathering their ideas and will revise them as they continue to learn about energy.

> **META NOTES**
>
> Avoid the misconception that a change of state, such as from a liquid to solid, is a chemical change. Make sure that students understand that a change of state is a physical change in matter. However, a change of state often occurs as a result of a chemical change.

Communicate Your Results: Share Your Ideas

10 min

Students share their analyses of the activities with the class.

How Do Hand Warmers Work?

10 min

Students read an explanation of the science of what they just observed.

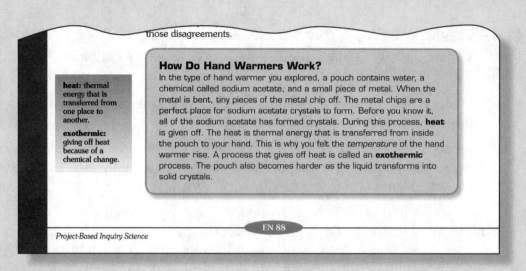

those disagreements.

heat: thermal energy that is transferred from one place to another.

exothermic: giving off heat because of a chemical change.

How Do Hand Warmers Work?
In the type of hand warmer you explored, a pouch contains water, a chemical called sodium acetate, and a small piece of metal. When the metal is bent, tiny pieces of the metal chip off. The metal chips are a perfect place for sodium acetate crystals to form. Before you know it, all of the sodium acetate has formed crystals. During this process, **heat** is given off. The heat is thermal energy that is transferred from inside the pouch to your hand. This is why you felt the *temperature* of the hand warmer rise. A process that gives off heat is called an **exothermic** process. The pouch also becomes harder as the liquid transforms into solid crystals.

EN 88

Project-Based Inquiry Science

○ Engage

Have students place their hands on their desks. Ask how the desk feels in terms of temperature. *(Students may describe the desk as cold.)* Discuss with the class that the desk feels cold because thermal energy from their hands is transferred to the desk as heat. Because their hands lose heat, they feel cold. Then ask how the hand warmer felt. *(Students should describe the hand warmer as warm.)* Let them know that the hand warmer felt warm because thermal energy was transferred from it to their hands. Because their hands absorbed heat, they felt warm.

△ Guide

Describe familiar examples of chemical changes, such as bread baking, silver tarnishing, iron rusting, and wood burning, to the class. Point out that during any chemical change, original substances are changed into new substances. Contrast a chemical change with a physical change by explaining that during a physical change, new substances are not formed. Instead, the original substances change in form or appearance. List several physical changes, such as bending metal, cutting wood, or freezing water into ice.

NOTES

....

....

....

....

In the exploration, you noticed the indicator for thermal energy, which is an increase in temperature. Hand warmers like the one you observed can be used again and again. To reuse the pouch after it cools off, you place it in boiling water for a few minutes. Heat from the hot water is transferred to the water in the pouch. In a short while, the crystals come apart. A process such as this, which requires an input of heat, is called an **endothermic** process. After the pouch cools off, it is ready to be used again.

You may think that the crystals of sodium acetate melted, but, in fact, they dissolved. When a crystal dissolves, tiny particles break off the crystal and mix completely with water. Eventually, all of the solid dissolves, and you see only a liquid inside the pouch. You may have seen this process if you have stirred sugar into tea. At first, you can see the crystals swirl around as you mix the tea, but after a while, they disappear because they have dissolved. The process of the sodium acetate crystals in the hand warmer coming out of the water and going back in when heated is a physical change.

There is another type of hand warmer that is not reusable. This type uses iron powder with water, salt, and air. The salt speeds up the exothermic reaction of the iron with oxygen in air so that a lot of heat is given off. This is a **chemical change** and produces a new, reddish-orange chemical, iron oxide. Iron oxide, or rust, cannot be easily transformed back into iron. Some of the indicators of a chemical change can be seen in this reaction, such as a change in color and heat being given off. Another indicator of a chemical change is the formation of a new substance in the form of a gas or a solid.

When a chemical change occurs, at least one new substance is made, and an energy transformation generally occurs. If the change is exothermic, chemical energy is transformed into thermal energy. If the change is endothermic, thermal energy is transformed into chemical energy.

endothermic: requires heat for a chemical change.

chemical change: a change that produces one or more new substances.

A burning candle gives off heat. Do you think this is an endothermic process or an exothermic process?

EN 89

ENERGY

Write the terms *exothermic* and *endothermic* on the board. Underline the prefix in each word. Explain that the prefix *exo-* means *out of* whereas the prefix *endo-* means *into*. This may help them remember the meanings of each term.

Reflect

10 min

Students answer questions to relate thermal energy, chemical energy, and heat.

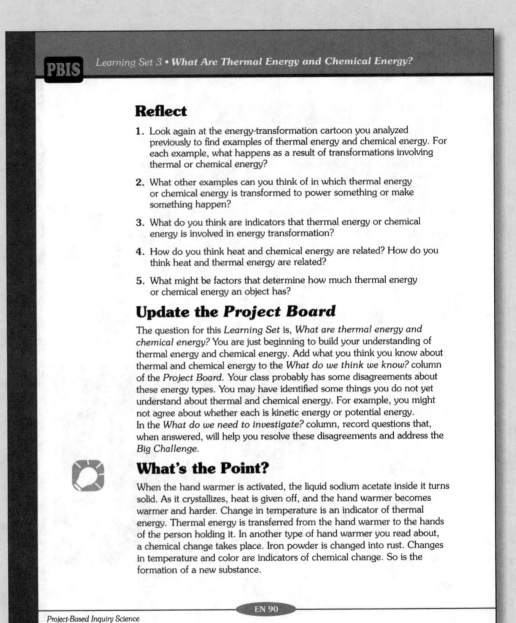

Reflect

1. Look again at the energy-transformation cartoon you analyzed previously to find examples of thermal energy and chemical energy. For each example, what happens as a result of transformations involving thermal or chemical energy?

2. What other examples can you think of in which thermal energy or chemical energy is transformed to power something or make something happen?

3. What do you think are indicators that thermal energy or chemical energy is involved in energy transformation?

4. How do you think heat and chemical energy are related? How do you think heat and thermal energy are related?

5. What might be factors that determine how much thermal energy or chemical energy an object has?

Update the *Project Board*

The question for this *Learning Set* is, *What are thermal energy and chemical energy?* You are just beginning to build your understanding of thermal energy and chemical energy. Add what you think you know about thermal and chemical energy to the *What do we think we know?* column of the *Project Board.* Your class probably has some disagreements about these energy types. You may have identified some things you do not yet understand about thermal and chemical energy. For example, you might not agree about whether each is kinetic energy or potential energy. In the *What do we need to investigate?* column, record questions that, when answered, will help you resolve these disagreements and address the *Big Challenge.*

What's the Point?

When the hand warmer is activated, the liquid sodium acetate inside it turns solid. As it crystallizes, heat is given off, and the hand warmer becomes warmer and harder. Change in temperature is an indicator of thermal energy. Thermal energy is transferred from the hand warmer to the hands of the person holding it. In another type of hand warmer you read about, a chemical change takes place. Iron powder is changed into rust. Changes in temperature and color are indicators of chemical change. So is the formation of a new substance.

EN 90

◇ Evaluate

Have students begin answering the *Reflect* questions by directing them back to the energy-transformation cartoons they examined earlier. Remind them that they have already looked for other types of energy in the cartoon. Now have them look for thermal energy and chemical energy. They also consider other examples, such as how in many power plants thermal energy is used to turn a turbine to produce electricity or how in a battery, chemical energy is used to produce electricity. Once students show that they recognize the use of thermal and chemical energy, evaluate their understanding of the indicators they used to identify each type of energy and factors that might relate to the amount of each type of energy. Use the following to assess their answers:

1. Students' answers will vary depending on the cartoon. In most cases, the examples will involve fire or an explosion. This leads to an object burning or being moved by the force of the explosion.

2. Students' answers will vary. Some examples of thermal energy that they may suggest are a stove, microwave oven, or the Sun. Some examples of chemical energy might be batteries, baking, or the combustion of gasoline in a car.

3. Students' answers will vary, depending on their knowledge base. Heat is an indicator of thermal energy. Chemical energy use may be indicated by heat, cold, change of color, a solid forming or a gas forming.

4. Students may have trouble linking thermal and chemical energy. They may suggest that heat can cause a chemical change, such as a match burning. Or that a chemical change can generate heat, as in an explosion. Students should know that heat and thermal energy are closely linked, if not the same thing.

5. Students should soon realize that the temperature of an object and the mass of the object are factors in determining the amount of thermal energy in an object. To determine the amount of chemical energy in an object is more difficult. Mass is one factor but the other factor is dependent upon the object's chemistry.

or chemical energy an s.

Update the *Project Board*

The question for this *Learning Set* is, *What are thermal energy and chemical energy?* You are just beginning to build your understanding of thermal energy and chemical energy. Add what you think you know about thermal and chemical energy to the *What do we think we know?* column of the *Project Board*. Your class probably has some disagreements about these energy types. You may have identified some things you do not yet understand about thermal and chemical energy. For example, you might not agree about whether each is kinetic energy or potential energy. In the *What do we need to investigate?* column, record questions that, when answered, will help you resolve these disagreements and address the *Big Challenge*.

Update the Project Board

5 min

Students add ideas about thermal and chemical energy to the Project Board.

△ Guide

Have students summarize what they learned about thermal and chemical energy. All students may not agree on the same ideas. Record all ideas on the *Project Board* along with questions about what students still need to learn.

Assessment Options

Targeted Concepts, Skills, and Nature of Science	How do I know if students got it?
Scientists often work together and then share their findings. Sharing findings makes new information available and helps scientists refine their ideas and build on others' ideas. When another person's or group's idea is used, credit needs to be given.	**ASK:** How was it helpful to analyze your observations about hand warmers with other students? **LISTEN:** Students might explain that they learned from other students or they realized observations they interpreted incorrectly.
Heat is the transfer of thermal energy from a substance at a higher temperature to a substance at a lower temperature.	**ASK:** What indicator did you use to conclude that heat was being transferred from the hand warmer into your hand? **LISTEN:** Students should describe how their hands felt warm as they absorbed heat.
The addition or removal of heat may result in a temperature change in a system.	**ASK:** What happened to the temperature of the toaster when it was used? **LISTEN:** Students should indicate that the temperature of the toaster increased because it became warmer.
Potential energy is stored energy, associated with position or condition.	**ASK:** What type of energy is stored in foods such as toast? **LISTEN:** Students should identify chemical potential energy in the toast.
Energy is absorbed or released during a chemical reaction.	**ASK:** What do all endothermic chemical changes have in common? **LISTEN:** Students should indicate that they all absorb heat.

Teacher Reflection Questions

- What difficulties did students have relating the toaster activity to the hand warmer activity? How might you make it easier for students to connect the two activities?

- How did you encourage students to use senses other than sight during the hand warmer activity? What suggestions can you make to help in the future?

- What did you do to help students understand the changes that took place inside the hand warmer? What can you try next time to present the concept while still keeping students focused on the changes in energy?

NOTES

NOTES

3.2 Investigate

What Factors Affect How Much Thermal Energy an Object or Substance Has?

◀ *2 class periods*
A class period is considered to be one 40 to 50 minute class.

Overview

Students relate a change in temperature to the transfer of heat. They conduct two experiments to compare the amount of thermal energy of samples of water. After analyzing their results and providing evidence to support their claims, students participate in an *Investigation Expo* and share their results. They read about factors that affect the amount of thermal energy, relate them to their experiments, and consider how they can apply what they have learned to the *Big Challenge*.

Targeted Concepts, Skills, and Nature of Science	Performance Expectations
Scientists often work together and then share their findings. Sharing findings makes new information available and helps scientists refine their ideas and build on others' ideas. When another person's or group's idea is used, credit needs to be given.	Students work together to conduct experiments and analyze their results.
Heat is the transfer of thermal energy from a substance at a higher temperature to a substance at a lower temperature.	Students recognize that heat is transferred from warmer water to cooler water.
Thermal energy is the energy of the particles of matter.	Students relate temperature and mass to the amount of thermal energy in a sample of matter.
The addition or removal of heat may result in a temperature change in a system.	Students analyze water at different temperatures to consider the amount of thermal energy in each.

Materials	
2 per group	Beaker, 1000 mL Straw Thermometer
1 per group	Warm water (35°C - 45°C), 400 mL Triple-beam balance Graduated cylinder, 100 mL
3 per group	Sealable plastic bags containing 100 g of frozen water (ice)
Experiment 1 **1 per group**	Cold water (15°C - 25°C), 400 mL
1 per student	*Thermal Energy in Water* page *Energy Types* page (started in *Learning Set 1*)
2 per student	Colored pencil or marker, each a different color

Homework Options

Reflection

- **Science Content:** How is thermal energy related to the mass of two samples at the same temperature? *(Students should recognize that for two samples at the same temperature, the sample with the greater mass has the greater amount of thermal energy.)*

- **Science Process:** What will happen if you place two samples at different temperatures next to one another? *(Students should explain that heat will be transferred from the sample with a higher temperature to the sample at a lower temperature.)*

Preparation for 3.3

- **Science Content:** How is thermal energy related to the temperature of two samples of identical material with different masses? *(Students should recognize that for two samples of identical material with equal mass, the sample with the higher temperature has the greater amount of thermal energy.)*

SECTION 3.2 IMPLEMENTATION

◀ *2 class periods**

3.2 Investigate

What Factors Affect How Much Thermal Energy an Object or Substance Has?

When you made observations of the hand warmer, you noticed that the temperature of the hand warmer changed. When you watched toast in the toaster, you observed that the heating elements warmed the toast. Each of these examples included a change in temperature. A change in temperature is an indication that heat has been transferred from one place to another.

All objects have some amount of thermal energy. Hotter objects have more thermal energy than cooler ones. When you increase the temperature of an object, it has more thermal energy. If the object is warmer than its surroundings, it will transfer some of its thermal energy into the surroundings as heat. One example of this is the hand warmer after it has been activated.

Why is thermal energy transferred? How is thermal energy related to heat and temperature? Is thermal energy a kind of kinetic energy, or is it potential energy? These are all good questions, and after you understand their answers, you will know how to put steps that use heat, fire, or even ice, into your Rube Goldberg machine.

You will start answering these questions by investigating the thermal energy of a single substance—water. You will run an experiment to compare the amount of thermal energy in three beakers of water. When you analyze your results, you will be able to identify two factors that affect the water's thermal energy.

Each group in the class will do either *Experiment 1* or *Experiment 2*. The groups doing *Experiment 1* will investigate the effects of temperature on water's thermal energy. The groups doing *Experiment 2* will investigate the effects of the mass of the water on its thermal energy.

Materials
- 2 beakers, 1000 mL
- warm water (35°C–45°C)
- 400 mL of cold water (15°C–25°C)
- 3 identical, sealable plastic bags, each containing 100 g of frozen water (ice)
- triple-beam balance
- 2 straws
- 2 thermometers
- 1 graduated cylinder, 100 mL
- 2 different-colored pencils or markers

ENERGY

3.2 Investigate

What Factors Affect How Much Thermal Energy an Object or Substance Has?

5 min

Students review what they have learned, preparing them for upcoming experiments.

○ Engage

Point out the different ideas students had at the end of the *Section 3.1*. Identify any questions they presented relating to thermal energy and temperature. Let them know that in this section, they will find answers to some of these questions.

*A class period is considered to be one 40 to 50 minute class.

Set Up Experiment 1

15 min

Students conduct an experiment to compare the thermal energy of a sample of warm water with a sample of cold water.

PBIS *Learning Set 3 • What Are Thermal Energy and Chemical Energy?*

Thermal Energy in Water			3.2.1
Name: _____		Date: _____	
	Beaker A or C Bag A or C	Beaker B or D Bag B or D	Unlabeled bag
Prediction			
Volume			
Initial temperature			
Time to melt			
Temperature after 5 min			
Temperature after 10 min			
Temperature after 15 min			

Set Up Experiment 1

Procedure

1. Label the two large beakers as A and B.

2. Pour 400 mL of cold water into Beaker A. Pour 400 mL of warm water into Beaker B.

3. Feel the sides of each beaker. Record your observations on your *Thermal Energy in Water* page.

4. Predict what would happen if you put the same mass of ice into each beaker. Which beaker do you think would melt the ice faster? Why? Record your predictions on your *Thermal Energy in Water* page. Then discuss your answers with your group and take notes of any differing opinions.

Set Up Experiment 2

Procedure

1. Label the two large beakers as C and D.

2. Pour 400 mL of warm water into Beaker C. Pour 200 mL of warm water into Beaker D.

3. Feel the sides of each beaker. Record your observations on your *Thermal Energy in Water* page.

4. Predict what would happen if you put the same mass of ice into each beaker. What will happen to the temperature of the water in each beaker? Why? Record your prediction on your *Thermal Energy in Water* page. Then discuss your answers with your group, and take notes of any differing opinions.

EN 92

Project-Based Inquiry Science

⬡ Get Going

Divide the class into groups after deciding which group will perform either *Experiment 1* or *Experiment 2*. Review the steps of the *Procedure* to make sure students in the groups performing this experiment understand what they are going to do. Have students get their *Thermal Energy in Water* page ready. Then distribute any necessary materials to students. Have students conduct the experiment and record their observations. Guide students to make their predictions and discuss their reasons for their predictions with their groups.

3.2

⬡ Get Going

Review the steps of the *Procedure* with students performing *Experiment 2*. Have students get their *Thermal Energy in Water* pages ready. Then distribute any necessary materials to students. Have students conduct the experiment and record their observations. Then guide students to make their predictions, and discuss their reasons for their predictions with their groups.

Set Up Experiment 2

10 min

Students conduct an experiment to compare the thermal energy of different masses of warm water.

NOTES

Run Experiment 1 and Experiment 2

10 min

Students observe ice in the beakers to measure changes in temperature.

Run Experiment 1 and Experiment 2

Procedure

5. You will work with three bags of ice. Label two of the bags A and B or C and D. Use the balance to find the mass of each bag and record the data on your *Thermal Energy in Water* page.

6. Measure the initial temperature of the water in both beakers.

7. If the warm water is below 35°C, pour it out and get new warm water. Your warm water should be between 35°C and 45°C. Record the temperature and volume of the water in each beaker on your *Thermal Energy in Water* page (Time=0 min). Leave a thermometer in each beaker.

8. Leave the unlabeled bag of ice on the table as a control. At the same time, place Bag A (or C) into Beaker A (or C) and Bag B (or D) into Beaker B (or D). Use the straws to hold the ice beneath the surface of the water in both beakers. Record the time that the bags went into the beakers.

9. Measure and record the temperature of the water in each beaker after 5 min and 10 min. Measure to the nearest 0.5°C. Gently swirl the water for 15 s to mix it before measuring the temperature each time.

EN 93

ENERGY

⬡ Get Going

Review Steps 5 through 11 with students. Make sure they understand what they are going to do with each beaker of water. Help students recognize that these steps complete *Experiment 1* and *Experiment 2*. Because the procedure is the same for both experiments, they are listed once. Here students are testing the predictions they made in the previous procedures.

10. After 15 min, remove the bags of ice from the beakers. Working quickly, measure and record the final temperature of the water in each beaker.

11. Working quickly, open Bag A (or C), pour the melted water into the graduated cylinder, and measure its volume. Be careful not to spill the water or let pieces of ice get into the graduated cylinder. Record the volume of water. Empty the graduated cylinder and repeat the process for Bag B (or D) and for the unlabeled bag.

Analyze Your Data

1. Begin your analysis by making a line graph of the temperatures you measured in the two beakers.

   • Label your graph clearly as "Experiment 1" or "Experiment 2."

   • Label the horizontal axis "Time" and divide it into minutes. For each beaker, you should have four data points—0, 5, 10, and 15 min.

   • Label the vertical axis "Temperature" and use 10°C increments from 0°C to 50°C.

   • Use one colored pencil or marker for graphing the data from Beaker A (or C) and another color for the data from Beaker B (or D).

   • For each beaker, plot the four data points and draw a line to connect the points. Include a key so people reading the graph will know which color represents which beaker.

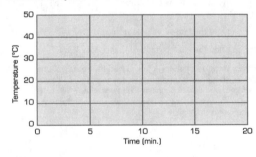

Project-Based Inquiry Science

Analyze Your Data

10 min

Students prepare a graph to represent the data from Experiments 1 *and* 2.

> **META NOTES**
>
> You may need to compare line graphs and bar graphs with students. Remind students that line graphs are most useful for representing variables that change continuously over time, such as temperature. Bar graphs are most useful for comparing separate quantities, such as volumes of water.

△ Guide

Explain that students will be making a Temperature-Time line graph to represent their data along with a bar graph. As students work on their graphs, walk around to make sure they are labeling axes properly. Assist any students who are struggling. Discuss with students how to identify trends in both types of graphs.

2. Set up a bar graph showing the volume of the water recovered from the three bags of ice.

- Use the same colors you used in your line graph for bags A, B, C, and D.

- Use a regular pencil or pen for the data from the unlabeled bag.

- Include a key that identifies the color used for each bag. Make the scale of your bar graph such that differences in your data are apparent.

- Label the graph clearly as "Experiment 1" or "Experiment 2."

3. Examine your data table and your graphs and answer these questions:

- Which beaker had the larger temperature change?

- Which ice bag had the largest volume of melted ice? Which had the least?

- What trend, if any, do you see in your line graphs?

Reflect

With your group, answer the questions. Be prepared to share the answers with the class.

1. What do you think caused the temperature of the water in each beaker to change? Why do you think the temperatures did not all change by the same amount?

2. Which ice bag had the largest volume of melted ice? Why?

3. Which ice bag had the least volume of melted ice? Why?

4. a) In *Experiment 1*, Beakers A and B had the same volume of water. However, the initial temperature of the water was different. How did this affect the volume of melted ice in each bag? Which do you think had more thermal energy before ice was added: the water in Beaker A or the water in Beaker B?

☐ Assess

Once students have finished their line graphs and bar graphs, tell them to answer Question 3. As they discuss, use the following guidelines to assess their understanding of the experiment they performed: .

- For *Experiment 1*, students should observe that Beaker B had the larger temperature change. For *Experiment 2*, students should observe that Beaker D had the larger temperature change.

- For *Experiment 1*, students should observe that Beaker B had the larger volume of melted water. For *Experiment 2*, students should observe that Beaker C had the larger volume of melted water. For *Experiment 1*, Beaker A had the smaller volume of melted ice. For *Experiment 2*, Beaker D had the smaller volume of melted water.

- For *Experiment 1*, students should note that both lines had a trend toward lower temperature with time. The line for Beaker B with the warm water has a steeper slope. For *Experiment 2*, students should note that both lines had a trend toward lower temperature with time. The line for Beaker D with only 200 mL of warm water has the steeper slope.

◇ Evaluate

Have students discuss answers to the *Reflect* questions with their groups. Encourage students to support each answer with evidence from their graphs. Tell students to discuss any differences they observe among their data.

1. Students will probably guess that the ice caused the temperature of the water in each beaker to decrease. They may correctly assume that the difference in temperature drop from beaker to beaker was due to either the difference in starting temperature *(Experiment 1)* or the difference in volume of warm water *(Experiment 2)*.

2. Students should report that Bag B of ice had the larger volume of melted water. They may suggest that it contained the most thermal energy. For *Experiment 2*, students should report that Bag C of ice had the larger volume of melted water. Students may suggest that Beaker C contained more thermal energy than Beaker D.

3. Students should report that in *Experiment 1*, Bag A of ice had a smaller volume of melted water. They may come to the understanding that Beaker A contained less thermal energy than Beaker B. In *Experiment 2*, students should report that Bag D of ice had a smaller volume of melted water. They should know that Beaker D contained less thermal energy.

4. **a)** Students should report that the beaker with the cooler water melted less ice. This beaker also had the smaller change in water temperature. Students should understand that the water in Beaker A contained more thermal energy.

Reflect

10 min

Students answer questions to better understand the experiments they conducted.

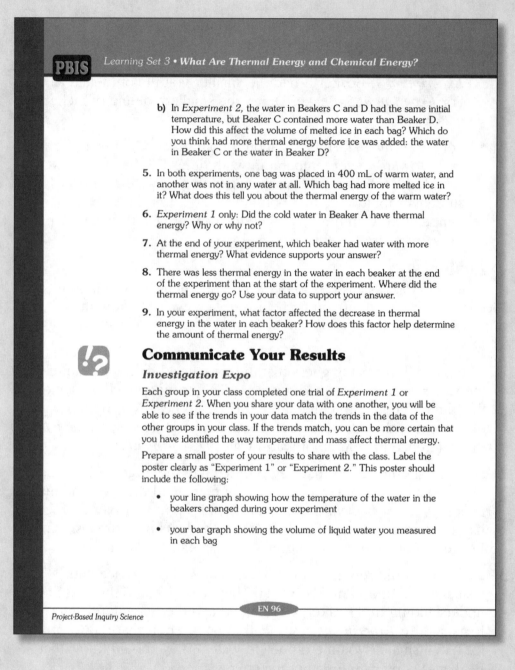

b) In *Experiment 2,* the water in Beakers C and D had the same initial temperature, but Beaker C contained more water than Beaker D. How did this affect the volume of melted ice in each bag? Which do you think had more thermal energy before ice was added: the water in Beaker C or the water in Beaker D?

5. In both experiments, one bag was placed in 400 mL of warm water, and another was not in any water at all. Which bag had more melted ice in it? What does this tell you about the thermal energy of the warm water?

6. *Experiment 1* only: Did the cold water in Beaker A have thermal energy? Why or why not?

7. At the end of your experiment, which beaker had water with more thermal energy? What evidence supports your answer?

8. There was less thermal energy in the water in each beaker at the end of the experiment than at the start of the experiment. Where did the thermal energy go? Use your data to support your answer.

9. In your experiment, what factor affected the decrease in thermal energy in the water in each beaker? How does this factor help determine the amount of thermal energy?

Communicate Your Results

Investigation Expo

Each group in your class completed one trial of *Experiment 1* or *Experiment 2*. When you share your data with one another, you will be able to see if the trends in your data match the trends in the data of the other groups in your class. If the trends match, you can be more certain that you have identified the way temperature and mass affect thermal energy.

Prepare a small poster of your results to share with the class. Label the poster clearly as "Experiment 1" or "Experiment 2." This poster should include the following:

- your line graph showing how the temperature of the water in the beakers changed during your experiment

- your bar graph showing the volume of liquid water you measured in each bag

EN 96

Project-Based Inquiry Science

b) Students should report that the beaker with the smaller volume of warm water melted less ice. This beaker also had the largest change in water temperature. Students will know that the water in Beaker C contained more thermal energy.

5. Students should report that the ice bag that was not placed in water had the smallest volume of melted water. Students should deduce that the warm water contained more thermal energy than air.

6. Students will opine that the cold water in Beaker A did have thermal energy because it did melt some water.

7. Students should recognize that in *Experiment 1,* Beaker B had more thermal energy than Beaker A, because it was warmer. This is shown by the greater volume of melted ice. In *Experiment 2,* students should recognize that Beaker C contained more thermal energy than Beaker D because it produced a greater volume of melted ice.

8. Students should understand that after the ice bags were removed, there was less thermal energy in each of the four beakers than before the experiments. The thermal energy was used to melt the ice. This is shown by the lower water temperature in each beaker.

9. Students should deduce that temperature showed the decrease in thermal energy in *Experiment 1,* because it was the variable tested. In *Experiment 2,* it was the mass of water in each beaker that affected the final temperature of the water. Mass or volume of water was the variable tested. Overall, the lower temperature indicated that the average kinetic energy of the water molecules is less than before each of the experiments.

△ Guide

Have groups prepare posters to summarize their data and conclusions. Make sure they label their posters according to the experiment they performed. Remind students to use the bulleted list in their text to guide them. Emphasize to groups that their posters should include a claim based on trends from their graphs. Also, they should use the *Reflect* questions to guide their thinking about claims and they should write their claim using the format that appears in the student text.

Communicate Your Results: *Investigation Expo*

30 min

Groups prepare posters summarizing the data and trends from their experiments and share to inform the rest of the class what they learned.

NOTES

....

....

....

....

....

....

- a claim about the factors that affect how much thermal energy is in water

  ◆ Use your answer to the last *Reflect* question to develop your claim.

  ◆ Your claim should be stated something like this:

    A factor that affects the amount of thermal energy in water is [*your factor*]. When [*factor*] is [*larger/higher/smaller/lower*], the water has [*more/less*] thermal energy.

- evidence to support your claim

- a comparison of your results to your predictions, what you know now that you did not know before this experiment, and any new questions you may have

As you look at other groups' posters, focus on two things:

- Notice the graphs on each of the posters. The measurements will not be exactly the same on all the posters, but the graphs should have similar shapes for each experiment. Notice if any of the graphs have different shapes from yours.

- Read the claims on each poster. How well do they match one another? Notice whether any other group stated any of your claims better than you did. Notice if any group made claims different from yours. Examine the evidence each group used to support their claims. Make sure you agree with the claims and evidence used to support each.

⬡ Get Going

Once posters are complete, have students set them up so others can view them. Allow students time to walk around and view the other posters. Tell students to look at the information carefully and consider the bulleted focus points in the student text. As they make their observations, they should be comparing graphs and analyzing trends between them.

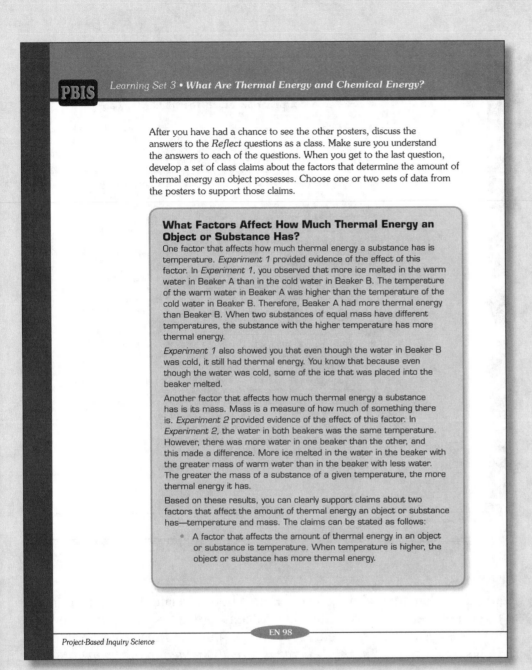

After you have had a chance to see the other posters, discuss the
answers to the *Reflect* questions as a class. Make sure you understand
the answers to each of the questions. When you get to the last question,
develop a set of class claims about the factors that determine the amount of
thermal energy an object possesses. Choose one or two sets of data from
the posters to support those claims.

What Factors Affect How Much Thermal Energy an Object or Substance Has?

One factor that affects how much thermal energy a substance has is
temperature. *Experiment 1* provided evidence of the effect of this
factor. In *Experiment 1*, you observed that more ice melted in the warm
water in Beaker A than in the cold water in Beaker B. The temperature
of the warm water in Beaker A was higher than the temperature of the
cold water in Beaker B. Therefore, Beaker A had more thermal energy
than Beaker B. When two substances of equal mass have different
temperatures, the substance with the higher temperature has more
thermal energy.

Experiment 1 also showed you that even though the water in Beaker B
was cold, it still had thermal energy. You know that because even
though the water was cold, some of the ice that was placed into the
beaker melted.

Another factor that affects how much thermal energy a substance
has is its mass. Mass is a measure of how much of something there
is. *Experiment 2* provided evidence of the effect of this factor. In
Experiment 2, the water in both beakers was the same temperature.
However, there was more water in one beaker than the other, and
this made a difference. More ice melted in the water in the beaker with
the greater mass of warm water than in the beaker with less water.
The greater the mass of a substance of a given temperature, the more
thermal energy it has.

Based on these results, you can clearly support claims about two
factors that affect the amount of thermal energy an object or substance
has—temperature and mass. The claims can be stated as follows:

- A factor that affects the amount of thermal energy in an object
  or substance is temperature. When temperature is higher, the
  object or substance has more thermal energy.

△ Guide

After students return to their seats, discuss the answers to the *Reflect*
questions as a class. Identify similarities and differences among the answers.
When all students understand the answers to each question, guide a
discussion to decide on a set of class claims. Make sure that students use the
Investigation Expo posters to support their claims.

What Factors Affect How Much Thermal Energy an Object or Substance Has?

5 min

Students read about how temperature and mass affect thermal energy, building on their understanding of their experiment results.

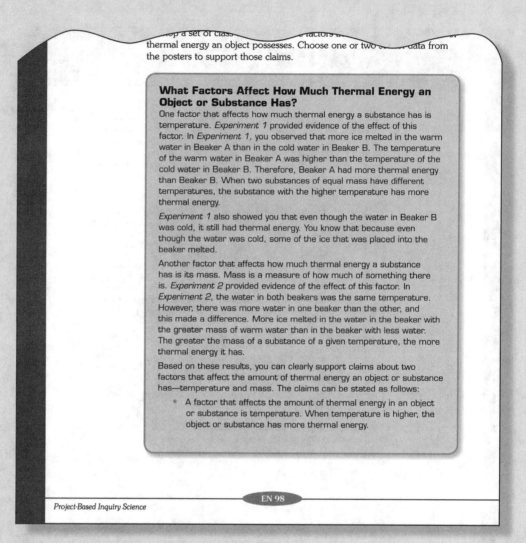

...op a set of class... ...factors th... ...thermal energy an object possesses. Choose one or two s... ...data from the posters to support those claims.

What Factors Affect How Much Thermal Energy an Object or Substance Has?

One factor that affects how much thermal energy a substance has is temperature. *Experiment 1* provided evidence of the effect of this factor. In *Experiment 1*, you observed that more ice melted in the warm water in Beaker A than in the cold water in Beaker B. The temperature of the warm water in Beaker A was higher than the temperature of the cold water in Beaker B. Therefore, Beaker A had more thermal energy than Beaker B. When two substances of equal mass have different temperatures, the substance with the higher temperature has more thermal energy.

Experiment 1 also showed you that even though the water in Beaker B was cold, it still had thermal energy. You know that because even though the water was cold, some of the ice that was placed into the beaker melted.

Another factor that affects how much thermal energy a substance has is its mass. Mass is a measure of how much of something there is. *Experiment 2* provided evidence of the effect of this factor. In *Experiment 2*, the water in both beakers was the same temperature. However, there was more water in one beaker than the other, and this made a difference. More ice melted in the water in the beaker with the greater mass of warm water than in the beaker with less water. The greater the mass of a substance of a given temperature, the more thermal energy it has.

Based on these results, you can clearly support claims about two factors that affect the amount of thermal energy an object or substance has—temperature and mass. The claims can be stated as follows:

- A factor that affects the amount of thermal energy in an object or substance is temperature. When temperature is higher, the object or substance has more thermal energy.

△ Guide

Read the student text with the class. Help students relate the information to the experiments they conducted. Ask them to write a statement in their own words relating thermal energy to temperature and mass. For example, students might write, *Thermal energy is directly related to the temperature and mass of a sample.*

3.2 Investigate

- A factor that affects the amount of thermal energy in an object or substance is mass. When the mass of an object or substance is greater (there is more of it), it has more thermal energy.

You also experienced one more factor that affects the amount of thermal energy in a substance. In *Experiment 1*, more ice in the bag of ice submerged in the cold water melted than in the bag of ice left on the table. Although the cold water was colder (had a lower temperature) than the air around the ice on the table, the ice in the cold water was able to absorb more thermal energy than the ice left on the table. How could this have happened? You will be able to answer this question after you read about how thermal energy raises temperatures in *Section 3.4*.

Reflect

1. Revise your *Energy Types* page. If you did not have thermal energy on your page before, add it now. Record indicators and factors that affect how much thermal energy an object or substance has.

2. What else do you still need to know about thermal energy in order to use thermal energy in the Rube Goldberg machine you are designing?

What's the Point?

Two factors that affect thermal energy are temperature and mass. The greater each factor, the greater the thermal energy a substance has. In the first experiment, the water in Beaker A was at a higher temperature than the water in Beaker B. You know that Beaker A had more thermal energy because it melted more ice. In the second experiment, the water in Beaker C and Beaker D both began at the same temperature. However, because there was more water in Beaker C, it had more thermal energy. The water in Beaker C melted more ice than the water in Beaker D.

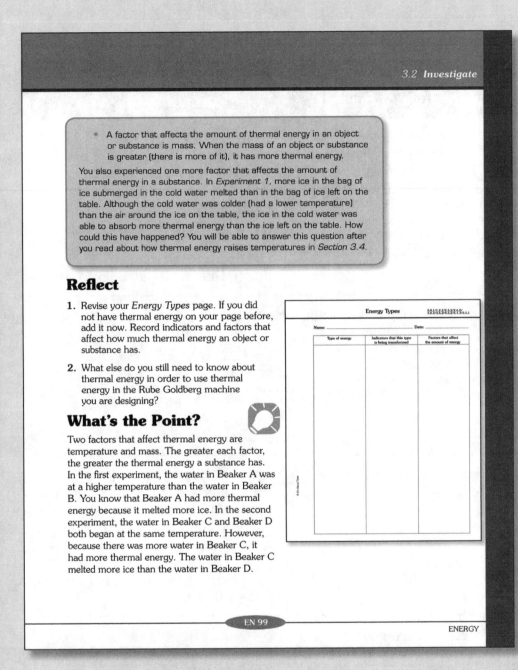

EN 99

ENERGY

Reflect

5 min

Students revise the Energy Types *page they developed in* Learning Set 1 *with the knowledge they have gained since the start of the Unit.*

△ Guide and Assess

Have students revise the *Energy Types* pages they completed earlier based on what they have learned about thermal energy. As students work, review the information they add to their tables for accuracy. Discuss with students what questions they still need to have answered about thermal energy. Encourage them to relate this information to their design for the *Big Challenge.*

Assessment Options

Targeted Concepts, Skills, and Nature of Science	How do I know if students got it?
Scientists often work together and then share their findings. Sharing findings makes new information available and helps scientists refine their ideas and build on others' ideas. When another person's or group's idea is used, credit needs to be given.	**ASK:** What did you discover by reviewing the posters of other students during the *Investigation Expo?* **LISTEN:** Students should identify some information they learned or perhaps whether or not their claims matched those of others during the *Investigation Expo.*
Heat is the transfer of thermal energy from a substance at a higher temperature to a substance at a lower temperature.	**ASK:** Why did the ice cubes melt in the experiment? **LISTEN:** Students should recognize that thermal energy was transferred as heat from the water to the ice cubes because the ice cubes had less thermal energy.
Thermal energy is the energy of the particles of matter.	**ASK:** Why does the amount of thermal energy depend on mass of the water? **LISTEN:** Students should recognize that the more particles of matter there are in a sample, the greater the amount of thermal energy there is.
The addition or removal of heat may result in a temperature change in a system.	**ASK:** Why does the temperature of a sample of water change when ice is added to it? **LISTEN:** Students should explain that heat is transferred from the water to the ice, causing the temperature of the water to decrease.

Teacher Reflection Questions

• What difficulties did students have following the procedure for their experiment? How could you simplify the process in the future?

• How did you guide students through the process of making graphs and interpreting them? Is there anything you would do differently?

• What method did you use to make sure all students played an active role in the experiments? What can you try next time to involve all students?

NOTES

....

....

....

....

....

....

....

....

....

....

NOTES

SECTION 3.3 INTRODUCTION

3.3 Explore

How Is Temperature Related to Thermal Energy?

◀ *2 class periods*

A class period is considered to be one 40 to 50 minute class.

Overview

Students conduct a thought experiment in which they model particles of matter by completing calculations involving distances traveled by marbles. They liken the average distances to temperature and the total distance to thermal energy. By relating their analyses to the heating or cooling of real-world objects, students begin to understand how the absorption or loss of heat affects the properties of matter. Students read information that differentiates between temperature and thermal energy and describes the units of each. Once students have a grasp of the two concepts, they have an opportunity to compare objects in terms of thermal energy using what they know about mass and temperature.

Targeted Concepts, Skills, and Nature of Science	Performance Expectations
Heat is the transfer of thermal energy from a substance at a higher temperature to a substance at a lower temperature.	Students predict the direction in which heat will flow by comparing substances at different temperatures.
Thermal energy is the energy of the particles of matter.	Students identify thermal energy as the total energy of the particles in a sample.
Temperature is the average kinetic energy of the particles of a substance.	Students identify temperature as the average kinetic energy of the particles in a sample.
The addition or removal of heat may result in a temperature change in a system.	Students recognize that the temperature of a substance can change when it absorbs or loses heat.

Materials	
1 per class **(optional)**	Model car or model airplane Thermometer

Homework Options

Reflection

- **Science Content:** What happens to the motion of the particles of matter as heat is absorbed? *(Students should recognize that the particles move faster and slightly farther apart as they absorb heat. This increases their average kinetic energy [temperature] and total energy [thermal energy].)*

- **Science Process:** What units are used to measure temperature and thermal energy? *(Students should know that temperature is measured in degrees Fahrenheit or Celsius, and thermal energy is measured in joules.)*

Preparation for 3.4

- **Science Process:** What indicators can you use to compare amounts of thermal energy? *(This question is meant to get students thinking about factors and indicators related to thermal energy, such as changes in temperature or state.)*

SECTION 3.3 IMPLEMENTATION

◀ *2 class periods* *

3.3 Explore

How Is Temperature Related to Thermal Energy?

You may have been surprised by the results of the experiment in *Section 3.2*. You may have thought that since the temperature of the water in Beakers C and D was the same, they would have the same amount of thermal energy. But the experiment showed something different. It showed that temperature and thermal energy are different. Two substances at the same temperature can have different amounts of thermal energy. To understand how this is possible, you will need to know more about temperature and thermal energy.

temperature: how hot or cold a substance or object is; a measure of the average kinetic energy of the particles in a substance.

What Are Temperature and Thermal Energy?

When scientists need to think about abstract ideas, they often use a model. You will do that now to imagine the relationship between temperature and thermal energy.

First, however, you will need to know just a little bit about temperature and thermal energy. You know that temperature has to do with how warm something feels. However, you do not know what happens to matter as it gets warmer. Matter is made of many, many small particles, too tiny to be seen. These particles are always moving. The more energy they have, the faster they move. When thermal energy in the form of heat is transferred from a warmer substance to a cooler substance, the particles in the cooler substance begin to move faster. The average energy of motion of the particles of the substance increases. Therefore, the temperature of the substance increases. The average energy of motion of particles in a substance is its kinetic energy. Therefore, **temperature** is the measure of the average kinetic energy of the particles of a substance. The thermal energy of the substance is the total energy of the substance. You can think of it as the sum of the kinetic energy of the particles. The thought experiment coming up will help you better understand this.

When a car sits in the Sun, its surface feels hot. What is happening to the molecules of matter to make the temperature of the car's surface rise?

3.3 Explore

How Is Temperature Related to Thermal Energy?

10 min

Students extend what they learned in Section 3.2.

What Are Temperature and Thermal Energy?

5 min

Students are given background knowledge for the upcoming activity.

△ **Guide**

Begin by asking students what they think happens when a hot water molecule bumps into a cold water molecule. Do both become hot? Do both become cold? Is there no change in either? Guide them to understand that energy is exchanged and the hot molecule becomes cooler (moves more slowly) and the cold molecule becomes warmer (moves faster). Then allow a few minutes to read about the difference between temperature and thermal energy.

*A class period is considered to be one 40 to 50 minute class.

Stop and Think

5 min

Students answer questions about the reading.

Stop and Think

1. Temperature is the average kinetic energy of the particles that make up a substance. Why do you think temperature would affect how much thermal energy a substance has?

2. Mass is the total amount of stuff in a substance, and thermal energy is the total energy of the particles in a substance. Why do you think mass would affect how much thermal energy a substance has?

When you discuss the answers as a class, notice any disagreements among your classmates. It is probably hard to agree on an answer. This is why a model will help.

A Thought Experiment

In this model, marbles are used to represent particles of matter. In matter, the particles are always moving. Some move more slowly, and some move more quickly. But they are always moving. In this model, the speed of each particle in a substance is represented by the speed of one marble as it rolls across the floor. Temperature is the average kinetic energy of all the particles. So, in this model, average kinetic energy represents temperature.

Finally, in this model, more marbles is a model for more mass. The more mass, the more thermal energy there is. So, in this model, total kinetic energy is used to represent thermal energy.

Think about these relationships, and follow the procedure to imagine how temperature and thermal energy are related.

Procedure

1. Make a copy of the table below to record your data.

Model of Marbles as Particles			
Number of marbles (represents mass)	Kinetic energy of each marble (in energy units)	Average kinetic energy of marbles (represents temperature)	Total kinetic energy of marbles (represents thermal energy)
10 marbles	4, 4, 6, 5, 4, 7, 3, 4, 5, 4		
20 marbles	4, 4, 6, 5, 4, 7, 3, 4, 5, 4, 8, 4, 4, 7, 4, 7, 3, 2, 3, 4		

ENERGY

△ Guide

Have the students discuss the questions with their groups to come to agreement on the answers. Listen for answers in discussions similar to the following:

1. Students may agree that temperature is one indicator of thermal energy in a substance. They should understand that the higher the temperature of a given amount of matter, the more thermal energy it contains.

2. Students should understand that each particle has its own thermal energy, therefore all the particles must be counted in order to know the total thermal energy.

○ Engage

Ask students if they were surprised by the results of *Experiment 2* in the *Section 3.2*. Point out that temperature and thermal energy are related, but they are not exactly the same. Tell students that in this section, they will explore the difference further.

△ Guide

Ask the class if they have ever built a model car or train. If possible, display an example. Describe how a model is used to represent a real object. Some models are simply smaller versions of the real object. Other models are ideas or concepts to describe a real phenomenon. Tell students that in this experiment, they will think about a model that shows the motion of particles of matter.

Make sure students understand how the marbles represent particles of matter. Emphasize that quantities and qualities of the marbles represent the quantities and qualities of the particles. Make sure students understand that the speed of the marbles relates to the speed of the particles, and that the temperature of the marbles relates to the average kinetic energy of the particle. Also point out that the more marbles there are, the more mass the particles have. Remind them that the more mass there is, the more thermal energy there is in the particles.

⬡ Get Going

Have students set up their copy of the table in the student text to record their data.

A Thought Experiment

25 min

Students imagine a model to compare thermal energy and temperature.

NOTES

....

....

....

....

....

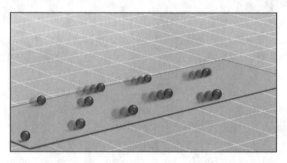

2. Begin by thinking about temperature. You will model that by averaging the kinetic energy of the marbles. Suppose that you have 10 identical marbles. They are all rolling across the floor at different speeds. The kinetic energy of each marble (in energy units) is given in the first row of the table. Calculate the average kinetic energy of the marbles. You can average the kinetic energy by dividing the sum of all the data values by 10. Record your data in the *Average Kinetic Energy of Marbles* column in the first row of the table.

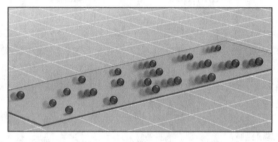

3. Now imagine that instead of 10 marbles, you have 20 marbles. Again, the marbles are identical, and each marble is moving across the floor at a different speed. Calculate the average kinetic energy of the marbles. You can find the average by adding all the data values in the second row of the table and dividing by 20. Record your data in the *Average Kinetic Energy of Marbles* column in the second row of the table.

EN 102

Project-Based Inquiry Science

△ Guide

Students may not fully grasp the concept of an average. Guide them to understand an average to be a value that describes most of the data in a set. An average is found by adding the data values, and then dividing by the number of values. As an example, show students how to calculate the average of a group of quiz grades. Point out that the average value may not match any particular data in the set. Then have students calculate and record the average for the speed of 10 marbles and 20 marbles.

4. Now consider thermal energy. Thermal energy is a measure of the total energy in a substance or object. In this model then, thermal energy is the total energy of the marbles, or their total kinetic energy. Which set of marbles do you think has more total energy—the set of 10 marbles or the set of 20 marbles? Why?

5. Calculate the total kinetic energy of the marbles in each set in the table. Record your data in the *Total Kinetic Energy of Marbles* column of the table.

Analyze Your Data

1. How does the average kinetic energy data in the two sets of marbles compare?

2. How does the total kinetic energy data in the two sets of marbles compare?

3. Why does the set of 20 marbles moving across the floor represent more thermal energy than the set of 10 marbles, even though the average kinetic energy of both sets of marbles is the same?

4. How do you think the thermal energy of a set of 40 marbles would compare to the thermal energy of the 10-marble and 20-marble sets if they all have the same average kinetic energy?

5. Think back to the experiment in the previous section. Imagine that Row 1 of your marble data table represents the water in Beaker D (the one with 200 mL of warm water). Imagine that Row 2 of the table represents the water in Beaker C (the one with 400 mL of warm water). How is the marble model like the water in those beakers?

The body temperature of each polar bear is 37°C (98.6°F). Which polar bear in the picture do you think has more thermal energy?

6. Use this model to develop a statement about why the water in Beaker C melted more ice than the water in Beaker D.

EN 103

ENERGY

Point out a *total* is very different from an *average*. Although they both depend on the same data, they are calculated in different ways. Have students calculate the total speed for 10 marbles and 20 marbles.

**Analyze
Your Data**

10 min

*Students review
the average speed
(temperature) and total
speed (total thermal
energy) values they
calculated.*

Analyze Your Data

1. How does the average kinetic energy data in the two sets of marbles compare?

2. How does the total kinetic energy data in the two sets of marbles compare?

3. Why does the set of 20 marbles moving across the floor represent more thermal energy than the set of 10 marbles, even though the average kinetic energy of both sets of marbles is the same?

4. How do you think the thermal energy of a set of 40 marbles would compare to the thermal energy of the 10-marble and 20-marble sets if they all have the same average kinetic energy?

5. Think back to the experiment in the previous section. Imagine that Row 1 of your marble data table represents the water in Beaker D (the one with 200 mL of warm water). Imagine that Row 2 of the table represents the water in Beaker C (the one with 400 mL of warm water). How is the marble model like the water in those beakers?

The body temperature of each polar bear is 37°C (98.6°F). Which polar bear in the picture do you think has more thermal energy?

6. Use this model to develop a statement about why the water in Beaker C melted more ice than the water in Beaker D.

EN 103

ENERGY

△ Guide

Have students discuss the questions in groups. If you find that most groups are having difficulty with particular questions, expand those discussions to the entire class. For example, you may need to help students relate this model to the water experiments in *Section 3.2*.

1. Students should observe that the calculation for the average speed of 10 marbles happens to be identical to the average speed for the set of 20 marbles.

2. Students should observe that the total speed for the set of 10 marbles is one half that for 20 marbles.

3. Students' answers will vary. Students may respond that the thermal energy of the 20 marbles could do more work than the thermal energy of the 10 marbles. Or, that it would take twice as much ice to cool down the 20 marbles.

4. Students should calculate that a set of 40 marbles would have twice the thermal energy of 20 marbles and four times the thermal energy of 10 marbles if each set had the same average speed.

5. Students should easily grasp the concept that, like the sets of 10 and 20 marbles, the beaker with 200 mL warm water contains one-half the total number of particles that the beaker with 400 mL.

6. Students' answers will vary. Listen for answers, such as, *The warm water in Beaker C melted more ice because it contained more thermal energy than the warm water in Beaker D.*

NOTES

What Is Temperature?

10 min

Students read about characteristics of temperature and thermal energy.

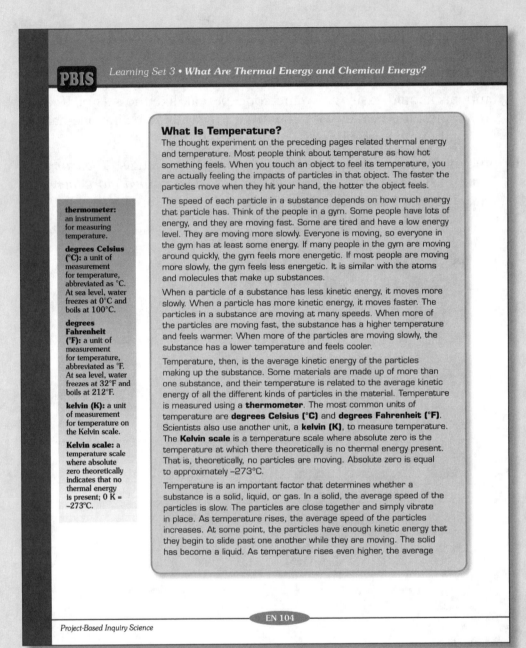

What Is Temperature?

The thought experiment on the preceding pages related thermal energy and temperature. Most people think about temperature as how hot something feels. When you touch an object to feel its temperature, you are actually feeling the impacts of particles in that object. The faster the particles move when they hit your hand, the hotter the object feels.

The speed of each particle in a substance depends on how much energy that particle has. Think of the people in a gym. Some people have lots of energy, and they are moving fast. Some are tired and have a low energy level. They are moving more slowly. Everyone is moving, so everyone in the gym has at least some energy. If many people in the gym are moving around quickly, the gym feels more energetic. If most people are moving more slowly, the gym feels less energetic. It is similar with the atoms and molecules that make up substances.

When a particle of a substance has less kinetic energy, it moves more slowly. When a particle has more kinetic energy, it moves faster. The particles in a substance are moving at many speeds. When more of the particles are moving fast, the substance has a higher temperature and feels warmer. When more of the particles are moving slowly, the substance has a lower temperature and feels cooler.

Temperature, then, is the average kinetic energy of the particles making up the substance. Some materials are made up of more than one substance, and their temperature is related to the average kinetic energy of all the different kinds of particles in the material. Temperature is measured using a **thermometer**. The most common units of temperature are **degrees Celsius (°C)** and **degrees Fahrenheit (°F)**. Scientists also use another unit, a **kelvin (K)**, to measure temperature. The **Kelvin scale** is a temperature scale where absolute zero is the temperature at which there theoretically is no thermal energy present. That is, theoretically, no particles are moving. Absolute zero is equal to approximately −273°C.

Temperature is an important factor that determines whether a substance is a solid, liquid, or gas. In a solid, the average speed of the particles is slow. The particles are close together and simply vibrate in place. As temperature rises, the average speed of the particles increases. At some point, the particles have enough kinetic energy that they begin to slide past one another while they are moving. The solid has become a liquid. As temperature rises even higher, the average

thermometer: an instrument for measuring temperature.

degrees Celsius (°C): a unit of measurement for temperature, abbreviated as °C. At sea level, water freezes at 0°C and boils at 100°C.

degrees Fahrenheit (°F): a unit of measurement for temperature, abbreviated as °F. At sea level, water freezes at 32°F and boils at 212°F.

kelvin (K): a unit of measurement for temperature on the Kelvin scale.

Kelvin scale: a temperature scale where absolute zero theoretically indicates that no thermal energy is present; 0 K = −273°C.

○ Engage

Hold up a thermometer to show the class. Ask students what the device measures. Most students will know that it is a thermometer and it measures temperature. Ask students if they can name two units of temperature. *(Students should name degrees Celsius and degrees Fahrenheit.)* Then ask students what the thermometer measures to determine temperature. Accept any reasonable answers. Then read the first part of the text together.

△ Guide

Remind students that all matter is made up of small particles that are in constant motion. Explain that the motion and arrangement of particles determines whether matter exists as a solid, liquid, or gas. Tell students to consider water as an example.

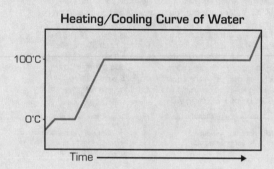

Heating/Cooling Curve of Water

TEACHER TALK

❝The solid form of water is ice. The particles in a sample of ice are held tightly in place. They can only vibrate in place. When ice is heated, the particles absorb energy and begin to move faster and farther apart. As this happens, its temperature increases. At 0°C (32°F), the particles move so fast that they break out of their fixed positions and the ice melts into liquid water. During this change, the temperature stays the same. If the liquid water is heated, the particles move even faster and farther apart. At 100°C (212°F), the particles move so fast that they escape the liquid and enter the air as a gas.❞

NOTES

....

....

....

....

....

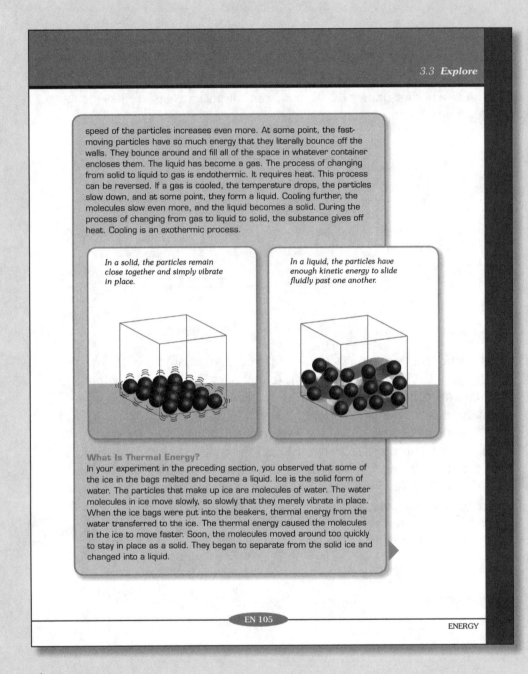

speed of the particles increases even more. At some point, the fast-moving particles have so much energy that they literally bounce off the walls. They bounce around and fill all of the space in whatever container encloses them. The liquid has become a gas. The process of changing from solid to liquid to gas is endothermic. It requires heat. This process can be reversed. If a gas is cooled, the temperature drops, the particles slow down, and at some point, they form a liquid. Cooling further, the molecules slow even more, and the liquid becomes a solid. During the process of changing from gas to liquid to solid, the substance gives off heat. Cooling is an exothermic process.

In a solid, the particles remain close together and simply vibrate in place.

In a liquid, the particles have enough kinetic energy to slide fluidly past one another.

What Is Thermal Energy?

In your experiment in the preceding section, you observed that some of the ice in the bags melted and became a liquid. Ice is the solid form of water. The particles that make up ice are molecules of water. The water molecules in ice move slowly, so slowly that they merely vibrate in place. When the ice bags were put into the beakers, thermal energy from the water transferred to the ice. The thermal energy caused the molecules in the ice to move faster. Soon, the molecules moved around too quickly to stay in place as a solid. They began to separate from the solid ice and changed into a liquid.

EN 105

ENERGY

△ Guide

Point out the diagrams in the student text. Emphasize to students that if two substances are identical in nature and mass, the sample with the higher temperature will have particles that move faster and farther apart. Ask students to think about a cup of hot tea and a glass of iced tea. Both contain the same types of particles, but the particles in the hot tea will have greater motion than the particles in the iced tea.

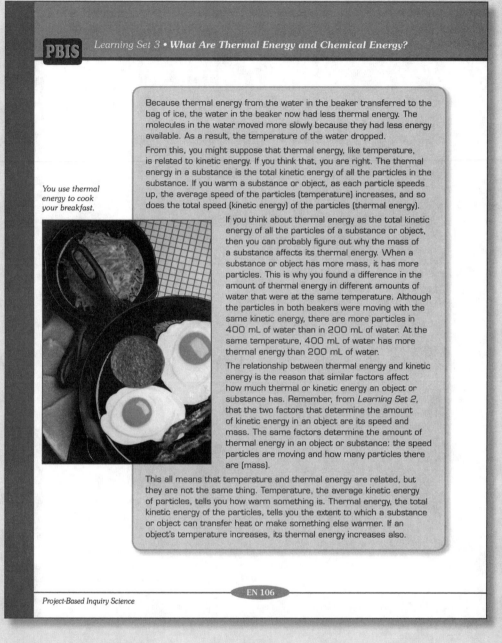

Because thermal energy from the water in the beaker transferred to the bag of ice, the water in the beaker now had less thermal energy. The molecules in the water moved more slowly because they had less energy available. As a result, the temperature of the water dropped.

From this, you might suppose that thermal energy, like temperature, is related to kinetic energy. If you think that, you are right. The thermal energy in a substance is the total kinetic energy of all the particles in the substance. If you warm a substance or object, as each particle speeds up, the average speed of the particles (temperature) increases, and so does the total speed (kinetic energy) of the particles (thermal energy).

You use thermal energy to cook your breakfast.

If you think about thermal energy as the total kinetic energy of all the particles of a substance or object, then you can probably figure out why the mass of a substance affects its thermal energy. When a substance or object has more mass, it has more particles. This is why you found a difference in the amount of thermal energy in different amounts of water that were at the same temperature. Although the particles in both beakers were moving with the same kinetic energy, there are more particles in 400 mL of water than in 200 mL of water. At the same temperature, 400 mL of water has more thermal energy than 200 mL of water.

The relationship between thermal energy and kinetic energy is the reason that similar factors affect how much thermal or kinetic energy an object or substance has. Remember, from *Learning Set 2*, that the two factors that determine the amount of kinetic energy in an object are its speed and mass. The same factors determine the amount of thermal energy in an object or substance: the speed particles are moving and how many particles there are (mass).

This all means that temperature and thermal energy are related, but they are not the same thing. Temperature, the average kinetic energy of particles, tells you how warm something is. Thermal energy, the total kinetic energy of the particles, tells you the extent to which a substance or object can transfer heat or make something else warmer. If an object's temperature increases, its thermal energy increases also.

EN 106

Project-Based Inquiry Science

△ Guide

Remind students what they learned in the experiment in the previous section. They discovered that two beakers of water at the same temperature did not have the same amount of thermal energy. The reason was because each beaker contained a different amount of water. Make sure students now understand that the difference arises because temperature is an average and thermal energy is a total.

Joules

5 min

Students are introduced to the units for energy and work.

However, because thermal energy depends on both temperature and mass, two objects at the same temperature do not necessarily have the same thermal energy.

Temperature and thermal energy are related in another important way. Temperature determines the direction in which thermal energy naturally flows—from warmer objects (higher temperature) to cooler objects (lower temperature). When a warmer object is in contact with a cooler object, the particles at the boundary collide. In each collision, kinetic energy is transferred from one particle to another. In collisions, the faster particles of the warmer object tend to lose some speed, and the slower particles in the cooler object tend to gain some speed. As a result, the warmer object becomes cooler, and the cooler object becomes warmer.

Joules

Scientists measure energy and work in units called **joules**. A joule is the amount of work required to lift a 100-g mass a distance of about 1 m. The unit is named after James Prescott Joule, who was a nineteenth century English physicist. He studied the relationship between heat, work, and energy. A joule is abbreviated as "J."

All types of energy can be measured in joules. Part of Joule's research was studying the relationship between thermal energy and work. Different types of energy are related by the amount of work they can do. The amount of work required to lift a 100-g mass to a height of 1 m is about the same as the thermal energy required to raise the temperature of 1 g of air by 1°C. By calculating energy amounts in joules, scientists can compare different types of energy and keep track of the amount of energy present as it is transformed from one type to another.

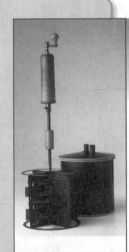

joule: a unit of measurement for energy, abbreviated as J; the amount of work required to lift a 100-g mass a distance of about 1 m.

Joule used a device similar to this one to measure the mechanical equivalent of heat.

META NOTES

Work and energy are closely related. Therefore, work and energy are measured in the same units. This is an important point to state for students so they do not become confused by seeing the same unit used in what may seem to be different measurements.

○ Engage

Let students know that James Prescott Joule was honored by naming the unit of energy after him because of his accomplishments in this area of science. Joule established the concept that different forms of energy are related and can be transformed into one another. In this way, he formed the basis for the law of conservation of energy. Also, point out that Joule's teacher was John Dalton, a pioneer in the field of chemistry.

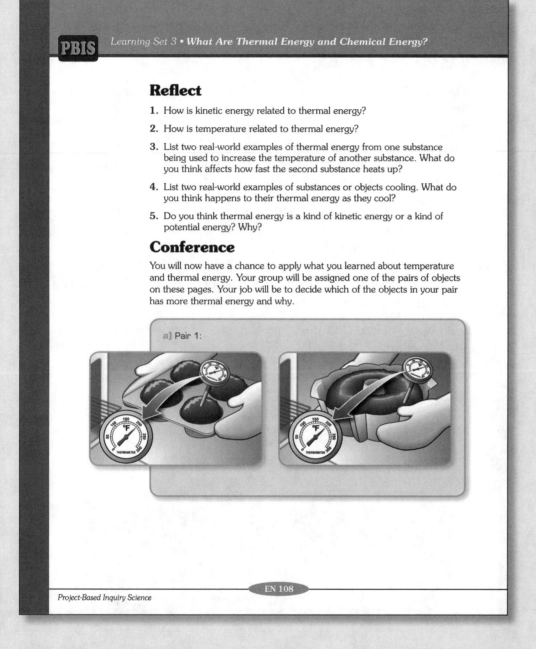

Reflect

1. How is kinetic energy related to thermal energy?

2. How is temperature related to thermal energy?

3. List two real-world examples of thermal energy from one substance being used to increase the temperature of another substance. What do you think affects how fast the second substance heats up?

4. List two real-world examples of substances or objects cooling. What do you think happens to their thermal energy as they cool?

5. Do you think thermal energy is a kind of kinetic energy or a kind of potential energy? Why?

Conference

You will now have a chance to apply what you learned about temperature and thermal energy. Your group will be assigned one of the pairs of objects on these pages. Your job will be to decide which of the objects in your pair has more thermal energy and why.

a) Pair 1:

Reflect

10 min

Students extend their observations from the experiments to real-world examples.

△ **Guide and Assess**

Have students answer the *Reflect* questions in their groups. Then lead a class discussion to share the answers.

1. Students should reply that particles of matter have kinetic energy because they have mass and are in motion. The total amount of kinetic energy of all the particles determines the total thermal energy of a sample.

2. Students should respond that while temperature is the average kinetic energy of the particles in a sample, it does not take into account the mass of all of the particles. Thermal energy is not an average, but rather a total.

3. Students' answers will vary. One response might be that heat is transferred from hot cocoa to a spoon. This causes the spoon to become warmer. The total thermal energy in the hot cocoa determines how fast the spoon heats up. Thermal energy is transferred as heat from substances at a higher temperature to substances at a lower temperature.

4. Students' answers will vary. One response might be that heat is transferred from a person's body through perspiration. As the perspiration evaporates, heat is taken from the person's body, causing the person to become cooler. When thermal energy is transferred away from a substance or object, the temperature of the substance decreases and the substance cools.

5. Students may realize that because thermal energy involves motion of particles, it is a form of kinetic energy.

Conference

10 min

Students compare sets of two objects in terms of thermal energy.

Conference

You will now have a chance to apply what you learned about temperature and thermal energy. Your group will be assigned one of the pairs of objects on these pages. Your job will be to decide which of the objects in your pair has more thermal energy and why.

a) Pair 1:

⬡ Get Going

Assign a pair of objects to each group. Tell students to look for indicators that tell something about thermal energy and temperature. Then have students to use these indicators to identify the object with the greater amount of thermal energy. Remind students that their descriptions should be thorough and use the correct terminology. Then have students answer the two bulleted questions based on their knowledge and observations of their pairs.

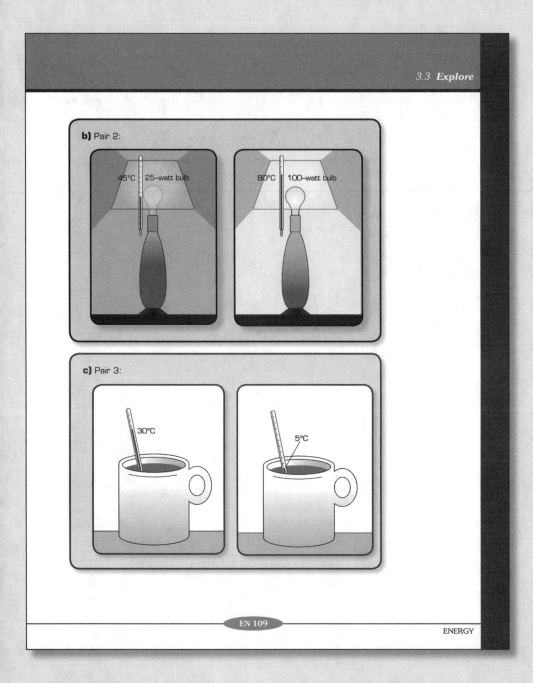

b] Pair 2:

45°C | 25-watt bulb

80°C | 100-watt bulb

c] Pair 3:

30°C

5°C

EN 109

ENERGY

Students should respond to the first bulleted question as follows:

Pair 1: The ice cubes will melt more quickly if placed in or next to the cake because it has more thermal energy than the cupcake.

Pair 2: The ice cubes will melt more quickly if placed next to the 100-watt bulb because it has more thermal energy than the 25-watt bulb.

Pair 3: The ice cubes will melt more quickly if placed in or next to the cup at 30°C because it has more thermal energy than the cup at 5°C.

Pair 4: The ice cubes will melt more quickly if placed in the larger oven because it has more thermal energy than the smaller oven.

Students should respond to the second bulleted question as follows:

Pair 1: The cake has more thermal energy than the cupcake because it has more mass.

Pair 2: The 100-watt bulb has more thermal energy because it has a higher temperature.

Pair 3: The cup at 30°C has more thermal energy because it has a higher temperature.

Pair 4: The larger oven has more thermal energy because it has more mass.

NOTES

....

....

....

....

....

....

....

....

....

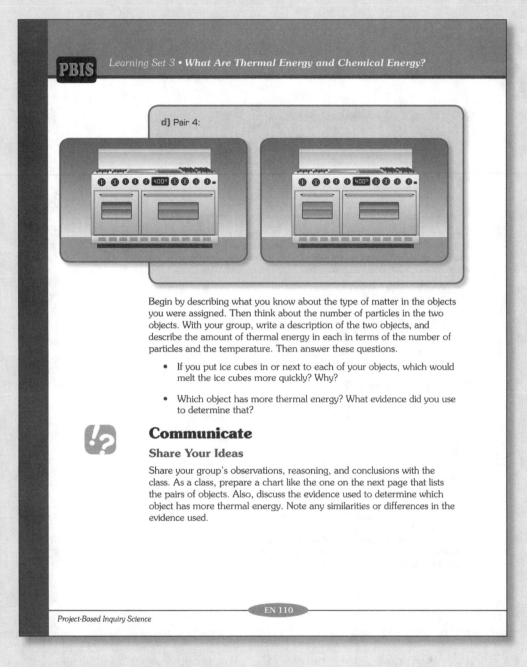

d) Pair 4:

Begin by describing what you know about the type of matter in the objects you were assigned. Then think about the number of particles in the two objects. With your group, write a description of the two objects, and describe the amount of thermal energy in each in terms of the number of particles and the temperature. Then answer these questions.

- If you put ice cubes in or next to each of your objects, which would melt the ice cubes more quickly? Why?

- Which object has more thermal energy? What evidence did you use to determine that?

Communicate

Share Your Ideas

Share your group's observations, reasoning, and conclusions with the class. As a class, prepare a chart like the one on the next page that lists the pairs of objects. Also, discuss the evidence used to determine which object has more thermal energy. Note any similarities or differences in the evidence used.

Communicate: Share Your Ideas

10 min

Students share their conclusions about the objects they examined.

△ Guide and Assess

Invite each group to share ideas, descriptions, and answers. Help students complete a chart to summarize what they found. For example, students should conclude that the large cake has more thermal energy than the cupcakes because the cake has the greater mass, even though the two are at the same temperature. Similarly, the 100-watt light bulb has more thermal energy because this bulb is a higher temperature than the other bulb, even though the bulbs are the same size.

Thermal Energy Table

Objects	More thermal energy	Less thermal energy
Pair 1		
Pair 2		
Pair 3		
Pair 4		

Then, as a class, take on a different challenge. You should have four objects in the *More Thermal Energy* column. Try to place these four objects in order of decreasing thermal energy, with the object with the most thermal energy on top. While doing this, consider the following questions:

- What evidence can you use to compare the thermal energy contained in objects made of different materials?

- Is it possible to compare the thermal energy of a cake with that of a light bulb? Why or why not?

- What additional information might you need in order to compare the thermal energy of objects made of different materials?

What's the Point?

Temperature is related to but not the same as thermal energy. Thermal energy and temperature both depend on the kinetic energy of the particles in a substance. The particles in a substance are moving at many different speeds. Particles moving at a slower speed have less kinetic energy. Particles moving at a faster speed have more kinetic energy. Temperature is a measure of the average kinetic energy of all the particles making up a substance. Temperature does not depend upon the mass of an object.

The thermal energy of a substance is a measure of the total kinetic energy of its particles. Therefore, the total number of particles contained in an object, or its mass, is a factor that determines how much thermal energy an object has. Thermal energy also depends on temperature: the higher the temperature of an object, the greater its kinetic energy. Thermal energy flows naturally from objects at a higher temperature to objects at a lower temperature. Energy is measured in units called joules.

EN 111

ENERGY

Once students come to agreement on the table, they should work together to arrange in order the four objects in the *More thermal energy* column. Students should use the bulleted questions in the student text to guide their discussions. Listen for the following in students' responses:

- Students may respond that they can use mass and temperature as evidence of greater or lesser thermal energy. Mass will be somewhat difficult to use as evidence since different materials will contain different amounts of thermal energy, even at the same temperature and mass.

- Students should reply that the thermal energy of the cake cannot be compared with that of a light bulb because the light bulb is continuing to receive energy in the form of electricity. It will not cool until it is turned off. The same can be said for the ovens.

- Students' answers will vary. It is not likely that any of the students will know about specific heat at this point.

NOTES

....

....

....

....

....

....

....

....

....

....

....

....

Assessment Options

Targeted Concepts, Skills, and Nature of Science	How do I know if students got it?
Heat is the transfer of thermal energy from a substance at a higher temperature to a substance at a lower temperature.	**ASK:** What happens when an ice cube melts in a glass of water? **LISTEN:** Students should describe how heat is transferred from the water to the ice cube.
Thermal energy is the energy of the particles of matter.	**ASK:** How did you relate the motion of marbles to thermal energy? **LISTEN:** Students should describe how they thought about and calculated the total kinetic energy of the marbles to model thermal energy.
Temperature is the average kinetic energy of the particles of a substance.	**ASK:** How did you relate the motion of marbles to temperature? **LISTEN:** Students should describe how they thought about and calculated the average kinetic energy the marbles traveled at to model temperature.
The addition or removal of heat may result in a temperature change in a system.	**ASK:** How does the motion of particles of matter change when they lose thermal energy? **LISTEN:** Students should recognize that the motion of the particles decreases and the particles lose kinetic energy.

Teacher Reflection Questions

- What problems did students encounter trying to model temperature and thermal energy by thinking about marbles? How can you help them to better understand the use of a model?

- What did you do to make sure students understood the meaning of an average? Is there anything you can do to more directly relate this mathematical topic to this science context?

- What convinced you that students grasped the difference between temperature and thermal energy? What misconceptions did you need to clarify?

NOTES

....

....

....

....

....

....

....

....

....

NOTES

3.4 Read

How Can You Compare the Thermal Energy of Two Different Types of Matter?

◀ *2 class periods*

A class period is considered to be one 40 to 50 minute class.

Overview

Students are presented with an example of two objects with the same mass and temperature. Unlike in the previous examples, students are told that the samples do not have the same amount of thermal energy because they are made of different materials. They learn about specific heat and how it determines the amount of thermal energy required to raise the temperature of a substance. Students read about how the specific heat of water can affect local climates. To understand how thermal energy is transferred, students learn three forms of heat transfer. They finish the section by identifying the Sun and Earth as sources of thermal energy.

Targeted Concepts, Skills, and Nature of Science	Performance Expectations
Every substance can be described by its specific heat.	Students discover that the specific heat of a substance determines the amount of thermal energy needed to raise the temperature of the substance.
Large bodies of water moderate nearby climates.	Students read how the specific heat of water causes large bodies of water to moderate climates over land.
Heat is transferred by conduction, convection, and radiation.	Students are introduced to three types of heat transfer.
The Sun is a source of heat energy.	Students learn that the Sun is the source of most energy on Earth.
Solar energy is a renewable energy resource.	Students read that energy from the Sun is a renewable energy resource and is a supply that cannot be used up.

ENERGY

Targeted Concepts, Skills, and Nature of Science	Performance Expectations
Geothermal energy is a renewable energy resource from Earth.	Students read that energy from beneath Earth's surface is renewable and is another source that will not be used up.

Materials	
1 per student	*Project Board* page
1 per class	Class *Project Board*

Homework Options

Reflection

- **Science Content:** What property of iron makes it possible to heat an iron pot more quickly than many other materials? *(Students should suggest that the specific heat of iron is low, meaning that a small amount of thermal energy can raise its temperature substantially.)*

- **Science Content:** What type of heat transfer occurs as a result of particles of matter colliding into one another? *(Students should recognize that this form of heat transfer is conduction.)*

Preparation for 3.5

- **Science Process:** What are some chemical reactions that you know? What are some ways you could investigate chemical energy to learn its indicators? *(These questions engage students to begin thinking about chemical energy and its indicators.)*

SECTION 3.4 IMPLEMENTATION

◄ *2 class periods**

3.4 Read

How Can You Compare the Thermal Energy of Two Different Types of Matter?

If two objects made of the same substance have different masses or temperatures, you can determine which has more thermal energy. If the objects have different masses but are otherwise the same, the one with more mass has more thermal energy. If the objects have different temperatures but are otherwise the same, the warmer one has more thermal energy. However, if two objects are made of different substances, you need more information to determine which object has more thermal energy.

The picture below shows a block of wood and a block of aluminum metal. Both blocks have been sitting on the table for some time and are at the same temperature. Both blocks also have the same mass. Up until now, mass and temperature are the only factors you have investigated for thermal energy. How can you decide whether the wood block or the aluminum block has more thermal energy?

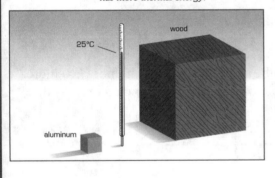

25°C

wood

aluminum

Identical masses of different materials can have different amounts of thermal energy, even at the same temperature. This means that *the material that makes up the substance* is a third factor that affects how much thermal energy a substance has. For example, 1 g of water at 25°C has about 10 times as much thermal energy as 1 g of iron at the same temperature.

Project-Based Inquiry Science

3.4 Read

How Can You Compare the Thermal Energy of Two Different Types of Matter?

15 min

Students compare amounts of thermal energy in different materials and are introduced to the concept of specific heat.

○ Engage

Ask students if they have ever run across a hot deck or beach to jump into a cool pool, lake, or ocean. If so, ask students to describe how much hotter the deck or sand felt than the water. Point out that the deck or sand and the water were exposed to the same amount of energy from the Sun. However, the different materials did not heat up in the same way. Use this example to lead into the discussion on thermal energy and types of materials.

*A class period is considered to be one 40 to 50 minute class.

△ Guide

Use the pictures of the wood and aluminum blocks to begin a discussion. Point out that both blocks are at the same temperature. Ask students what this might mean about thermal energy. Most students will predict that the blocks have the same amount of thermal energy. Point out that in the previous section they compared the same material—water. These two blocks are made of different materials and students should understand that they cannot assume that the amount of thermal energy is the same.

△ Guide

To help students understand the mathematical relationship, work out several examples with the class.

TEACHER TALK

"Suppose you have 100 g of iron. To find the amount of thermal energy needed to raise the temperature 1°C, multiply the mass by the specific heat of iron.

$$100 \text{ g} \times 0.449 \text{ J/g} \bullet °C = 44.9 \text{ J}$$

Now suppose you also have 100 g of water.

$$100 \text{ g} \times 4.184 \text{ J/g} \bullet °C = 418.4 \text{ J}$$

You can see that it requires about 10 times as much energy to increase the temperature of the sample of water by the same amount as the sample of iron."

NOTES

....

....

....

....

....

....

Scientists use a measurement called **specific heat** to describe how much thermal energy is required to raise the temperature of different substances. The units for specific heat are joules per gram per degree Celsius (J/g•°C). The specific heat of water is 4.184 J/g•°C. This means it takes 4.184 J of thermal energy to raise the temperature of 1 g of water by 1°C.

Two important things to remember about specific heat are:

- The greater the specific heat of a material, the more thermal energy is required to raise its temperature.

- The greater the specific heat of a material, the more thermal energy it has compared to some other material with the same mass and temperature.

The specific heat of iron is 0.449 J/g•°C. This means that if you have some water and a piece of iron with the same mass and temperature as the water, the water has about 10 times as much thermal energy as the iron. Water also needs 10 times as much thermal energy as iron does to raise its temperature by 1°C. In fact, water's specific heat is greater than the specific heat of every type of metal.

specific heat: the heat required to raise the temperature of 1 g of a substance 1°C.

Because water has a high specific heat, it takes a lot of energy to heat water to boiling, but once water is hot, it will remain hot for a long time. The high specific heat of water makes it a good substance for storing thermal energy. This is one reason water is often used in cooking.

If you think about hard-boiling eggs, you may be able to better appreciate just how special water's specific heat is. Suppose you want to hard-boil an egg. All of the particles in the egg need to be heated completely to hard-boil it. You know from your experiment with the ice and water that thermal energy from warm water can transfer into a substance submerged in the water. The way people normally hard-boil eggs is to submerge the eggs in water, turn the heat up to boil the water, and then let the eggs boil in the water and absorb its thermal energy. People usually allow the water to boil for about 5 min to hard-boil the eggs. Then they remove the eggs from the water and cool them.

However, because water has such high specific heat, there is a way to hard-boil eggs using less energy. You can use the thermal energy from the burner to bring the water with the eggs to a boil, and then turn off the burner. The water will stay hot long enough to fully cook the eggs without extra energy from the burner.

META NOTES

Students may find the unit of specific heat confusing. It may help to define specific heat as the amount of heat needed to raise the temperature of one gram of a substance by one degree Celsius. Then underline each part in the unit.

Stop and Think

10 min

Students answer questions to focus their understanding of specific heat.

The table below shows the specific heat of different materials with which you are familiar.

Specific Heat Table	
Material	**Specific heat (J/g-°C)**
Air (nitrogen)	1.03
Aluminum	0.897
Diamond	0.510
Iron	0.449
Polyethylene (PET, a type of plastic)	1.79
Sand (quartz)	0.742
Water	4.186

Stop and Think

1. Which material listed in the table requires the greatest amount of energy for 1 g to be heated by 1°C?

2. You are choosing a material that can store a lot of thermal energy but not get very hot (not reach a high temperature). Would you choose a material with a low or high specific heat? Give reasons for your answer.

3. A container of water can be heated by adding hot water or a piece of hot metal. If the mass of the water is equal to the mass of the metal, which material will have the greater effect on the water's temperature? Justify your answer.

4. On a hot day, which would you expect to have a higher temperature, sand or water, if they have the same mass? Why?

5. Think back to the experiment you did with the water and ice. More of the ice submerged in cold water melted than the ice in the bag sitting on the table. The water was cooler than the air in the classroom. Why did the cold water melt more ice than the warm air?

△ Guide and Assess

Review the table with students so they know what information is present in each column. Then discuss the answers to the questions as a class. Help students apply the information in the table to the situations described. Make sure they understand that the specific heat is related to the rate at which the temperature of a substance increases as it absorbs energy.

1. Students should use the table to indicate that water requires the greatest amount of energy to raise the temperature of 1 g by 1°C.

2. Students may recognize that a substance with a high specific heat will contain more thermal energy than a substance with a low specific heat at the same temperature.

3. Students should respond that the substance with the highest specific heat will have the greatest effect on the temperature of the water because, at a given temperature, it contains the most thermal energy. The metal in the table with the highest specific heat is aluminum.

4. Students should deduce that sand will be hotter than water on a hot day. Sand has a lower specific heat and so a given amount of thermal energy from the Sun will raise its temperature more.

5. Students should state that the cold water melted more ice than the warm air because it contained more thermal energy than the air.

NOTES

....

....

....

....

....

....

....

....

....

How Specific Heat of Water Affects Climate

10 min

Students relate specific heat to changes in climate near large bodies of water.

How Specific Heat of Water Affects Climate

You may know that the climate near a large lake or near the ocean is milder than the climate farther inland. A milder climate means that it is less hot in the summer and less cold in the winter. Temperatures near a large lake or the ocean are milder because of the specific heat of the water compared to the specific heat of land. Water absorbs heat slowly and also releases heat slowly. Land absorbs heat more quickly, but it also releases its heat more quickly.

During the summer, when the weather is warmer, the land absorbs thermal energy from the air more quickly than the water does, so the temperature of the land rises faster than the temperature of the water. When the land temperature rises, air that is above land far from large bodies of water receives thermal energy from below and becomes warmer. Air that is above a large body of water receives less thermal energy from below. So air that is farther inland is generally warmer in the summer than air close to lakes or oceans.

In the fall when the air is cooler, less thermal energy is available. As the land and water cool in the fall, the water retains more of the thermal energy it absorbed during the summer. During cold weather, the land cools more quickly, so in winter it has less thermal energy to transfer to the air above it. Because its specific heat is lower than the water, the air above large bodies of water receives a larger transfer of thermal energy from below than air that is inland. So the air near lakes and oceans is generally warmer in the winter than inland air. The larger the lake, the more thermal energy it has stored up to heat the air around it. This keeps temperatures more moderate near large bodies of water.

Which will warm up faster, the water or the sand in this coastal area?

○ Engage

Ask students to describe the climate where they live. If students have difficulty, tell student that climate describes the overall weather conditions over a long period of time. Tell students that climate partly depends on latitude. For example, the climate is warmer near the Equator than in regions farther from the Equator. If a world map is available, point to specific locations and describe its climate. Let students know that there are some exceptions to this general rule.

For example, high mountains in Tibet (28° N latitude) are colder than New York City (43° N latitude). Then read through the information about how large bodies of water affect local climates.

◇ **Evaluate**

When students have finished reading, ask a volunteer to summarize the information. Make sure students recognize that because of water's high specific heat, it heats up and cools off more slowly than most other substances. This makes a large body of water warmer in winter and cooler in summer than the nearby land.

NOTES

....

....

....

....

....

....

....

....

....

....

....

....

How Does Thermal Energy Raise the Temperature of a Substance?

20 min

Students learn about three types of heat transfer—conduction, convection, and radiation.

How Does Thermal Energy Raise the Temperature of a Substance?

In the experiment in *Section 3.2,* when you put bags of ice into the beakers of water, the ice began to melt. Thermal energy was transferred from the warm water to the ice. The thermal energy heated the ice, so some of it melted and became water. At the same time, the loss of thermal energy cooled the water in the beaker. How did this happen?

conduction: the transfer of thermal energy by direct contact.

Heat is thermal energy that is transferred from one object or substance into another object or substance. You have read that heat naturally flows from hotter objects to colder objects. This transfer of thermal energy can happen in three different ways—through *conduction, convection,* and *radiation.*

Recall that when two substances at different temperatures are in contact with each other, the faster-moving particles of the warmer object collide with slower-moving particles in the cooler object. After many collisions, the particles in the cooler object have speeded up, and the particles in the warmer object have slowed down. Eventually, the two objects end up at the same temperature. This process is called **conduction**. Conduction occurs when two objects are in direct contact with each other. In conduction, the colder object gains thermal energy. The hotter object loses the same amount of thermal energy.

When you hard-boil eggs, heat moves by conduction from the burner to the pot, then from the pot to the water, then from the water to the eggs.

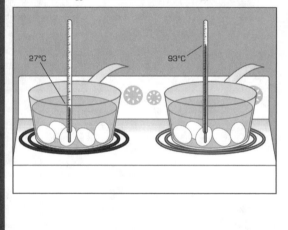

27°C   93°C

In the experiment in *Section 3.2,* the water in the beakers was not in direct contact with the ice. Thermal energy from the water was first transferred to the plastic bag. It was then transferred from the plastic bag to the ice, which was in direct contact with the bag. There are other familiar examples of conduction. When you hard-boil eggs on an electric stove, heat from the burner transfers by conduction to the pot, warming it up. The pot then

---

◯ Engage

Ask students to imagine putting a spoon into a cup of hot tea. Tell students that after some amount of time, the handle of the spoon will feel warm. Students may be familiar with similar experiences. Describe to students how heat is transferred from the end of the spoon in the tea to the handle by conduction. Check students' understanding of this process by asking them to think of any examples of conduction they have experienced.

△ Guide

If time allows, challenge students to model conduction. They might use marbles or other items to represent particles of matter, or students themselves might show the transfer of heat through their movement.

NOTES

....

....

....

....

....

....

....

....

....

....

....

....

....

META NOTES

Convection is the process through which heat is transferred beneath Earth's surface. There, the lower portion of a molten layer of magma known as the asthenosphere is heated by Earth's interior. The heated material rises as cooler material sinks into its place. As the material flows, it is believed to carry parts of Earth's crust known as lithospheric plates. This movement explains how continents move slowly over time.

META NOTES

Convection depends on changes in density. When a substance, such as water, is warmed, the particles spread out a little. This makes the warm substance less dense than the substance when it is cool. A denser substance sinks in a less-dense substance. In a pot of water, the cooler, denser water at the top sinks and warmer, less-dense water at the bottom rises. If a heat source continuously heats the water at the bottom, the cycle will continue.

transfers heat to water inside the pot. The water then transfers heat to the shells of the eggs, and the shells transfer heat to the insides of the eggs.

Another way to transfer thermal energy is through **convection**. You may know that warm air rises and cool air sinks. This is an example of convection. An electric space heater that is near the floor warms the air near it by conduction. This warm air rises, and cooler air rushes in to take its place. The cooler air is heated by the space heater, so it rises, and again cooler air takes its place. Eventually, the thermal energy released by the space heater is able to spread throughout a room by the rising and falling of air in the room. This movement of warmer air to cooler air is convection.

convection: the transfer of thermal energy by the movement of a fluid, such as water or air.

Convection will also occur in a beaker of water when an ice bag is placed in the water. The water near the ice becomes cooler by the transfer of thermal energy into the ice bag. This cooler water sinks toward the bottom of the beaker. It is replaced by warmer water rising from the bottom of the beaker. The entire beaker of water then cools off as it loses thermal energy to the bag of ice.

The oven in your kitchen is another example of convection. The food sits on racks near the center of the oven, while the heating elements are near the sides, top, or bottom. Thermal energy from the heating elements reaches the food by the convection of the air inside the oven.

Another way to transfer thermal energy is by radiation. Radiation occurs when some of the thermal energy in an object is converted into *electromagnetic waves* that spread outward from the object. You will learn more about electromagnetic waves in *Learning Set 4*.

Baking is usually done in a convection oven. In a convection oven, the heating element or flame warms the air near it. As that air warms, it rises, and cooler air takes its place. A fan speeds up the movement of the air.

Convection and conduction can transfer thermal energy only through matter, but radiation can transfer energy through matter or through empty space. This is why the Sun is able to transfer thermal energy to Earth. The Sun emits radiation in the form of electromagnetic waves. This radiation can travel through the empty space between the Sun and Earth. When matter absorbs radiation from the Sun, the particles of the matter move faster. When this happens, the thermal energy of the matter increases. Similarly, when matter emits radiation, the matter can lose thermal energy.

EN 117

ENERGY

△ Guide

Point out the picture of the oven in the student text. Using this image, walk students through the process of convection. Describe how the air at the bottom of the oven is heated by the coils. This warm air rises and cooler air above it sinks into its place. The cooler air is then heated until it becomes warm and the process is repeated. This movement of air forms a pattern known as a convection current.

Another example of radiation is when you heat hot chocolate or popcorn in a microwave oven. Microwaves are a type of electromagnetic wave. The microwaves are generated in the oven and then absorbed by the food inside the oven. The thermal energy of the food increases when the absorbed radiation increases the speed of the particles that make up the food.

Microwave ovens use electromagnetic waves.

Your body warms up when the matter in your body absorbs radiation from the Sun.

Often, all three processes—conduction, convection, and radiation—occur at the same time. Remember the example of the oven in your kitchen. Thermal energy is transferred to air particles in contact with the heating elements by conduction. The movement of warmer air rising and cooler air sinking spreads thermal energy throughout the oven by convection. You can see the heating elements glowing because they are so hot. This glowing is an indicator of radiation. The heating elements are emitting electromagnetic waves, some of which are visible light that you can see. These electromagnetic waves also warm the air in the oven.

Reflect

List five different objects or machines that are used to transfer thermal energy from one place to another. Describe briefly the method by which each transfers thermal energy, and then classify each as using conduction, convection, radiation, or some combination of these. Be sure to cover each of these three processes at least once in your examples.

Project-Based Inquiry Science

○ Engage

Ask students how they think heat travels to Earth from the Sun. If students suggest convection, explain that the heat travels through a vacuum in space. Therefore, there is no matter to rise and fall, so this cannot be correct. If students suggest conduction, explain that heat is transferred in this way only when matter is in contact with a heat source. The Sun is very far from Earth so this cannot be correct. Explain that this heat is transferred by a different method known as radiation. Discuss examples of radiation using the pictures in the student text.

Reflect

5 min

Students apply what they have learned about heat transfer and think of examples in their lives.

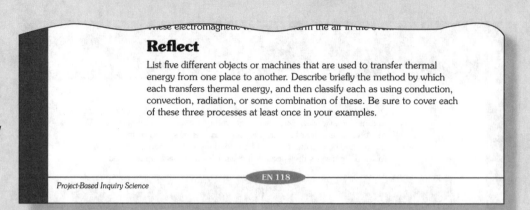

Reflect

List five different objects or machines that are used to transfer thermal energy from one place to another. Describe briefly the method by which each transfers thermal energy, and then classify each as using conduction, convection, radiation, or some combination of these. Be sure to cover each of these three processes at least once in your examples.

Project-Based Inquiry Science   EN 118

△ Guide and Assess

Have students work in their groups to come up with examples of heat transfer. Challenge students to identify each form of heat transfer and to include at least one example of each type of heat transfer. You may need to provide an example to begin the discussion. For example, you might suggest that a pot of water on a stove comes to a boil as a result of convection. When students have had a few minutes to work together, allow groups to share their lists with the class. Correct any mislabeled examples. Students' answers will vary, but may include the following examples:

- *stoves (gas, electric, wood, coal) (All can be examples of conduction, convection, and radiation)*

- *fireplace (gas, electric, wood, coal) (All can be examples of conduction, convections, and radiation)*

- *microwave (radiation)*

- *Sun (radiation)*

- *soldering iron, pressing iron (conduction)*

- *heat lamp (mostly radiation)*

- *baseboard heater (convection)*

NOTES

....

....

....

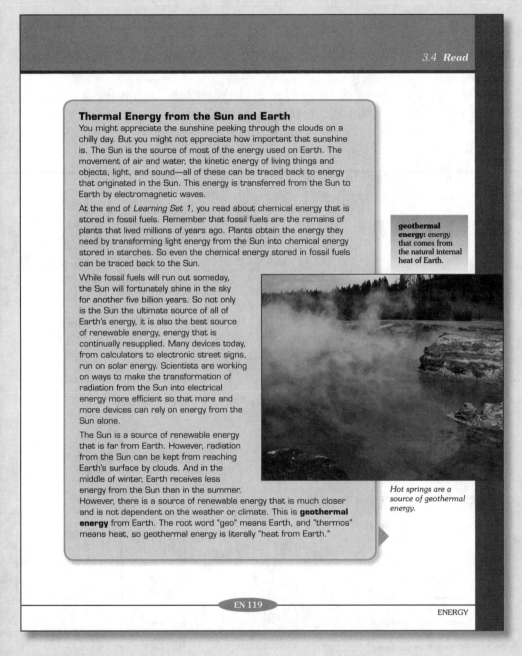

3.4 Read

Thermal Energy from the Sun and Earth

You might appreciate the sunshine peeking through the clouds on a chilly day. But you might not appreciate how important that sunshine is. The Sun is the source of most of the energy used on Earth. The movement of air and water, the kinetic energy of living things and objects, light, and sound—all of these can be traced back to energy that originated in the Sun. This energy is transferred from the Sun to Earth by electromagnetic waves.

At the end of *Learning Set 1*, you read about chemical energy that is stored in fossil fuels. Remember that fossil fuels are the remains of plants that lived millions of years ago. Plants obtain the energy they need by transforming light energy from the Sun into chemical energy stored in starches. So even the chemical energy stored in fossil fuels can be traced back to the Sun.

While fossil fuels will run out someday, the Sun will fortunately shine in the sky for another five billion years. So not only is the Sun the ultimate source of all of Earth's energy, it is also the best source of renewable energy, energy that is continually resupplied. Many devices today, from calculators to electronic street signs, run on solar energy. Scientists are working on ways to make the transformation of radiation from the Sun into electrical energy more efficient so that more and more devices can rely on energy from the Sun alone.

The Sun is a source of renewable energy that is far from Earth. However, radiation from the Sun can be kept from reaching Earth's surface by clouds. And in the middle of winter, Earth receives less energy from the Sun than in the summer. However, there is a source of renewable energy that is much closer and is not dependent on the weather or climate. This is **geothermal energy** from Earth. The root word "geo" means Earth, and "thermos" means heat, so geothermal energy is literally "heat from Earth."

geothermal energy: energy that comes from the natural internal heat of Earth.

Hot springs are a source of geothermal energy.

EN 119

ENERGY

Thermal Energy from the Sun and Earth

10 min

Students read about the most abundant energy resources.

META NOTES

The Sun is only an average-sized star. As in other stars, nuclear reactions release huge amounts of energy in the form of heat and light. During these reactions, hydrogen atoms are fused together to form helium atoms. The Sun has enough "fuel" to last for hundreds of millions, if not billions, of years.

○ Engage

Ask students to name one major characteristic that makes Earth different from the other planets in the solar system. Guide students to recognize that Earth is the only planet on which water exists as a liquid. This is because the global temperature of Earth is warm enough to maintain liquid water. It is not so hot that the water evaporates or boils, and not so cold that all the water is frozen. Earth's temperature range results mainly from its position relative to the Sun.

PBIS

△ Guide

As students learn that the Sun is Earth's major source of energy, describe the following examples:

- Remind students of the water cycle they read about earlier when they were introduced to hydroelectric power. Point out that the Sun provides the energy necessary for water to flow through the water cycle.

- Uneven heating in the atmosphere by the Sun causes winds that produce wind power.

- Plants use sunlight to make food. The energy stored in that food is trapped when plants die. Describe to students how the remains of plants from millions of years ago formed fossil fuels that are used today.

Let students know that fossil fuels are known as non-renewable resources. Once they are used up, they will not be replaced in nature. The Sun's energy, however, is a renewable resource. It is constantly being replaced.

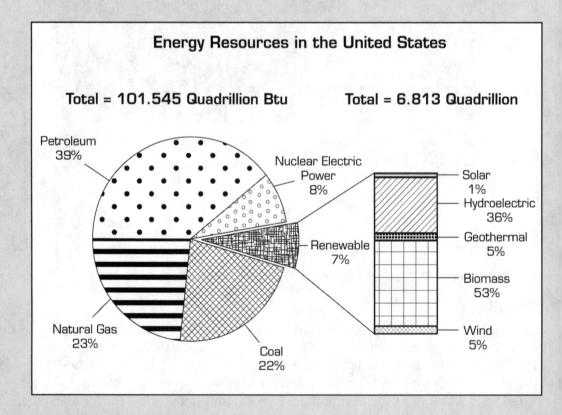

Energy Resources in the United States

Total = 101.545 Quadrillion Btu Total = 6.813 Quadrillion

Petroleum 39%
Nuclear Electric Power 8%
Natural Gas 23%
Coal 22%
Renewable 7%
Solar 1%
Hydroelectric 36%
Geothermal 5%
Biomass 53%
Wind 5%

Geothermal energy is thermal energy that comes from Earth's interior. This thermal energy is constantly being released at the surface, but it is released in greater amounts in certain locations. Volcanoes and hot springs are two examples of places that receive a large amount of geothermal energy.

In Iceland, where there are numerous cracks in Earth's crust, scientists have found ways to use the large amounts of available geothermal energy that is released through these cracks. Iceland is cold, but almost 90 percent of the energy needed to heat buildings and generate electricity in Iceland comes from geothermal energy. The geothermal energy is absorbed by water or steam in pipes far underground. The water or steam is then pumped to the locations that need to be heated.

In the United States, California uses the most of this clean, renewable energy source. Even so, geothermal energy today provides less than 1 percent of the world's population's energy needs.

This geothermal power plant in Iceland provides electricity to thousands of people.

Reflect

1. What are examples of the use of thermal energy in your home? What processes do these examples use to transfer thermal energy from one location to another?

2. What are the advantages of geothermal energy? Why is it not used everywhere to heat homes and generate electricity?

3. Do you think thermal energy is a kind of kinetic energy or a kind of potential energy?

EN 120

Project-Based Inquiry Science

△ Guide

Students may be unfamiliar with geothermal energy. Discuss what it is and its origin. Tell students that geothermal energy makes up less than half of one percent of the energy resources in the United States, but has a greater potential for use in the future.

Reflect

5 min

Students relate what they have read to real applications and earlier ideas.

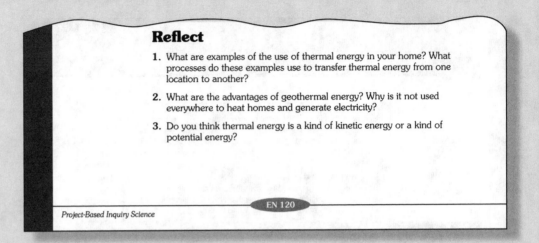

Reflect

1. What are examples of the use of thermal energy in your home? What processes do these examples use to transfer thermal energy from one location to another?

2. What are the advantages of geothermal energy? Why is it not used everywhere to heat homes and generate electricity?

3. Do you think thermal energy is a kind of kinetic energy or a kind of potential energy?

EN 120

Project-Based Inquiry Science

△ Guide and Assess

Have students discuss the questions in their groups. Then have groups share their answers. Note that students are again being asked the same question about whether thermal energy is kinetic or potential. Rather than simply repeating their earlier answers, encourage students to reconsider the question based on what they have learned. New information may support their earlier ideas, which is fine, or it might contradict their earlier ideas.

1. Students' answers will vary, but should be more specific and accurate than when this question was asked earlier.

2. Students should respond that geothermal energy is a renewable resource and cannot be exhausted. It is not used in more locations because its use requires cracks in Earth's crust.

3. Student should answer that thermal energy is a form of kinetic energy.

NOTES

....

....

....

....

Update the *Project Board*

It is time now to revisit the *Project Board.* Perhaps some of the questions you had about energy have been answered. Examine the questions in the *What do we need to investigate?* column. For which ones do you now know the answers? Record what you know now about thermal energy in the *What are we learning?* column.

You have a lot of evidence for what you know about thermal energy. Make sure you record evidence that supports what you have learned in the *What is our evidence?* column. If you have more questions, record them in the *What do we need to investigate?* column.

What's the Point?

Temperature, mass, and the type of material are factors that affect the thermal energy of an object. When two materials being compared are different, the temperature and the mass can be the same, but one material may contain more thermal energy than the other. Specific heat is a measure of the heat required to raise the temperature of one gram of a substance 1°C. Material with the higher specific heat will have more thermal energy than material with lower specific heat if they both have the same mass and temperature.

Thermal energy can be transferred from one place to another through conduction, convection, or radiation. Conduction is the transfer of thermal energy by objects or substances that are touching. Convection is the transfer of thermal energy by a moving fluid (liquid or gas). Radiation is the transfer of thermal energy by electromagnetic waves.

Two renewable sources of thermal energy are solar energy and geothermal energy. Solar energy is thermal energy transferred from the Sun through radiation. Geothermal energy is thermal energy that comes from Earth's interior.

EN 121

ENERGY

Update the *Project Board*

5 min

Students add new ideas and questions to the Project Board.

△ Guide

Work with students to review the questions on the *Project Board.* If any questions have been answered, add the answers in the appropriate column. Have students suggest new ideas to include, as well as any new questions that have arisen.

TEACHER TALK

❝What did you learn about thermal energy from your experiments? What is the evidence that can support that idea?

What did you learn about the transfer of thermal energy that is not on the *Project Board*? What should we write as evidence?**❞**

Assessment Options

Targeted Concepts, Skills, and Nature of Science	How do I know if students got it?
Every substance can be described by its specific heat.	**ASK:** How is water unusual in terms of specific heat? **LISTEN:** Students should recognize that the specific heat of water is higher than any other common substance.
Large bodies of water moderate nearby climates.	**ASK:** How does an ocean affect nearby land climates in winter? **LISTEN:** Students should explain that the water moderates a climate by keeping it warmer than nearby regions at the same latitude.
Heat is transferred by conduction, convection, and radiation.	**ASK:** How is radiation different from conduction and convection? **LISTEN:** Students should answer that radiation does not require matter for transport.
The Sun is a source of heat energy.	**ASK:** What is the original source of most energy on Earth? **LISTEN:** Students should identify the Sun as Earth's primary source of energy.

Targeted Concepts, Skills, and Nature of Science	How do I know if students got it?
Solar energy is a renewable energy resource.	**ASK:** What does it mean to say that solar energy is renewable? **LISTEN:** Students should understand that the Sun's energy is continuously produced and will not be used up.
Geothermal energy is a renewable energy resource from Earth.	**ASK:** What type of energy is associated with volcanoes and hot springs? **LISTEN:** Students should identify geothermal energy as the heat transfer type from volcanoes and hot springs.

Teacher Reflection Questions

- What difficulties arose when students were introduced to specific heat? How were you able to avoid any confusion?

- How were you able to relate specific heat to climate? Are there any examples you can describe to help students understand these concepts?

- What convinced you that students were able to differentiate among the three types of heat transfer? What can you do differently next time?

NOTES

....

....

....

....

....

NOTES

3.5 Explore

How Do You Know When Chemical Energy Is Involved?

◀ *2 class periods*

A class period is considered to be one 40 to 50 minute class.

Overview

Students conduct investigations involving chemical change. The class is divided into groups and each group investigates a different example of a chemical change. Students look for indicators that suggest that a chemical change has occurred and there has been a change in the amount of energy. They analyze their results and share them with the class. They read about indicators of chemical energy and then update the *Project Board* with new information and questions they have from their investigations and class discussions.

Targeted Concepts, Skills, and Nature of Science	Performance Expectations
Scientists often work together and then share their findings. Sharing findings makes new information available and helps scientists refine their ideas and build on others' ideas. When another person's or group's idea is used, credit needs to be given.	Students work together to complete investigations in which they observe a chemical change.
During a chemical change, the original substances are changed into new substances with different properties.	Students cause substances to change into different properties.
Chemical energy is potential energy stored in the bonds that hold matter together.	Students consider the chemical energy stored in the substances they observe.
Some chemical changes absorb thermal energy and others release thermal energy.	Students determine whether thermal energy is released or absorbed during chemical changes.

Materials

Investigation 1	15 mL vinegar
1 per group	10 g (about 1 tsp) baking soda
	Small flask
	Graduated cylinder, 100 mL
	Rubber balloon
	Funnel
	Roll of paper towels
	Plastic teaspoon
Investigation 2	25 mL vinegar
1 per group	5 g (about ½ tsp) table salt
	Graduated cylinder, 100 mL
	Roll of paper towels
	10-oz plastic cup
	Plastic teaspoon
5 per group	Dull, stained pennies
Investigation 3	25 mL vinegar
1 per group	10 g (about 1 tsp) table salt
	Graduated cylinder
	Roll of paper towels
	10-oz plastic cup
	Plastic teaspoon
20 per group	Stained pennies
Investigation 4	Effervescent antacid tablet
1 per group	30 mL water
	Small flask
	Graduated cylinder, 100 mL
	Rubber balloon
	Funnel

Materials	
1 per class	Class *Project Board*

Activity Setup and Preparation

Make sure students are using pennies dated before 1982. During that year, the U.S. Mint changed the composition of the penny from 95 percent copper to 97.5 percent zinc.

Homework Options

Reflection

- **Science Content:** What are some indicators that suggest a chemical change has taken place? *(Students' answers may include a change in temperature, a change in color, or the production of bubbles or a precipitate.)*

Preparation for 3.6

- **Science Content:** How might you use indicators to compare amounts of chemical energy? *(This question is meant to get students thinking about amounts of chemical energy rather than simply the presence of chemical energy.)*

NOTES

....

....

....

....

....

....

NOTES

SECTION 3.5 IMPLEMENTATION

◄ *2 class periods**

3.5 Explore

How Do You Know When Chemical Energy Is Involved?

Indicators of chemical reactions can be found almost anywhere you look. Some reactions are very fast, such as an explosion of dynamite. But some can happen slowly, over days or weeks. The ripening of fruit is an example of a slow chemical reaction. Perhaps you have seen a green tomato on the vine. If you have ever eaten a green tomato, you know that more than color makes a ripe tomato. When a tomato is green, its odor, flavor, and texture are different from when it has ripened. A change in color or odor is evidence that chemical energy is involved.

In this section, you will carry out several investigations to look for other indicators of chemical energy. With this knowledge, you will be able to identify when chemical energy is involved in an energy transformation. Knowing the indicators will also help you investigate factors that determine the amount of chemical energy involved. You may find it challenging to involve chemical energy in an energy transformation in your Rube Goldberg machine. An understanding of the factors will help you control the amount of chemical energy released, so your machine operates properly.

The change of color and odor as a tomato ripens indicates that chemical energy is involved.

Each group in the class will be assigned one of four investigations. Each of these investigations shows one example of a chemical change. A chemical change occurs when one or more new substances form from the atoms or molecules present in the original substance or substances. Each group will do one of the activities and then share their understanding with others.

Before getting started, read the procedure for your investigation, and gather your materials.

Project-Based Inquiry Science

EN 122

3.5 Explore

How Do You Know When Chemical Energy Is Involved?

10 min

Students are introduced to the task of the section and review the procedure they will follow with their groups.

As with all lab investigations, students must wear safety goggles, tie back hair, and secure any loose clothing.

○ Engage

Assign an *Investigation* to each group. Have students read through the steps of their *Investigation* with their groups and discuss what they are going to do. Address any questions or concerns at this time. Distribute the materials for students to observe before starting their investigations and suggest that each student in the group perform a different function during the procedures.

*A class period is considered to be one 40 to 50 minute class.

ENERGY

Investigation 1: Vinegar and Baking Soda

30 min

Students assigned to this investigation observe what happens when vinegar and baking soda are mixed.

Tell students to clean up any spills immediately to avoid accidents.

Investigation 1: Vinegar and Baking Soda

Procedure

1. Put 10 g (1 tsp) of baking soda into the balloon, using the funnel. Remove the funnel and clean the inside of the funnel with a paper towel.

2. Measure 15 mL of vinegar, using the graduated cylinder.

3. Using the clean funnel, pour the vinegar into the small flask.

4. While someone holds the small flask, stretch the opening of the balloon over the mouth of the small flask. Make sure that none of the baking soda gets into the flask.

5. Holding the flask and balloon upright, empty the baking soda from the balloon into the flask. Hold the balloon onto the flask tightly so it does not fall off.

Materials
- 15 mL of vinegar
- 10 g of baking soda (about 1 tsp)
- 1 small flask
- 1 graduated cylinder, 100 mL
- 1 rubber balloon
- 1 funnel
- paper towels
- 1 plastic teaspoon

Step 3	Step 4	Step 5

6. Observe the balloon and flask for the next 5 min. During this time, touch the outside of the flask from time to time to make observations of temperature changes. Record your observations. Make sure to record the differences you see in the flask and the balloon, as well as any temperature changes you might feel.

EN 123

ENERGY

⬡ Get Going

Before the group begins the investigation, make sure all students know their roles and what they have to do during the procedure. They may want to divide roles by having one student pour the baking soda, another student clean the funnel between Steps 1 and 2, and one student pour the vinegar. They should also determine which pair of students will place the balloon over the flask.

When the group is set up, have them start their investigation. Emphasize that they should use the diagram in the student text to ensure that they are following the procedure correctly. Remind students to record their observations as they occur and to be as thorough as possible.

NOTES

....

....

....

....

....

....

....

....

....

....

....

....

Investigation 2: Vinegar, Copper, and Salt

30 min

Students assigned to this investigation observe what happens when pennies are added to a salt–vinegar solution.

Investigation 2: Vinegar, Copper, and Salt

Materials
- 5 dull, stained pennies
- 25 mL of white vinegar
- 5 g of table salt (about ½ tsp)
- 1 graduated cylinder, 100 mL
- paper towels
- 1 plastic 10-oz cup
- 1 plastic teaspoon

Procedure

1. Examine the pennies and record your observations of their appearance.

2. Using the graduated cylinder, measure 25 mL of vinegar, and pour it into the plastic cup. Measure about 5 g (½ tsp) of table salt. Add it to the vinegar and stir with the spoon until the salt dissolves.

3. Place the coins in the salt-vinegar solution.

4. Observe the cup for the next 5 min. During this time, touch the outside of the cup from time to time to make observations of temperature changes. Record your observations. Make sure to record any changes you see in the liquid and the pennies, as well as any temperature changes you might feel.

5. Using the spoon, remove the coins from the salt and vinegar solution. Rinse them with water and place them on a paper towel to dry.

6. Examine the pennies, and record what they look like. Note any differences between the way the coins look now and the way they looked before they were put into the solution.

Investigation 3: Vinegar, Salt, and Metals

Materials
- 2 steel nails
- 2 steel screws
- 25 mL of white vinegar
- 10 g table salt (about 1 tsp)
- 1 graduated cylinder, 100 mL
- 20 stained pennies
- paper towels
- 1 10-oz plastic cup
- 1 plastic teaspoon

Procedure

1. Examine the nails and screws. Record your observations of how they look.

2. Using the graduated cylinder, measure 25 mL of vinegar, and pour it into the plastic cup. Measure about 10 g (1 tsp) of table salt. Add it to the vinegar and stir with the spoon until the salt dissolves.

3. Place 10 pennies in the salt-vinegar solution and wait 10 min.

4. Remove the pennies from the salt-vinegar solution, rinse them, and place them on a paper towel to dry. Compare the 10 pennies that were in the solution with the 10 pennies that were not treated. Record your observations.

EN 124

⬡ Get Going

Make sure each group member knows his or her role before starting the procedure. Remind students that they must record their observations of the pennies before measuring and mixing the liquids in the procedure. Point out to students that they should gently touch the cup when making their observations in Step 4 so they do not spill the solution and disrupt the investigation. Also remind students to record their observations as they occur and to be as thorough as possible.

○ Get Going

Before starting the procedure, make sure group members have been assigned roles and know what they should do. The group should decide if there will be a pair to make the salt-vinegar solution, or if there should be one student to do it. They should decide who will add and remove the pennies and who will do the same for the nails and screws. Once this has been determined, let the group begin. Remind students to record their observations of the nails and screws before mixing the liquids.

Investigation 3: Vinegar, Salt, and Metals

30 min

Students in this group observe a mixture of vinegar and salt with types of metals.

NOTES

....

....

....

....

....

....

....

....

....

....

....

....

ENERGY

5. Using the diagram as a guide, place the steel nails and screws into the same vinegar solution. Lean one of the steel nails against the side of the cup so only about one-half of it is in the solution. The other nail and the screws should be completely submerged in the liquid.

6. Observe the cup for the next 10 min. During this time, touch the outside of the cup from time to time to make observations of temperature changes. Record your observations. Make sure to record any changes you see in the liquid and the nails, as well as any temperature changes you might feel.

7. After 10 min, use the spoon to remove the nails and screws from the solution. Place them on a paper towel to dry.

8. Examine the nails and screws again, and record your observations. Touch the nails and screws, and record what they feel like. Note any differences in the nails and screws from before they were put into the solution and after they came out of the solution. Compare the bottom half of the nail that was in the solution to the top half of the nail that was not in the solution.

Investigation 4: Antacid

Procedure

1. Insert the antacid tablet into the balloon. You may have to break the tablet so the pieces fit through the opening in the balloon.

2. Measure 30 mL of water using the graduated cylinder.

Materials
- 1 effervescent antacid tablet
- 30 mL water
- 1 small flask
- 1 graduated cylinder, 100 mL
- 1 rubber balloon
- 1 funnel

EN 125

ENERGY

△ Guide

When the group comes to Step 5, make sure they use the diagram in the student text to guide their placement of the nails and screws in the cup. Remind students to record their observations as they occur and to be as thorough as possible.

3. Using the funnel, pour the water into the small flask.

4. Hold the balloon so that the tablet cannot fall out, and stretch the open end of the balloon over the top of the flask.

5. Holding the flask and balloon upright, empty the tablet from the balloon into the flask. Hold the balloon onto the flask tightly so it does not fall off. The illustration for *Investigation 1* may help you see how to do this.

6. Observe the balloon and the flask for the next 10 min. During this time, touch the outside of the flask from time to time to make observations of temperature changes. Record your observations. Make sure to record the differences you see in the flask and the balloon, as well as any temperature changes you might feel.

Analyze Your Results

Use the observations and results from your group's investigation to answer the following questions.

1. How did the appearance of the materials you worked with change? Describe any changes.

2. Did you observe any changes in heat, light, or sound? Describe any observed changes.

3. Which of the changes you observed do you think are indicators that chemical energy was used?

4. Do you think chemical energy is a type of kinetic energy or a type of potential energy? Why?

Communicate

Share Your Results

Each group will share the results of its investigation with the class. When it is your turn to present, begin with a brief description of your investigation, including the materials used. Then share your observations and results. If you have pennies, nails, or screws to show, show them to the class, and tell the class what they looked like before you put them into the liquid. Then report the indicators of chemical energy that you identified.

EN 126

Investigation 4: Antacid

30 min

Students in this group observe a mixture of antacid and water.

⬡ Get Going

Before starting the procedure, students should know what role they are performing during the investigation. They should decide how the antacid tablet will be put into the balloon in Step 1, either by one group member or a pair of students. They should also choose a student to add the water to the graduated cylinder and then the flask. They should also decide who will place the balloon on the flask.

Analyze Your Results

10 min

Students answer questions to interpret the results of the investigations.

Analyze Your Results

Use the observations and results from your group's investigation to answer the following questions.

1. How did the appearance of the materials you worked with change? Describe any changes.

2. Did you observe any changes in heat, light, or sound? Describe any observed changes.

3. Which of the changes you observed do you think are indicators that chemical energy was used?

4. Do you think chemical energy is a type of kinetic energy or a type of potential energy? Why?

△ Guide and Assess

Have groups discuss their results by answering the questions. Tell students to consider all of their observations as they attempt to answer the questions. Let students know that they will be sharing their results with the class. As students answer these questions, circulate the classroom and listen for the following in discussions:

1. For *Experiment 1,* students should report that the mixture of vinegar and baking soda bubbled and foamed. The balloon expanded because a gas had formed. The flask got colder.

   For *Experiment 2,* students should report that the pennies became cleaner and shinier. The cup did not change temperature.

   For *Experiment 3,* students should report that the nails and screws became rusty while the pennies became cleaner and shinier. There was no change in temperature.

   For *Experiment 4,* students should report that the mixture of water and antacid tablet bubbled and foamed. The balloon expanded because a gas had formed. The flask got colder.

2. For *Experiment 1,* students should describe how the flask became colder. Perhaps there might have been some bubbling noises.

   For *Experiment 2,* students should not report that there were only color changes.

   For *Experiment 3,* students should not report that there were color changes and some shape changes.

   For *Experiment 4,* students should describe that the flask became colder. It is also possible that there may have been some bubbling noises.

3. For *Experiment 1,* students should respond that the bubbling and gas formation indicate chemical changes. The temperature change also is an indicator.

For *Experiment 2,* students should respond that the color changes indicate that chemical energy had been used.

For *Experiment 3,* students should respond that the color changes indicate that chemical energy had been used.

For *Experiment 4,* students should respond that the bubbling and gas formation indicate chemical changes. The temperature change also is an indicator.

4. Students' answers may vary, but try to lead them to conclude that the chemical energy was present before anything happened, so it must be potential energy.

NOTES

....

....

....

....

....

....

....

....

....

Communicate: Share Your Results

20 min

Groups share their results with the class.

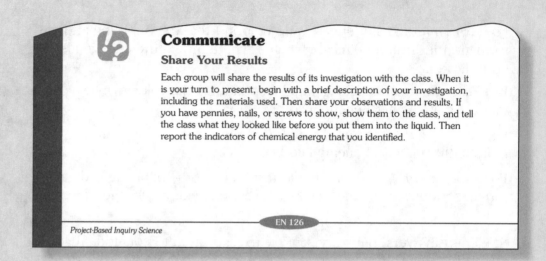

Communicate

Share Your Results

Each group will share the results of its investigation with the class. When it is your turn to present, begin with a brief description of your investigation, including the materials used. Then share your observations and results. If you have pennies, nails, or screws to show, show them to the class, and tell the class what they looked like before you put them into the liquid. Then report the indicators of chemical energy that you identified.

Project-Based Inquiry Science

EN 126

Get Going

Allow each group to present their results to the class. Ask students to describe what they did, what they observed, and what they learned from their observations. Tell students to include any indicators they identified.

Also discuss with students what they should be listening for in other groups' presentations. Encourage them to ask questions if they have any and remind them to be respectful when doing so.

Once all groups have presented, work with a class to answer the questions relating to the *Big Challenge*. Make a list of the questions students still need answered so they can be added to the *Project Board*.

NOTES

As you listen, make sure you understand what each group did, what their results were, and what indicators they identified. If you do not understand something, be sure to ask for more information.

After all of the presentations, make a class list of indicators of chemical energy. If there are questions about some of the indicators, discuss these questions. You may want to ask questions of the groups that suggested each indicator. Make sure there is agreement on the final list.

Then, as a class, answer these questions that relate to the *Big Challenge*:

- Which of the changes you observed can be used to provide energy to something else?

- How might one of these changes be used as a step in the *Big Challenge*?

- What else do you need to know about chemical energy to use chemical energy in the machine you are designing?

What Are Indicators of Chemical Energy?

The indicators for chemical energy are similar to indicators for a chemical change. The indicators include temperature change, change in color, giving off light and sound, formation of a solid from solution (precipitation), or formation of bubbles in a solution (gas formation). A fireworks display is a good example of chemical reactions giving off light and sound.

One indication of a chemical reaction is the formation of bubbles. In this model of an erupting volcano, baking soda and vinegar react to produce foamy bubbles.

What Are Indicators of Chemical Energy?

< 5 min

Students note indicators of chemical energy when a match is lit.

⭘ Engage

Break a wooden match as students watch. Then take another match, light it, and let it burn for ten seconds before extinguishing it. Ask students which match underwent a chemical change. Ask them to explain why they chose the match that burned. Ask them for indicators of chemical change that they just witnessed in your demonstration. Then let them read the selection.

Update the *Project Board*

5 min

Students add new ideas and questions to the Project Board.

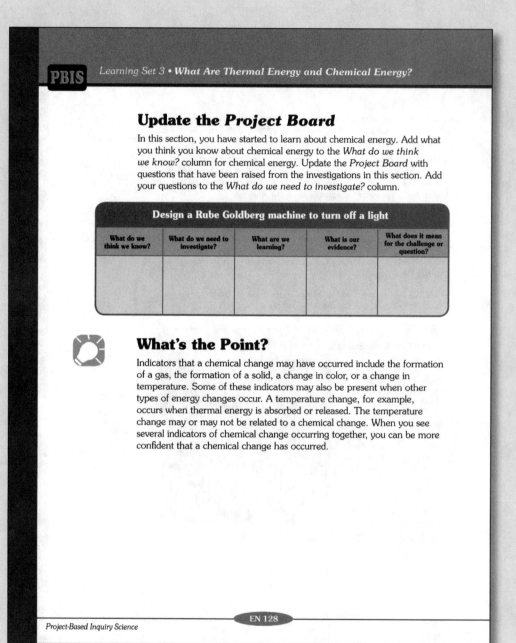

Update the *Project Board*

In this section, you have started to learn about chemical energy. Add what you think you know about chemical energy to the *What do we think we know?* column for chemical energy. Update the *Project Board* with questions that have been raised from the investigations in this section. Add your questions to the *What do we need to investigate?* column.

Design a Rube Goldberg machine to turn off a light				
What do we think we know?	What do we need to investigate?	What are we learning?	What is our evidence?	What does it mean for the challenge or question?

What's the Point?

Indicators that a chemical change may have occurred include the formation of a gas, the formation of a solid, a change in color, or a change in temperature. Some of these indicators may also be present when other types of energy changes occur. A temperature change, for example, occurs when thermal energy is absorbed or released. The temperature change may or may not be related to a chemical change. When you see several indicators of chemical change occurring together, you can be more confident that a chemical change has occurred.

△ Guide

Work with students to review their ideas and questions about chemical energy. Record the information on the *Project Board*.

Assessment Options

Targeted Concepts, Skills, and Nature of Science	How do I know if students got it?
Scientists often work together and then share their findings. Sharing findings makes new information available and helps scientists refine their ideas and build on others' ideas. When another person's or group's idea is used, credit needs to be given.	**ASK:** How was it helpful to conduct the investigation with other students? **LISTEN:** Students should describe that they were able to work together and to combine their observations in their groups.
During a chemical change, the original substances are changed into new substances with different properties.	**ASK:** How can you determine that a chemical change occurred? **LISTEN:** Students should describe the indicators they have observed, including the fact that substances could not be turned back into the original substances.
Chemical energy is potential energy stored in the bonds that hold matter together.	**ASK:** What was the source of energy released during the experiments? **LISTEN:** Students should recognize that chemical energy stored in the substances was released during experiments.
Some chemical changes absorb thermal energy and others release thermal energy.	**ASK:** What indicator can you use to detect a release of thermal energy? **LISTEN:** Students might mention that the final substances felt warmer or colder than the original substances.

Teacher Reflection Questions

- What procedural problems did students face during the investigations? How can you avoid these problems in the future?

- How did you make sure that students shared the responsibilities of the investigations? What might you do differently?

- Did students make the connection between the reading and the investigations? What could you do to make the connection more obvious?

NOTES

3.6 Investigate

What Factors Influence How Much Chemical Energy a Substance Has?

◀ *3 class periods*

A class period is considered to be one 40 to 50 minute class.

Overview

Students are introduced to chemical changes as chemical reactions by first considering the example of fireworks. They review the procedure for an experiment to complete a chemical reaction involving an antacid tablet in water. Each group uses a different amount of an antacid tablet to observe how it affects the volume of carbon dioxide gas produced. The buildup of carbon dioxide gas makes a film canister cap travel some distance through the air. Students relate the distance to the amount of chemical energy. Following the investigation, students read about how chemical energy is involved in the reaction as well as how combustion reactions are examples of exothermic reactions. Students also consider pollutants produced by some chemical reactions. The class updates the *Project Board* with new data and questions they have. They move on to a *More to Learn* section and read about how chemical energy is involved in the living processes of photosynthesis and cell respiration.

Targeted Concepts, Skills, and Nature of Science	Performance Expectations
Scientists often work together and then share their findings. Sharing findings makes new information available and helps scientists refine their ideas and build on others' ideas. When another person's or group's idea is used, credit needs to be given.	Students work together to conduct experiments in which they manipulate the amount of an antacid tablet in a chemical reaction.
During a chemical change, the original substances are changed into new substances with different properties.	Students observe how a change in substances during a chemical reaction can result in the motion of a film canister cap.

ENERGY

Targeted Concepts, Skills, and Nature of Science	Performance Expectations
Chemical energy is potential energy stored in the bonds that hold matter together.	Students read about chemical energy stored in food and fuels.
Plants change the energy of sunlight into chemical energy during photosynthesis.	Students read how energy is involved in the process of photosynthesis.
The cells of living things break down food during cell respiration to obtain energy.	Students read how energy is used by living things.

Materials

1 per group	Effervescent antacid tablet Water Film canister with cap Roll of paper towels Graduated cylinder, 10 mL Meter stick
1 per student	Safety goggles *Chemical Reactions* page *Energy Types* page
several per group	Colored candies

NOTES

....

....

....

....

....

Activity Setup and Preparation

Each group will use a different amount of an antacid tablet in their investigation. You may want to break up the tablets before class to save time. Break the antacid tablets into $\frac{1}{4}$, $\frac{1}{2}$, and $\frac{3}{4}$ size pieces. Each group will need five samples of the same size. Also, before class, designate an area to use a launch site for the film canisters.

Homework Options

Reflection

- **Science Content:** What happens to atoms of matter during a chemical reaction? *(Students should explain that bonds between atoms are broken, atoms are rearranged, and new bonds are formed.)*

- **Science Content:** How are photosynthesis and cell respiration related? *(Students should suggest that they are opposite processes because energy is stored during photosynthesis and released for use during cell respiration.)*

NOTES

....

....

....

....

....

....

....

NOTES

SECTION 3.6 IMPLEMENTATION

3.6 Investigate

What Factors Influence How Much Chemical Energy a Substance Has?

You now know several of the indicators of chemical energy. However, you do not yet know what factors affect how much chemical energy a substance has. In this section, you will vary the amount of antacid tablet used in a **chemical reaction** and measure how that affects the chemical energy that is released.

Each group will use a different amount of the antacid tablet—¼ tablet, ½ tablet, ¾ tablet, or 1 tablet. Each group will repeat the procedure multiple times and average their results. After each group has reported their results to the class, you will be able to see how changing the amount of one chemical in a reaction can change the chemical energy that is released.

> **chemical reaction:** a process in which a new substance or substances are formed when atoms from the original substance or substances are rearranged.

Fireworks are grand displays of chemical energy. Think about what factors determine the amount of chemical energy released in each display shown here.

EN 129

ENERGY

3.6 Investigate

What Factors Influence How Much Chemical Energy a Substance Has?

10 min

Students learn what a chemical reaction is to prepare them for the chemical reactions they will investigate in the section.

○ Engage

Ask students to look at the photographs in the student text. Point out that they have observed several physical and chemical changes throughout this Unit. Tell students that a chemical change is also known as a chemical reaction and that displays of fireworks involve chemical reactions.

*A class period is considered to be one 40 to 50 minute class.

TEACHER TALK

"In this section, you will work in groups to investigate what happens when you place an antacid tablet in water. I know some of you conducted a similar investigation in the previous section. However this time, each group will use a different portion of an antacid tablet. You will find out how the size of the tablet affects your results."

NOTES

....

....

....

....

....

....

....

....

....

....

....

....

In this chemical reaction, the antacid will react with water to produce a gas. The reaction will occur in a film canister. You will be using the chemical energy released from the reaction to shoot film canisters into the air. It will be fun to watch, like fireworks. And, just as when you are watching fireworks, you will have to stay out of the way when the film canisters fall back to the ground. You will compare how much chemical energy was released by measuring how high and how far the film canisters travel.

Set up a launch site in your classroom. Everyone will need to stay outside the launch-site area except for the students who are launching a film canister. You will use a vertical scale to measure how high each film canister flies. Two students in each group will launch a film canister. The others in the group will observe its launch and measure how high and how far it travels.

Read through the entire procedure. Before you begin, you will make a prediction that relates the height and distance the canister flies to the amount of antacid used. You will need to connect this prediction to the amount of chemical energy that is used to propel the canister.

Materials
- bubbling antacid tablets
- water
- 1 film canister with cap
- paper towels
- 1 tape measure
- 1 graduated cylinder, 10-mL
- meter sticks
- saftey goggles

⚠️

Put your safety goggles on and leave them on for the remainder of this investigation.

Procedure

1. Prepare five samples of antacid tablet that are all the right size, according to the amount you have been assigned. You will use the samples in five trials.

2. Measure 10 mL of water in a graduated cylinder and pour it into a film canister. Wait until your group is called to the launch site.

3. Make your prediction about how high and far the canister will travel. Record it on your *Chemical Reactions* page.

⚠ Guide

Describe what students will be observing in this investigation. Review all safety procedures and requirements. Emphasize that they must wear safety goggles and they must not aim their film canisters at any people or windows. Once you are confident that all students understand these precautions, assign each group a different portion of an antacid tablet. Then distribute the materials to each group.

Procedure

20 min

Students use mixtures of antacid tablets in water to shoot a film canister cap some distance.

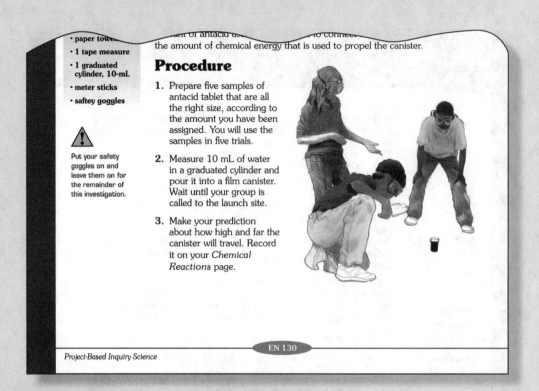

• paper towe
• 1 tape measure
• 1 graduated cylinder, 10-mL
• meter sticks
• saftey goggles

⚠️

Put your safety goggles on and leave them on for the remainder of this investigation.

...t of antacid u... ...o conne.. the amount of chemical energy that is used to propel the canister.

Procedure

1. Prepare five samples of antacid tablet that are all the right size, according to the amount you have been assigned. You will use the samples in five trials.

2. Measure 10 mL of water in a graduated cylinder and pour it into a film canister. Wait until your group is called to the launch site.

3. Make your prediction about how high and far the canister will travel. Record it on your *Chemical Reactions* page.

EN 130

Project-Based Inquiry Science

◯ Get Going

Before groups have their turn at the launch site, have students record their predictions on their *Chemical Reactions* pages. Then guide groups in taking turns using the launch site. Two students in the groups should quickly place the antacid tablet in the canister, place the cap back on, and turn it upside down. Make sure that groups have designated a group member to measure the height the film canister travels. Watch to make sure that all students are making their measurements in the same way. They should measure from where the canister lands to the X marked on the floor. Remind students to record their data as they collect it.

When all groups have collected their data, have students calculate the average. If needed, remind students to add the data and divide by the number of values in the data set.

3.6 Investigate

4. When your group is called to the launch site, two of you should move quickly to the center of the site. One student will put the antacid in the film canister containing the water and move away. The other will quickly place the cap on the canister, turn it upside down, place it at the center of the "X" marked on the floor, and step back. A third group member will stand near the vertical scale and be ready to observe how high the canister flies.

5. When the canister lands, use the tape measure to measure the distance from the "X" to where the canister landed.

6. Record your data in the correct columns of the data table.

7. After your group has run all of your trials, calculate the average height your canister traveled by adding all the values for height and dividing the sum by 5, which is the number of trials. Repeat to calculate the average distance from the "X."

Chemical Reactions			3.6.1

Name: .... Date: ....

For Your Group:

= Your tablet size ($\frac{1}{4}$, $\frac{1}{2}$, $\frac{3}{4}$, or 1 tablet)

	Height	Distance	Your prediction:
Trial 1			
Trial 2			
Trial 3			
Trial 4			
Trial 5			

For your Class

Film Canister Launches (Average Data)

	$(\frac{1}{4}$ tablet)		$(\frac{1}{2}$ tablet)		$(\frac{3}{4}$ tablet)		(1 tablet)	
	Height	Distance	Height	Distance	Height	Distance	Height	Distance
Group 1								
Group 2								
Group 3								
Group 4								
Group 5								
Group 6								
Group 7								
Group 8								
Class average								

Stop and Think

1. What variables were changed, or manipulated, in this investigation? What variables were controlled?

2. As each group presents its data, what trends should you look for?

3. What indicator(s) of chemical energy did you observe in this investigation?

4. What factor that controls the amount of chemical energy did you investigate?

Stop and Think

10 min

Students discuss the investigation they completed.

◇ **Evaluate**

Have groups answer the *Stop and Think* questions. Students should recognize that the size of the antacid tablet is the manipulated variable and the distance the canister moves is the dependent variable. All other variables must be held constant. Students should relate the size of the antacid tablet to the distance and indicate if their predictions were correct.

Listen for the following as students discuss the answers with their groups:

1. Students should identify the manipulated variable as the size of tablet added to the canister. They should also know that the amount of water was held constant.

2. Students should realize that the expected trend is that the more tablet used, the greater the distance traveled.

3. Students should know that the indicator of chemical energy was the generation of a gas.

4. Students should state that the factor controlling amount of chemical energy is the mass of the tablet used.

NOTES

Communicate

Share Your Results

The entire class observed the film canisters as they were launched. Now each group will share its data, including the averages they calculated. Make a poster that contains your data table and the average of all your data. Also, prepare a graph of the class averages. On the *x*-axis, plot the portion of the tablet used (¼, ½, ¾, 1). On the *y*-axis, plot either the height or the distance. As each group presents, record their data in the bottom chart of your *Chemical Reactions* page. When all groups have presented, discuss the following questions:

- What trends do you see in the data?

- What factor(s) did you identify that affect how much chemical energy a reaction releases?

- Did the data support your predictions? Why or why not?

- What do you think would happen if you used the same amount of substance in each canister but made the type of substance the variable? For example, if you tested equal amounts of antacid and aspirin against each other, what do you think would happen?

- What other factor(s) do you think affect how much chemical energy is released by a chemical reaction?

> **Chemical Energy**
> Almost all matter has the potential to react and release chemical energy. Matter is made of atoms, such as carbon, hydrogen, and oxygen. One way that atoms are arranged is in molecules. One of the most familiar molecules is water. Two atoms of hydrogen and one atom of oxygen are bonded together to form one molecule of water.
>
> When the bonding between atoms or molecules changes in any way, a chemical reaction occurs. Bonds in the original substance or substances are broken, and the atoms form different combinations of atoms, with new bonds holding them together.

Communicate: Share Your Results

20 min

Students make posters to summarize their group results and the class results.

◯ Get Going

Have groups prepare posters that summarize the results of their investigation. Help students complete graphs representing the class averages. Allow each group to present their posters. Then discuss the bulleted questions in the student text with the class. Help students consider other factors that can be tested. Encourage students to share their ideas, even if they are unsure about the results.

Chemical Energy

20 min

Students read about the nature of chemical energy.

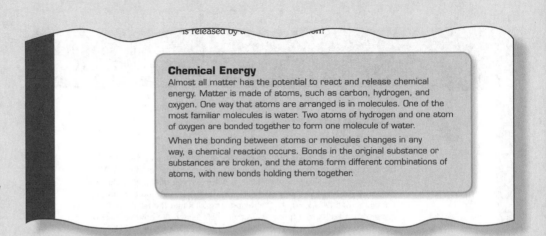

is released by

Chemical Energy

Almost all matter has the potential to react and release chemical energy. Matter is made of atoms, such as carbon, hydrogen, and oxygen. One way that atoms are arranged is in molecules. One of the most familiar molecules is water. Two atoms of hydrogen and one atom of oxygen are bonded together to form one molecule of water.

When the bonding between atoms or molecules changes in any way, a chemical reaction occurs. Bonds in the original substance or substances are broken, and the atoms form different combinations of atoms, with new bonds holding them together.

⃝ Engage

Distribute colored candies to groups of students. Challenge students to arrange the same number of each color candy in two different ways. For example, they might have:

Arrangement A:

2 blue candies + 1 red candy + 1 blue candy + 3 yellow candies

Arrangement B:

3 yellow candies + 1 red candy + 3 blue candies

When students are finished, explain that they have modeled a chemical reaction.

NOTES

....

....

....

....

....

....

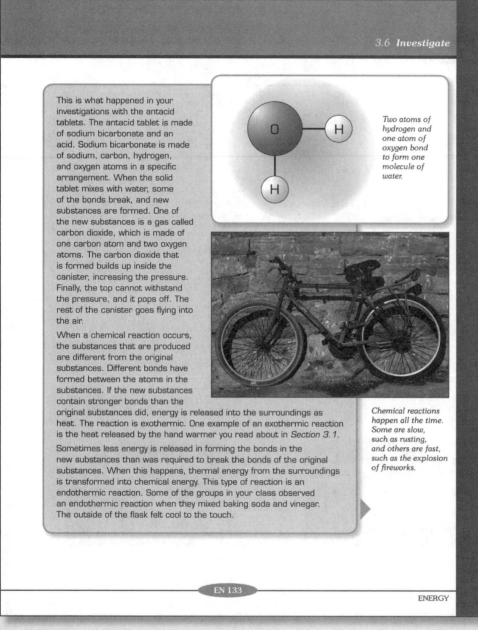

3.6 Investigate

This is what happened in your investigations with the antacid tablets. The antacid tablet is made of sodium bicarbonate and an acid. Sodium bicarbonate is made of sodium, carbon, hydrogen, and oxygen atoms in a specific arrangement. When the solid tablet mixes with water, some of the bonds break, and new substances are formed. One of the new substances is a gas called carbon dioxide, which is made of one carbon atom and two oxygen atoms. The carbon dioxide that is formed builds up inside the canister, increasing the pressure. Finally, the top cannot withstand the pressure, and it pops off. The rest of the canister goes flying into the air.

When a chemical reaction occurs, the substances that are produced are different from the original substances. Different bonds have formed between the atoms in the substances. If the new substances contain stronger bonds than the original substances did, energy is released into the surroundings as heat. The reaction is exothermic. One example of an exothermic reaction is the heat released by the hand warmer you read about in *Section 3.1*.

Sometimes less energy is released in forming the bonds in the new substances than was required to break the bonds of the original substances. When this happens, thermal energy from the surroundings is transformed into chemical energy. This type of reaction is an endothermic reaction. Some of the groups in your class observed an endothermic reaction when they mixed baking soda and vinegar. The outside of the flask felt cool to the touch.

Two atoms of hydrogen and one atom of oxygen bond to form one molecule of water.

Chemical reactions happen all the time. Some are slow, such as rusting, and others are fast, such as the explosion of fireworks.

△ Guide

As students begin to read, guide them to understand that during a chemical reaction, bonds between atoms are broken apart and the atoms are rearranged in different ways. The number and types of atoms do not change, but the arrangement does. Whenever atoms are rearranged, chemical energy is involved.

Review the explanation of the chemical reaction that took place in the film canister. Make sure students understand why they made the observations they did.

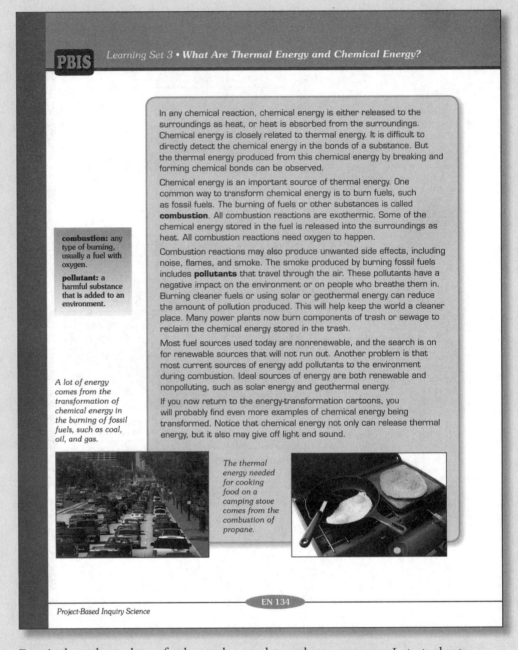

In any chemical reaction, chemical energy is either released to the surroundings as heat, or heat is absorbed from the surroundings. Chemical energy is closely related to thermal energy. It is difficult to directly detect the chemical energy in the bonds of a substance. But the thermal energy produced from this chemical energy by breaking and forming chemical bonds can be observed.

Chemical energy is an important source of thermal energy. One common way to transform chemical energy is to burn fuels, such as fossil fuels. The burning of fuels or other substances is called **combustion**. All combustion reactions are exothermic. Some of the chemical energy stored in the fuel is released into the surroundings as heat. All combustion reactions need oxygen to happen.

Combustion reactions may also produce unwanted side effects, including noise, flames, and smoke. The smoke produced by burning fossil fuels includes **pollutants** that travel through the air. These pollutants have a negative impact on the environment or on people who breathe them in. Burning cleaner fuels or using solar or geothermal energy can reduce the amount of pollution produced. This will help keep the world a cleaner place. Many power plants now burn components of trash or sewage to reclaim the chemical energy stored in the trash.

Most fuel sources used today are nonrenewable, and the search is on for renewable sources that will not run out. Another problem is that most current sources of energy add pollutants to the environment during combustion. Ideal sources of energy are both renewable and nonpolluting, such as solar energy and geothermal energy.

If you now return to the energy-transformation cartoons, you will probably find even more examples of chemical energy being transformed. Notice that chemical energy not only can release thermal energy, but it also may give off light and sound.

combustion: any type of burning, usually a fuel with oxygen.

pollutant: a harmful substance that is added to an environment.

A lot of energy comes from the transformation of chemical energy in the burning of fossil fuels, such as coal, oil, and gas.

The thermal energy needed for cooking food on a camping stove comes from the combustion of propane.

Remind students how fuels are burned to release energy. Let students know that a chemical reaction in which a fuel is burned in oxygen is called a combustion reaction. Ask students to name examples of combustion reactions, such as when a candle is burned, a firework explodes, or gasoline is burned in a car's engine.

Tell students that all combustion reactions are exothermic. Some energy is released as light or sound, but most of the energy is released as heat, or thermal energy. Have students think about what happens when a log is burned. It turns into a small pile of ashes.

Now tell students that the mass of the substances that go into a chemical reaction is not the same as the mass of the substances produced. The mass of a pile of ashes is clearly less than the mass of the original log. Ask students what might have happened to the missing mass. Explain that the mass is not really missing. When a log burns, it also produces substances in the form of gases. The gases escape into the air. Tell students that if you could measure the mass of the gases and the ashes, the total would be equal to the mass of the log.

Now that students know that gases are released during the process of combustion, explain that some of the gases are considered to be pollutants. Tell students that a pollutant is a substance that harms the environment or living things.

NOTES

....

....

....

....

....

....

....

....

....

....

3.6 Investigate

Reflect

10 min

Students answer questions to consider processes that involve chemical energy.

Reflect

1. What are some indicators that chemical energy is released as thermal energy by a chemical reaction?

2. What are some factors that determine how much chemical energy an object possesses? How could you find out if there are more?

3. What are some good reasons for burning coal? What are some reasons to avoid burning coal?

4. Is chemical energy kinetic energy or potential energy? What is your evidence?

5. Add chemical energy to your *Energy Types* page. Record indicators that chemical energy is being used and factors that affect the amount of energy.

Energy Types		
Name:		Date:
Type of energy	Indicators that this type is being transformed	Factors that affect the amount of energy

Update the Project Board

Record what you have learned about chemical energy in the *What are we learning?* column. For each item you list, add evidence for it to the *What is our evidence?* column. Add any new questions you have to the *What do we need to investigate?* column.

What's the Point?

Chemical energy is stored in chemical bonds between atoms in a substance. During chemical reactions, a transformation occurs between chemical energy and thermal energy. In an exothermic reaction, chemical energy is transformed into thermal energy and released to the surroundings. In an endothermic reaction, some of the thermal energy in the surroundings is transformed into chemical energy. Light and sound can also be released in chemical reactions. A combustion reaction is one example of an exothermic reaction. It occurs when a fuel is burned.

EN 135

ENERGY

☐ Assess

Use the following to assess students' understanding:

1. Students should remember that in some of the reactions, the flask grew hot or grew cold.

2. Students should understand that the amount of substance is a factor that determines how much chemical energy is available. They would have to experiment further to identify any other factors.

3. Students should respond that coal is a good source of thermal energy because it is plentiful and relatively inexpensive. They may know that the use of coal has its drawbacks because it is a large source of pollution.

4. Students should now understand that chemical energy is a form of potential energy because it is present, even when no reaction is happening. This is like a ball sitting atop a hill or a fully compressed spring.

5. Students should record that the factors that determine the amount of chemical energy are the amount (mass) of reactants and the nature of the chemical reaction itself. They should also record light, change in temperature, sound, formation of a gas, and formation of a solid precipitate as indicators of a chemical reaction.

△ Guide

Discuss the ideas students have developed from this section. Have students identify the evidence for each idea. Record this information along with any new questions to the *Project Board*.

Update the Project Board

5 min

Students add new ideas and questions to the Project Board.

NOTES

....

....

....

....

....

....

....

....

More to Learn: *Chemical Energy and You*

15 min

Students learn about chemical energy in living processes.

META NOTES

It is a common misconception that plants only carry out photosynthesis process and animals only carry out cell respiration processes. Guide students to understand that plants carry out both processes.

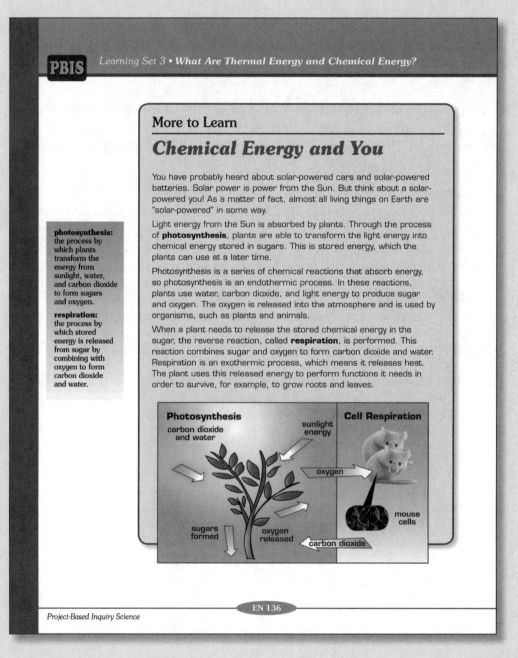

More to Learn

Chemical Energy and You

You have probably heard about solar-powered cars and solar-powered batteries. Solar power is power from the Sun. But think about a solar-powered you! As a matter of fact, almost all living things on Earth are "solar-powered" in some way.

Light energy from the Sun is absorbed by plants. Through the process of **photosynthesis**, plants are able to transform the light energy into chemical energy stored in sugars. This is stored energy, which the plants can use at a later time.

Photosynthesis is a series of chemical reactions that absorb energy, so photosynthesis is an endothermic process. In these reactions, plants use water, carbon dioxide, and light energy to produce sugar and oxygen. The oxygen is released into the atmosphere and is used by organisms, such as plants and animals.

When a plant needs to release the stored chemical energy in the sugar, the reverse reaction, called **respiration**, is performed. This reaction combines sugar and oxygen to form carbon dioxide and water. Respiration is an exothermic process, which means it releases heat. The plant uses this released energy to perform functions it needs in order to survive, for example, to grow roots and leaves.

photosynthesis: the process by which plants transform the energy from sunlight, water, and carbon dioxide to form sugars and oxygen.

respiration: the process by which stored energy is released from sugar by combining with oxygen to form carbon dioxide and water.

Photosynthesis
carbon dioxide and water
sunlight energy

Cell Respiration
oxygen
mouse cells
sugars formed
oxygen released
carbon dioxide

△ Guide

Review the terms *photosynthesis* and *cell respiration*. Use the diagram to show that they are opposite processes. The products of photosynthesis are used in cell respiration and the products of cell respiration are used in photosynthesis.

More to Learn

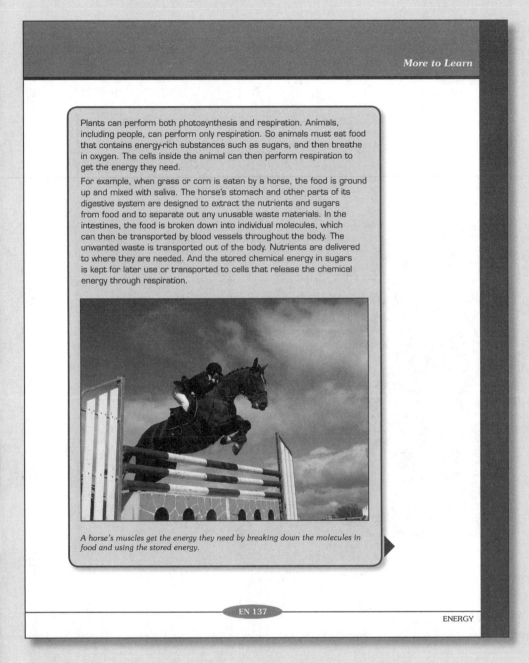

Plants can perform both photosynthesis and respiration. Animals, including people, can perform only respiration. So animals must eat food that contains energy-rich substances such as sugars, and then breathe in oxygen. The cells inside the animal can then perform respiration to get the energy they need.

For example, when grass or corn is eaten by a horse, the food is ground up and mixed with saliva. The horse's stomach and other parts of its digestive system are designed to extract the nutrients and sugars from food and to separate out any unusable waste materials. In the intestines, the food is broken down into individual molecules, which can then be transported by blood vessels throughout the body. The unwanted waste is transported out of the body. Nutrients are delivered to where they are needed. And the stored chemical energy in sugars is kept for later use or transported to cells that release the chemical energy through respiration.

A horse's muscles get the energy they need by breaking down the molecules in food and using the stored energy.

△ Guide

Help students recognize that cells in all living things need energy to carry out life functions. Plants change the energy of sunlight into chemical energy stored as food and in their structure. They use some of the energy and store the rest. Animals that eat plants then absorb the stored energy.

Every cell in your body is constantly using the chemical energy from sugars to carry out life processes, such as growing, dividing, or doing work. Take for example your muscle cells. Inside the muscle cells, the process of respiration releases thermal energy. The muscle cells are able to further transform some of this thermal energy into kinetic energy by shrinking or expanding. This is how you use muscles to push things, pull things, run, and jump, and for all the other movements you make.

The chemical energy that is stored in food can be measured in **Calories**. A Calorie is about 240 times as much energy as a joule. If you consume more Calories of food than your body needs, the excess energy is stored, often as fat. This is why you gain weight if you eat more food than you need. If you do not eat enough food to provide the energy your body needs, then your body uses some of its stored energy to perform life processes. In this case, you will lose weight.

Calorie: a unit of energy used to describe the amount of energy in food, also called a kilocalorie.

Climbing up a flight of stairs in your home uses only about one Calorie. Heavy exercise can use several hundreds of Calories an hour. Even when sleeping in your bed, your body uses about 60 Calories of energy per hour to perform necessary life processes.

Your body is really a living, breathing chemical factory. All of the functions your body carries out require the chemical energy stored in the food you eat. Your body contains stored chemical energy, the same way all living things, and the remains of living things, contain stored chemical energy. Part of what makes you alive is that your body can transform the chemical energy in food into thermal energy through respiration and then further transform that thermal energy to carry out various needs.

The muscles in people also need the stored energy in food.

META NOTES

The calorie (with a lowercase c) was an older unit used before joules. One calorie is 4.18 J. The Calorie used to measure energy in foods (with an uppercase C) is really a kilocalorie, or 1,000 calories. This means that one food Calorie equals 4180 J.

[Note: This does not match the SE text exactly, but this is correct. Please advise.]

○ Engage

Tell students that 1 lb of fat stores 3500 Calories. That means to burn 1 lb, a person needs to burn 3500 more Calories than the person eats. Use this example to help students understand that energy is stored in food and in fat. The body uses energy to carry out its functions and stored as excess energy.

Assessment Options

Targeted Concepts, Skills, and Nature of Science	How do I know if students got it?
Scientists often work together and then share their findings. Sharing findings makes new information available and helps scientists refine their ideas and build on others' ideas. When another person's or group's idea is used, credit needs to be given.	**ASK:** What did you learn from the investigations of the other groups? **LISTEN:** Students should describe information they gathered from listening to the results of other students.
During a chemical change, the original substances are changed into new substances with different properties.	**ASK:** How were the substances produced during the investigations different from the starting materials, antacid tablet and water? **LISTEN:** Students might describe that the solid and the liquid combine to form a gas, carbon dioxide.
Chemical energy is potential energy stored in the bonds that hold matter together.	**ASK:** What is required for bonds between atoms to be formed? **LISTEN:** Students should recognize that chemical energy is used in the formation of bonds.
Plants change the energy of sunlight into chemical energy during photosynthesis.	**ASK:** What energy transformation takes place during photosynthesis? **LISTEN:** Students should explain that light energy is changed to chemical energy stored in sugars, fats, and starch.
The cells of living things break down food during cell respiration to obtain energy.	**ASK:** During what process do living things break down food to release energy? **LISTEN:** Students should identify cell respiration as the process through which living things obtain energy.

Teacher Reflection Questions

- What difficulties did students have in completing the investigation? What could you do to help them get the proper results?

- What evidence do you have that students understood the concepts of combustion and pollutants?

- How did you manage the *More to Learn* segment on living things? What ideas do you have for next time?

NOTES

Back to the Big Challenge

Design a Rube Goldberg Machine to Turn Off a Light

◀ $1\frac{1}{2}$ *class periods*

A class period is considered to be one 40 to 50 minute class.

Overview

Students begin by returning to their energy-transformation cartoons to identify thermal energy and chemical energy. They work together to identify indicators of each type of energy as well as the effects of each type of energy. Students develop claims and explanations about thermal and chemical energy in terms of whether they represent kinetic or potential energy. Using their explanations, students go on to design steps for their own Rube Goldberg machines that use and produce thermal energy or chemical energy. Students share their ideas and interact to learn from each other's designs, and they relate what they learn to the *Big Challenge*.

Targeted Concepts, Skills, and Nature of Science	Performance Expectations
Scientists often work together and then share their findings. Sharing findings makes new information available and helps scientists refine their ideas and build on others' ideas. When another person's or group's idea is used, credit needs to be given.	Students share their ideas about thermal and chemical energy, and how they can be related to designing a Rube Goldberg machine.
Scientific knowledge is developed through observations, recording and analysis of data, and development of explanations based on evidence.	Students develop explanations about thermal and chemical energy.
Energy exists in different forms and can be changed from one form to another.	Students look for forms of energy that exist before and after a step in their energy-transformation cartoons.
Thermal energy is the energy of the particles of matter.	Students design a step for their Rube Goldberg machines that uses or produces thermal energy.

335

Targeted Concepts, Skills, and Nature of Science	Performance Expectations
Chemical energy is potential energy stored in the bonds that hold matter together.	Students design a step for their Rube Goldberg machines that uses or produces chemical energy.

Materials	
1 per student	*Energy-transformation Cartoon* page *Create Your Explanation* page *My Rube Goldberg Machine* page *Project Board* page
1 per class	Class *Project Board*

Homework Options

Reflection

- **Science Content:** What criteria do you use to decide if a form of energy is kinetic or potential? *(Students may describe deciding whether motion is involved, and how the energy can be used to cause something to change to determine the type of energy.)*

- **Science Process:** Why must you use evidence to develop an explanation? *(Students should explain that evidence includes data and observations used to support a claim. These are essential parts of a scientific explanation.)*

BACK TO THE BIG CHALLENGE IMPLEMENTATION

Learning Set 3

Back to the Big Challenge

Design a Rube Goldberg machine to turn off a light.

The *Big Challenge* you are working on in this Unit is *Design a Rube Goldberg machine to turn off a light*. You have ideas about the last step and about how to transfer energy to that last step. What about the other steps of your machine? You now know enough about thermal energy and chemical energy to imagine how they might help your Rube Goldberg machine turn off a light. Using what you now know, you will choose a way of transforming thermal energy or chemical energy to get a machine started, and you will design steps that will transform thermal energy or chemical energy into the energy your machine needs to turn off a light. But first you will think once more about whether thermal energy and chemical energy are kinetic energy or potential energy and how they can be transformed to do work. You will need to know these things to make your design successful.

Reflect

To help you think about thermal energy and chemical energy, you will examine the energy-transformation cartoons from the Unit *Introduction* again. Identify the steps that involve thermal energy and chemical energy in your group's cartoon. Record these on an *Energy-transformation Cartoon* page. Then for each of these steps, answer the following questions. Be prepared to share your answers with the class.

1. How do you know the step involves thermal energy or chemical energy? What are the indicators?

2. How does the step transform thermal energy or chemical energy?

EN 139

ENERGY

Learning Set 3

Back to the Big Challenge

5 min

Students revisit the goal of the Big Challenge *by summarizing what they have learned about energy.*

○ Engage

Ask students what they found interesting about thermal or chemical energy. Have them describe something they learned that they did not know before completing this section. Then challenge them to think about how they can use what they learned to design their Rube Goldberg machine.

*A class period is considered to be one 40 to 50 minute class.

Reflect

10 min

Students review the energy-transformation cartoons in terms of thermal and chemical energy.

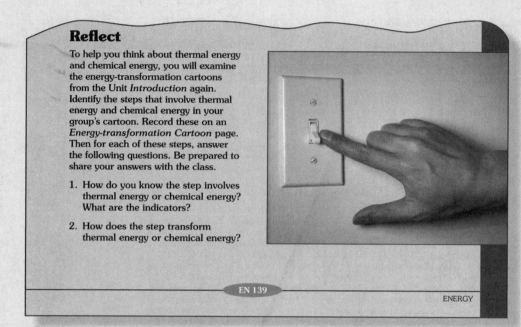

Reflect

To help you think about thermal energy and chemical energy, you will examine the energy-transformation cartoons from the Unit *Introduction* again. Identify the steps that involve thermal energy and chemical energy in your group's cartoon. Record these on an *Energy-transformation Cartoon* page. Then for each of these steps, answer the following questions. Be prepared to share your answers with the class.

1. How do you know the step involves thermal energy or chemical energy? What are the indicators?

2. How does the step transform thermal energy or chemical energy?

EN 139

ENERGY

LOOKING AHEAD

Students have looked at the energy-transformation cartoons already, and they will continue to look at them several more times throughout the Unit. To engage students, point out that they will be looking for something different each time.

△ Guide

Have students work in their groups to review their energy-transformation cartoons. Ask them to discuss answers to the questions listed. Tell students to narrow their search to either thermal energy or chemical energy. Encourage students to suggest their best possible answers based on what they know.

1. Students' answers will vary depending on the cartoon and the steps selected. In general, the indicator for thermal energy is heat, so the step might use a match, a fire, an explosion, the Sun, an oven or any other device that can generate heat. Students may have more difficulty identifying indicators of chemical energy, as it is a form of potential energy. The cartoon may show chemicals being mixed in beakers or something burning. Combustion is an indicator of chemical energy.

2. Students' answers will vary depending on the cartoon and the steps selected.

3. Students' answers will vary depending on the cartoon and the steps selected.

4. Students' answers will vary depending on the cartoon and the steps selected. In general, students can be expected to use one of the factors controlling that type of energy to either increase the energy or to decrease the energy.

3. What are the effects of each step, and what kind of energy is produced by each step?

4. How could you change the effects of each step?

5. Does thermal energy act more like kinetic energy or potential energy? Which answers to the other questions support your answer?

6. Does chemical energy act more like kinetic energy or potential energy? Which answers to the other questions support your answer?

Explain

Working with your group, develop two claims and explanations. One claim should answer the question, "Is thermal energy kinetic energy or potential energy, and how does it do work?" The other should answer the question, "Is chemical energy kinetic energy or potential energy, and how does it do work?" Use a different *Create Your Explanation* page for each of your claims.

After you have recorded your two claims, work with your group to develop explanations. Remember that an explanation has four parts: a claim, evidence, science knowledge, and an explanation. The evidence in each of your explanations will come from the data collected earlier in this *Learning Set* and your analysis of the cartoons. The science knowledge in each will come from what you have been reading. Each of your explanation statements should tie together your claim, evidence, and science knowledge. Your explanations should help somebody reading them to understand how you came up with them.

Plan Your Design

With your group, consider how you can involve thermal energy or chemical energy in your design of a machine to turn off a light. You can revisit the energy-transformation cartoons to get ideas.

5. Students should explain that thermal energy is more like kinetic energy because its effect can be seen as it is happening. Students' answers to Question 1 will support this answer.

6. Students should explain that chemical energy is more like potential energy because it cannot be seen. It is only known to be present when it is transformed into another kind of energy. The answer to Question 1 supports this answer.

Explain

10 min

Students work together to develop a claim and an explanation.

META NOTES

It will be challenging for students to work thermal energy and chemical energy into their designs. It may make it easier to remind them that they do not have to build their design, but it should be safe if someone does build it.

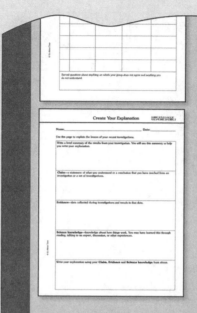

...or p... ...ergy? Which a... ...other questions support your answer?

Explain

Working with your group, develop two claims and explanations. One claim should answer the question, "Is thermal energy kinetic energy or potential energy, and how does it do work?" The other should answer the question, "Is chemical energy kinetic energy or potential energy, and how does it do work?" Use a different *Create Your Explanation* page for each of your claims.

After you have recorded your two claims, work with your group to develop explanations. Remember that an explanation has four parts: a claim, evidence, science knowledge, and an explanation. The evidence in each of your explanations will come from the data collected earlier in this *Learning Set* and your analysis of the cartoons. The science knowledge in each will come from what you have been reading. Each of your explanation statements should tie together your claim, evidence, and science knowledge. Your explanations should help somebody reading them to understand how you came up with them.

Plan Your Design

△ Guide and Assess

Keep students in their groups. Make sure each student has two *Create Your Explanation* pages each. Have students work together to develop the two claims described. Remind them to write one claim on each page.

Review the four parts of an explanation with students. Read through the paragraph together to make sure students know where to find the information they need to develop the explanations. Visit each group to evaluate their explanations and suggest areas for improvement.

Plan Your Design

20 min

Students incorporate steps using and producing thermal and chemical energy in their designs.

Plan Your Design

With your group, consider how you can involve thermal energy or chemical energy in your design of a machine to turn off a light. You can revisit the energy-transformation cartoons to get ideas.

△ Guide

Review with students what they need to do. Use the energy-transformation cartoons to help them think of ideas.

Make sure student understand that they are designing one step that *uses* one of these forms of energy and one step that *produces* one of these forms of energy. Encourage students to be creative, and tell them that they will have opportunities to revise their designs through the remainder of the *Learning Set*.

Design two sets of steps that involve thermal energy or chemical energy to turn off a light. One should begin with a step that transforms thermal energy or chemical energy into another form of energy. The other should begin with a step that transforms another form of energy into thermal or chemical energy. Both sets of steps should end with a step that turns off a light. You may use as few or as many steps in each of your designs as you want.

Sketch your steps on a *My Rube Goldberg Machine* page, and label your sketch to show what type of energy is transformed into what other type of energy in each step. If you borrowed any ideas from other groups, be sure to record which group you borrowed the ideas from. It is important to give credit for ideas you borrow from others.

You will need to think carefully through how the steps pass energy to each other. Each step has to be able to pass energy smoothly to the next step, and the separate pieces of your machine need to work together to complete the task.

Communicate

Plan Briefing

When it is time for you to present your designs to the class, show your sketches one at a time. For each, describe the steps, and tell the class how energy is transformed from one step to another step. Try to be brief. If you are unsure about how to describe some energy transformations in your steps, ask the class for help.

Observe everyone's designs carefully, and listen to their descriptions of how energy will be transferred from step to step. If you think a group has not described an energy transformation well, raise your hand and ask for more information or offer a more complete description. Remember to be courteous and respectful. If a group asks for advice, offer your ideas.

Notice all of the different ideas your classmates have about transforming energy and about involving thermal energy and chemical energy in their machines. You might want to borrow some of those ideas later. When you borrow ideas, you will need to remember which group you borrowed your ideas from and give them credit. Record ideas you might want to remember at the bottom of your *My Rube Goldberg Machine* page. Remember to record which group presented each idea.

Communicate: *Plan Briefing*

10 min

Students present their design sketches to the class.

As students critique one another's work, remind them that the goal of such comments is to help improve their designs rather than to criticize their work. Similarly, point out that students can use the ideas of others. This is different from stealing or copying ideas as long as credit is given appropriately. Relate this sharing of ideas to the process through which scientists build off one another's ideas.

△ Guide and Evaluate

Allow each group to present their sketches to the class. Have each student from the group explain part of his or her ideas and what science knowledge the design is based on. Invite students to comment on the sketches to point out any flaws in the design.

Reflect

10 min

Students work together to review the design ideas presented.

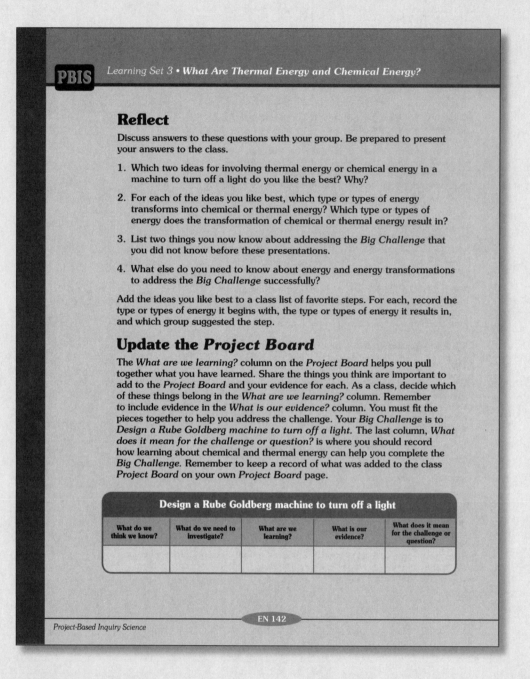

Reflect

Discuss answers to these questions with your group. Be prepared to present your answers to the class.

1. Which two ideas for involving thermal energy or chemical energy in a machine to turn off a light do you like the best? Why?

2. For each of the ideas you like best, which type or types of energy transforms into chemical or thermal energy? Which type or types of energy does the transformation of chemical or thermal energy result in?

3. List two things you now know about addressing the *Big Challenge* that you did not know before these presentations.

4. What else do you need to know about energy and energy transformations to address the *Big Challenge* successfully?

Add the ideas you like best to a class list of favorite steps. For each, record the type or types of energy it begins with, the type or types of energy it results in, and which group suggested the step.

Update the *Project Board*

The *What are we learning?* column on the *Project Board* helps you pull together what you have learned. Share the things you think are important to add to the *Project Board* and your evidence for each. As a class, decide which of these things belong in the *What are we learning?* column. Remember to include evidence in the *What is our evidence?* column. You must fit the pieces together to help you address the challenge. Your *Big Challenge* is to *Design a Rube Goldberg machine to turn off a light*. The last column, *What does it mean for the challenge or question?* is where you should record how learning about chemical and thermal energy can help you complete the *Big Challenge*. Remember to keep a record of what was added to the class *Project Board* on your own *Project Board* page.

Design a Rube Goldberg machine to turn off a light				
What do we think we know?	What do we need to investigate?	What are we learning?	What is our evidence?	What does it mean for the challenge or question?

△ Guide

Ask students to work in their groups to discuss the ideas presented. Have them discuss answers to the questions listed. As you walk around the room, find out if students correctly identify the types of energy discussed. Then lead a class discussion to list the best-designed steps.

△ Guide

Work as a class to summarize what students have learned about thermal and chemical energy, and the evidence they have to support their ideas. Add this information to the *Project Board*. Students also proposed steps they could use in their designs. Record how students used their ideas to relate to the *Big Challenge*.

Assessment Options

Targeted Concepts, Skills, and Nature of Science	How do I know if students got it?
Scientists often work together and then share their findings. Sharing findings makes new information available and helps scientists refine their ideas and build on others' ideas. When another person's or group's idea is used, credit needs to be given.	**ASK:** What ideas did you learn by listening to other groups? **LISTEN:** Students should describe any improvements or additions they made to their designs based on the presentations, and they should give credit to the proper students.
Scientific knowledge is developed through observations, recording and analysis of data, and development of explanations based on evidence.	**ASK:** How did your group come to agreement about your explanation? **LISTEN:** Students should describe the process through which they used to develop their explanation and the information that supported them.
Energy exists in different forms and can be changed from one form to another.	**ASK:** What types of energy were present before and after the steps you analyze in the energy-transformation cartoon? **LISTEN:** Students should describe the step they chose, and identify the energy before and after that step occurred.

Update the Project Board
10 min

Students add new information to the Project Board.

ENERGY

Targeted Concepts, Skills, and Nature of Science	How do I know if students got it?
Thermal energy is the energy of the particles of matter.	**ASK:** In what way can thermal energy be used in your Rube Goldberg design? **LISTEN:** Students should explain how they might use thermal energy in their design, such as increasing thermal energy so an object releases heat that can be used to perform some task.
Chemical energy is potential energy stored in the bonds that hold matter together.	**ASK:** In what ways can you release chemical energy in your design? **LISTEN:** Students may recognize that substances need to change into other substances to release chemical energy.

Teacher Reflection Questions

- What difficulties did students have in designing steps for their Rube Goldberg machines? How were you able to help students to learn from each other's ideas?

- What evidence do you have that students have begun to connect thermal and chemical energy to other concepts they need to accomplish the *Big Challenge?*

- How did you get students to contribute to the discussion of what to put on the *Project Board?* What other ideas do you have?

LEARNING SET 4 INTRODUCTION

Learning Set 4

How Can Sound and Light Be Forms of Energy?

◀ **13 class periods**

A class period is considered to be one 40 to 50 minute class.

Students investigate the characteristics of sound and light as energy.

Overview

Students begin thinking of light and sound as energy by looking for uses of sound and light in everyday objects. They use their observations to formulate an initial description of sound energy and light energy. Students go on to investigate factors that affect sound energy and identify indicators of changes produced by sound energy. To understand how sound energy travels, students work with a coiled spring to model a longitudinal wave. They investigate properties of waves and factors that affect wave speed. After their introduction to sound, students move on to observe a demonstration involving light. They compare factors that affect properties of sound and make claims to summarize their conclusions.

Targeted Concepts, Skills, and Nature of Science	Section
Scientists often work together and then share their findings. Sharing findings makes new information available and helps scientists refine their ideas and build on others' ideas. When another person's or group's idea is used, credit needs to be given.	4.1, 4.2, 4.3, 4.4, 4.5
Studying the work of different scientists provides understanding of scientific inquiry and reminds students that science is a human endeavor.	4.5
Scientists must keep accurate and descriptive records of what they do so they can share their work with others and consider what they did, why they did it, and what they want to do next.	4.2
Energy is the ability to cause change or do work.	4.1, 4.2
Sound is the transfer of energy as longitudinal waves that cannot travel through a vacuum.	4.1, 4.2, 4.3

Targeted Concepts, Skills, and Nature of Science	Section
Visible light is a small band within the electromagnetic spectrum, which is energy that travels in the form of waves.	4.1, 4.5
The ear is the human organ that detects sound.	4.2
Mechanical waves can be described as longitudinal waves or transverse waves.	4.3
The speed of sound depends on the medium through which it travels.	4.3
Waves involve a transfer of energy from one place to another.	4.3
Light can be described by a particle nature.	4.4
Light can be described by its intensity.	4.4
Light can be described by a wave nature.	4.5
White light is made up of different colors of light.	4.5
The electromagnetic spectrum arranges radiation in terms of frequency and wavelength.	4.5
Light travels at different speeds in different materials.	4.5
The eye is the human organ that detects light.	4.5
Light interacts with surfaces through reflection and refraction.	4.5

Students' Initial Conceptions and Capabilities	• Students usually believe that energy can be destroyed or created because they think that energy is something that makes things happen and is expended in processes (Watts, 1983a).

NOTES

....

....

Understanding for Teachers

In this *Learning Set,* students will be observing examples of sound and light. They will need to consider how sound and light carry energy, what factors affect the amount of energy, and what indicators they can use to identify the energy.

Sound and Light Waves

Sound travels as a longitudinal wave. All sounds are caused by vibrations. A sound wave travels away from the source of the vibration in all directions, disturbing particles of matter. As the particles are disturbed, they vibrate from rest. This creates compressions where particles are squeezed together and rarefactions where particles are pulled apart. In this type of wave, the energy moves parallel to the direction of vibration. Because sound waves travel by disturbing matter, sound waves cannot travel through a vacuum.

Light travels as a transverse wave. A light wave is produced by the vibration of an electric charge. It creates a vibrating electric field and a vibrating magnetic field. The vibrating fields can travel through a vacuum or they can travel through matter. The high points of a transverse wave are called crests and the low points are called troughs.

All waves can be described by basic characteristics of wavelength, frequency, and amplitude. One wavelength is the distance from one point on a wave to an identical point on the next wave. For example, the distance between two compressions of a sound wave or two crests of a light wave is one wavelength. Frequency describes the number of waves passing a point in a given amount of time. Amplitude describes how far the wave vibrates from a resting position.

Wave Types

Students are introduced to light waves in this section. However, they discover that light waves are just one type of electromagnetic waves. Other types of electromagnetic waves include radio waves, microwaves, X-rays, ultraviolet light, and gamma rays. These waves are organized in a spectrum in order of wavelength and frequency. Visible light makes up only a small portion of the spectrum and visible light can be further divided into different colors of light.

Characteristics of Light Energy

In addition to its wave nature, light can be described by a particle nature as photons of energy. Some characteristics of light can be explained by one model or the other. Neither model can explain all of the characteristics of light by itself. As a result, light is said to have a wave-particle duality.

For many purposes, light can be described as a ray traveling between two points. When light strikes a surface, it can be transmitted through the surface, it can be reflected from the surface, or it can be absorbed. If the light is transmitted, the light may be refracted as it changes speed from one medium to another.

The Speed of Light and the Speed of Sound

Sound and light can both be described by their speed. Light travels at 3×10^8 m/s in a vacuum. Its speed is slower in all other media, and the difference depends on the properties of the medium. Sound travels much more slowly than light. It can travel through most types of matter, but it travels fastest through solids and slowest through gases. The speed of sound depends on the elasticity and temperature of the medium.

Sound is detected by the human ear and light is detected by the human eye. Both organs gather energy and transform this energy into a signal that can be interpreted by the brain.

NOTES

....

....

....

....

....

....

....

....

....

....

....

4.0

Learning Set 4

How Can Sound and Light Be Forms of Energy?

Sound and light energy are a big part of daily life for many living organisms. Sound energy makes it possible for many animals to communicate and to react to situations around them. Light energy brightens the day and illuminates the night. Light also provides the energy on which almost all life on Earth depends. In this *Learning Set,* you will find out what sound and light energy are and how they may be applied to the challenge for this Unit.

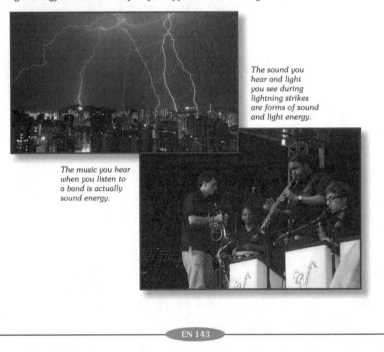

The sound you hear and light you see during lightning strikes are forms of sound and light energy.

The music you hear when you listen to a band is actually sound energy.

EN 143

ENERGY

Learning Set 4

How Can Sound and Light Be Forms of Energy?

5 min

Students begin to consider light energy and sound energy in their everyday lives.

○ Engage

Use the photographs in the student text to begin a discussion of the role sound and light plays in students' lives. Discuss ways that sound and light protect them, such as sirens and lights on a rescue vehicle, or traffic lights and signs. Lead into a discussion about relaxing sights and sounds, such as the sound and sight of ocean waves along a shore. Allow students to take the discussion in different directions as long as they mention examples of

*A class period is considered to be one 40 to 50 minute class.

sound and lights. Then focus them back on the idea that sound and light are forms of energy that are useful in everyday life and can also be useful for accomplishing the *Big Challenge*.

NOTES

....

....

....

....

....

....

....

....

....

....

....

....

....

....

....

....

SECTION 4.1 INTRODUCTION

4.1 Understand the Question

Think About Sound Energy and Light Energy

◀ *1 class period*
A class period is considered to be one 40 to 50 minute class.

Overview

Students are introduced to the concept of light and sound as energy. They examine examples that involve sound and light to look for indicators of change. Together, they complete a chart of examples and indicators. In their groups, students investigate sound or light using common objects. They share their ideas to try to define sound energy and light energy, and identify the factors that determine the amount of each. Using what they have discovered, students analyze the energy-transformation cartoons again to look for examples of light and sound energy. They consider additional examples and start thinking about comparing different amounts of energy. Any questions or new data is added to the *Project Board* at the end of this section.

Targeted Concepts, Skills, and Nature of Science	Performance Expectations
Scientists often work together and then share their findings. Sharing findings makes new information available and helps scientists refine their ideas and build on others' ideas. When another person's or group's idea is used, credit needs to be given.	Students work together to examine objects that involve either sound or light energy.
Energy is the ability to cause change or do work.	Students look for evidence of change as indicators of sound or light energy.
Sound is the transfer of energy as longitudinal waves that cannot travel through a vacuum.	Students consider how sound energy causes change.
Visible light is a small band within the electromagnetic spectrum, which is energy that travels in the form of waves.	Students consider how light energy causes change.

351

Materials	
1 per *sound* group	Small mallet Bowl of water Set of wind chimes with hollow tubes
2 per *sound* group	Tuning forks of different pitches Inflated balloons, two sizes
1 per *light* group	Table lamp with 25-W bulb Table lamp with 60-W bulb Photovoltaic-powered device Magnifying lens
2 or 3 per *light* group	Colored filters (red, green, or blue)
1 per student	*Sound Energy and Light Energy Explorations* page *Energy-Transformations Cartoon* page *Project Board* page
1 per class	Class *Project Board*

Homework Options

Reflection

- **Science Content:** How do you know that light energy is involved in an action? *(Students should indicate that light can be seen, so the presence or absence of light indicates a change in light energy.)*

Preparation for 4.2

- **Science Process:** What is one way to recognize that a sound transfers energy? *(Students might suggest that a sound can cause matter to vibrate.)*

SECTION 4.1 IMPLEMENTATION

◀ *1 class period**

4.1 Understand the Question

Think About Sound Energy and Light Energy

It may seem strange to think about sound or light as energy. For this reason, you will begin your exploration of sound and light by thinking about your experiences with them. This will help you identify what you already know and help you feel more comfortable thinking about them as types of energy.

Sound and light energy improve the quality of your life in many ways.

EN 144

Project-Based Inquiry Science

4.1 Understand the Question

Think About Sound Energy and Light Energy

10 min

Students begin to think of light and sound as energy by considering familiar examples.

○ Engage

Use the photographs to begin a discussion about examples of sound and light. Discuss common uses and ask students to describe characteristics of sound and light from experience. Let them know that in this section, students will learn about these examples in terms of energy.

---

*A class period is considered to be one 40 to 50 minute class.

Get Started

5 min

Students think of examples of light and sound as energy and complete a chart describing the indicators and effects. They start to ask questions which will prepare them for further investigation.

Get Started

One way to think about sound and light as energy is to think about ways sound and light change things. For example, earlier in this Unit you observed that light from a flashlight made the flags of a radiometer move. This is an example of light energy providing energy to move something.

> **vibrate:** to move back and forth.

To begin to understand sound as energy, you might think about a time when you were very close to very loud music, perhaps at a concert, in a car, or at home. When the music is loud, you can feel the bass notes thump in your chest or stomach. The energy in the sound makes your eardrums and the things around you **vibrate**.

Where else have you seen light used to provide energy? What are other ways sound provides energy? With your group, list examples of light energy and sound energy in the first row of a *Sound Energy and Light Energy Explorations* page.

Then, using your examples, work with your group to fill in the rest of the chart. List indicators that can tell you whether light energy or sound energy is present. List anything you know about factors that affect how much light or sound is present. For example, you know you can flip a switch to make lights go on, and you can turn a dial to raise the sound level of a TV or radio. Also, record any questions that come up and any ideas you are not sure about.

Communicate

Share Your Ideas

Briefly share your ideas with your class. Notice what your class agrees about and any disagreements. By the end of this *Learning Set,* you will know much more about both sound energy and light energy.

⬡ Get Going

Have students meet with their groups to think of examples where light and sound provide energy. Once they have their ideas, tell them to identify the indicators. If needed, give students an example to think about, such as opera singers that can shatter glass using the sounds of their voices. The indicators would be the sound itself and then the glass vibrating until it broke into pieces. For every idea that the groups come up with, they should record its indicator on their *Sound Energy and Light Energy Explorations* pages. Also make sure that groups are recording any questions or ideas they are not sure about.

⬡ Get Going

Ask a representative from each group to go over the list from their *Sound Energy and Light Energy Explorations* page. Encourage groups to add ideas to their lists as they listen and to note any ideas with which they disagree.

Communicate: Share Your Ideas

10 min

Students share their lists with the class.

NOTES

Mess About

15 min

Students explore a set of either sound sources or light sources to look for indicators of energy.

Mess About

In this activity, you will *mess about* to find out more about sound energy or light energy. You are going to explore either a set of sound sources or a set of light sources. After you have spent some time exploring your assigned items, you will share with the class what you observed.

Explore the items you have been given, and try doing different things with them. Explore how each item can be used to make something change. Look for indicators that energy is present. Imagine how each item might be causing changes. See if you can figure out how to increase or decrease the amount of sound energy or light energy. Be creative. Keep in mind the question for this *Learning Set: How can sound and light be forms of energy?*

Materials

Sound Groups:
- 2 tuning forks of different pitches
- small mallet
- bowl of water
- 1 set of wind chimes with hollow tubes
- 2 inflated balloons, two sizes

Light Groups:
- table lamp with 25-W bulb
- table lamp with 60-W bulb
- photovoltaic-powered device
- magnifying lens
- 2 or 3 colored filters (red, green, or blue)

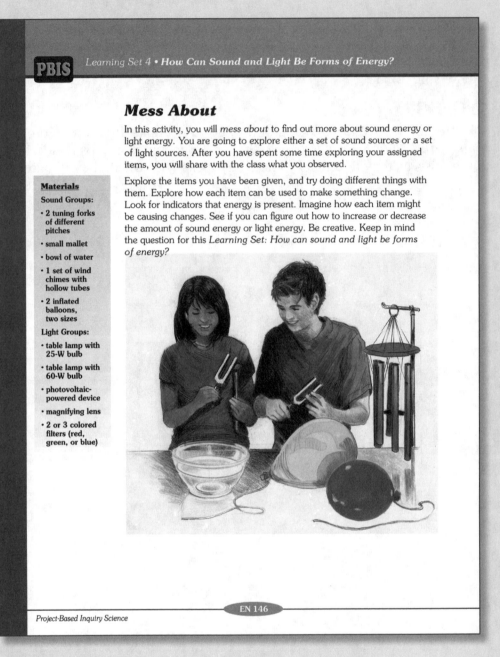

◯ Get Going

Distribute a set of materials to each group. If possible, have even numbers of groups investigate the same materials. Review basic safety procedures, such as not looking directly into a light source and not touching a hot light bulb. Then let students mess about. Encourage them to think creatively about ways to use the objects to cause changes.

As you explore, work together to answer the following questions. Record your answers, and be prepared to share your answers with the class.

1. What do you think sound (or light) energy is? What are the indicators that sound (or light) energy is present?

2. How can you determine how much sound (or light) energy an object possesses?

3. If you can, sort the objects in order of increasing sound (or light) energy. What makes that easy or difficult?

4. How does your distance from the source of sound (or light) energy make it easier or harder to determine how much energy is present?

5. What do you think might be factors that determine how much sound or light energy is emitted by an object? How can you find out?

Communicate

Share Your Ideas

Since none of the groups explored both types of energy, you will need to share what you observed with the rest of the class. One of the *sound* groups will present to the class what they observed about sound energy. The other *sound* groups will add more detail as needed. Then one of the *light* groups will present to the class, and other *light* groups will add to their presentation.

When it is your group's turn to present, tell the class how you explored your objects, and share your answers to the questions. If your group is presenting, begin by presenting the objects you explored. Show how they operate and the changes they cause. Then, present what you did to change the energy of the object. Finally, share what you think the indicators are for your type of energy and the factors that affect how much energy is present.

If you are one of the groups adding to the presentation, tell the class which explorations you did that were the same as those already presented. Then present in detail other ways you explored your objects. Include the indicators and factors you identified and any disagreements you have with other groups.

As students discover ways to use the energy for their objects, have them use the questions in the student text to guide them. Tell each group to record their answers to the questions.

1. Students' answers will vary. Some students may have a good understanding of what sound is, but fewer will have an in-depth understanding of light. They should know that the primary indicator for sound energy is hearing a sound. Similarly, the best indicator of

light energy is seeing light. Sound energy can also be seen as ripples on a bowl of water using a tuning fork.

2. Students should explain that the amount of sound can be heard with the ears and can be loud, soft, or just average in intensity. Light may be described as very faint or very bright.

3. Students may find it difficult to place the various examples of sound (or light) in order of increasing energy. One reason for the difficulty is that sound comes in various tones and pitches. Similarly, light comes in various colors.

4. Students should know that sound (or light) decreases in intensity with increasing distance.

5. Students' answers will vary, but most will not have a good idea of what the factors controlling the amount of sound or light are. Students may have some good ideas about how to find out what the factors are.

Communicate: Share Your Ideas

10 min

Students share their observations about sound and light energy.

---

light energy is emitted by an object? How can you find out?

Communicate

Share Your Ideas

Since none of the groups explored both types of energy, you will need to share what you observed with the rest of the class. One of the *sound* groups will present to the class what they observed about sound energy. The other *sound* groups will add more detail as needed. Then one of the *light* groups will present to the class, and other *light* groups will add to their presentation.

When it is your group's turn to present, tell the class how you explored your objects, and share your answers to the questions. If your group is presenting, begin by presenting the objects you explored. Show how they operate and the changes they cause. Then, present what you did to change the energy of the object. Finally, share what you think the indicators are for your type of energy and the factors that affect how much energy is present.

If you are one of the groups adding to the presentation, tell the class which explorations you did that were the same as those already presented. Then present in detail other ways you explored your objects. Include the indicators and factors you identified and any disagreements you have with other groups.

△ Guide

Choose a *sound* group to start the class discussion. Have them describe what they did and share their answers to the questions. Let the other *sound* groups share their observations. Invite other groups who investigated sound to add to the presentations. Encourage *light* groups to ask questions so they understand what was done. Tell students in the *light* groups that they should be taking notes on their *Sound Energy and Light Energy Exploration* pages during presentations.

As you listen, take notes on your *Sound Energy and Light Energy Explorations* page. Make sure you understand what other groups did to explore their type of energy. Listen, too, for anything that sound energy and light energy have in common. If you do not understand what a group did, or if you do not agree with their indicators or factors, ask a question. Remember to be respectful, even if you disagree.

When the presentations are done, discuss what light energy and sound energy might have in common. Then, identify questions you still have about sound and light energy and any suggestions you have about further investigations.

Reflect

Return to the energy-transformation cartoon your group analyzed previously in the Unit *Introduction*. Look at it again, and find energy transformations you think are caused by sound energy and light energy. On an *Energy-transformation Cartoon* page, record the steps that use sound energy and light energy, and fill in the boxes in the row beside each step. Then answer the questions on the next page. Be prepared to share your answers with the class.

Then choose a *light* group to share their observations. Ask them to describe what they did and share their answers to the questions. Then have the other *light* groups present their observations. Encourage students who studied sound to ask questions so they understand what was done. They should record their notes from these presentations on their *Sound Energy and Light Energy Explorations* pages.

Lead students in a discussion about the similarities between the investigations. Make sure that students identify indicators of each type of energy by some type of change they observed.

Reflect

10 min

Students reexamine the energy-transformation cartoons in terms of sound and light energy.

△ Guide

Let students examine the energy-transformation cartoons they considered earlier. Review some of the things they look for each time, such as examples of kinetic and potential energy or thermal and chemical energy. Now, let students know they should look for indicators of sound and light energy.

Ask students to answer the questions, which extend the concepts to additional examples and focus their attention on measuring energy.

1. Students' answers will vary depending on the cartoon being examined. Amplified sound is used to physically move marbles in one cartoon. The Sun's rays are focused with a magnifying glass to start a fire in another instance. Students might also suggest that light is used by the running dog seeing a hot dog that is just out of reach.

2. Students should state that the indicator of sound energy is the sound itself, or stimulation of the eardrum. They should also realize that the indicator for light is the stimulation of the retina of the eye.

3. Students should identify that indicators of sound energy in a muted television program would be the sight of people's mouths moving, or cars, trucks, and trains moving.

4. Students might suggest that reflections off the wall would indicate that light was being emitted by a television in the next room.

5. Students might suggest that electrical factors, such as a volume control, are one way to control sound and light energy. A three-way light can be controlled by the position of a switch.

6. Students' answers will vary, but their suggestions should take into account the different pitches of sound and the different colors of light.

1. In the cartoon, how do sound energy and light energy make things happen?

2. What are the indicators that sound energy is present? What are the indicators that light energy is present?

3. Suppose you were watching a television program with the mute button on. What indicators would tell you that sound energy was emitted in the action occurring in the program?

4. Suppose you were in another room, listening to a television program, but you could not see the screen. What indicators would tell you that light energy was emitted in the action occurring in the program?

5. What might be factors that determine how much sound energy or light energy is emitted by an object?

6. How do you think you can investigate an object to determine how much sound energy or light energy it emits?

Energy-transformation Cartoon				
Name:			Date:	

Fill in the letter of the step you are analyzing. Then fill in other information about that step.

Name of your machine:			Purpose of your machine:	
Step	Changes/Work done	Energy type in	Energy types out	Indicators of energy transformations

Record questions about anything on which your group does not agree and anything you do not understand.

Update the *Project Board*

In the *What do we think we know?* column, record the indicators you have identified for sound energy and light energy and the factors you think affect how much sound or light energy an object possesses. In the *What do we need to investigate?* column, record questions about issues your class still disagrees about or that you are unsure about. Also, record any ideas you have about investigations that will help you better understand sound and light energy.

What's the Point?

Sound is an indicator for sound energy. Light is an indicator for light energy. However simple this may seem, it is also the case that both sound energy and light energy are complex.

Update the Project Board

10 min

Students add ideas and questions to the Project Board.

Update the *Project Board*

In the *What do we think we know?* column, record the indicators you have identified for sound energy and light energy and the factors you think affect how much sound or light energy an object possesses. In the *What do we need to investigate?* column, record questions about issues your class still disagrees about or that you are unsure about. Also, record any ideas you have about investigations that will help you better understand sound and light energy.

△ Guide

Students have been introduced to the concepts of sound and light energy. As a class, summarize what they have discovered. Record the ideas in the *What do we think we know?* column of the *Project Board*. Then invite students to describe any questions they have about sound and light. Remind students of the questions they recorded on their *Sound Energy and Light Energy Explorations* pages at the beginning of this section. If they have not already answered these, they may add these to the *What do we need to investigate?* column.

NOTES

Assessment Options

Targeted Concepts, Skills, and Nature of Science	How do I know if students got it?
Scientists often work together and then share their findings. Sharing findings makes new information available and helps scientists refine their ideas and build on others' ideas. When another person's or group's idea is used, credit needs to be given.	**ASK:** How did discussing indicators of sound and light energy give you new ideas? **LISTEN:** Students should describe how they shared their ideas and developed a more complete list than they had alone. Depending on if they were in a *light* group or a *sound* group, they should mention how they learned of the other type of energy. They learn from each other as the investigated one type, shared their observations of it, and heard observations of the other type.
Energy is the ability to cause change or do work.	**ASK:** What do all indicators of energy have in common? **LISTEN:** Students should explain that they identify some type of change.
Sound is the transfer of energy as longitudinal waves that cannot travel through a vacuum.	**ASK:** What senses did you use to observe indicators of sound energy? **LISTEN:** Students may list hearing, touch, and sight as senses used to identify indicators of sound energy.
Visible light is a small band within the electromagnetic spectrum, which is energy that travels in the form of waves.	**ASK:** What were the differences you observed among the objects that used light energy? **LISTEN:** Students may describe specific characteristics, such as how some sources of light energy were brighter than others.

Teacher Reflection Questions

- How did you guide students to think of ideas about examples of sound and light energy? What could you do to help them identify the indicators of each?

- How were you able to help students stay focused as they examined the energy-transformation diagrams again? What might you try next time?

- What evidence do you have that students understand that sound and light carry energy?

NOTES

4.2 Explore

What Factors Affect Sound Energy?

◀ *2 class periods*

A class period is considered to be one 40 to 50 minute class.

Overview

Students conduct one of four investigations to explore factors that affect sound energy. In one investigation, students use the sound of their voices to cause grains of rice on a piece of taut plastic cling wrap to vibrate. In another investigation, students compare the thickness and tension of rubber bands to the sounds they make when plucked. In a third investigation, students vibrate a ruler in different ways to compare the resulting sounds. In the fourth investigation, students use a tuning fork to cause a cork suspended on a string to vibrate. The class compiles a table summarizing the investigations by relating factors to the effects they have on sound energy. Groups reflect on the observation of other groups and come up with explanations for these changes. They share their explanation and the class develops an explanation they agree on. They update the *Project Board* and then learn how to measure sound using decibels. The section concludes with a *More to Learn* where students read how sounds are heard by the eardrum.

Targeted Concepts, Skills, and Nature of Science	Performance Expectations
Scientists often work together and then share their findings. Sharing findings makes new information available and helps scientists refine their ideas and build on others' ideas. When another person's or group's idea is used, credit needs to be given.	Students work together to conduct investigations involving sound energy in different situations. They share their observations, informing the rest of the class about more factors that affect sound energy.
Scientists must keep accurate and descriptive records of what they do so they can share their work with others and consider what they did, why they did it, and what they want to do next.	Students describe their observations using a combination of senses.

Targeted Concepts, Skills, and Nature of Science	Performance Expectations
Energy is the ability to cause change or do work.	Students recognize that some change is produced by sound energy.
Sound is the transfer of energy as longitudinal waves that cannot travel through a vacuum.	Students discover that sound can transfer energy to other objects, such as from a voice to rice on plastic cling wrap.
The ear is the human organ that detects sound.	Students learn about the parts of the ear and how they work together to detect sound.

Materials

Investigation 1 **1 per group**	Jar covered with taut plastic cling wrap $8\frac{1}{2}$ in. x 11 in. paper, curled into a funnel shape Rubber band
1 per group	Grains of raw rice
Investigation 2 **2 per group**	Matching thick rubber bands Matching thin rubber bands
4 per group	Cans of different heights, open at one end
Investigation 3 **1 per group**	Ruler Desk
Exploration 4 **1 per group**	Tuning fork Small mallet (to strike tuning fork) Cork on a string
1 per student	*Create Your Explanation* page *Project Board* page
1 per class	Class *Project Board*

Homework Options

Reflection

- **Science Content:** What evidence suggests that sound energy is passing through a material? *(Students might suggest that the material vibrates as sound passes through it.)*

- **Science Content:** How do scientists compare sounds in terms of the energy passing through a given area in a given time? *(Students should describe the decibel scale that describes sounds in order of intensity.)*

Preparation for 4.3

- **Science Content:** How does sound travel from its source to your ear? *(This question is intended to have students consider the way in which sounds travel through matter.)*

NOTES

....

....

....

....

....

....

....

....

....

....

ENERGY

NOTES

SECTION 4.2 IMPLEMENTATION

4.2 Explore

What Factors Affect Sound Energy?

Lullabies and soothing sounds from nature can calm babies and help them go to sleep.

There are some sounds that are so soothing they can put you to sleep. Other sounds can actually be painful to your ears. Some sounds can make your whole body feel like it is vibrating. Although it may seem strange to think about sound having energy, it is the energy in sound that can make your ears hurt. When you observed a tuning fork striking the side of a bowl of water earlier in this *Learning Set,* you could clearly see that sound is associated with vibrations. In this section, you will explore the factors that influence the amount of energy in sounds, how sound energy is transformed from other types of energy, and how sound energy can do work.

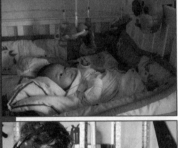

The most obvious indicator for sound energy appears simple. If you hear a sound, sound energy is present. However, the human hearing range is narrower than that of many other animals. Also, people tend to lose part of their hearing as they grow older, and some people are hard of hearing. This suggests that sometimes when sound energy is present, you cannot detect it with your ears.

Some sounds are so loud they can harm the human ear if proper protection is not worn.

You will begin with an exploration. Each group will carry out one of the following four explorations and then report to the class. Some groups will explore how different sounds have different effects. Some groups will explore what affects the loudness of sounds. Some will explore what affects the *pitch* of a sound—how high or low it is. Afterward, you will report to one another. As a class, you will be able to identify factors that affect how sound is produced and how sound travels. You will also identify factors that affect how much sound energy reaches your ears.

Project-Based Inquiry Science

4.2 Explore

What Factors Affect Sound Energy?

5 min

Students prepare to explore factors that affect sound.

○ Engage

Ask students to describe different types of sounds—pleasant sounds, scary sounds, violent sounds, and so on. Lead them to recognize that there are many different types of sounds. Elicit adjectives that describe the various sounds so students begin thinking about the different properties of sounds.

△ Guide

Assign an *Exploration* to each group. Review what each group will be doing, and then distribute the materials.

*A class period is considered to be one 40 to 50 minute class.

Exploration 1: Talking to Rice

15 min

Students simulate a small drum head using plastic cling wrap.

Exploration 1: Talking to Rice

Take a few pieces of rice and place them on the plastic cling wrap covering the top of the jar. Start by talking quietly near the jar. Be careful not to blow your breath on the rice. You might read this paragraph aloud if you cannot think of anything to say. Observe the rice as you are talking. Begin to talk more loudly, and then even more loudly, and continue observing the rice.

How does the movement of the rice change as the loudness of your voice changes? Each group member should have a chance to talk to the rice.

Repeat the procedure, this time talking to the rice through the funnel. On a piece of paper, record your observations of how each change you make affects the rice.

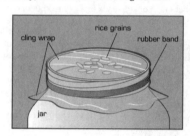
cling wrap · rice grains · rubber band · jar

Materials
- jar covered with taut plastic cling wrap
- 5 grains of rice, raw
- 8 x 11 paper curled into a funnel shape
- rubber band

Exploration 2: Music from Rubber Band Cans

Each member of your group should take a rubber band. Pluck the rubber band, and listen carefully to the sound it makes. Explore what happens to the sound of each rubber band as you change its tension from loose to tightly stretched. Record your observations. Then stretch each rubber band over the open end of a can and pluck it. Change the tension in the rubber band and pluck it again. Record observations on a piece of paper of all the ways you pluck the rubber band and the different sounds you hear.

Materials
- 2 matching rubber bands, thick
- 2 matching rubber bands, thin
- 4 cans of different heights, open at one end

EN 151

ENERGY

⬡ Get Going

Tell students to assemble the materials as described. Use the diagram to guide any students having difficulty. Remind students to be careful of their breath when speaking next to the jar. Point out that they are testing the sound waves from their voice, and that they do not want to disrupt the experiment with their breath. Make sure students observe the movement of the rice and record their observations as they make them.

4.2

⬡ Get Going

Tell students to assemble the materials as described. Remind them to use the diagram in the student text to guide their assembly if they are having difficulty. Guide students to change one factor at a time to listen for its effects. For example, they might listen to the thin rubber band and then the thick rubber band on the same can. Then they might do the same for the other cans.

Exploration 2: Music from Rubber Band Cans

15 min

Students stretch rubber bands over cans to listen to the sounds they make.

NOTES

....

....

....

....

....

....

....

....

....

....

....

Exploration 3: A Ruler as a Percussion Instrument

15 min

Students use a vibrating ruler to make sound.

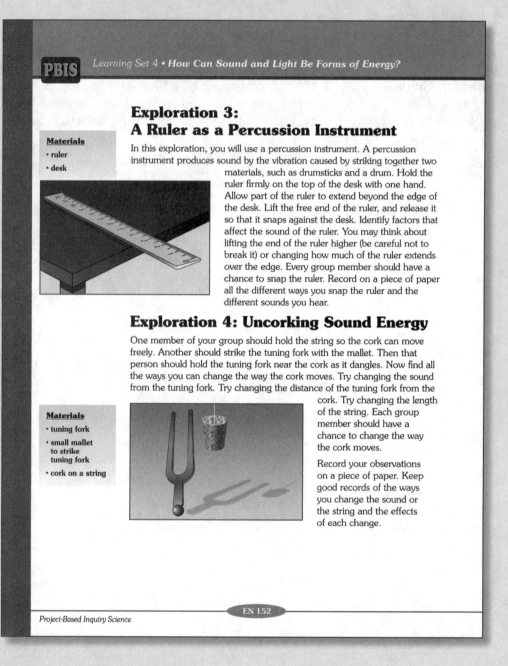

Exploration 3: A Ruler as a Percussion Instrument

Materials
- ruler
- desk

In this exploration, you will use a percussion instrument. A percussion instrument produces sound by the vibration caused by striking together two materials, such as drumsticks and a drum. Hold the ruler firmly on the top of the desk with one hand. Allow part of the ruler to extend beyond the edge of the desk. Lift the free end of the ruler, and release it so that it snaps against the desk. Identify factors that affect the sound of the ruler. You may think about lifting the end of the ruler higher (be careful not to break it) or changing how much of the ruler extends over the edge. Every group member should have a chance to snap the ruler. Record on a piece of paper all the different ways you snap the ruler and the different sounds you hear.

Exploration 4: Uncorking Sound Energy

One member of your group should hold the string so the cork can move freely. Another should strike the tuning fork with the mallet. Then that person should hold the tuning fork near the cork as it dangles. Now find all the ways you can change the way the cork moves. Try changing the sound from the tuning fork. Try changing the distance of the tuning fork from the cork. Try changing the length of the string. Each group member should have a chance to change the way the cork moves.

Materials
- tuning fork
- small mallet to strike tuning fork
- cork on a string

Record your observations on a piece of paper. Keep good records of the ways you change the sound or the string and the effects of each change.

⬡ Get Going

Have students use the diagram in the student text to guide their placement of the ruler. If necessary, show them where to place their hand to hold the ruler in place. Also, caution the students not to pull on the ruler too hard to avoid breaking it. Guide students to change one factor at a time to listen for its effects. For example, they might let the ruler extend 2 in. over the edge and listen for the sound it makes. Then they might try 4 in., 6 in., and 8 in. Make sure students record their observations as they make them.

○ Get Going

Tell students to assemble the materials as described. Use the diagram to guide any students having difficulty. Let them start testing different variations in the setup of their exploration. For example, they might begin testing different distances to the cork. Then they might vary the length of the string. Make sure students record each change they make and their observations of each effect.

Exploration 4: Uncorking Sound Energy

15 min

Students use tuning forks to move a cork suspended on a string.

NOTES

Analyze Your Data

10 min

Students answer questions to focus their thoughts from the investigations.

Analyze Your Data

Use the observations and results from your group's investigation to answer the following questions.

1. What did you observe with your senses of sight, hearing, and touch?

2. In what ways were you able to change the sound you were investigating?

3. In what ways did you observe sound changing?

4. What indicators for sound energy did you observe?

5. What type(s) of material was the sound traveling through?

6. What factors did you observe that affected the amount of sound energy? What is your evidence?

Communicate

Share Your Ideas

Each group investigated an object that made sound. Now, each group will share the results of its exploration with the class.

If yours is the first group to present an exploration, begin with a brief description, including the materials used. Then share your group's observations, reasoning, and conclusions with the class. Provide a summary for the class. Make sure you identify any factors you identified that affect the amount of sound energy.

If your group is adding to what was presented, begin by reporting your ideas about the indicators and factors that were different from those presented. Present any indicators and factors you identified that were not already presented.

Listen carefully as each group presents. If you do not understand something, be sure to ask for more information. As you listen, make sure you understand what each group did, what their results were, and what factors they identified. If there are questions about some of the factors, discuss those questions. You may want to ask questions of the groups that suggested each factor.

As a class, prepare a table like the one shown on the next page that lists the results of the explorations.

ENERGY

△ Guide and Assess

Have students answer the questions about what they observed with their groups. Remind students to consider factors and indicators related to sound energy. Remind them to record their answers.

1. Depending on the instrument they explored, students' answers will vary. Students that *talked to the rice* may say that they saw the rice bounce around on the plastic cling wrap. Students that made music from rubber bands around a can may describe how they *heard*

different tones from the rubber bands. They could also see the rubber bands vibrate. The ruler was an audible instrument. They also may have been able to *feel* the vibrations on the desk. Students who explored the tuning fork and cork could *see* the effect of sound waves on the string and cork.

2. Students with the rice should describe how they altered the intensity of their voice and saw its effects reflected in the movement of the rice. Student who explored the rubber bands should describe how they changed the tension of the rubber bands to make different sounds. Students who explored the ruler should describe how they changed the length of the ruler to change the sounds produced. Students who explored the cork, string, and tuning fork should describe how they changed the length of the string and the intensity of the tuning fork to get different patterns.

3. Depending on the instrument they explored, students' answers will vary. With rice, students should report that the louder the voice, the more movement the rice showed. With rubber bands, students should have observed that the sound took on a higher pitch as the tension increased. With rulers, students should report that the sound became louder as the ruler was bent more. Also, students will report that the shorter the ruler, the higher the pitch of the "thwack." Using a tuning fork, students should describe how the string and cork vibrated more when the tuning fork was closer to the cork.

4. Depending on the instrument they explored, students' answers will vary. For rice, students should have observed the increased movement (kinetic energy) of the rice as an indicator. For rubber bands, students may report that sound was an indicator for sound energy. Also, they may have observed the vibration of the rubber bands. For the rulers, students should report that sound was an indicator of sound energy. For the tuning fork and cork, students should report that the sound energy was indicated by the movement (kinetic energy) of the string and cork.

5. Students should respond that the sound energy in each case was carried by air primarily.

6. Students may conclude that, in each case, the controlling factor was the amount of kinetic energy put into the instrument which controlled the loudness of the sound and, therefore, the amount of sound energy produced.

Communicate: Share Your Ideas

10 min

Students share their answers to the Analyze Your Data *questions, informing the rest of the class of the factors that affect their sound explorations.*

What is your evidence?

Communicate

Share Your Ideas

Each group investigated an object that made sound. Now, each group will share the results of its exploration with the class.

If yours is the first group to present an exploration, begin with a brief description, including the materials used. Then share your group's observations, reasoning, and conclusions with the class. Provide a summary for the class. Make sure you identify any factors you identified that affect the amount of sound energy.

If your group is adding to what was presented, begin by reporting your ideas about the indicators and factors that were different from those presented. Present any indicators and factors you identified that were not already presented.

Listen carefully as each group presents. If you do not understand something, be sure to ask for more information. As you listen, make sure you understand what each group did, what their results were, and what factors they identified. If there are questions about some of the factors, discuss those questions. You may want to ask questions of the groups that suggested each factor.

As a class, prepare a table like the one shown on the next page that lists the results of the explorations.

EN 153

ENERGY

△ Guide

Allow each group to present their ideas and answers. After all the groups have presented, complete the chart together as a class. Encourage students to be as descriptive as they can when completing the chart.

NOTES

....

....

....

....

....

....

PBIS   *Learning Set 4 • How Can Sound and Light Be Forms of Energy?*

Sound Energy Chart			
Exploration	Description of sounds	Material sound travels through	Factors affecting sound energy
1. Talking to rice			
2. Music from rubber band cans			
3. A ruler as a percussion instrument			
4. Uncorking sound energy			

Reflect

1. What happens to sound vibrations when you hit or pluck something with more force? With less force?

2. Describe what happens to sound when the length of an object is changed. Why do you think this is so?

3. An object made a sound, and then you heard it. How do you think the sound traveled from the source to your ears?

4. If a flashlight were shining in your eyes, you could stop the light with your hand or a piece of paper. What happens when you try to stop sound with your hand or a piece of paper?

5. How do you think sound energy causes changes?

6. Do you think sound energy is a type of kinetic energy or a type of potential energy? Why?

Explain

You are now ready to try to explain how each factor you identified affects sound energy. Use a different *Create Your Explanation* page to record each of your claims.

Reflect

10 min

Students discuss questions to extend their observations from the investigations.

◇ Evaluate

After completing the chart, have the class discuss each of the *Reflect* questions. Make sure students realize that these should be their best answers based on what they now know. Tell students they will continue to learn about sound and light, and will have more opportunities to define these forms of energy later in the Unit.

1. Students should respond that when something is hit or plucked with more force, more sound energy is generated. It follows that, with less force, less sound energy is generated.

2. Students should understand that when the length of an object is changed, the pitch of the sound it can make will change. A longer object will have a lower tone; a shorter object will have a higher tone.

3. Students should understand that the sound traveled through air from the source to their ears.

4. Students should reply that sound cannot be stopped by inserting an object between the source and their ears. Sound can travel around objects.

5. Students should respond that sound energy causes vibratory changes in the substance it travels through. In air, it sets up alternating compression regions.

6. Students should state that because sound energy is a moving force, it is probably kinetic energy.

Explain

10 min

Students try to explain the relationships between the factors they observed and their effects on energy.

Explain

You are now ready to try to explain how each factor you identified affects sound energy. Use a different *Create Your Explanation* page to record each of your claims.

△ **Guide**

Ask volunteers to describe in their own words what they do when they explain something. Then review the four features of a good science explanation.

Use the statement template given to give an example, such as *When the thickness of a rubber band increases, sound energy decreases*. Make sure students provide supporting examples for any statement. For instance, a student might state that he or she determined this because the sound became deeper as the thickness of the rubber band increases. Once students understand what to do, have them work in their groups to write an explanation.

Remember that a good explanation has four parts:

- your claim

- your evidence

- your science knowledge

- a statement connecting your claim to your evidence and the science you know

Start by making a claim about how a factor you identified affects sound energy. Try to state your claim this way:

When [*your factor*] [*increases/decreases*], sound energy [*increases/decreases/stays the same*].

Describe the evidence from the explorations that supports your claim. Write a statement that uses your evidence and science knowledge that supports your claim. This will be your explanation. Write your explanation statement so it tells why the factor you have chosen affects sound energy.

As you are working on your explanation, remember to use all of your science knowledge, as well as evidence from your investigations, explorations, and readings, to support your explanation. Science knowledge is knowledge about how things work. This knowledge can come through readings, discussion, talking to an expert, or other experiences. You may include information that you read in this *Learning Set* or knowledge you have gained in other classes. Do not worry if you cannot create a perfect explanation. Just work with the information you have for now. You will have opportunities later to revise your claims and explanations.

Conference

Share Your Explanations

When everyone is finished, you will share your explanations with the class. Record each group's explanation. As a class, come to agreement on an explanation about how each factor you have identified affects sound energy.

EN 155

ENERGY

NOTES

....

....

Conference: Share Your Explanations

10 min

Students share their explanations of the factors that affect sound energy.

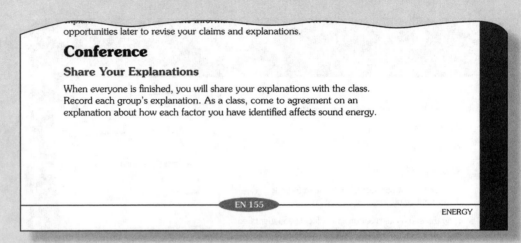

opportunities later to revise your claims and explanations.

Conference

Share Your Explanations

When everyone is finished, you will share your explanations with the class. Record each group's explanation. As a class, come to agreement on an explanation about how each factor you have identified affects sound energy.

EN 155

ENERGY

⬡ Get Going

Have each group present their explanation to the class. Allow other groups to ask questions or identify disagreements. Work through disagreements with students so the class can develop one complete list of factors and their effects.

NOTES

....

....

....

....

....

....

....

....

Update the *Project Board*

In this section, you explored sound energy. You identified indicators of sound energy and the changes caused by the involvement of sound energy. Update the *Project Board* by adding ideas from your explorations in the *What do we think we know?* column. Be sure to add to the *Project Board* the ideas your group agreed on and areas you are not sure about. You may have questions about the relationship between sound energy and vibrations. You may have ideas for investigations to find out more about sound energy. Record your questions and ideas for investigations in the *What do we need to investigate?* column.

Design a Rube Goldberg machine to turn off a light				
What do we think we know?	What do we need to investigate?	What are we learning?	What is our evidence?	What does it mean for the challenge or question?

intensity: the amount of electricity, light, heat, or sound energy per unit area per unit time.

decibel: a measurement used to compare the intensity of different sounds. Each increase of 10 decibels is a sound intensity 10 times greater.

Measuring Sound Energy

You may have heard loud sounds, such as a jet plane taking off, and soft sounds, such as a raindrop hitting a window. To compare different sounds, scientists measure sound **intensity**, the energy passing through a given area in a given time. One way to measure sound intensity is to compare sounds using units called **decibels**. A 50-decibel sound has an intensity 10 times greater than a 40-decibel sound. A 60-decibel sound has an intensity 10 times greater than a 50-decibel sound, or 100 times greater than a 40-decibel sound. For example, normal conversation has a sound intensity of about 60 decibels. This is 100 times greater than the intensity of sound in a quiet room, 40 decibels. In the front row of a rock concert, sound intensity can be 120 decibels, which is 1,000,000 times greater than the intensity of normal conversation.

Update the Project Board

5 min

Students think about ideas and questions to add to the Project Board.

META NOTES

A scale based on multiples of 10 is also known as a logarithmic scale. A sound assigned an intensity level of 0 dB corresponds to an intensity of 1×10^{-12} W/m^2. A sound assigned an intensity level of 10 dB corresponds to an intensity of 1×10^{-11} W/m^2, which is 10 times more intense. A sound assigned an intensity level of 20 dB corresponds to an intensity of 1×10^{-10} W/m^2, which is 100 times more intense.

△ Guide

Discuss with students the ideas and concepts they have learned about sound energy. Record this information on the *Project Board*. Note any topics about which there is disagreement. Ask students to present any questions they need to have answered in order to complete the *Big Challenge*. Record the questions and ideas for investigation on the *Project Board*.

Measuring Sound Energy

10 min

Students read about units of measure used to describe sound.

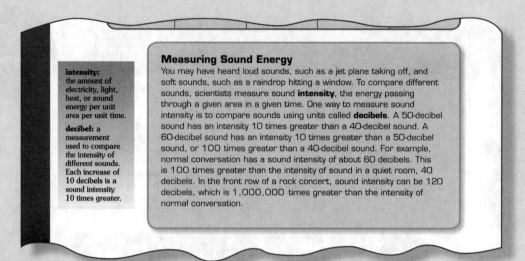

intensity: the amount of electricity, light, heat, or sound energy per unit area per unit time.

decibel: a measurement used to compare the intensity of different sounds. Each increase of 10 decibels is a sound intensity 10 times greater.

Measuring Sound Energy

You may have heard loud sounds, such as a jet plane taking off, and soft sounds, such as a raindrop hitting a window. To compare different sounds, scientists measure sound **intensity**, the energy passing through a given area in a given time. One way to measure sound intensity is to compare sounds using units called **decibels**. A 50-decibel sound has an intensity 10 times greater than a 40-decibel sound. A 60-decibel sound has an intensity 10 times greater than a 50-decibel sound, or 100 times greater than a 40-decibel sound. For example, normal conversation has a sound intensity of about 60 decibels. This is 100 times greater than the intensity of sound in a quiet room, 40 decibels. In the front row of a rock concert, sound intensity can be 120 decibels, which is 1,000,000 times greater than the intensity of normal conversation.

△ Guide

Remind students of some of the sounds they might have described earlier at the beginning of the section. Now ask students to organize those sounds in terms of loudness, or sound intensity. Tell students to use the *Sound Intensity Decibel Scale* as a guide.

NOTES

4.2 Explore

The louder a sound source is, the more sound energy it is emitting, and the greater the sound intensity. However, as you may have discovered, sound intensity also depends on your distance from the sound source. The farther you are from the source, the lower the sound intensity. You can think of the sound source as emitting its energy in all directions. Farther from the source, the same amount of energy is covering a bigger area, so the intensity decreases. This spreading out of the sound energy is called **dispersion**.

Sound Intensity Decibel Scale

Decibels	Example of sound
130	ambulance siren
120	loud rock music (front row); jet engine
110	symphony orchestra
100	power saw
90	subway train
80	vacuum cleaner
70	street noise
60	people talking
50	private office
40	quiet room in home
30	library
20	whisper
10	breathing
0	threshold of hearing

dispersion:
the spreading out of energy as it travels away from the source of the energy. The decrease in intensity as distance from an energy source increases.

META NOTES

Of all Americans who suffer from hearing loss, roughly one fourth of those cases can be described as noise-induced hearing loss (NIHL). NIHL can be caused by either one-time exposure to loud sound or to long-term exposure over an extended period of time. A sound, such as from a bulldozer idling at 85 dB, can cause damage in as little as 8 hours. Listening to music on earphones at a level of 100 dB 15 minutes per day can cause permanent damage.

NOTES

....

....

....

What's the Point?

Indicators for sound energy include sounds that are heard and vibrations. Additional indicators include seeing a sound source as it produces sound, for example, seeing contact between two objects. Most examples of motion are also indicators of sound energy.

The factors that determine the amount of sound energy include characteristics of the sound source and the substance through which the sound is traveling. To increase sound energy, you can increase the force being applied to make an object vibrate. It takes work to increase sound energy.

Sound intensity also depends on how loud the source is and on the distance from the source. The farther you are from a sound source, the lower the intensity of the sound you hear. You can compare intensity of different sounds using the decibel scale.

You can change the pitch of a sound by changing the length of the vibrating part of an object. The shorter the part that vibrates, the higher the pitch. You also can change pitch by changing only the tension in an elastic material that vibrates. For a given length, increasing the tension makes the pitch higher. Pitch can affect how sound energy is transmitted. Sounds can cause vibration of nearby objects, depending on their length or shape.

A police car is a source of both sound energy and light energy.

NOTES

....

....

....

More to Learn

How Do You Hear Sound?

Ears are the sense organs that detect sound. In the ear, vibrations of air are transformed into nerve impulses that are transmitted to the brain for interpretation. Think about the outside of your ears. This is the part with which you are most familiar, because you can see it. The outer part is shaped like a funnel to direct sound into the smaller part and into a narrow tube. This narrow tube, called the **ear canal**, carries the sound inside the ear to the **eardrum**. The eardrum is a tightly stretched **membrane** like the surface of a musical drum. When sound energy reaches the eardrum, the membrane of the eardrum begins to vibrate. The vibrations are then transmitted to the middle ear.

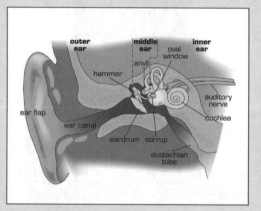

The middle ear starts at the inside of the eardrum. Inside the middle ear are the three smallest bones in the human body. They are the **hammer**, **anvil**, and **stirrup**. Each bone is named for its shape. The eardrum first transmits the vibrations to the hammer. The hammer then transmits the vibrations to the anvil, which, in turn, transmits the

ear canal: a tubelike structure connecting the external ear to the eardrum.

eardrum: the membrane separating the outer ear from the inner ear.

membrane: a layer of tissue that serves as a covering, connection, or lining.

hammer: the first in a series of three small bones in the middle ear.

anvil: the second in a series of three small bones in the middle ear.

stirrup: the third in a series of three small bones in the middle ear.

More to Learn: How Do You Hear Sound?

10 min

Students learn about the parts of the ear.

○ Engage

Ask students the age-old question, *If a tree falls in a forest and no one is there to hear it, does it make a sound?* Explain that one reason there is no simple answer is because the ear is the organ that detects a sound. An ear changes vibrations in air into signals that the brain detects as sound.

vibrations to the stirrup. Vibrations from the stirrup are transmitted to another membrane covering an opening called the **oval window.** The oval window separates the middle ear from the inner ear.

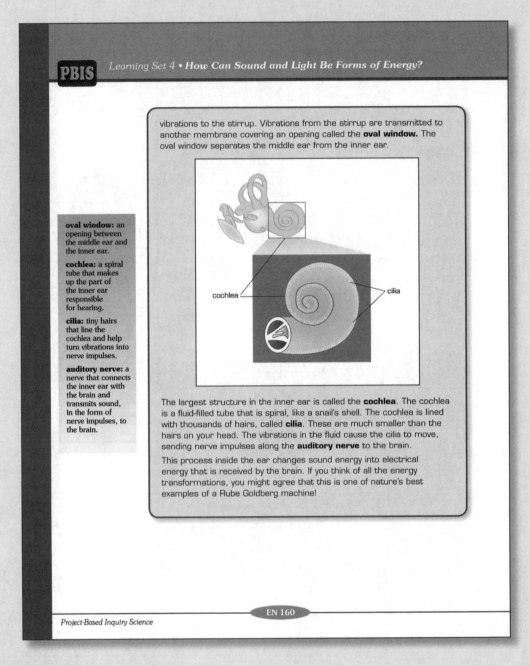

cochlea

cilia

oval window: an opening between the middle ear and the inner ear.

cochlea: a spiral tube that makes up the part of the inner ear responsible for hearing.

cilia: tiny hairs that line the cochlea and help turn vibrations into nerve impulses.

auditory nerve: a nerve that connects the inner ear with the brain and transmits sound, in the form of nerve impulses, to the brain.

The largest structure in the inner ear is called the **cochlea**. The cochlea is a fluid-filled tube that is spiral, like a snail's shell. The cochlea is lined with thousands of hairs, called **cilia**. These are much smaller than the hairs on your head. The vibrations in the fluid cause the cilia to move, sending nerve impulses along the **auditory nerve** to the brain.

This process inside the ear changes sound energy into electrical energy that is received by the brain. If you think of all the energy transformations, you might agree that this is one of nature's best examples of a Rube Goldberg machine!

EN 160

Project-Based Inquiry Science

△ **Guide**

Review with students the parts of the ear. Have students make a simple sketch of the ear. Ask them to use captions to describe the role of each part in their own words.

Assessment Options

Targeted Concepts, Skills, and Nature of Science	How do I know if students got it?
Scientists often work together and then share their findings. Sharing findings makes new information available and helps scientists refine their ideas and build on others' ideas. When another person's or group's idea is used, credit needs to be given.	**ASK:** How did you work together in your groups to investigate sound energy? **LISTEN:** Students should describe the roles the members of their groups played in the investigation.
Scientists must keep accurate and descriptive records of what they do so they can share their work with others and consider what they did, why they did it, and what they want to do next.	**ASK:** Why was it important to keep detailed records of your observations about sound? **LISTEN:** Students should recognize that they needed detailed explanations to compare their results to other groups, and to complete the chart relating factors to their effects.
Energy is the ability to cause change or do work.	**ASK:** What changes did you observe in your investigation? **LISTEN:** Students should describe what effect they used as an indicator of sound energy.
Sound is the transfer of energy as longitudinal waves that cannot travel through a vacuum.	**ASK:** What type of motion was observed each time sound energy was involved? **LISTEN:** Students might suggest that vibration was involved in each investigation.
The ear is the human organ that detects sound.	**ASK:** How are nerve impulses sent from the ear to the brain? **LISTEN:** Students should describe how cilia in the cochlea move as a result of vibrations and send impulses along the auditory nerve.

Teacher Reflection Questions

- How did you make sure students manipulated only one variable at a time? What could you do to guide them in the future?

- What did you do to help students identify both factors and indicators? Are there examples you could give to help them recognize this relationship?

- What evidence did you have that convinced you that students understand how to make a claim using evidence they observed? What might you try next time?

NOTES

SECTION 4.3 INTRODUCTION

4.3 Explore

How Are Sound and Light Energy Transmitted?

◀ *2 class periods*

A class period is considered to be one 40 to 50 minute class.

Overview

Students manipulate a coiled spring to investigate factors that affect the speed of a wave. In their groups, they participate in a race using a coiled spring and a rope to test waves in different materials. From this activity, they learn about the properties of mechanical waves, including wavelength, frequency, wave speed, and wave amplitude. Students use the new information they learn to revise their earlier explanations of how factors affect sound. At the end of the section, students read about seismic waves in a *More to Learn* section.

Targeted Concepts, Skills, and Nature of Science	Performance Expectations
Scientists often work together and then share their findings. Sharing findings makes new information available and helps scientists refine their ideas and build on others' ideas. When another person's or group's idea is used, credit needs to be given.	Students share their findings about factors that affect mechanical waves.
Mechanical waves can be described as longitudinal waves or transverse waves.	Students demonstrate mechanical waves using a rope and a coiled spring.
Sound is the transfer of energy as longitudinal waves that cannot travel through a vacuum.	Students learn that sound requires a medium through which to travel.
Wave energy can be described in terms of frequency, wavelength, and amplitude.	Students relate the classroom wave activity to real sound and light energy through frequency, wavelength, and amplitude.
Waves involve a transfer of energy from one place to another.	Students learn that sound involves the transfer of energy, but not matter.

Materials	
1 per group	Coiled spring Rope that is longer than the coiled spring Stopwatch with second hand Small piece of paper, about 1.5 cm x 5 cm (about 0.5 in. x 2 in.) *Mechanical Wave Investigation* page
1 per class (optional)	Bowl or pan filled with water Pebble

Activity Setup and Preparation

The race activity in this section requires space for each group to work. Before class, you may want to designate areas for each group to conduct their race. When deciding where to place the areas, consider that each group will need to stretch out the coiled spring and the rope, and will need the appropriate space for the students holding these and making observations.

Homework Options

Reflection

- **Science Content:** How is wavelength related to frequency in a sound wave? *(Students should recognize that as wavelength increases, frequency decreases.)*

- **Science Content:** How is a longitudinal wave different from a transverse wave? *(Students should describe how the direction in which a longitudinal wave moves is parallel to the direction of vibration of the particles of matter. In a transverse wave, the direction of the wave is perpendicular to the direction of vibration of the particles of matter.)*

Preparation for 4.4

- **Science Content:** When someone is talking to you, how do you know who it is? What are the factors that control sound energy? *(These questions will start students thinking about the characteristics of sound energy and the factors controlling them.)*

SECTION 4.3 IMPLEMENTATION

4.3 Explore

How Are Sound and Light Energy Transmitted?

When you throw a ball, the kinetic energy of the moving ball is transferred along with the ball. If you throw a ball at a piece of paper, the paper will move when the ball strikes it. The movement of the paper indicates that the piece of paper now has some of the kinetic energy from the ball. You experienced this same phenomenon in the previous section when you held a vibrating tuning fork close to a dangling cork. The kinetic energy of the tuning fork made the dangling cork move. But something was different in the tuning-fork example. The tuning fork never touched the cork, yet the cork still moved. Somehow, the energy from the tuning fork was transferred to the cork without touching it.

How did the energy from the vibrating tuning fork travel between the tuning fork and the cork if they never touched one another? The answer is that the sound energy from the tuning fork traveled in **waves** toward the cork. When the energy in the waves was transmitted to the cork, the cork moved. Scientists use the idea of waves to describe how sound energy travels and is transferred. They also use the idea of waves to describe how light energy travels and is transferred. This means that everything you see and hear comes to you in the form of waves. So, to include sound and light energy in your Rube Goldberg machine, you must know something about waves.

Mechanical Waves—Off to the Races

Your group is going to hold races between a wave in a rope and a wave in a coiled spring. At the same time, you will explore factors that affect the speed of a **mechanical wave**. A mechanical wave is a transfer of energy without a transfer of material. The material a wave moves through is called a **medium**. In this case, the rope and coiled spring are the medium that your waves will travel through. As you do your exploration, pay attention to the direction each wave travels and the direction the rope and coiled spring travel. You will each have a chance to create waves.

wave: a disturbance that travels through a medium from one place to another.

mechanical wave: a transfer of energy through a medium without a transfer of the medium.

medium: the material through which a mechanical wave travels.

Materials
- coiled spring
- rope that is longer than the coiled spring
- stopwatch with second hand
- small piece of paper about 1.5 cm by 5 cm (about 0.5 in. by 2 in.)

EN 161

ENERGY

4.3 Explore

How Are Sound and Light Energy Transmitted?

5 min

Students are introduced to the idea that sound travels as waves.

⭘ Engage

Ask students if they have ever thrown a stone into a pond or dropped one into a puddle. Have a volunteer describe what happens to the water. You may want to consider demonstrating ripples in a pan or bowl of water for the students to observe. Discuss with students how the water vibrates up and down and how the ripples move outward from the point of impact in concentric circles.

*A class period is considered to be one 40 to 50 minute class.

Ask them what happens to a floating object when the ripples move past the object. Point out that this is like what happened to the cork when the tuning fork was struck. Challenge them to imagine ripples of sound waves moving out from the tuning fork in three dimensions, bumping into the cork, as well as your ears.

△ Guide

Once students have considered water waves, discuss the definition of mechanical waves. Tell students that they will be conducting an investigation to learn more about mechanical waves.

Mechanical Waves—Off to the Races

Your group is going to hold races between a wave in a rope and a wave in a coiled spring. At the same time, you will explore factors that affect the speed of a **mechanical wave**. A mechanical wave is a transfer of energy without a transfer of material. The material a wave moves through is called a **medium**. In this case, the rope and coiled spring are the medium that your waves will travel through. As you do your exploration, pay attention to the direction each wave travels and the direction the rope and coiled spring travel. You will each have a chance to create waves.

stopwatch with second hand

- small piece of paper about 1.5 cm by 5 cm (about 0.5 in. by 2 in.)

⬡ Get Going

Review the procedure with students as you distribute the materials to each group. Before they begin their race, make sure that each group member knows their role and understands which piece of equipment they will be using for the activity. There should be two students to manipulate the coiled spring and two students to manipulate the rope. There should also be a student to act as the starter and another to act as the recorder. Let them know that they will rotate these roles throughout the activity so that each group member has had a turn in each.

Mechanical Waves—Off to the Races

20 min

Students use a coiled spring and a rope to investigate the nature of mechanical waves.

NOTES

....

....

....

....

PBIS *Learning Set 4 • How Can Sound and Light Be Forms of Energy?*

Procedure

1. Two students in your group will each hold one end of the coiled spring. Hold the spring on the ground with some tension so there is a little space between the coils. One student will generate a wave in the spring. To do this, squeeze part of the spring by bringing a handful of coil edges together and then letting them go. This type of wave is called a *longitudinal* or *compressional wave*. The other student should hold the spring fixed in place on the ground. Have each student practice making a longitudinal wave travel the length of the coiled spring until you are ready to start the first race.

2. A third and fourth student will each hold an end of the rope. They will stand next to the students holding the coiled spring, and hold the rope in a straight line on the ground. One student will generate a wave with a rapid side-to-side motion. This type of wave is called a *transverse wave*. The other student should hold the rope fixed in place on the ground. Practice making a transverse wave until you are ready to start the first race.

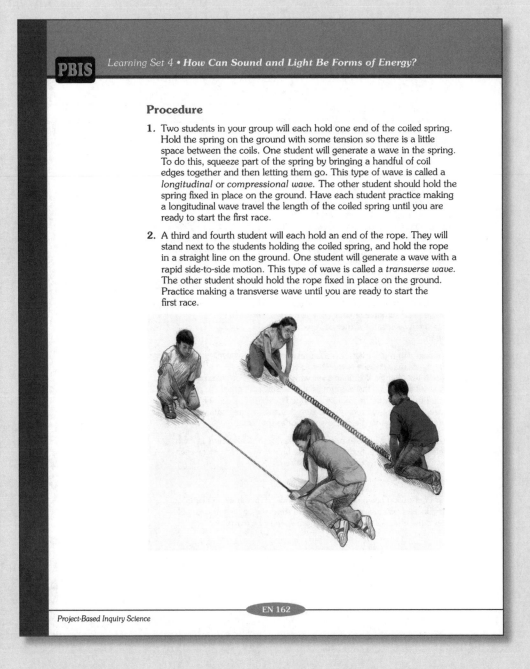

EN 162

Project-Based Inquiry Science

△ Guide

Walk the class through the steps before they begin the procedure on their own. Point out that when students are investigating a longitudinal, or compressional wave, they will use the coiled spring. Also point out that the rope represents a transverse wave. Later, they will read more about these waves, this is now only an introduction to the terms. Also, make sure that students understand which section of the *Mechanical Wave Investigation* page coordinates with each step.

3. A fifth student will be the starter, and a sixth student will be the recorder. Students will get a chance to change roles so all students can generate a wave. The starter will start the race by counting down: "Ready, set, go!" At the sound of "go," each team will generate its wave, and the starter will start the stopwatch.

The starter can call a mis-start if the waves are not produced at the same time. When the first wave reaches the students at the other end, the starter will stop the stopwatch. The recorder will record the winner of the race and record the winning time in the *Race data* table on a *Mechanical Wave Investigation* page. For the first race, nothing is recorded in the *Factors changed* column.

4. After the first trial, discuss the waves you observed and summarize your observations about the waves in the *Other observations* column.

5. Continue with more trials. In each trial, the losing team may choose one factor to change to see if the change will make their wave go faster. For example, you may want to change the amount of side-to-side motion of the rope. Record the factor in the *Factors changed* column. Record the factor before the start of the race. Make sure that the factors changed will not cause any damage to the coiled spring or to the rope.

6. After all students have had one turn in each role, both teams in each race should change a factor. Record the factors changed before each race. Then run the race and record the results.

7. Repeat *Steps 5* and *6*.

8. After your group has completed two rounds of race trials, make a list of the factors you investigated in the *Summary of observations* table. Record the effect of each factor on the speed of a wave.

Mechanical Wave Investigation 4.3.1

Name: _____ Date: _____

Race data

Race Number	Winner	Winning time	Factors changed	Other observations
1				
2				
3				
4				
5				
6				
7				
8				

Summary of observations

Wave speed	Wave reflection

EN 163

ENERGY

△ Guide

Have each group move to their designated area and start their race. Make sure that after the first trial, each group takes time to discuss their observations and record them in the *Other observations* column of the *Mechanical Wave Investigation* page. Then, let the groups move on to their next trial and rotate roles. As they run their trials, make sure teams are recording the factors they change. By the time that groups have reached Step 8, they should have completed two rounds of trials and should now record their data in the *Summary of observations* section.

9. Fold a small rectangle of paper in half and place it over one of the coils of the coiled spring near the fixed end. Also place a small piece of paper on the rope near the fixed end. Send a wave down the coiled spring and the rope. Notice what happens to the paper as the wave pulse goes by. Observe what happens to the wave when it reaches the fixed end of the coiled spring or rope. Record your observations in the *Wave reflection* box in the *Summary of observations* table on the *Mechanical Wave Investigation* page.

Stop and Think

1. In what direction did the coils of the spring move as the wave moved from one end of the coiled spring to the other?

2. A dictionary definition of compressional is "the state of being compressed." A dictionary definition of longitudinal is "placed or running lengthwise." Explain why compressional or longitudinal wave is a suitable name for the type of wave you made on the coiled spring.

3. In what direction did the rope move as the wave moved from one end of the rope to the other?

4. A dictionary definition of transverse is "in a crosswise direction." Another definition is "at right angles (perpendicular) to the long axis." Why is transverse a good name for the wave you generated and observed on the rope?

5. Does the speed of the wave depend on how much you moved the rope sideways to generate the wave? Use evidence from your investigation to answer this question.

6. Does the speed of the wave depend on how many coils you squeezed together? Use evidence from your investigation to answer this question.

7. You observed that the paper attached close to the fixed end of the spring or rope "jumped" as the wave went by. At first, the paper was at rest and had no (kinetic) energy. When it started to move, you know that it had gained kinetic energy. Where did this energy come from?

8. What happened to the wave pulse when it reached the fixed end of the spring or rope?

△ Guide

If needed, assist groups with the placement of the folded paper rectangle. It should be placed over the coil, forming a tent. The paper over the rope should not be folded and simply laid on top of the rope.

Stop and Think

5 min

Students summarize their investigation by answering the Stop and Think *questions.*

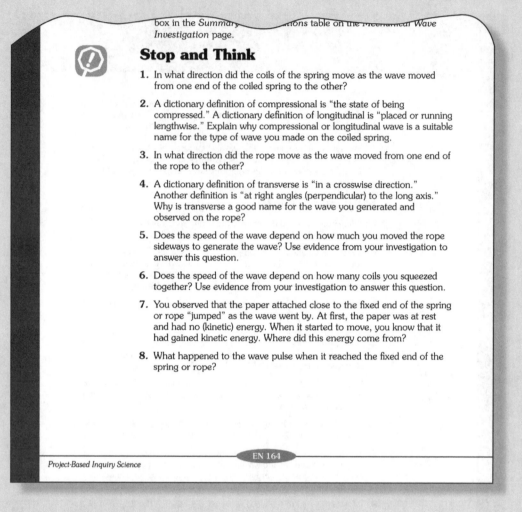

box in the *Summary* ~~questions~~ table on the *Mechanical Wave Investigation* page.

! Stop and Think

1. In what direction did the coils of the spring move as the wave moved from one end of the coiled spring to the other?

2. A dictionary definition of compressional is "the state of being compressed." A dictionary definition of longitudinal is "placed or running lengthwise." Explain why compressional or longitudinal wave is a suitable name for the type of wave you made on the coiled spring.

3. In what direction did the rope move as the wave moved from one end of the rope to the other?

4. A dictionary definition of transverse is "in a crosswise direction." Another definition is "at right angles (perpendicular) to the long axis." Why is transverse a good name for the wave you generated and observed on the rope?

5. Does the speed of the wave depend on how much you moved the rope sideways to generate the wave? Use evidence from your investigation to answer this question.

6. Does the speed of the wave depend on how many coils you squeezed together? Use evidence from your investigation to answer this question.

7. You observed that the paper attached close to the fixed end of the spring or rope "jumped" as the wave went by. At first, the paper was at rest and had no (kinetic) energy. When it started to move, you know that it had gained kinetic energy. Where did this energy come from?

8. What happened to the wave pulse when it reached the fixed end of the spring or rope?

Project-Based Inquiry Science

EN 164

△ Guide and Assess

As a class, discuss answers to the *Stop and Think* questions. Have students consider all the factors they tested during the activity. Allow them to consider additional factors that could not be tested in this way.

1. Students should have observed the coils moving parallel (in the same direction) as the wave, making a longitudinal wave.

2. Students should note that the wave they observed in the coil was a compressional wave, because it had a region of compression which moved the length of the coil. Because it moved the length and was parallel to the length, it is a longitudinal wave.

3. Students should have observed that the rope moved up and down, making a transverse wave.

4. Students should recognize that "crosswise direction" and "at right angles (perpendicular) to the long axis" have the same meaning and describes how the ropes moved perpendicular to the direction of the wave.

5. Students should describe how they did not observe a change in the speed of the wave when they varied the side-to-side distance. They could have changed the wavelength and the frequency, but not the speed of the wave.

6. Students should respond that they did not observe a change in the speed of the wave when they varied the number of coils compressed. They could have changed the wavelength and the frequency, but not the speed of the wave.

7. Students should recognize that the kinetic energy of the paper came from the energy in the wave.

8. Students should describe how when the wave pulse reached the end of the spring or rope, it was reflected back.

NOTES

....

....

....

....

....

....

....

....

Characteristics of Waves

10 min

Students read about types of mechanical waves.

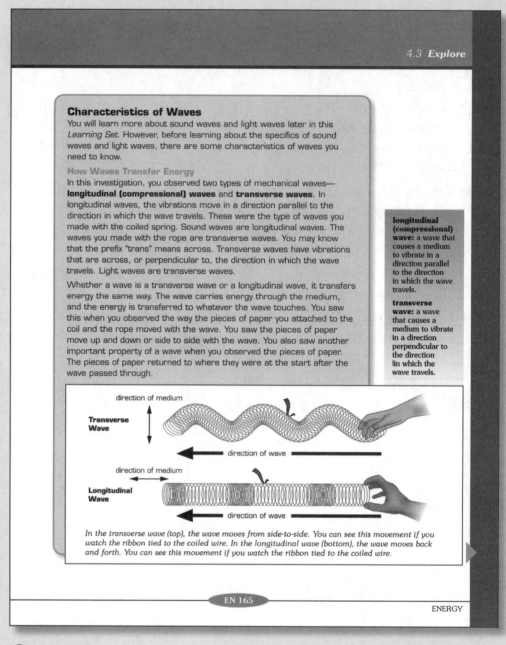

Characteristics of Waves

You will learn more about sound waves and light waves later in this *Learning Set*. However, before learning about the specifics of sound waves and light waves, there are some characteristics of waves you need to know.

How Waves Transfer Energy

In this investigation, you observed two types of mechanical waves—**longitudinal (compressional) waves** and **transverse waves**. In longitudinal waves, the vibrations move in a direction parallel to the direction in which the wave travels. These were the type of waves you made with the coiled spring. Sound waves are longitudinal waves. The waves you made with the rope are transverse waves. You may know that the prefix "trans" means across. Transverse waves have vibrations that are across, or perpendicular to, the direction in which the wave travels. Light waves are transverse waves.

Whether a wave is a transverse wave or a longitudinal wave, it transfers energy the same way. The wave carries energy through the medium, and the energy is transferred to whatever the wave touches. You saw this when you observed the way the pieces of paper you attached to the coil and the rope moved with the wave. You saw the pieces of paper move up and down or side to side with the wave. You also saw another important property of a wave when you observed the pieces of paper. The pieces of paper returned to where they were at the start after the wave passed through.

longitudinal (compressional) wave: a wave that causes a medium to vibrate in a direction parallel to the direction in which the wave travels.

transverse wave: a wave that causes a medium to vibrate in a direction perpendicular to the direction lin which the wave travels.

direction of medium

Transverse Wave

direction of wave

direction of medium

Longitudinal Wave

direction of wave

In the transverse wave (top), the wave moves from side-to-side. You can see this movement if you watch the ribbon tied to the coiled wire. In the longitudinal wave (bottom), the wave moves back and forth. You can see this movement if you watch the ribbon tied to the coiled wire.

EN 165

ENERGY

○ Engage

Ask students if they have ever been to a sporting event where the fans did "the wave." Have one volunteer describe the "human wave" and ask one or two other students what are the defining features of a "human wave." Ask, *when you see it, how do you know it is a wave? Do people move? In which direction?* Tell them that this "wave" at sporting events has something in common with sound and light waves.

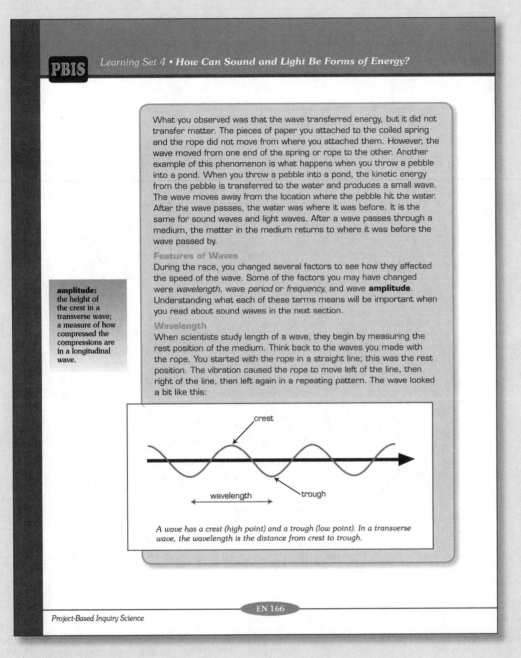

What you observed was that the wave transferred energy, but it did not transfer matter. The pieces of paper you attached to the coiled spring and the rope did not move from where you attached them. However, the wave moved from one end of the spring or rope to the other. Another example of this phenomenon is what happens when you throw a pebble into a pond. When you throw a pebble into a pond, the kinetic energy from the pebble is transferred to the water and produces a small wave. The wave moves away from the location where the pebble hit the water. After the wave passes, the water was where it was before. It is the same for sound waves and light waves. After a wave passes through a medium, the matter in the medium returns to where it was before the wave passed by.

Features of Waves

During the race, you changed several factors to see how they affected the speed of the wave. Some of the factors you may have changed were *wavelength,* wave *period* or *frequency,* and wave **amplitude**. Understanding what each of these terms means will be important when you read about sound waves in the next section.

Wavelength

When scientists study length of a wave, they begin by measuring the rest position of the medium. Think back to the waves you made with the rope. You started with the rope in a straight line; this was the rest position. The vibration caused the rope to move left of the line, then right of the line, then left again in a repeating pattern. The wave looked a bit like this:

crest

wavelength

trough

A wave has a crest (high point) and a trough (low point). In a transverse wave, the wavelength is the distance from crest to trough.

amplitude: the height of the crest in a transverse wave; a measure of how compressed the compressions are in a longitudinal wave.

△ Guide

Make sure that students can differentiate between longitudinal and transverse waves. Use the coiled spring from the activity to demonstrate an example of each. To show a longitudinal wave, lay the coiled spring on a flat surface and push the end inward and then pull it out. This should send a wave along the spring from one end to the other. Then move the end of the coiled spring back and forth perpendicular to the spring. This should set up a transverse wave. In both instances, show students that the coiled spring itself does not move. Instead, a wave travels along it.

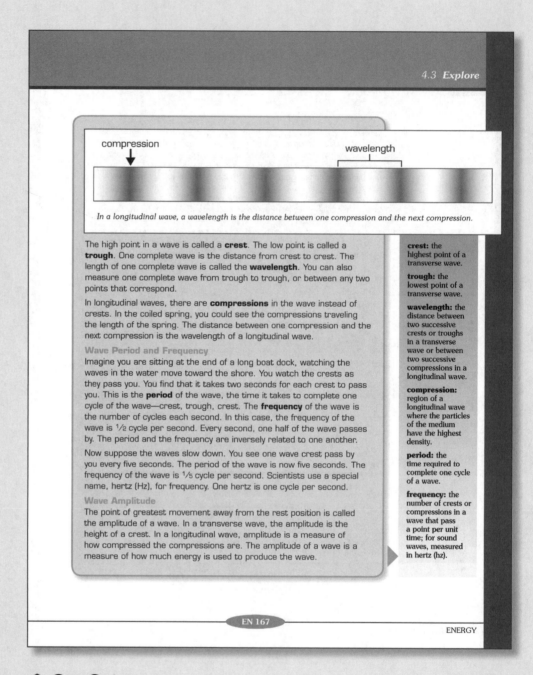

In a longitudinal wave, a wavelength is the distance between one compression and the next compression.

The high point in a wave is called a **crest**. The low point is called a **trough**. One complete wave is the distance from crest to crest. The length of one complete wave is called the **wavelength**. You can also measure one complete wave from trough to trough, or between any two points that correspond.

In longitudinal waves, there are **compressions** in the wave instead of crests. In the coiled spring, you could see the compressions traveling the length of the spring. The distance between one compression and the next compression is the wavelength of a longitudinal wave.

Wave Period and Frequency

Imagine you are sitting at the end of a long boat dock, watching the waves in the water move toward the shore. You watch the crests as they pass you. You find that it takes two seconds for each crest to pass you. This is the **period** of the wave, the time it takes to complete one cycle of the wave—crest, trough, crest. The **frequency** of the wave is the number of cycles each second. In this case, the frequency of the wave is ½ cycle per second. Every second, one half of the wave passes by. The period and the frequency are inversely related to one another.

Now suppose the waves slow down. You see one wave crest pass by you every five seconds. The period of the wave is now five seconds. The frequency of the wave is ⅕ cycle per second. Scientists use a special name, hertz (Hz), for frequency. One hertz is one cycle per second.

Wave Amplitude

The point of greatest movement away from the rest position is called the amplitude of a wave. In a transverse wave, the amplitude is the height of a crest. In a longitudinal wave, amplitude is a measure of how compressed the compressions are. The amplitude of a wave is a measure of how much energy is used to produce the wave.

crest: the highest point of a transverse wave.

trough: the lowest point of a transverse wave.

wavelength: the distance between two successive crests or troughs in a transverse wave or between two successive compressions in a longitudinal wave.

compression: region of a longitudinal wave where the particles of the medium have the highest density.

period: the time required to complete one cycle of a wave.

frequency: the number of crests or compressions in a wave that pass a point per unit time; for sound waves, measured in hertz (hz).

ENERGY

⬡ Get Going

Read through the text on *Wave Amplitude*. Make sure students recognize that amplitude can be measured above and below the line representing rest position. Review the descriptions of wavelength, frequency, and amplitude. Have groups work together to make a model of each type of mechanical wave. For example, students might make a drawing or glue a string to a poster board. Tell students to label the *wavelength, crest,* and *trough* or *compression.*

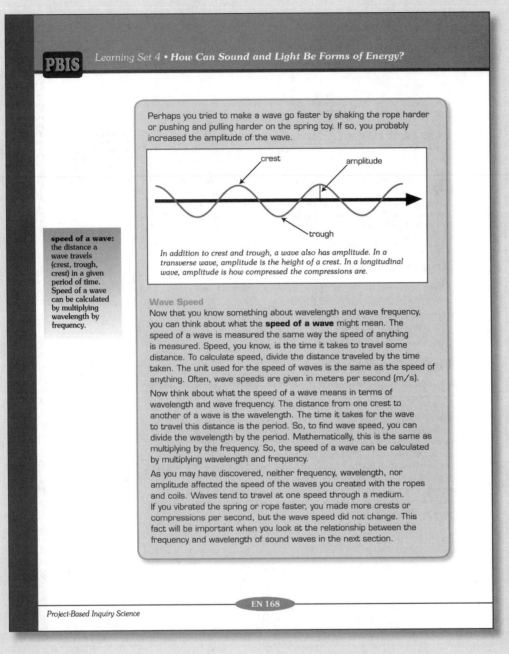

Perhaps you tried to make a wave go faster by shaking the rope harder or pushing and pulling harder on the spring toy. If so, you probably increased the amplitude of the wave.

crest   amplitude

trough

In addition to crest and trough, a wave also has amplitude. In a transverse wave, amplitude is the height of a crest. In a longitudinal wave, amplitude is how compressed the compressions are.

speed of a wave: the distance a wave travels (crest, trough, crest) in a given period of time. Speed of a wave can be calculated by multiplying wavelength by frequency.

Wave Speed

Now that you know something about wavelength and wave frequency, you can think about what the **speed of a wave** might mean. The speed of a wave is measured the same way the speed of anything is measured. Speed, you know, is the time it takes to travel some distance. To calculate speed, divide the distance traveled by the time taken. The unit used for the speed of waves is the same as the speed of anything. Often, wave speeds are given in meters per second (m/s).

Now think about what the speed of a wave means in terms of wavelength and wave frequency. The distance from one crest to another of a wave is the wavelength. The time it takes for the wave to travel this distance is the period. So, to find wave speed, you can divide the wavelength by the period. Mathematically, this is the same as multiplying by the frequency. So, the speed of a wave can be calculated by multiplying wavelength and frequency.

As you may have discovered, neither frequency, wavelength, nor amplitude affected the speed of the waves you created with the ropes and coils. Waves tend to travel at one speed through a medium. If you vibrated the spring or rope faster, you made more crests or compressions per second, but the wave speed did not change. This fact will be important when you look at the relationship between the frequency and wavelength of sound waves in the next section.

△ Guide

As you discuss the *Wave Speed* reading, use the diagram to show the relationship between frequency and wavelength. Help students understand that these quantities are inversely proportional. Guide them to understand that as one quantity increases, the other decreases.

Reflection of Waves

One more important characteristic of waves is **reflection**. When you throw a ball at a hard wall, the ball will bounce back. The ball **reflects** off the wall. Reflection means to turn back from a hard surface. You observed the same thing happening with the waves you created. When a wave reached the end of the coiled spring or rope, you saw that the wave was reflected back. Because waves carry energy, when a wave reflects back, the energy in the wave is also reflected. This is what happened with the waves you made in the ropes and coils. When each wave reached the fixed end of the rope or coil, the wave was reflected back, and so was the energy in the wave.

reflection: when the medium and energy in a wave is turned back from a hard surface.

reflect: to turn back from a hard surface.

Stop and Think

1. Draw a series of transverse waves. Label the wavelength, amplitude, trough, and crest of one of the waves.

2. What is the difference between wave speed and wave frequency? Use the examples of water waves in your answer.

3. What factor or factors affect the speed of a wave?

What's the Point?

Energy can be transferred by mechanical waves. When energy is transferred in this way, there is no transfer of matter. Two types of mechanical waves are longitudinal waves and transverse waves. In a longitudinal wave, the medium vibrates parallel to the direction in which the wave is traveling. In a transverse wave, the medium vibrates perpendicular to the direction in which the wave is traveling. Waves are described by the properties of wavelength, frequency, and amplitude. However, the speed of a wave does not depend on any of these factors. The speed of a wave depends on the medium through which it is traveling. Reflection is another important property of waves. Reflection is what happens when a wave meets a hard surface and bounces off of it. The reflected wave carries its energy with it as it reflects off the hard surface.

ENERGY

To introduce the *Reflection* of Waves, ask the students if they have heard an echo and use their experiences to reinforce the concept. For light waves, you might want to use a mirror and show how light waves are reflected.

⬡ Get Going

As a class, discuss answers to the *Stop and Think* questions. Have students consider all the wave characteristics they read about.

1. Students should be able to complete a sketch of transverse waves and label the sketch properly.

2. Students should respond that wave speed measures how fast one wave travels from Point A to Point B and has units of meters per second (m/s). Wave frequency is a measure of how many waves pass a given point each second and has units of cycles per second.

3. Students should respond that the nature of the medium, the sound wave travels through, is one factor that can affect the speed of a wave.

Stop and Think

5 min

Students consolidate their understanding of the reading by answering the Stop and Think *questions.*

NOTES

....

....

....

....

....

....

....

....

More to Learn: Seismic Waves

10 min

Students read about a specific type of waves— seismic waves.

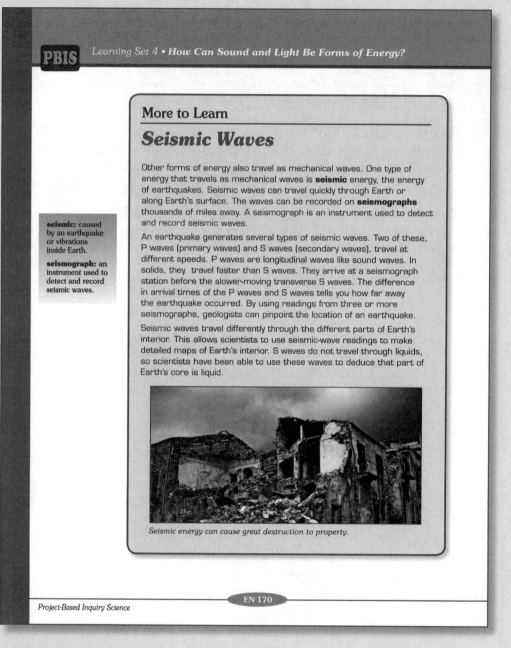

More to Learn

Seismic Waves

Other forms of energy also travel as mechanical waves. One type of energy that travels as mechanical waves is **seismic** energy, the energy of earthquakes. Seismic waves can travel quickly through Earth or along Earth's surface. The waves can be recorded on **seismographs** thousands of miles away. A seismograph is an instrument used to detect and record seismic waves.

An earthquake generates several types of seismic waves. Two of these, P waves (primary waves) and S waves (secondary waves), travel at different speeds. P waves are longitudinal waves like sound waves. In solids, they travel faster than S waves. They arrive at a seismograph station before the slower-moving transverse S waves. The difference in arrival times of the P waves and S waves tells you how far away the earthquake occurred. By using readings from three or more seismographs, geologists can pinpoint the location of an earthquake.

Seismic waves travel differently through the different parts of Earth's interior. This allows scientists to use seismic-wave readings to make detailed maps of Earth's interior. S waves do not travel through liquids, so scientists have been able to use these waves to deduce that part of Earth's core is liquid.

seismic: caused by an earthquake or vibrations inside Earth.

seismograph: an instrument used to detect and record seismic waves.

Seismic energy can cause great destruction to property.

EN 170

Project-Based Inquiry Science

○ Engage

Explain to students that Earth's crust is broken into several large pieces, known as *lithospheric plates*. Tell them that these plates move very slowly over time. Point out that in some places, plates get caught on one another as they slide in opposite directions. As they do, tension can build up between them. At some point, the plates suddenly shift in such a way that they release large amounts of energy. This shift results in an earthquake. That energy travels away from the center of the earthquake in all directions, much like the ripples in the water the class observed at the beginning of this section. Then go on to review seismic energy and waves.

Assessment Options

Targeted Concepts, Skills, and Nature of Science	How do I know if students got it?
Scientists often work together and then share their findings. Sharing findings makes new information available and helps scientists refine their ideas and build on others' ideas. When another person's or group's idea is used, credit needs to be given.	**ASK:** What ideas did you learn by listening to other groups? **LISTEN:** Students should identify factors they had not considered or observations they overlooked.
Mechanical waves can be described as longitudinal waves or transverse waves.	**ASK:** What are two types of mechanical waves you learned about in this section? **LISTEN:** Students should identify longitudinal waves and transverse waves and describe the characteristics of each.
Sound is the transfer of energy as longitudinal waves that cannot travel through a vacuum.	**ASK:** Which type of wave can you use to model a sound wave? **LISTEN:** Students should describe a sound wave as a longitudinal wave.
Wave energy can be described in terms of frequency, wavelength, and amplitude.	**ASK:** What are the three characteristics that describe any wave? **LISTEN:** Students should know that all waves have frequency, wavelength, and amplitude.

Targeted Concepts, Skills, and Nature of Science	How do I know if students got it?
Waves involve a transfer of energy from one place to another.	**ASK:** Why doesn't water move out of the oceans with the waves? **LISTEN:** Students should recognize that waves do not transfer matter, such as water. Waves transfer energy. Mechanical waves transfer energy by causing particles of matter to vibrate.

Teacher Reflection Questions

- What concepts in this section were most difficult for students? What can you do to help students with these concepts?

- What convinced you that students understood the characteristics of waves? What might you do differently next time?

- How were you able to keep students participating in the class discussions? What can you do to encourage this participation?

NOTES

....

....

....

....

....

....

....

4.4 Read

How Does Sound Energy Travel?

◀ *3 class periods*

A class period is considered to be one 40 to 50 minute class.

Overview

Students read about the speed of sound and how it travels through a medium. The concept of pitch is introduced and its relationship to wave frequency is outlined. The last part of the reading solidifies students' understanding of amplitude and reflection in terms of loudness and the echo effect. They have the opportunity to revise and share their explanations of factors that affect sound energy before updating the *Project Board*.

Targeted Concepts, Skills, and Nature of Science	Performance Expectations
Scientists often work together and then share their findings. Sharing findings makes new information available and helps scientists refine their ideas and build on others' ideas. When another person's or group's idea is used, credit needs to be given.	Students work together in groups and as a class to share their ideas and knowledge. They then revise their explanation of factors that affect sound waves.
The speed of sound depends on the medium through which it travels.	Students find out that the speed of sound is not constant.
Sound carries energy from one place to another, but does not transfer matter.	Students learn that matter is used to transfer sound energy, but matter is not actually transferred itself.
Sound cannot travel in a vacuum.	Students learn that sound travels by the transfer of energy from particle to particle.

Materials	
1 per student	*Project Board* page
1 per class	Class *Project Board*

Homework Options

Reflection

- **Science Content:** How does sound energy travel through any medium? *(Students should recall that sound travels through any medium—solid, liquid, gas—by energy transfer from particle to particle.)*

- **Science Content:** What is the relationship between the frequency of a wave and its wavelength? *(Students should know that frequency and wavelength have a reciprocal relationship. The larger one is, the smaller the other is. High frequency—short wavelength, low frequency—long wavelength)*

Preparation for 4.5

- **Science Content:** Sound was described as a wave that carries energy. What observations suggest that light might have a wave nature as well? *(This question is intended to start students thinking about indicators that suggest wave characteristics of light.)*

NOTES

....

....

....

....

....

....

....

SECTION 4.4 IMPLEMENTATION

◀ *3 class periods**

4.4 Read

How Does Sound Energy Travel?

Think of the ripples of water in a pond when you toss in a pebble. The ripples start at the point where the pebble hits the water. The ripples spread out from this point in all directions. The ripples are small waves, and they keep making larger and larger circles as they spread out. The waves can travel for quite a while after the pebble enters the water.

Now imagine people standing around the pond. Could they all hear the pebble when it goes into the water? No matter where you stand, you should hear the splash. Could the sound also be a kind of wave, like the ripples in the pond?

Scientists often use models to help visualize things that cannot be seen. A model that shows sound traveling as waves can help you to understand many of the characteristics of sound. Sound travels from one place to another in the form of longitudinal waves, similar to the waves you made with the coiled spring. Recall that in longitudinal waves, the vibrations move in a direction parallel to the direction in which the wave travels.

Sound can travel through all forms of matter, but it travels better through most solids than liquids, and better through most liquids than gases. Most of the sounds you hear result from sound waves that travel to your ear through air, which is a mixture of gases.

A pebble dropped into a pond will make concentric circles of waves.

Speed of Sound

You already know that when a wave moves through a medium, it does not carry the matter in the medium with it. It is the same with sound waves. When a sound wave moves through a medium, it does not carry the medium along with it. Sound waves start with a vibration in matter. The waves travel when the kinetic energy of the vibration is transferred from particle to particle of the matter.

EN 171

ENERGY

4.4 Read

How Does Sound Energy Travel?

5 min

Students think about ripples in water and start to relate the qualities to sound waves.

◯ Engage

Discuss with the class that in 1947, Charles Yeager became the first pilot to travel faster than the speed of sound. When he did so, he was flying at 293 m/s (about 655 mi/h). However, the speed of sound in air at room temperature is 340 m/s (about 760 mi/h). Explain that the key to Yeager's feat was taking advantage of temperature. Air temperature decreases with altitude. At an altitude of 12,000 m, the temperature is about -65°C (-85°F) and speed of sound is 290 m/s (about 650 mi/h). By flying at this altitude, Yeager was able to fly faster than the speed of sound.

*A class period is considered to be one 40 to 50 minute class.

△ Guide

Point out to students that the speed of sound depends on several factors—the state of matter, the properties of the medium, and the temperature. Use the reading to review the explanation of how speed depends on the state of matter. Also tell students that as temperature decreases within a substance, the movement of the particles slows down. This causes sound waves to be transferred more slowly than at higher temperatures.

NOTES

Think back to the Newton's cradle you explored in *Learning Set 2*. The balls in the middle hardly move at all, yet kinetic energy is transferred from one end to the other. In much the same way, a mechanical wave can carry energy through a medium without moving matter through the medium.

The speed of sound is 343 m/s (meters per second) in air at room temperature. You may have read about aircraft that go faster than the speed of sound. They are called *supersonic*. However, there is no single speed of sound. Sound travels more slowly in cold air and faster in hot air. Sound travels even faster through water, at 1443 m/s. The speed of sound is different in different materials.

pitch: how high or low a sound is.

The speed of sound depends on the particles of the medium the sound wave is moving through. Because the particles in a solid are tightly packed together, sound waves can quickly transfer energy from particle to particle in a solid. The particles in liquids are less tightly packed, so the sound travels more slowly than in most solids. Gas particles are farther apart, so the speed of sound is slowest when it moves through gases.

The arrangement of particles in solids, liquids, and gases affects the speed of sound through the media. Sound travels slowest through gases and fastest through solids. This is because in solids, the particles are closest together, and in gases, they are farthest apart.

Relating Characteristics of Sound to Wave Characteristics

One characteristic of sound is its **pitch**. Pitch is how high or low a sound is. The pitch of a sound is related to the sound wave's frequency. When you hear a high-pitched sound, you are hearing sound waves with a high frequency. A low-pitched sound is from a wave that has a low frequency. The human ear can hear sounds from about 100 Hz (hertz) up to about 18,000 Hz. Other animals are able to hear lower- and higher-frequency sounds.

Relating Characteristics of Sound to Wave Characteristics

5 min

Students read about pitch and its relationship to sound's wave frequency.

⃝ Engage

Ask students to describe the difference between a soprano voice and a bass voice. They will likely use the term *pitch* in their explanation. Ask them whether the sound wave of the soprano has a higher frequency (more cycles per second) or a lower frequency. You might also relate their descriptions to the instruments they played in an earlier activity. The shorter, tauter ruler or rubber band had a higher pitch.

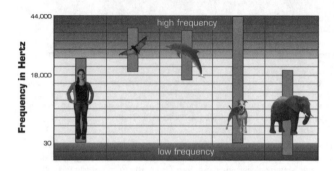

Different animals can hear a range of different frequencies of sound. Look at the graph to see which animal hears the greatest range of sound and which hears the smallest range.

As you observed in your mechanical-wave race in the previous section, the speed of a wave is not affected by the frequency of the wave. In air, high-frequency sound waves and low-frequency sound waves both travel at 343 m/s. How is this possible? The speed of any wave depends on both its frequency and wavelength. The longer the wavelength, the lower the frequency. The shorter the wavelength, the higher the frequency. With higher-frequency waves, more compressions pass by you each second, but the distance between compressions is smaller. You can see in the diagram that a higher frequency wave has a shorter wavelength than a lower frequency wave.

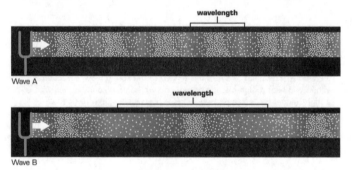

Which of the two longitudinal waves has the higher frequency? How do you know?

ENERGY

NOTES

....

....

You read earlier that sound energy and intensity depend on how loud the source is. You compared intensity of different sounds using the decibel scale. The wave model can be used to explain the loudness of a sound. The louder the sound, the greater the energy. When you generated the waves in the rope, the more you moved the rope away from the rest position, the greater the amplitude of the wave you generated. It required more energy from you to move the rope the greater distance, so you transferred more energy to the rope. The amplitude of the wave was related to the energy transferred to the rope. The same is true for sound. The greater the amplitude of the sound wave, the greater the energy carried by the wave. Therefore, the louder the sound is.

Have you ever heard an echo? If you yell loudly in an empty gymnasium, you will hear the yell repeated shortly after. What you hear is the reflection of the sound off the hard walls of the gymnasium. Just as the wave you generated in the coiled spring or rope reflected from the fixed end, sound waves reflect off hard surfaces.

Stop and Think

1. Why does sound travel better through a solid than through air?

2. How is the pitch of a sound related to the frequency of a sound wave?

3. How is the loudness of a sound related to the amplitude of a sound wave?

4. Use the wave model of sound to describe what happens when you hear an echo.

Revise Your Explanation

With your group, revisit the explanations you wrote in *Section 4.2*. Use what you have learned about waves to revise or add to your claims about the factors that affect sound energy. Then use what you have read to revise the science knowledge and your explanation statement.

Conference

Share Your Explanations

When everyone is finished, share your claims and explanations with the class. As each group shares their revised claims and explanations, record

EN 174

Stop and Think

10 min

Students consider what they have read and answer the Stop and Think *questions.*

1. Students should answer that the particles in a solid are touching each other causing energy to be transferred more quickly and more efficiently.

2. Students should know that a higher-pitched sound has a higher frequency than one with a lower pitch.

3. Students should respond that loudness is directly related to the amplitude of a sound wave.

4. Students should describe how a wave strikes a barrier, such as a canyon wall, and is reflected back.

Revise Your Explanation

5 min

Students consider their progress toward understanding sound and revise earlier explanations.

Revise Your Explanation

With your group, revisit the explanations you wrote in *Section 4.2*. Use what you have learned about waves to revise or add to your claims about the factors that affect sound energy. Then use what you have read to revise the science knowledge and your explanation statement.

△ **Guide**

Have students meet with their groups. Remind students of the explanation they came up with in *Section 4.2*. Using what they have read, they should add to these. Remind groups that every claim they make needs to be supported by evidence.

Conference: Share Your Explanations

10 min

Students share their revised explanations with the class.

Conference

Share Your Explanations

When everyone is finished, share your claims and explanations with the class. As each group shares their revised claims and explanations, record

△ **Guide**

Allow students to share their revised explanations, as well as their reasons for any changes. If any students have decided not to revise their explanation, make sure they present the reasons for their decision.

NOTES

....

....

....

....

....

....

....

4.4 Read

the explanations. Revise the classroom poster that has the full set of claims and explanations.

Update the *Project Board*

Think about the results of your explorations in *Sections 4.2* and *4.3*, as well as what you have read about waves in this section. Record what you learned about sound waves in the *What are we learning?* column of the *Project Board*. Every time you add something to this column, remember to add supporting evidence in the *What is our evidence?* column.

Again, it is important to recognize any questions you may have. Well-developed questions can guide your learning. Any questions you have about sound energy should be recorded in the *What do we need to investigate?* column.

Design a Rube Goldberg machine to turn off a light				
What do we think we know?	What do we need to investigate?	What are we learning?	What is our evidence?	What does it mean for the challenge or question?

What's the Point?

Sound waves are longitudinal waves that can travel through many kinds of matter. Sound waves, like other mechanical waves, are described by the properties of wavelength, frequency, wave speed, and amplitude. Amplitude is a measure of the energy used to create the wave. The greater the amplitude, the greater the energy of the wave and the louder the sound. The pitch of a sound is related to frequency. When you hear a high-pitched sound, the frequency of the wave is greater than that of a low-pitched sound. The speed of sound is generally fastest in solids and slowest in gases. A wave model can account for reflection of sound waves and why the speed of sound in a medium is the same for waves with different frequencies.

Update the Project Board

5 min

Students add ideas and questions about waves to the Project Board.

△ Guide

Once all groups have shared their explanations, ask the class to consider how their understanding of sound has changed throughout the *Learning Set*. Remind them of the wave explorations they performed in *Section 4.3* and the following readings that described what they modeled. Guide students to decide which parts of these activities should be placed in the *What are we learning?* and *What is our evidence?* columns. Also guide them to think of any questions they have about this new knowledge. They should record these in the *What do we need to investigate?* column.

Assessment Options

Targeted Concepts, Skills, and Nature of Science	How do I know if students got it?
Scientists often work together and then share their findings. Sharing findings makes new information available and helps scientists refine their ideas and build on others' ideas. When another person's or group's idea is used, credit needs to be given.	**ASK:** What ideas about waves did you learn by listening to other groups? **LISTEN:** Students should identify the ideas and questions they had not considered.
The speed of sound depends on the medium through which it travels.	**ASK:** Why does sound travel more slowly through air than through wood? **LISTEN:** Students should describe how the energy of sound is transferred through particles of matter. They should recognize that the particles of solids are closer together than the particles of a gas, causing the waves to travel more slowly through air.
Sound carries energy from one place to another, but does not transfer matter.	**ASK:** If sound is caused by the movement of air particles, why is there no transfer of matter? **LISTEN:** Students should respond that the air particles may compress when sound energy passes through, but they do not move overall.
Sound cannot travel in a vacuum.	**ASK:** How loud would a sound have to be to travel from Earth to the Moon? **LISTEN:** Students should reply that sound cannot travel through the vacuum between Earth and the Moon.

Teacher Reflection Questions

- How were you able to connect the concept of pitch in this section to the actual frequency of sound waves? What might you try next time?

- What difficulties did students have understanding that sound travels more slowly in cold air? How might you help them with this in the future?

- How were you able to engage students in discussing the readings about sound and how it travels? What can you do to keep them engaged in further discussions?

NOTES

....

....

....

....

....

....

....

....

....

....

NOTES

4.5 Investigate

What Factors Affect the Intensity of Light Energy?

◀ **3 class periods**

A class period is considered to be one 40 to 50 minute class.

Overview

Students think back to the radiometer demonstration to engage them in thinking about light as energy. The class observes a demonstration involving light patterns produced on a wall by a flashlight at different distances. In group investigations, they determine how the distance to a light source affects the area illuminated and intensity for three different light sources. The procedure involves each group working with one light source. As groups take turns performing their investigations, the other groups make observations of that group's light source and records their data. Students consider the particle nature of light by learning about photons as packets of energy. They then observe a demonstration to discover how the angle of sunlight varies with latitude.

Targeted Concepts, Skills, and Nature of Science	Performance Expectations
Scientists often work together and then share their findings. Sharing findings makes new information available and helps scientists refine their ideas and build on others' ideas. When another person's or group's idea is used, credit needs to be given.	Students work together in groups and as a class to gather data to relate the characteristics of light to the brightness of, and distance to, a light source.
Light can be described by a particle nature.	Students learn that one model of light involves packets of energy called *photons*.
Light can be described by its intensity.	Students observe factors that affect the intensity of light.

Materials	
1 per group	Light source (either a flashlight, table lamp with 25-W bulb, or table lamp with 60-W bulb)
	Poster board with a 2 cm x 2 cm opening in the center
	Laminated poster board with a 2 cm x 2 cm grid
	Washable marker
	Masking tape
1 per student	*Effect of Distance and Source Brightness on Light Intensity* page
	Energy Types page
	Create Your Explanation page
	Project Board page
1 per class	Class *Project Board*
	Sphere
	Flashlight
1 per class (optional)	Solar-powered calculator

Homework Options

Reflection

- **Science Content:** What happens to the area illuminated by a flashlight as the light source moves closer? (*Students should recall that the area illuminated by the flashlight decreases as the light source moves closer.*)

- **Science Content:** In a flashlight, chemical energy stored in a battery is converted to electrical energy. The electrical energy passes through a bulb, where it is converted to heat and light. How do you think the strength of the battery affects the intensity of the light? (*Students may directly relate the strength of the battery to the intensity of light by suggesting that a weaker battery produces a fainter light.*)

Preparation for 4.6

- **Science Content:** Sound was described as a wave that carries energy. What observations suggest that light might have a wave nature as well? (*This question is intended to start students thinking about indicators that suggest wave characteristics of light.*)

4.5 Investigate

What Factors Affect the Intensity of Light Energy?

It may seem odd to you to think about light as energy. However, you did see that when a flashlight was held close to a radiometer, the flags moved more than when the flashlight was held farther away. So, clearly, the light somehow provided energy to the radiometer. You may be wondering how light can provide energy and how light from the Sun can heat Earth. You may also be wondering how light can power devices such as a calculator. Like sound, light energy can travel in waves. In this section, you will investigate light energy and identify factors that affect the amount of light energy emitted by a light source. Your investigations will also help you understand the relationship between light that you see and light energy.

Demonstration

Watch as your teacher shines the light from a flashlight on a classroom wall. The beam will make a circle of light on the wall. The teacher will move the flashlight closer to the wall and away from the wall. Work in groups to discuss what is happening during the demonstration.

Analyze Your Data

In your group, discuss the following questions:

1. What do you think is happening when the circle of light becomes larger? What about when it becomes smaller?

2. Do you think the light energy emitted by the flashlight changes at any point in the demonstration? If so, how?

3. When a flashlight is close to the wall, the illuminated area is a small circle. How do you think the intensity of the light in the small circle compares with the intensity when the light makes a big circle? In other words, how does the intensity of light striking the wall relate to the distance of the flashlight from the wall?

EN 176

Project-Based Inquiry Science

4.5 Investigate

What Factors Affect the Intensity of Light Energy?

5 min

Students recall the radiometer demonstration to prepare for a new demonstration about light energy.

○ Engage

If one is available, display a solar-powered calculator to initiate a class discussion about devices powered by sunlight. Ask students if they know of other examples, such as heating systems in homes or swimming pools. Guide students to realize that sunlight can do work, and the intensity of the light affects the amount of work it can do.

Demonstration

5 min

Students observe light from a flashlight at different distances from a wall.

understand the relationship between light that you see and light energy.

Demonstration

Watch as your teacher shines the light from a flashlight on a classroom wall. The beam will make a circle of light on the wall. The teacher will move the flashlight closer to the wall and away from the wall. Work in groups to discuss what is happening during the demonstration.

Analyze Your Data

⬡ Get Going

Emphasize to students that they should pay close attention to the demonstration, as they will later discuss it with their groups. Darken the overhead lights in the classroom and close blinds if possible. Shine a flashlight on a wall. With the flashlight on, step away from the wall. Then step back toward the wall. Have students observe the size of the circle made by the flashlight and how bright the circle is.

Analyze Your Data

10 min

Students discuss their observations from the flashlight demonstration.

Analyze Your Data

In your group, discuss the following questions:

1. What do you think is happening when the circle of light becomes larger? What about when it becomes smaller?

2. Do you think the light energy emitted by the flashlight changes at any point in the demonstration? If so, how?

3. When a flashlight is close to the wall, the illuminated area is a small circle. How do you think the intensity of the light in the small circle compares with the intensity when the light makes a big circle? In other words, how does the intensity of light striking the wall relate to the distance of the flashlight from the wall?

△ Guide and Assess

Review terms that students have encountered already, such as *intensity* and *dispersion*. Then have students discuss the questions within their groups. Listen for students' answers to reflect an understanding that the light is more intense when the circle is small and bright than when it is large and dim. Also listen to make sure they recognize that the light intensity decreases as the distance from the wall increases.

1. Student answers will vary, but all should recognize that when the flashlight is farther from the wall, the circle of light is larger and less intense (dimmer). When the circle of light is smaller (and brighter), the flashlight is closer to the wall.

2. Students should state that the light energy of the flashlight is constant.

3. Students should realize that the light reflected from the wall is more intense as the flashlight is moved closer to the wall.

4. How can you use the area illuminated by a flashlight at different distances to determine how the intensity of light at the wall is related to distance from the source?

5. Suppose you repeat the demonstration, using two flashlights, one of which is brighter and more powerful. Describe the circles of light that will be produced if both flashlights make circles of light that are the same size. How do you think the brightness of the light source will affect light intensity at the wall?

How Does Distance Affect Light Intensity?

The data from the demonstration suggest that as light energy spreads out over a larger area, it decreases in intensity. But you do not know for sure, because you have observed this using the light of just one flashlight. What if the light source was different? Would the same thing happen? You are going to investigate to find the answers.

In this investigation, three lab stations will be set up around the classroom, each using a different light source. Your group will have a chance to run the procedure at least once at one of the lab stations. You will watch as other groups run the procedure at other lab stations. It will be important for you to record observations at all three lab stations. Record your data in an *Effect of Distance and Source Brightness on Light Intensity* page.

EN 177

ENERGY

4. Students' answers will vary. Those who understand what is happening will respond that there is an inverse relationship between distance from the wall and the intensity of the light. The shorter the distance, the more intense the light.

5. Students should understand that the more-powerful flashlight will have a more intense circle of reflected light than the less-powerful flashlight. The brightness of the light source will be reflected as a brighter circle of light.

How Does Distance Affect Light Intensity?

5 min

Students relate the intensity of light to different light sources.

How Does Distance Affect Light Intensity?

The data from the demonstration suggest that as light energy spreads out over a larger area, it decreases in intensity. But you do not know for sure, because you have observed this using the light of just one flashlight. What if the light source was different? Would the same thing happen? You are going to investigate to find the answers.

In this investigation, three lab stations will be set up around the classroom, each using a different light source. Your group will have a chance to run the procedure at least once at one of the lab stations. You will watch as other groups run the procedure at other lab stations. It will be important for you to record observations at all three lab stations. Record your data in an *Effect of Distance and Source Brightness on Light Intensity* page.

○ Get Going

Assign each group to one lab station. Depending on the size of your class, some lab stations may have more than one group. Students should have their *Effect of Distance and Source Brightness on Light Intensity* pages ready to record their observations.

△ Guide

Review the procedure as a class. Make sure that all students understand what they are to do. Make sure they understand that the procedure requires them to shine the light three times, each from a different distance to the wall. Give the groups time to decide who will hold the poster with the square hole, who will turn on the light source, and who will outline the illuminated area.

NOTES

....

....

....

....

....

....

4.5

PBIS

Procedure

1. When it is your turn to set up a station using one of the three light sources, start by taping to the wall your group's laminated poster board with the grid. Make sure you know which light source you are using so you will record your data in the proper place on your *Effect of Distance and Source Brightness on Light Intensity* page.

2. Position a desk so a light source on it is 100 cm from the wall. One student in the group will hold the poster board with the square hole vertically on the desk. Position it so the hole is right in front of the light source.

3. A second student will turn on the light source and hold it up to the board so the light shines through the hole and strikes the laminated poster board on the wall.

4. A third student will use a marker to outline the illuminated area on the laminated plastic. Estimate the area by counting the grid squares contained inside the outline. Label the area "Produced by source at 100 cm. Area = _____ cm². " Write the area you estimated on the blank line.

5. Notice the intensity of the light striking the laminated poster board. You will not be able to rank the intensity until you have seen other illuminated areas. Until then, look at the center of the illuminated area, where the light intensity is greatest, and notice how intense it is.

6. Repeat *Steps 2–5,* but this time, move the desk so the light source and the poster board with the hole are 50 cm from the wall. Record your data. Notice if the intensity of light in the illuminated area is greater or smaller than it was when the light was held 100 cm from the poster board.

7. Repeat *Steps 2–5,* but this time, move the desk so the light source and poster board are 25 cm from the wall. Record your data. Notice if the intensity of light in the illuminated area is greater or smaller than it was when the light was held 50 cm from the poster board.

8. Record the relative intensity of the illuminated areas. Which was most intense? Which was least intense? Which was in the middle?

Materials

- one light source: flashlight, table lamp with 25-W bulb, or table lamp with 60-W bulb
- 1 poster board with a 2 cm x 2 cm opening in the center
- 1 poster board, laminated and with 2 cm x 2 cm grid
- 1 washable marker
- masking tape

Project-Based Inquiry Science

Procedure

5 min

Groups test the effects of distance on the intensity of three different light sources.

Remind students not to look directly into the light sources and to use care when handling the bulbs.

If necessary, show students how to estimate area using a grid. Read through the following *Watching the Procedure* section with the class and have each group conduct their investigation.

Watching the Procedure

10 min

Students record their observations of other groups' light source investigations.

Watching the Procedure

When your group is watching another group carry out the procedure, you will not get to set up the station. However, you will need to record the data that group is collecting and judge the relative intensity of the illuminated areas.

1. Make sure you know which light source the group is using, and make sure you always know how far away from the laminated board they are positioning the light source.

2. Each time the group running the procedure creates an illuminated area, notice how large it is, and make sure they tell you how many square centimeters they measured. If you cannot hear the size, ask them to repeat it. Record the size of each illuminated area.

3. Notice the intensity of the light in each illuminated area. Observe how the intensity changes as the distance from the light to the laminated board changes. Notice, too, the differences in intensity between the illuminated areas created by the different light sources. Make notes so you will remember these differences.

4. You will need to rank the intensity of the illuminated areas produced by each of the light sources at each distance from the laminated board. So, if you need to, go back and observe a procedure a second time so you can be more exact about the intensity of light at different distances and using different light sources.

Effect of Distance and Source Brightness on Light Intensity 4.5.1

Name: _____ Date: _____

Light source	Distance to wall (cm)	Area illuminated at wall (cm²)	Intensity rating (scale of 1 to 10)
25-W bulb	25		
	50		
	100		
60-W bulb	25		
	50		
	100		
flashlight	25		
	50		
	100		

△ Guide

Discuss with the class how they will be observing the investigations of other groups. Point out where they should record data on their *Effect of Distance and Source Brightness on Light Intensity* pages. Remind them that they will have to rank the intensity of illumination of each light source, so they should keep this in mind as they make their observations.

Analyze Your Data

1. Begin by doing your best to rank the intensity of the light in the illuminated areas you observed, and graph the results. Which light source and distance produced the most intense illumination? Which produced the least intense illumination? Which ones were very similar to each other? Assign a number between 1 and 10 to the intensity of the light in each illuminated area.

2. What relationship do you see between the size of the illuminated area and the distance of the light source from the wall?

3. What relationship do you see between the size of the illuminated area and the intensity of the illuminated area when the light source is the same?

4. What relationship do you see between the brightness of the light source and the size of the illuminated area?

5. What relationship do you see between the brightness of the light source and the intensity of the illuminated area when the light sources are the same distance from the illuminated area?

Communicate

Share Your Results

Although all of the groups did the same investigation, different groups may have analyzed the results differently.

When it is your group's turn to present, show the class your data table. As you show your data table and graph, tell the class how you ranked the intensity of the illuminated areas, and point out the trends you see.

As you listen to the other groups, notice ways in which each group's data are similar to yours and ways in which their data are different. Notice the relationships groups are proposing between distance and area, area and light intensity, or distance and light intensity. For each presentation, decide if you agree. As always, if you do not understand what is being presented, ask questions. If you think the data are not trustworthy, also ask questions about that. Remember to be respectful, even if you disagree with a group.

Analyze Your Data

10 min

Students construct and interpret a graph to represent their data.

△ Guide and Assess

Have students answer the *Analyze Your Data* questions with their groups. As students work, circulate the room to monitor and review students' graphs. Recognize that there can be different approaches to summarizing this data. For example, students could plot distance on the *x*-axis, and area or intensity on the *y*-axis. They would need to graph the data for each light source on a different graph. In this case, distance would be the independent variable and the variables they observed would be dependent variables. Another approach is to plot the type of light source on the *x*-axis and factors such as area or intensity on the *y*-axis. Students would need to graph the data for each distance on a different graph. A third approach would be to plot area versus intensity. Whatever students choose, make sure they recognize that both the light source and the distance were manipulated throughout this investigation.

Use the following to assess students' understanding of the investigation results:

1. Students should respond that the distance of 25 cm produced the most-intense light for each source. The 100 cm distance produced the least-intense light. The 60-W bulb produced a more-intense light than the 25-W bulb. Unless the flashlight is a very powerful one, it probably produced the least-intense light at each distance.

2. Students should observe that there is a direct relationship between distance from the wall and the size of the illuminated area. The farther from the wall, the larger the illuminated area.

3. Students should note that there is an inverse relationship between the size of the illuminated area and the intensity of the illuminated area. The larger the illuminated area, the less intense the light is.

4. Students should respond that there is no relationship between the brightness of the light source and the size of the illuminated area. All light sources had approximately the same size illuminated area.

5. Students should recognize that the brightest light source produced the most-intensely illuminated area for each distance.

NOTES

....

....

....

....

....

....

....

Communicate

Share Your Results

Although all of the groups did the same investigation, different groups may have analyzed the results differently.

When it is your group's turn to present, show the class your data table. As you show your data table and graph, tell the class how you ranked the intensity of the illuminated areas, and point out the trends you see.

As you listen to the other groups, notice ways in which each group's data are similar to yours and ways in which their data are different. Notice the relationships groups are proposing between distance and area, area and light intensity, or distance and light intensity. For each presentation, decide if you agree. As always, if you do not understand what is being presented, ask questions. If you think the data are not trustworthy, also ask questions about that. Remember to be respectful, even if you disagree with a group.

Communicate: Share Your Results

10 min

Students share their conclusions from the investigation.

META NOTES

Unlike a flashlight, which produces a beam of light that disperses, a laser produces a concentrated beam of light. The light is said to be monochromatic because it consists of only one color of light, and it is coherent because all the light waves travel together in the same way. A laser beam could not have been used for this activity.

△ Guide and Assess

Allow groups to share their results. Help students explain the reason for any discrepancies. Work together to summarize the relationships being suggested. Do not discount any ideas at this point. Allow students to express their claims. They will have opportunities to revise them as they continue to learn more about light energy.

NOTES

4.5 Investigate

Reflect

Discuss the following questions as a group. Be prepared to share your answers with the class.

1. How do the graphs of different groups compare? What are the similarities and differences?

2. Based on the graphs, develop a statement about the relationship between the distance from the light source and the intensity of light at the poster board.

3. Based on the graphs, develop a statement about the relationship between the brightness of the light source and the intensity of light at the poster board.

4. Develop a statement about the relationship between the amount of illuminated area and the intensity of light at the poster board.

5. Develop a statement about the relationship between the amount of illuminated area and the distance from the poster board.

6. Now think back to the radiometer. As the flashlight was brought closer to the radiometer, the flags moved faster. Based on what you observed in this experiment and on your observations of the radiometer, what do you think is the relationship between light intensity and light energy?

7. What are two factors that determine the available amount of light energy?

8. Do you think light energy is a type of kinetic energy or a type of potential energy? Why?

Reflect

10 min

Students answer questions to analyze their observations and apply them to other situations involving light.

△ Guide and Assess

Have each group discuss the *Reflect* questions. Point out that they should consider not only their own results, but those of the other groups as well. Listen as students develop their statements. Go around the room and ask students what evidence they used to reach these statements. Make sure they can explain their logic for identifying light energy as either kinetic energy or potential energy.

1. Students should observe that when the same independent and dependent variables are graphed, the graphs of different groups are similar. The biggest differences are in judging the intensity of the light by each group.

2. Students should report that as the distance of the light from the poster board increased, the intensity of the light decreased.

3. Students should report that as the light source increased in intensity, the intensity of the light in the illuminated area increased.

4. Students should report that as the distance from the poster board increased, the intensity of the light in the illuminated area decreased.

5. Students should report that as the distance of the light from the poster board increased, the size of the illuminated area increased.

6. Students should recognize that as the light energy increases, the intensity of the light increases.

7. Students should deduce that the intensity of the light source and the distance from the light source are two factors in determining the amount of light energy.

8. Students will probably state that light energy is a form of kinetic energy because it moves from Point A to Point B. Forms of potential energy that they have experienced cannot be seen directly.

NOTES

Why Does Light Intensity Decrease With Distance From the Source?

10 min

Students read about the relationship between light intensity and distance from the light source.

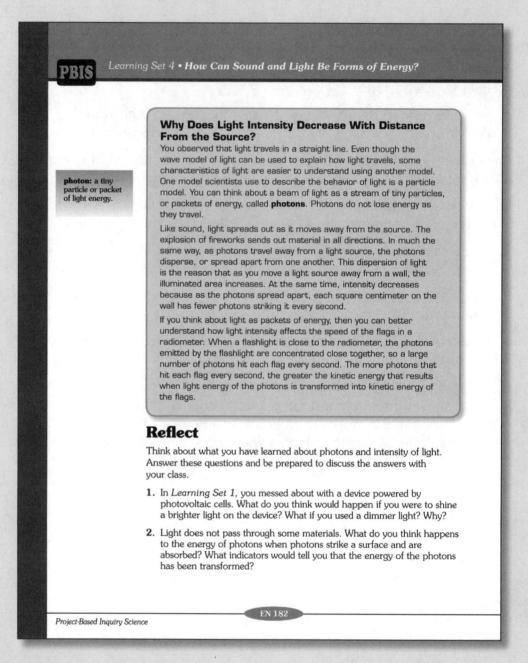

Why Does Light Intensity Decrease With Distance From the Source?

You observed that light travels in a straight line. Even though the wave model of light can be used to explain how light travels, some characteristics of light are easier to understand using another model. One model scientists use to describe the behavior of light is a particle model. You can think about a beam of light as a stream of tiny particles, or packets of energy, called **photons**. Photons do not lose energy as they travel.

photon: a tiny particle or packet of light energy.

Like sound, light spreads out as it moves away from the source. The explosion of fireworks sends out material in all directions. In much the same way, as photons travel away from a light source, the photons disperse, or spread apart from one another. This dispersion of light is the reason that as you move a light source away from a wall, the illuminated area increases. At the same time, intensity decreases because as the photons spread apart, each square centimeter on the wall has fewer photons striking it every second.

If you think about light as packets of energy, then you can better understand how light intensity affects the speed of the flags in a radiometer. When a flashlight is close to the radiometer, the photons emitted by the flashlight are concentrated close together, so a large number of photons hit each flag every second. The more photons that hit each flag every second, the greater the kinetic energy that results when light energy of the photons is transformed into kinetic energy of the flags.

Reflect

Think about what you have learned about photons and intensity of light. Answer these questions and be prepared to discuss the answers with your class.

1. In *Learning Set 1*, you messed about with a device powered by photovoltaic cells. What do you think would happen if you were to shine a brighter light on the device? What if you used a dimmer light? Why?

2. Light does not pass through some materials. What do you think happens to the energy of photons when photons strike a surface and are absorbed? What indicators would tell you that the energy of the photons has been transformed?

EN 182

Project-Based Inquiry Science

△ Guide

Have students imagine a beam of light as a circle of marbles moving out from a central point. Tell students that the marbles are touching when they start moving, but that as they move out in a circle they get farther and farther apart. Have students read through their text. Describe to them how the more marbles (photons) that hit the same point on the wall, the greater the intensity of the light at that point.

Guide and Assess

Have groups discuss answers to the *Reflect* questions. Encourage students to give their best answers based on what they have learned and observed thus far. Point out that their answers do not have to be perfect, but they should be supported by evidence. Allow several minutes for the entire class to share their answers and identify any disagreements.

1. Students should describe how with a brighter source of light, the flags will spin faster and with a dimmer source of light, the flags will spin more slowly. This is because available light energy is greater with a brighter source.

2. Students might guess that when a photon is absorbed, the energy is transformed into heat. The indicator for this transformation would be an increase in temperature.

Reflect

10 min

Students answer questions to relate what they have learned about light to other situations.

NOTES

....

....

....

....

....

....

....

....

....

....

....

3. How do you know that light travels faster than sound? (Hint: Give an example of something that produces sound and light at the same time.)

4. Why do you think light is sometimes called "visible light?" What other kinds of light have you heard about or read about?

Explain

It is time to update your *Energy Types* page or use a new *Energy Types* page to record what you know about light energy.

You are also ready now to try to explain how each factor you identified affects light energy. Use a different *Create Your Explanation* page to record each of your claims.

Start by making a claim about how a factor you identified affects light energy. Try to state your claim this way:

When [*your factor*] [*increases/decreases*], light energy [*increases/decreases/stays the same*].

Describe the evidence from the explorations that supports your claim. Record science knowledge from what you have read. Then develop a statement that uses your evidence and science knowledge and tell why the factor you chose affects light energy. This will be your explanation.

As you are working on your explanation, remember to use all your science knowledge, as well as evidence from your investigations, explorations, and readings, to support your explanation. Science knowledge is knowledge about how things work. This knowledge can come through readings, discussion, talking to an expert, or other experiences. You may include what you read in this *Learning Set* or knowledge you have gained in other classes. Do not worry if you cannot create a perfect explanation. Just work with what you know for now. You will have opportunities later to revise your claims and explanations.

EN 183

ENERGY

3. Students should respond that when lightning strikes, both light and sound are produced. However, the light can be seen well before the thunder is heard.

4. Students may respond that they have heard of ultraviolet light, or may even know that the light we can see is only part of a continuous electromagnetic spectrum.

△ Guide

Ask volunteers to describe in their own words what they do when they "explain" something. Then review the four features of a good science explanation. Use the statement template given to give examples, such as *When the distance from a light source increases, light energy decreases.* Make sure students provide supporting examples for any statement. For example, a student might state that he or she determined this because the light became dimmer as the distance between the source and the poster board increases. Once students understand what to do, have them work in their groups to write an explanation.

Explain

10 min

Students explain the relationships between the factors they observed and their effects on light energy.

NOTES

Conference: Share Your Explanations

10 min

Students share their explanations of the factors that affect light energy.

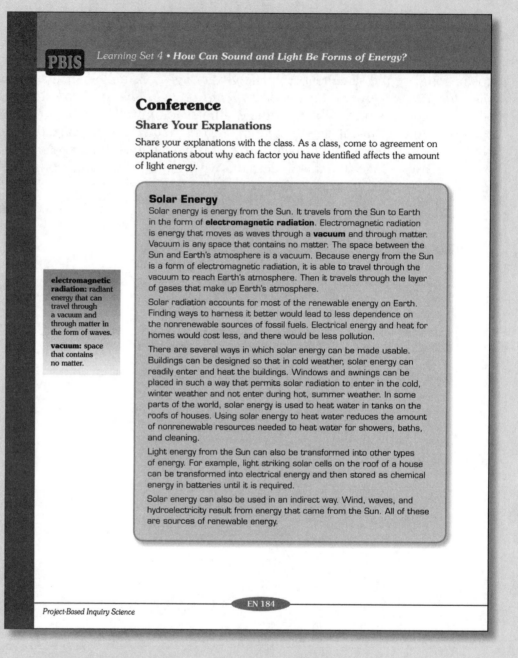

Conference

Share Your Explanations

Share your explanations with the class. As a class, come to agreement on explanations about why each factor you have identified affects the amount of light energy.

Solar Energy

Solar energy is energy from the Sun. It travels from the Sun to Earth in the form of **electromagnetic radiation**. Electromagnetic radiation is energy that moves as waves through a **vacuum** and through matter. Vacuum is any space that contains no matter. The space between the Sun and Earth's atmosphere is a vacuum. Because energy from the Sun is a form of electromagnetic radiation, it is able to travel through the vacuum to reach Earth's atmosphere. Then it travels through the layer of gases that make up Earth's atmosphere.

Solar radiation accounts for most of the renewable energy on Earth. Finding ways to harness it better would lead to less dependence on the nonrenewable sources of fossil fuels. Electrical energy and heat for homes would cost less, and there would be less pollution.

There are several ways in which solar energy can be made usable. Buildings can be designed so that in cold weather, solar energy can readily enter and heat the buildings. Windows and awnings can be placed in such a way that permits solar radiation to enter in the cold, winter weather and not enter during hot, summer weather. In some parts of the world, solar energy is used to heat water in tanks on the roofs of houses. Using solar energy to heat water reduces the amount of nonrenewable resources needed to heat water for showers, baths, and cleaning.

Light energy from the Sun can also be transformed into other types of energy. For example, light striking solar cells on the roof of a house can be transformed into electrical energy and then stored as chemical energy in batteries until it is required.

Solar energy can also be used in an indirect way. Wind, waves, and hydroelectricity result from energy that came from the Sun. All of these are sources of renewable energy.

electromagnetic radiation: radiant energy that can travel through a vacuum and through matter in the form of waves.

vacuum: space that contains no matter.

EN 184

Project-Based Inquiry Science

△ Guide

Have each group take turns sharing their explanations with the class. Then guide a class discussion to come to an agreement on a class explanation. Encourage students to ask questions about other groups' explanations they did not understand. If they disagreed with any explanation, they should also share this, but remind them to support every argument with evidence.

△ Guide

Point out that the topic of solar energy has come up throughout the Unit, but now students have a formal definition of this type of energy. Remind students how sunlight is involved in the water cycle, in the formation of wind, and in the production of fossil fuels. Read through the examples as a class, and point out that it is solar energy that powered the calculator from the beginning of the section.

Solar Energy

10 min

Students read about solar energy.

NOTES

Reflect

5 min

Students answer questions about solar energy.

META NOTES

Students may find it difficult to understand that solar energy from the Sun can be found in what they may consider the darkness of space. Explain that a spacecraft operating near the Sun uses solar panels to absorb energy from the Sun. The International Space Station, for example, relies on solar energy for most of its power needs. Farther out in the solar system, however, light from the Sun is not intense enough to provide all of the energy a spacecraft needs. Spacecraft at these distances must therefore rely on alternative energy sources.

Even the nonrenewable sources come from solar energy. Solar energy is transformed by plants into chemical energy through the process of *photosynthesis*. The energy stored in fossil fuels comes from the chemical energy stored in plants or eaten by animals millions of years ago.

Reflect

Answer the following questions in your group. Be prepared to share your answers with the class.

1. Why do you think a house that uses solar energy needs to store chemical energy in batteries?

2. What is the source of almost all energy on Earth? Justify your answer.

Update the *Project Board*

Think about the results of the demonstration and the investigation, as well as what you have read. Record what you learned about light energy in the *What are we learning?* column of the *Project Board*. Do not forget to add supporting evidence to the *What is our evidence?* column.

Again, it is important to recognize any questions you may have. Well-developed questions can guide your learning. Any questions you have about light energy should be recorded in the *What do we need to investigate?* column.

What's the Point?

Light intensity depends mainly on two factors: the strength (brightness) of the light source and distance from the source. Close to the source, the intensity is greatest. As you move farther away from the light source, intensity decreases. This can be explained with a particle model of light in which photons emitted by the light source travel outward in all directions. As the photons move farther from the source, they spread apart, and fewer photons pass through each unit area. A brighter light source emits more photons. This is what makes it brighter.

△ Guide

Have students answer the *Reflect* questions with their groups. Encourage students to make predictions about the situations described based on what they have observed and learned.

1. Students should recognize that the Sun does not shine at night and solar power needs to be stored in batteries for nighttime use.

2. Students may choose to respond by listing each type of energy—solar, wind, tidal, water, coal, gas, oil, nuclear, geothermal—but should recognize that almost all of our energy comes from the Sun, except for nuclear and geothermal.

△ Guide

As a class, summarize the new ideas that students have learned about light energy. Record the ideas as well as the supporting evidence on the *Project Board*. Then ask students what questions they have about light energy and how it might be used in the *Big Challenge*. Add these questions to the *Project Board* as well.

Update the Project Board

5 min

Students add ideas from the demonstration and investigation to the Project Board.

NOTES

....

....

....

....

....

....

....

....

....

....

More to Learn: Why Is It so Much Warmer Near the Equator Than at the North Pole and South Pole?

5 min

Students consider how climate varies with location on Earth.

More to Learn

Why Is It so Much Warmer Near the Equator Than at the North Pole and South Pole?

The same Sun strikes all parts of Earth, but different parts of Earth have very different climates. Do you know why?

In February, the Arctic Circle is a frozen mass of snow and ice. To the south, there may be four feet of snow in Vermont and New York. Meanwhile, in southern Florida, people are swimming in the warm waters of the Atlantic Ocean or the Gulf of Mexico. Traveling even farther south, at the Equator, it is hot and steamy, with tropical plants and animals thriving in the rain forests. All of these locations are warmed by the same Sun at the same time. Why are there such extreme differences in the heating of Earth? The answer to this question has to do with intensity of light from the Sun and its duration.

Project-Based Inquiry Science

EN 186

○ Engage

Ask students how the climate at the North Pole is different from the climate where they live. *(Without specifics, students should recognize that the North Pole is much colder than locations in the United States.)* Ask students what they know about the South Pole. Make sure students realize that the South Pole is a frigid location, despite having "South" in its name. Read through the text to be sure that students recognize that both of Earth's poles have extremely cold climates.

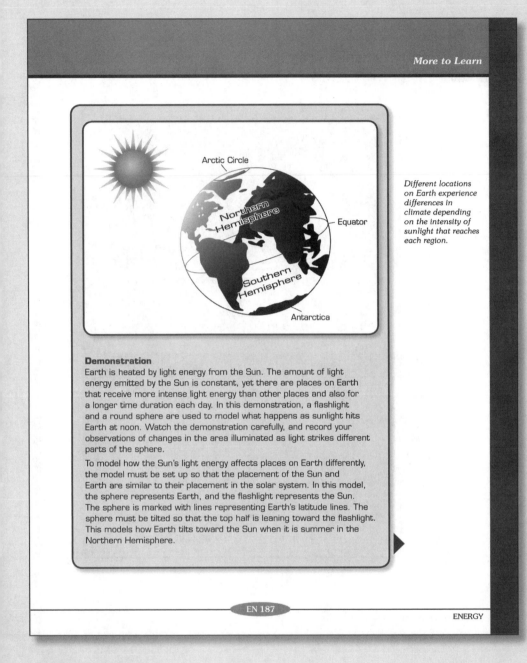

More to Learn

Arctic Circle

Northern Hemisphere

Equator

Southern Hemisphere

Antarctica

Different locations on Earth experience differences in climate depending on the intensity of sunlight that reaches each region.

Demonstration

Earth is heated by light energy from the Sun. The amount of light energy emitted by the Sun is constant, yet there are places on Earth that receive more intense light energy than other places and also for a longer time duration each day. In this demonstration, a flashlight and a round sphere are used to model what happens as sunlight hits Earth at noon. Watch the demonstration carefully, and record your observations of changes in the area illuminated as light strikes different parts of the sphere.

To model how the Sun's light energy affects places on Earth differently, the model must be set up so that the placement of the Sun and Earth are similar to their placement in the solar system. In this model, the sphere represents Earth, and the flashlight represents the Sun. The sphere is marked with lines representing Earth's latitude lines. The sphere must be tilted so that the top half is leaning toward the flashlight. This models how Earth tilts toward the Sun when it is summer in the Northern Hemisphere.

EN 187

ENERGY

Demonstration

5 min

Students observe a demonstration to see how the angle of light from the Sun varies with latitude in the summer.

○ Engage

Let students know that they will now see how the Sun warms Earth. Describe the demonstration to the class. Show students the sphere that will represent Earth, then identify which locations they should focus on. Then ask for a volunteer to assist in the demonstration. Guide that student to measure 30 cm (about 1 ft) from the sphere. Tell the class that this is the location of the Sun.

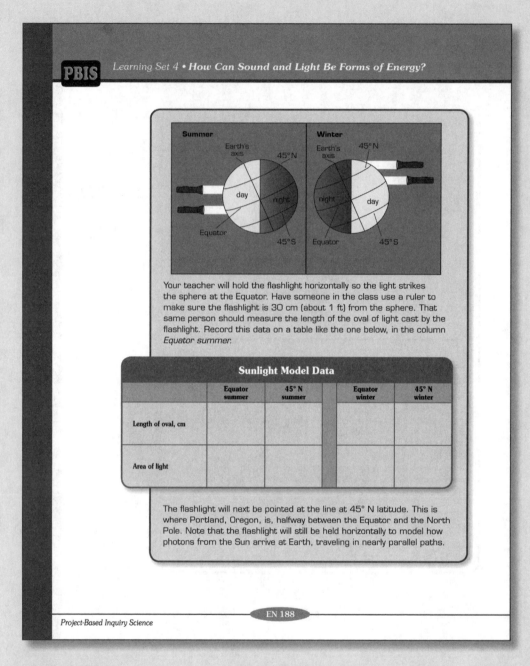

Your teacher will hold the flashlight horizontally so the light strikes the sphere at the Equator. Have someone in the class use a ruler to make sure the flashlight is 30 cm (about 1 ft) from the sphere. That same person should measure the length of the oval of light cast by the flashlight. Record this data on a table like the one below, in the column *Equator summer*.

Sunlight Model Data

	Equator summer	45° N summer		Equator winter	45° N winter
Length of oval, cm					
Area of light					

The flashlight will next be pointed at the line at 45° N latitude. This is where Portland, Oregon, is, halfway between the Equator and the North Pole. Note that the flashlight will still be held horizontally to model how photons from the Sun arrive at Earth, traveling in nearly parallel paths.

EN 188

⬡ Get Going

Have students create a data table similar to the one shown in the student text. Show students how to measure the length of the oval formed by the flashlight. Once students are comfortable with the method, ask a volunteer to measure the length of the oval in each position. Tell all students to record the measurements in their data tables.

More to Learn

Someone should measure to make sure the flashlight is still 30 cm from the sphere and then measure the length of the oval of light. Record this number in the *45° N summer* column of your table.

Analyze Your Data

1. Use the equation for calculating the area of a circle to calculate the approximate area of the ovals of light from the flashlight. Although they are ovals, you can get a good enough approximation of the relationship of their sizes by treating them as circles. Divide the length of the oval by two to get the radius. Square that and multiply it by pi (*π*): 3.14. Record the approximate area of each oval in its column.

2. What do you notice about the relationship of the area of each oval? Which has a larger area? Which has a smaller area?

3. What does that tell you about the light intensity at the Equator versus Portland, Oregon? Which receives more light energy from the Sun?

Demonstration

The flashlight will now be moved to the other side of Earth. This models the relationship between Earth and the Sun in the Northern Hemisphere in the winter. Repeat the measurements you did earlier. First, measure the oval produced at the Equator and then at 45° N latitude. In both cases, use the ruler to make sure the flashlight is 30 cm from the sphere. Measure the length of the oval in each case. Record the measurements in the *Equator winter* and the *45° N winter* columns of your table.

Analyze Your Data

1. Calculate the approximate area of each oval of light from the flashlight, and record the area of each in its column.

2. Compare the areas of the winter and summer Equator ovals. How do they compare? What does this tell you about the amount of light energy they receive from the Sun in the summer and winter?

3. Compare the areas of the ovals produced at 45° latitude in the summer and the winter. What does this tell you about the light intensity at 45° N latitude in the summer and the winter? When does Portland, which is at 45° N latitude, receive more light energy from the Sun, in the summer or in the winter?

Analyze
Your Data

10 min

Students use the data from the demonstration to answer questions and make predictions.

△ Guide and Assess

Have each group discuss answers to the questions, and then share the answers with the class.

1. The area of a circle is calculated as:

$$A = \pi r^2 \text{ or } = \pi \left(\frac{d}{2}\right)^2$$

For example, for an oval which is 5 cm long, the area is approximately:

$$\pi \left(\frac{5}{2}\right)^2 = 20 \text{ cm}^2$$

2. Students should observe that the oval at the Equator has less area than the oval at 45°N latitude (Portland, Oregon).

3. Students should understand that the light intensity is greater at the Equator than at 45°N latitude (Portland, Oregon). Therefore, the Equator receives more light energy per square meter.

Demonstration

5 min

Students observe a demonstration to see how the angle of light from the Sun varies with latitude in the winter.

Demonstration

The flashlight will now be moved to the other side of Earth. This models the relationship between Earth and the Sun in the Northern Hemisphere in the winter. Repeat the measurements you did earlier. First, measure the oval produced at the Equator and then at 45° N latitude. In both cases, use the ruler to make sure the flashlight is 30 cm from the sphere. Measure the length of the oval in each case. Record the measurements in the *Equator winter* and the *45° N winter* columns of your table.

⬡ Get Going

Following the description in the student text, perform the demonstration again, this time on the other side of the sphere. Point out to students that they are observing winter in the Northern Hemisphere.

Analyze Your Data

10 min

Students use the data from the demonstration to answer questions and make predictions.

your ta...

Analyze Your Data

1. Calculate the approximate area of each oval of light from the flashlight, and record the area of each in its column.

2. Compare the areas of the winter and summer Equator ovals. How do they compare? What does this tell you about the amount of light energy they receive from the Sun in the summer and winter?

3. Compare the areas of the ovals produced at 45° latitude in the summer and the winter. What does this tell you about the light intensity at 45° N latitude in the summer and the winter? When does Portland, which is at 45° N latitude, receive more light energy from the Sun, in the summer or in the winter?

△ Guide and Assess

Have each group discuss answers to the questions and then share the answers with the class.

1. Check students' answers to make sure they are using the area equation correctly and recording their answers. Knowing the measurements, make sure that students have performed the calculations correctly.

2. Students should observe that the area of the oval at the Equator in the winter is similar to that in the summer. This means that the amount of light energy that reaches the surface will be about the same.

3. Students should notice that the area of the oval is greater in the winter at 45°N latitude than in the summer. This means that, per square meter, more light energy is received in the summer than in the winter.

NOTES

4. Why it is warmer in the summer than in the winter in Portland? Include what you understand about the tilt of Earth and its relationship to the Sun in the summer and winter.

5. To calculate how much more light energy Portland gets in the summer than in the winter, calculate the ratio of the area of the 45° N latitude in the summer to the area of the 45° N latitude in the winter.

6. Now do the same for the two Equator measurements.

7. Why is the temperature near the Equator about the same all year? Use what you know about light energy to answer this question.

8. Why is it so much colder at the North and South Poles than it is at the Equator?

Reflect

Answer these questions with your group, and be prepared to discuss them with the class.

1. Suppose you stay outside from noon to 3:00 PM on a sunny day in winter. Compare this to staying outside from noon to 3:00 PM on a sunny day in summer. In which case would you be more likely to get a sunburn? Why?

2. You are asked to make measurements of the oval of light hitting the model Earth at 45° S latitude in the Southern Hemisphere. Estimate from the data already collected what you would expect the length of the oval to be at 45° S latitude when it is summer in the Northern Hemisphere. What will the length of the oval be at 45° S latitude when it is winter in the Northern Hemisphere?

3. The demonstration showed how the Sun's rays strike Earth at around noon. In a single day, however, the sun rises low in the East, moves across the sky, and sets low in the West. At what time(s) of day is the intensity of sunlight the greatest? At what time(s) of day is the intensity of sunlight the least?

EN 190

4. Students should understand that the axis of Earth is tilted toward the Sun in the summer and causes the solar radiation to be more direct in the summer (smaller oval). More light energy per square meter is received in Portland, making the climate warmer.

5. Students' answers will vary depending on the data, but the ratio should be greater than 1.

6. Students should calculate that the ratio of the areas to be about 1.

7. Students should describe how the amount of light energy received at the Equator, per square meter, is about the same in the winter as in the summer. This keeps the temperature at about the same point all year around.

8. Students should recognize that very little direct sunlight is received at the North Pole and South Pole, whether it is summer or winter. This keeps those regions very cold.

☐ Assess

Have students answer these questions with their groups. As students discuss, listen for the following:

1. Students should recognize that the sunlight is more direct during summer and therefore makes it more likely that they would get a sunburn in summer than in winter.

2. Students should make predictions based on their data, keeping in mind that it is winter in the Southern Hemisphere when it is summer in the Northern Hemisphere.

3. Students should recognize that the reason for the Sun's apparent motion is Earth's rotation. As a result, the sunlight is most intense at noon and least intense near sunrise and sunset.

Reflect

5 min

Students answer questions to apply their knowledge to new situations.

Assessment Options

Targeted Concepts, Skills, and Nature of Science	How do I know if students got it?
Scientists often work together and then share their findings. Sharing findings makes new information available and helps scientists refine their ideas and build on others' ideas. When another person's or group's idea is used, credit needs to be given.	**ASK:** How did you refine your conclusions about the relationships between a light source and the intensity of light based on the input of other students? **LISTEN:** Students may mention a relationship or observation they had not considered or that their group did not investigate.

Targeted Concepts, Skills, and Nature of Science	How do I know if students got it?
Light can be described by a particle nature.	**ASK:** Which model of light considers the particle nature of light? **LISTEN:** Students should describe the particle model of light as involving packets of energy called photons.
Light can be described by its intensity.	**ASK:** What can you do to increase the brightness of light produced on a kitchen table by an overhead lamp? **LISTEN:** Students should apply what they have learned to make suggestions, such as moving the lamp closer to the table or by replacing the lamp's bulb with a brighter one.

Teacher Reflection Questions

- How were you able to connect the models in this section to the actual event, such as light striking Earth at different times of the year? What might you try next time?

- What difficulties did students have calculating the area illuminated by the light? How might you help them with this in the future?

- How were you able to engage students in discussing the differences among their results? What can you do to keep them engaged in further discussions?

4.6 Explore

How Does Light Behave Like a Wave?

◄ 3 class periods

A class period is considered to be one 40 to 50 minute class.

Overview

Students observe a demonstration in which a pencil is placed in water in different ways. Through these observations, they begin to think about factors that affect the path of light. Students think about similarities between sound waves and light waves. The speed of light is presented, followed by the concepts of reflection, diffraction, and refraction of light. They read about the electromagnetic spectrum, which shows students that visible light makes up only a small portion of all electromagnetic waves. Students conclude the section by adding claims and supporting evidence to the *Project Board* about what they learned in this section. In the *More to Learn* section that follows, students learn how the eye transforms the light it receives into an image interpreted by the brain.

Targeted Concepts, Skills, and Nature of Science	Performance Expectations
Scientists often work together and then share their findings. Sharing findings makes new information available and helps scientists refine their ideas and build on others' ideas. When another person's or group's idea is used, credit needs to be given.	Students share their ideas about the properties of light.
Light can be described as having a wave nature.	Students discover that light has wave characteristics in addition to its particle characteristics.
Visible light is a small band within the electromagnetic spectrum, which is energy that travels in the form of waves.	Students examine the placement of visible light in the electromagnetic spectrum.

Targeted Concepts, Skills, and Nature of Science	Performance Expectations
White light is made up of different colors of light.	Students discover that white light can be separated into individual colors according to wavelength.
The electromagnetic spectrum arranges radiation in terms of frequency and wavelength.	Students recognize the arrangement of the electromagnetic spectrum according to wavelength and frequency.
Light travels at different speeds in different materials.	Students learn that light travels fastest in a vacuum and at slower speeds in other materials.
The eye is the human organ that detects light.	Students learn about the parts of the eye and how it forms images that are interpreted by the brain.
Light interacts with surfaces through reflection and refraction.	Students investigate reflection, diffraction, and refraction.

Materials

1 per class	Pencil
	Glass of water
	Cloth
	Tennis ball
1 per student	*Create Your Explanation* page
	Project Board page
1 per class	Class *Project Board*

NOTES

....

....

....

450

Homework Options

Reflection

- **Science Content:** Why is light described by a wave-particle duality? *(Students should explain that some characteristics of light can be explained by a wave model and others can be explained by the particle model.)*

- **Science Content:** How does the energy carried by gamma rays compare to that of radio waves? *(Students should explain that gamma rays have shorter wavelengths and higher frequencies, which indicates that they carry more energy.)*

NOTES

....

....

....

....

....

....

....

....

....

....

....

NOTES

SECTION 4.6 IMPLEMENTATION

◀ 3 class periods*

4.6 Explore

How Does Light Behave Like a Wave?

Your experience with light energy has suggested that light travels from point A, a source, to point B, a surface, in a straight line. You have learned about two factors that affect the light intensity at the surface: the brightness of the source and the distance of point B from the source. Light spreads out as it travels away from the source, and this can be modeled using a particle model of light.

However, this particle model is not a perfect model of light energy. Other factors exist that can be modeled only by thinking of light as a wave. The intensity of light can be affected by the characteristics of those waves.

When you place a straw in water, it looks like the straw is broken. Why do you think it looks that way?

Demonstration

You will observe as your teacher inserts a pencil into a cup in a variety of situations. Record your observations on paper at each step.

1. The pencil is inserted into the cup and pulled out. Record your observations of the pencil.

2. The cup is filled with water. The pencil is inserted into the water, pulled out of the water, and finally inserted back into the water. Record your observations.

3. The cup is covered with a cloth. After the cloth is removed, record your observations of how the pencil has changed.

4. While still in the water, the pencil is moved slowly, tipped from left to center to right and back again several times. Record your observations of how the pencil appears in the left position, the center position, and the right position.

EN 191

ENERGY

4.6 Explore

How Does Light Behave Like a Wave?

5 min

Students begin to consider light as a wave.

◯ Engage

Use the idea of water waves to introduce the concept of light waves.

TEACHER TALK

"Have you ever seen waves in an ocean, lake, or even in a pond? How would you describe them? Do they have high points and low points? Do they carry water with them? What do you think water waves have to do with the light you see?"

*A class period is considered to be one 40 to 50 minute class.

Demonstration

10 min

Students observe a demonstration involving the appearance of a pencil in water.

the charac......... ...... those waves.

Demonstration

You will observe as your teacher inserts a pencil into a cup in a variety of situations. Record your observations on paper at each step.

1. The pencil is inserted into the cup and pulled out. Record your observations of the pencil.

2. The cup is filled with water. The pencil is inserted into the water, pulled out of the water, and finally inserted back into the water. Record your observations.

3. The cup is covered with a cloth. After the cloth is removed, record your observations of how the pencil has changed.

4. While still in the water, the pencil is moved slowly, tipped from left to center to right and back again several times. Record your observations of how the pencil appears in the left position, the center position, and the right position.

EN 191

ENERGY

⬡ Get Going

Tell students to observe the pencil closely as you perform the demonstration. Explain that the pencil itself is not changing, but the appearance of the pencil is. Give students an opportunity to record their observations after each step. Repeat any steps as needed.

NOTES

....

....

....

....

....

....

5. Record your observations of the pencil after it is taken out of the cup of water.

Analyze Your Data

1. How does your eye see the pencil when the teacher first shows it? Make a sketch showing the path of light rays from the pencil to your eyes.

2. How did the pencil appear when placed into the empty cup?

3. How is the path the light takes different after the pencil is placed in the water? Make a sketch showing the path of light rays from the pencil to your eyes that would match your observations.

4. Identify factors that affected the pencil's appearance.

5. Why do you think the pencil appeared to change and then was restored to its original form?

Communicate Your Results

Share Your Ideas

As a class, share your observations. Discuss any differences in observations. If you do not understand what a person is presenting, or if you disagree about the observations, ask a question. Remember to be respectful.

Make a class list of the factors that affect the pencil's appearance. Note any disagreements. Later you will have a chance to put questions on the *Project Board* that will help you settle those disagreements.

The squares on the bottom of a swimming pool look crooked when water is in the pool.

Analyze Your Data

10 min

Students discuss their observations of the pencil demonstration, engaging them in thinking about how their eyes see light.

△ Guide and Assess

Explain to students that they can see objects because light travels from the object to their eyes. Then have students discuss the questions in their groups. Join in any discussions during which students are having difficulty suggesting answers. Remind students that they should give their best answers based on what they know now, but they will learn more as they complete the section.

1. Students should describe the pencil as appearing straight and unbroken. They should sketch a straight line to describe the light rays from the pencil to their eyes.

2. Students should describe how the pencil did not change in appearance when placed in the empty cup.

3. Students should answer that the pencil looks broken when placed in the water. They should sketch it showing a straight line where the top of the pencil is out of the water, but must use two straight lines to show the light rays for the pencil in the water.

4. Students should identify the surface of the water as a factor affecting the pencil's appearance.

5. Students may respond that the water distorted, or bent, the light rays.

Communicate Your Results: Share Your Ideas

5 min

Students share their analysis with the class.

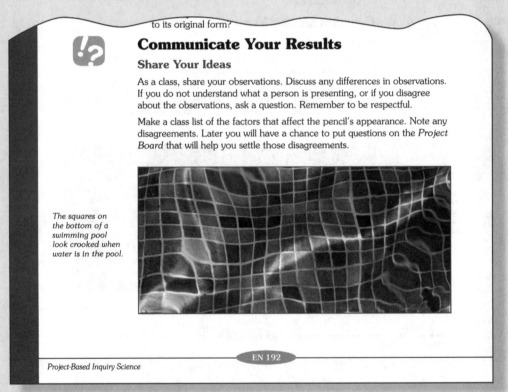

to its original form?

Communicate Your Results

Share Your Ideas

As a class, share your observations. Discuss any differences in observations. If you do not understand what a person is presenting, or if you disagree about the observations, ask a question. Remember to be respectful.

Make a class list of the factors that affect the pencil's appearance. Note any disagreements. Later you will have a chance to put questions on the *Project Board* that will help you settle those disagreements.

The squares on the bottom of a swimming pool look crooked when water is in the pool.

EN 192

Project-Based Inquiry Science

△ Guide

Lead a class discussion to summarize the ideas of each group. Welcome all ideas at this point, and address them throughout the section. Remind students that they should be listening for ideas and questions that they can later add to the *Project Board*.

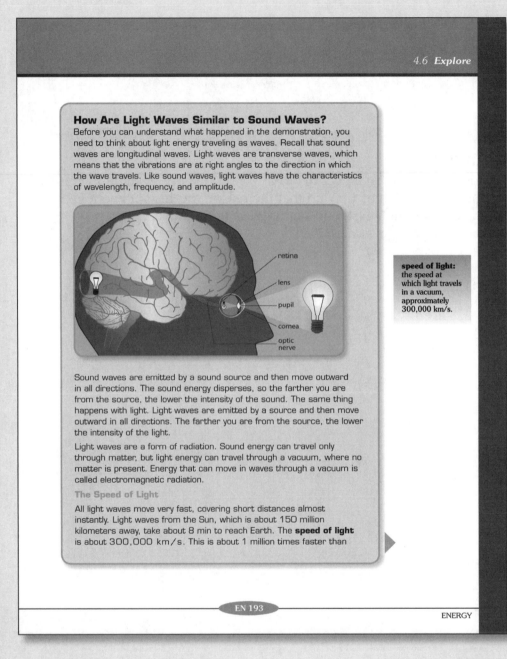

4.6 Explore

How Are Light Waves Similar to Sound Waves?

Before you can understand what happened in the demonstration, you need to think about light energy traveling as waves. Recall that sound waves are longitudinal waves. Light waves are transverse waves, which means that the vibrations are at right angles to the direction in which the wave travels. Like sound waves, light waves have the characteristics of wavelength, frequency, and amplitude.

retina

lens

pupil

cornea

optic nerve

speed of light: the speed at which light travels in a vacuum, approximately 300,000 km/s.

Sound waves are emitted by a sound source and then move outward in all directions. The sound energy disperses, so the farther you are from the source, the lower the intensity of the sound. The same thing happens with light. Light waves are emitted by a source and then move outward in all directions. The farther you are from the source, the lower the intensity of the light.

Light waves are a form of radiation. Sound energy can travel only through matter, but light energy can travel through a vacuum, where no matter is present. Energy that can move in waves through a vacuum is called electromagnetic radiation.

The Speed of Light

All light waves move very fast, covering short distances almost instantly. Light waves from the Sun, which is about 150 million kilometers away, take about 8 min to reach Earth. The **speed of light** is about 300,000 km/s. This is about 1 million times faster than

ENERGY

How Are Light Waves Similar to Sound Waves?

10 min

Students relate light waves to sound waves.

META NOTES

Light waves are very different from transverse waves on a rope. A light wave consists of vibrating electric and magnetic fields. The fields vibrate at right angles to each other and to the direction of motion of the wave.

△ Guide

Remind students of longitudinal and transverse waves. Make sure students recall that sound travels as longitudinal waves. Then point out that light can be described by transverse waves. Unlike waves on a rope, light waves and other electromagnetic waves do not carry energy by disturbing particles of matter. Tell students that this makes it possible for light to travel through the vacuum of space, whereas sound cannot.

ENERGY

The Speed of Light

5 min

Students are introduced to the speed of light.

META NOTES

Students may have difficulty appreciating the magnitude of the speed of light. It may help to offer some additional examples. For example, use a clock or stopwatch to measure 1 s. Then explain that if a beam of light curved around Earth, it would make almost 8 complete trips in 1 s.

META NOTES

Because distances in space are so vast, scientists use a unit of distance known as the light-year. One light-year is the distance light can travel in one year, which is about 9,500,000,000,000 km.

called electromagnetic radiation.

The Speed of Light

All light waves move very fast, covering short distances almost instantly. Light waves from the Sun, which is about 150 million kilometers away, take about 8 min to reach Earth. The **speed of light** is about 300,000 km/s. This is about 1 million times faster than

○ **Engage**

Ask students if they have ever heard anyone say that, "Nothing travels faster than the speed of light." Explain that the reason for this comment is that light travels extremely fast, and nothing has been found to exceed it.

NOTES

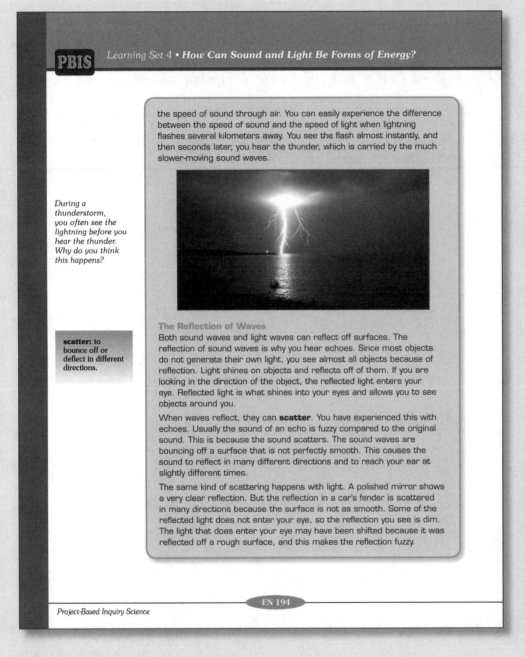

the speed of sound through air. You can easily experience the difference between the speed of sound and the speed of light when lightning flashes several kilometers away. You see the flash almost instantly, and then seconds later, you hear the thunder, which is carried by the much slower-moving sound waves.

During a thunderstorm, you often see the lightning before you hear the thunder. Why do you think this happens?

scatter: to bounce off or deflect in different directions.

The Reflection of Waves

Both sound waves and light waves can reflect off surfaces. The reflection of sound waves is why you hear echoes. Since most objects do not generate their own light, you see almost all objects because of reflection. Light shines on objects and reflects off of them. If you are looking in the direction of the object, the reflected light enters your eye. Reflected light is what shines into your eyes and allows you to see objects around you.

When waves reflect, they can **scatter**. You have experienced this with echoes. Usually the sound of an echo is fuzzy compared to the original sound. This is because the sound scatters. The sound waves are bouncing off a surface that is not perfectly smooth. This causes the sound to reflect in many different directions and to reach your ear at slightly different times.

The same kind of scattering happens with light. A polished mirror shows a very clear reflection. But the reflection in a car's fender is scattered in many directions because the surface is not as smooth. Some of the reflected light does not enter your eye, so the reflection you see is dim. The light that does enter your eye may have been shifted because it was reflected off a rough surface, and this makes the reflection fuzzy.

The Reflection of Waves

10 min

Students read about how light waves reflect from surfaces.

META NOTES

The law of reflection states that the angle at which light strikes a surface, the angle of incidence, equals the angle at which the light leaves the surface, the angle of reflection. Students may discover this if they roll a ball against a wall.

○ Engage

Have a volunteer sit on the floor and roll a tennis ball straight toward the wall. Allow the class to watch the ball return to the volunteer after bouncing off the wall. Then have the volunteer roll the ball at an angle to the wall. Allow the class to watch the ball bounce off the wall away from the volunteer. Help students understand that the ball is reflected from the wall much like light is reflected from a surface.

△ Guide

Use the ball example to understand that light bounces off a surface during reflection. Help students understand the difference between diffuse reflection, during which reflected waves scatter, and mirror reflection, during which a clear image is formed.

Then explain to students that light can also bend. When light bends, it makes your eye think the light came from a different place than it really did. This is when objects in water can look bent or broken.

NOTES

....

....

....

....

....

....

....

....

....

....

....

4.6

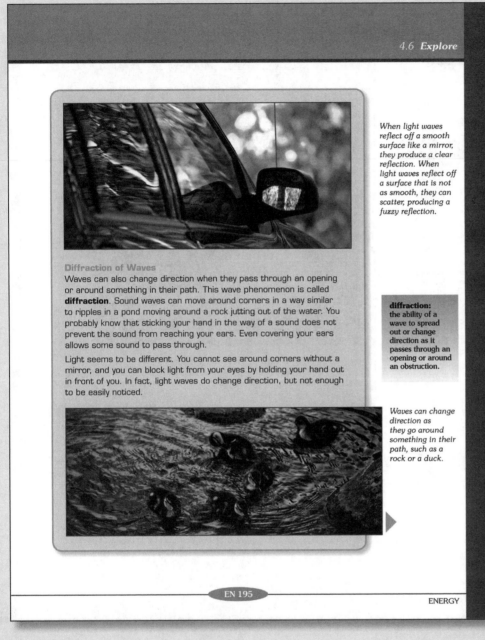

4.6 *Explore*

When light waves reflect off a smooth surface like a mirror, they produce a clear reflection. When light waves reflect off a surface that is not as smooth, they can scatter, producing a fuzzy reflection.

Diffraction of Waves

Waves can also change direction when they pass through an opening or around something in their path. This wave phenomenon is called **diffraction**. Sound waves can move around corners in a way similar to ripples in a pond moving around a rock jutting out of the water. You probably know that sticking your hand in the way of a sound does not prevent the sound from reaching your ears. Even covering your ears allows some sound to pass through.

Light seems to be different. You cannot see around corners without a mirror, and you can block light from your eyes by holding your hand out in front of you. In fact, light waves do change direction, but not enough to be easily noticed.

diffraction: the ability of a wave to spread out or change direction as it passes through an opening or around an obstruction.

Waves can change direction as they go around something in their path, such as a rock or a duck.

EN 195

ENERGY

Diffraction of Waves

5 min

Students read about how waves move around objects by diffraction.

⭕ Engage

Have students block their image of you using their hands. Then, have students attempt to block your voice (as you continue talking) by using their hands in the same way. Tell them that light cannot go around corners, but that sound can due to diffraction.

Refraction of Waves

< 5 min

Students read about how light is bent by refraction.

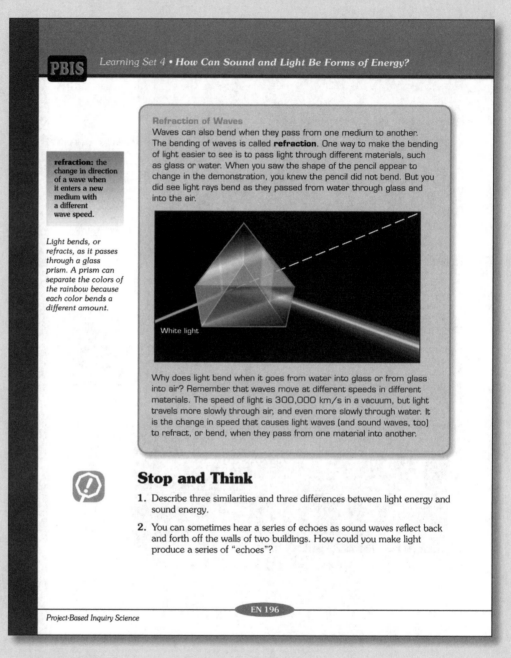

refraction: the change in direction of a wave when it enters a new medium with a different wave speed.

Light bends, or refracts, as it passes through a glass prism. A prism can separate the colors of the rainbow because each color bends a different amount.

Refraction of Waves

Waves can also bend when they pass from one medium to another. The bending of waves is called **refraction**. One way to make the bending of light easier to see is to pass light through different materials, such as glass or water. When you saw the shape of the pencil appear to change in the demonstration, you knew the pencil did not bend. But you did see light rays bend as they passed from water through glass and into the air.

White light

Why does light bend when it goes from water into glass or from glass into air? Remember that waves move at different speeds in different materials. The speed of light is 300,000 km/s in a vacuum, but light travels more slowly through air, and even more slowly through water. It is the change in speed that causes light waves (and sound waves, too) to refract, or bend, when they pass from one material into another.

Stop and Think

1. Describe three similarities and three differences between light energy and sound energy.

2. You can sometimes hear a series of echoes as sound waves reflect back and forth off the walls of two buildings. How could you make light produce a series of "echoes"?

EN 196

Project-Based Inquiry Science

⬡ Get Going

Tell students that when light strikes a boundary between two materials at an angle, one side of the wave changes speed before the other. This causes the light to bend in a process known as refraction.

△ Guide and Assess

Have students discuss answers to the *Stop and Think* questions. Listen as students use what they have learned about light.

1. Student may identify some of the following as similarities in their answers:

   - travel in waves

   - transport energy, not matter

   - have characteristic wavelength, frequency, amplitude

   - diminish in intensity with distance from source

   - can be reflected, refracted, and diffracted

   They may identify some of the following differences between light energy and sound energy:

   - light energy can travel through a vacuum, sound energy cannot

   - light energy can be stopped by a barrier between source and object, sound energy cannot be stopped entirely

   - light energy is perceived by the eyes, sound energy by the ears

   - light energy has an electric field and a magnetic field, sound energy travels through particles

   - light is about 1 million times as fast as sound

   - light travels in transverse waves while sound travels in longitudinal waves

2. Students may respond that light could be reflected back and forth many times by placing two mirrors facing each other.

Stop and Think

10 min

Students answer questions to focus their ideas about light energy.

NOTES

....

....

Revise Your Explanations

5 min

Students revise earlier explanations of light.

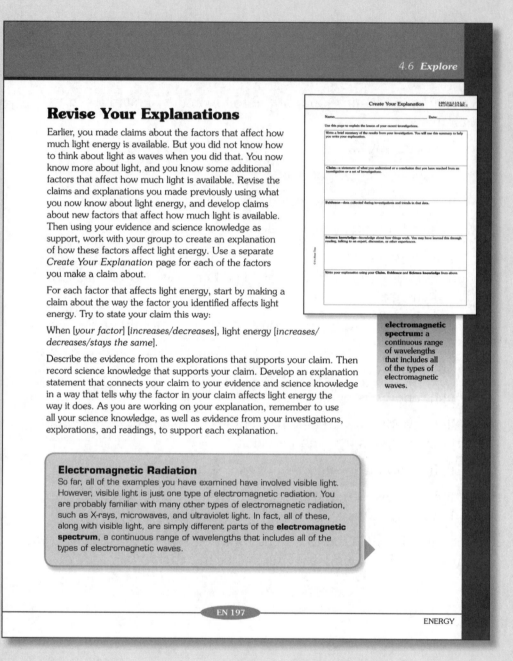

Revise Your Explanations

Earlier, you made claims about the factors that affect how much light energy is available. But you did not know how to think about light as waves when you did that. You now know more about light, and you know some additional factors that affect how much light is available. Revise the claims and explanations you made previously using what you now know about light energy, and develop claims about new factors that affect how much light is available. Then using your evidence and science knowledge as support, work with your group to create an explanation of how these factors affect light energy. Use a separate *Create Your Explanation* page for each of the factors you make a claim about.

For each factor that affects light energy, start by making a claim about the way the factor you identified affects light energy. Try to state your claim this way:

When [*your factor*] [*increases/decreases*], light energy [*increases/decreases/stays the same*].

Describe the evidence from the explorations that supports your claim. Then record science knowledge that supports your claim. Develop an explanation statement that connects your claim to your evidence and science knowledge in a way that tells why the factor in your claim affects light energy the way it does. As you are working on your explanation, remember to use all your science knowledge, as well as evidence from your investigations, explorations, and readings, to support each explanation.

electromagnetic spectrum: a continuous range of wavelengths that includes all of the types of electromagnetic waves.

> **Electromagnetic Radiation**
>
> So far, all of the examples you have examined have involved visible light. However, visible light is just one type of electromagnetic radiation. You are probably familiar with many other types of electromagnetic radiation, such as X-rays, microwaves, and ultraviolet light. In fact, all of these, along with visible light, are simply different parts of the **electromagnetic spectrum**, a continuous range of wavelengths that includes all of the types of electromagnetic waves.

ENERGY

△ Guide

Ask students to think back to their explanations from *Section 4.5*. Have them take out their *Create Your Explanation* pages from that section. Advise them to decide what new things they have learned about light in their groups. Then guide them to discuss how they can apply these to their earlier explanations. Emphasize that they should listen to each other's ideas and be respectful when making arguments in their discussions. Remind them that every claim they make needs to be supported by science knowledge or evidence.

◯ Engage

Ask students if they have ever cooked food in a microwave oven, talked on a cell phone, or had an X-ray taken of their teeth. Explain that these examples involve other forms of electromagnetic radiation. Use the diagram of the electromagnetic spectrum to point out the various forms of radiation.

Electro-magnetic Radiation

10 min

Students learn about other types of electromagnetic radiation.

NOTES

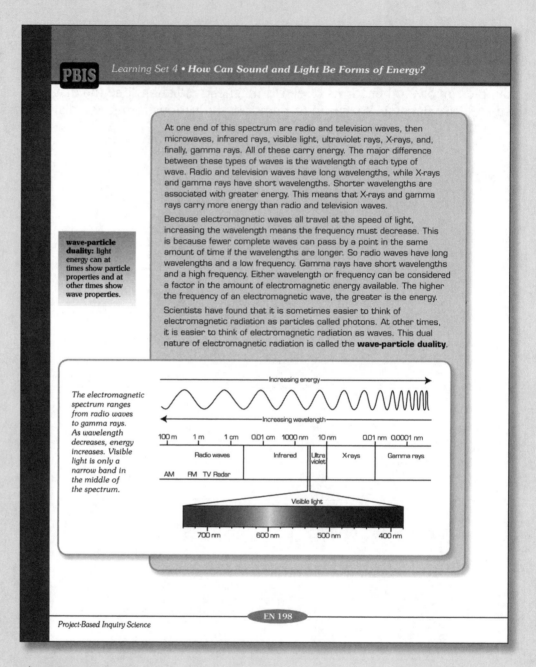

At one end of this spectrum are radio and television waves, then microwaves, infrared rays, visible light, ultraviolet rays, X-rays, and, finally, gamma rays. All of these carry energy. The major difference between these types of waves is the wavelength of each type of wave. Radio and television waves have long wavelengths, while X-rays and gamma rays have short wavelengths. Shorter wavelengths are associated with greater energy. This means that X-rays and gamma rays carry more energy than radio and television waves.

Because electromagnetic waves all travel at the speed of light, increasing the wavelength means the frequency must decrease. This is because fewer complete waves can pass by a point in the same amount of time if the wavelengths are longer. So radio waves have long wavelengths and a low frequency. Gamma rays have short wavelengths and a high frequency. Either wavelength or frequency can be considered a factor in the amount of electromagnetic energy available. The higher the frequency of an electromagnetic wave, the greater is the energy.

Scientists have found that it is sometimes easier to think of electromagnetic radiation as particles called photons. At other times, it is easier to think of electromagnetic radiation as waves. This dual nature of electromagnetic radiation is called the **wave-particle duality**.

wave-particle duality: light energy can at times show particle properties and at other times show wave properties.

The electromagnetic spectrum ranges from radio waves to gamma rays. As wavelength decreases, energy increases. Visible light is only a narrow band in the middle of the spectrum.

Increasing energy

Increasing wavelength

| 100 m | 1 m | 1 cm | 0.01 cm | 1000 nm | 10 nm | 0.01 nm | 0.0001 nm |

Radio waves   Infrared   Ultra violet   X-rays   Gamma rays

AM   FM   TV Radar

Visible light

700 nm   600 nm   500 nm   400 nm

△ **Guide**

Remind students that waves can be described by wavelength and frequency. Have students determine how the spectrum is arranged in terms of these quantities. Help students recognize that frequency increases in one direction of the spectrum as wavelength decreases.

4.6 Explore

Conference

Share Your Explanations

Share your claims and explanation statements with the class. As you listen to other groups, notice how well their claims match your claims. Notice whether any other group stated any of your claims better than you did. Notice if any group made claims different from yours. Examine the evidence each group used to support its claims. Make sure you agree with the claims and evidence used to support each. Notice the explanation statements of other groups. You may notice that some groups expressed their explanations better than your group did.

Revise Your Explanations

As a class, revise the set of claims and explanations about light energy. Make sure everybody agrees with each claim and understands each explanation statement.

Update the *Project Board*

The question for this section of the Unit is *How does light behave like a wave?* Add what you now know about light as a wave to the *What are we learning?* column. Do not forget to add evidence to the *What is our evidence?* column for every entry.

What's the Point?

Light refracts, or bends, when it passes from one material into another material because the speed of the waves changes. Electromagnetic waves are transverse waves that can travel though a vacuum. Visible light is a small portion of the electromagnetic spectrum. All the waves in the electromagnetic spectrum travel at the speed of light (300,000 km/s in a vacuum). The waves in the electromagnetic spectrum differ in wavelength and frequency. As wavelength increases, frequency decreases. If other factors are the same, electromagnetic waves with lower frequency have less energy than electromagnetic waves with higher frequency.

Conference: Share Your Explanations

10 min

Students share their revised explanations of light.

⚠ Guide

Allow students to share their revised explanations, as well as their reasons for any changes. If any students have decided not to revise their explanation, make sure they present the reasons for their decision.

Update the Project Board

5 min

*Students add ideas
and questions to the
Project Board.*

explanation statement.

Update the *Project Board*

The question for this section of the Unit is *How does light behave like
a wave?* Add what you now know about light as a wave to the *What are
we learning?* column. Do not forget to add evidence to the *What is our
evidence?* column for every entry.

What's the Point?

△ **Guide**

Invite students to share their ideas about light along with their questions.
Encourage students to suggest investigations they would like to conduct
to learn more about light. Record all information on the *Project Board* in
the appropriate columns. Note any topics students disagree on so you can
revisit them later.

NOTES

4.6

More to Learn

How Do You See Light?

pupil: the circular opening in the center of the iris that controls the amount of light that enters the eye.

iris: a flat, colored, ring-shaped membrane with an adjustable circular opening at the center.

lens: a structure in the eye that changes shape to focus light and images onto the retina.

retina: the layer at the back of the inside of the eye containing cells that respond to light and color.

optic nerve: cells that transmit electrical signals from the retina to the brain.

cones: cells that respond to bright light, responsible for color detection and sharpness of vision.

rods: light-sensitive cells responsible for vision in dim light.

Eyes are the sense organs that detect light waves. In the eye, light energy and color information are transformed into nerve impulses (electrical energy). This energy is sent to your brain for interpretation. Think about the front of your eyes. This is the part that you are most familiar with, since you can see it. In the center is the **pupil**, which is an opening that allows light to come into the eye. The **iris** is a membrane that surrounds the pupil. The iris is the part that determines the color of your eyes. The iris also controls the size of the pupil and the amount of light that comes into the eye. Just behind the pupil and iris is the **lens**, which focuses light into the back of the eye. In the back of the eye is the **retina**, which is made of cells that receive the light energy and react to its intensity by sending an impulse to the brain. The signals are sent to the brain along the **optic nerve**.

The retina is the place in the eye where light energy is transformed into chemical energy. The retina is made up of **cones** and **rods**. The rods respond to the overall intensity of light coming into the eye. The rods are more sensitive to light than the cones, so they are used in night vision. Cones are primarily responsible for identifying color differences in light.

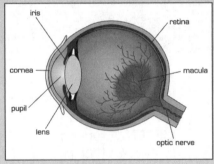

Light energy enters the eye, is converted into chemical energy in the retina, and then transformed into electrical energy in signals sent to the brain. The eye is another example of one of nature's Rube Goldberg machines.

EN 200

More to Learn: How Do You See Light?

10 min

Students learn how the human eye forms images.

META NOTES

In some eyes, the image is formed in front of or behind the retina which make it fuzzy when interpreted by the brain. Corrective lenses, such as eyeglasses or contact lenses, can change the way in which light is bent to make sure the image forms correctly.

△ Guide

Read through the information about the eye together. Use the diagram to identify the parts of the eye. Make sure that students can trace the path of light and signals using the diagram of light traveling through the brain in the *How Are Light Waves Similar to Sound Waves?* textbox earlier in the section.

Assessment Options

Targeted Concepts, Skills, and Nature of Science	How do I know if students got it?
Scientists often work together and then share their findings. Sharing findings makes new information available and helps scientists refine their ideas and build on others' ideas. When another person's or group's idea is used, credit needs to be given.	**ASK:** What did you learn by reviewing the claims of other groups? **LISTEN:** Students should mention if other claims supported theirs or differed from theirs.
Light can be described by a wave nature.	**ASK:** What type of wave best describes light? **LISTEN:** Students should identify light as a transverse wave.
Visible light is a small band within the electromagnetic spectrum, which is energy that travels in the form of waves.	**ASK:** How would you describe the portion of the electromagnetic spectrum made up of visible light? **LISTEN:** Students should describe a relatively small portion of the spectrum.
White light is made up of different colors of light.	**ASK:** What characteristic of light determines the order of colors in a rainbow? **LISTEN:** Students should explain that each color of light has a different wavelength.
The electromagnetic spectrum arranges radiation in terms of frequency and wavelength.	**ASK:** How is wavelength related to energy in electromagnetic waves? **LISTEN:** Students should explain that waves with greater wavelengths, such as radio waves and microwaves, carry less energy than waves with shorter wavelengths, such as gamma rays.

Targeted Concepts, Skills, and Nature of Science	How do I know if students got it?
Light travels at different speeds in different materials.	**ASK:** What is significant about the speed of light in a vacuum? **LISTEN:** Students might recall that this is the fastest known speed in the universe.
The eye is the human organ that detects light.	**ASK:** What are the roles of rods and cones in the eye? **LISTEN:** Students should describe how they interpret the color and intensity of light that enters the eye.
Light interacts with surfaces through reflection and refraction.	**ASK:** Why does light bend when it enters a new medium? **LISTEN:** Students should describe that the speed of light changes as it enters a new medium. Much like in their model, if light enters at an angle, part of the light changes speed before the other, causing it to bend.

Teacher Reflection Questions

- How were you able to engage students to answer questions before they knew the complete answers? How can you help students with this?

- How did you get students to ask each other specific questions about their claims or ideas? What can you do to encourage this in the future?

- What difficulties did students have understanding the extremely high speed of light? What might you try next time?

NOTES

Back to the Big Challenge

Design a Rube Goldberg Machine to Turn Off a Light

◀ $1\frac{1}{2}$ *class periods*

A class period is considered to be one 40 to 50 minute class.

Overview

Students analyze their energy-transformation cartoons once more to look for indicators of sound and light energy. They develop claims and explanations about sound and light energy in terms of whether they represent kinetic or potential energy. Students use their explanations to design steps for their own Rube Goldberg machines that use and produce sound energy or light energy. Students share their ideas and interact to learn from each other's designs and they relate what they learn to the *Big Challenge*.

Targeted Concepts, Skills, and Nature of Science	Performance Expectations
Scientists often work together and then share their findings. Sharing findings makes new information available and helps scientists refine their ideas and build on others' ideas. When another person's or group's idea is used, credit needs to be given.	Students share their ideas about sound and light energy, and how they can be related to designing a Rube Goldberg machine.
Scientific knowledge is developed through observations, recording and analysis of data, and development of explanations based on evidence.	Students develop explanations about sound and light energy.
Energy exists in different forms and can be changed from one form to another.	Students look for forms of energy that exist before and after a step in their energy-transformation cartoons.
Sound is the transfer of energy as longitudinal waves that cannot travel through a vacuum.	Students design a step for their Rube Goldberg machines that uses or produces sound energy.

Targeted Concepts, Skills, and Nature of Science	Performance Expectations
Visible light is a small band within the electromagnetic spectrum, which is energy that travels in the form of waves.	Students design a step for their Rube Goldberg machines that uses or produces light energy.

Materials	
1 per student	*Energy-transformation Cartoon* page *Create Your Explanation* page *My Rube Goldberg Machine* page *Project Board* page
1 per class	Class *Project Board*

Homework Options

Reflection

- **Science Content:** Suppose someone is sitting at a piano, but you have earplugs that prevent you from hearing sound. What can you do to determine if a sound is being produced by the piano? *(Students may recognize that they can feel the piano for a vibration. This question may help students to recognize ways to use sound in their Rube Goldberg designs.)*

- **Science Process:** Why is it important to let other students ask questions about your design or to make suggestions about it? *(Students should recognize that scientists build on the ideas of others, and they can only consider their results valid after others have reviewed and repeated them.)*

Learning Set 4

Back to the Big Challenge

Design a Rube Goldberg Machine to Turn Off a Light

The *Big Challenge* you are working on for this Unit is *Design a Rube Goldberg machine to turn off a light*. You have considered how thermal energy and chemical energy might be involved in a Rube Goldberg machine that will turn off a light. You now know enough about light energy and sound energy to imagine how light energy or sound energy might be involved in your machine. You will soon be designing a set of steps that transform light energy or sound energy into another form of energy. However, before doing that, you will think once more about whether light energy and sound energy are kinetic energy or potential energy and how they do work.

Reflect

To help you think about light energy and sound energy, you will examine the energy-transformation cartoons again from the *Introduction* to this Unit. Identify the steps that show light energy and sound energy transformations in your group's cartoon, and record them on an *Energy-transformation Cartoon* page. Fill in the blocks in the row for each step you identify. Then for each step, answer these questions. Be prepared to share your answers with the class.

1. How do you know the step involves light energy or sound energy transformations? What are the indicators?

2. How does the step transform light energy or sound energy?

Energy-transformation Cartoon

Name: _____ Date: _____

Fill in the letter of the step you are analyzing. Then fill in other information about that step.

Name of your machine: _____ Purpose of your machine: _____

Step	Changes/Work done	Energy type in	Energy types out	Indicators of energy transformations

Record questions about anything on which your group does not agree and anything you do not understand.

EN 201

ENERGY

Learning Set 4

Back to the Big Challenge

5 min

Students revisit the goal of the Big Challenge *by summarizing what they have learned about light and sound energy.*

○ Engage

Ask students to think of a task that is accomplished through sound. Perhaps students have seen or used a device that can turn an appliance on and off by clapping. In this way, help students start thinking about how they can use sound and light to accomplish the *Big Challenge*.

*A class period is considered to be one 40 to 50 minute class.

Reflect

10 min

Students review the energy-transformation cartoons in terms of light and sound energy.

Reflect

To help you think about light energy and sound energy, you will examine the energy-transformation cartoons again from the *Introduction* to this Unit. Identify the steps that show light energy and sound energy transformations in your group's cartoon, and record them on an *Energy-transformation Cartoon* page. Fill in the blocks in the row for each step you identify. Then for each step, answer these questions. Be prepared to share your answers with the class.

1. How do you know the step involves light energy or sound energy transformations? What are the indicators?

2. How does the step transform light energy or sound energy?

Energy-transformation Cartoon

Name: _____ Date: _____

Fill in the letter of the step you are analyzing. Then fill in other information about that step.

Name of your machine:		Purpose of your machine:	
Step	Changes/Work done	Energy type in	Energy types out	Indicators of energy transformations

Record questions about anything on which your group does not agree and anything you do not understand.

EN 201

ENERGY

△ Guide and Assess

Have students work in their groups to review the energy-transformation cartoons and discuss answers to the *Reflect* questions. They should first identify if each step shows light energy or sound energy, and then record it on their *Energy-transformations Cartoon* page. Then they should further analyze the steps by answering the questions in the student text. Remind students that every group member should contribute and the final answers of the group should be agreed upon by all. When groups have answered the questions, have a class discussion sharing them. Use the following guidelines to assess students' understanding:

1. Students should indicate that a step involves light energy by analyzing the cartoon for evidence of light causing action, such as using a magnifying glass to intensify the Sun's rays to start a fire. Students should also indicate that a step involves sound energy by finding evidence that a force carried by air caused an action, such as a loudspeaker causing marbles to move.

2. Students' answers will vary depending on the cartoon and step selected. In the example of light energy in the answer to Question 1, light energy is turned into heat energy to ignite an object to release chemical energy. The sound example in the answer to Question 1 shows sound energy transformed into kinetic energy.

3. What are the effects of each step, and what kind of energy is produced by each step?

4. How could you change the effects of each step?

5. Does light energy act more like kinetic energy or potential energy? Which answers to the other questions support your answer?

6. Does sound energy act more like kinetic energy or potential energy? Which answers to the other questions support your answer?

Explain

Working with your group, develop two claims and explanations. One claim should answer the question, "Is light energy kinetic energy or potential energy, and how can it do work?" The other should answer the question, "Is sound energy kinetic energy or potential energy, and how can it do work?" Use a different *Create Your Explanation* page for each of your claims.

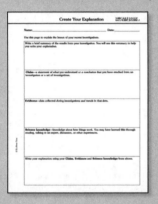

After you have recorded your two claims, work with your group to develop explanation statements. Remember that an explanation has four parts: a claim, evidence, science knowledge, and an explanation statement. The evidence in each of your explanations will come from the data collected earlier in this *Learning Set,* the data recorded on your *Energy Types* pages, and your observations of the energy-transformation cartoons. The science knowledge in each will come from what you have been reading. Each of your explanation statements should tie together your claim, evidence, and science knowledge. They should help somebody reading them to understand how you came up with your explanation, and why light energy or sound energy is a type of kinetic energy or potential energy.

⏺ Communicate

Share Your Explanations

Share your explanations with the class. As a class, come to agreement on an explanation about how each factor you have identified affects light energy.

3. Students' answers will vary depending on the cartoon and step selected. In the example of light energy used in the answer to Question 1, light energy is turned into heat energy to ignite an object to release chemical energy. The sound example used in the answer to Question 1 shows sound energy transformed into kinetic energy.

4. Students' answers will vary depending on the cartoon and the step selected. In the light energy example from the answer to Question 1, the effect could be changed by doing it on a cloudy day, by using a larger or smaller magnifying glass, or by using more or less fuel. In the sound example above, the effect could be changed by increasing or decreasing the amplitude of the speaker, or by increasing or decreasing the mass of the marbles.

5. Students may answer that light energy is more like kinetic energy, because it goes from one place to another and it can be seen. They may support this with their knowledge that light comes in packets of photons and the results of the radiometer demonstration.

6. Students may answer that sound energy is more like kinetic energy because, it travels from place to place and can be heard. The potential energy sources they are familiar with—gravitational, chemical, and electrical—do not show the energy available before it is released.

Explain

10 min

Students work together in their groups to develop a claim and an explanation.

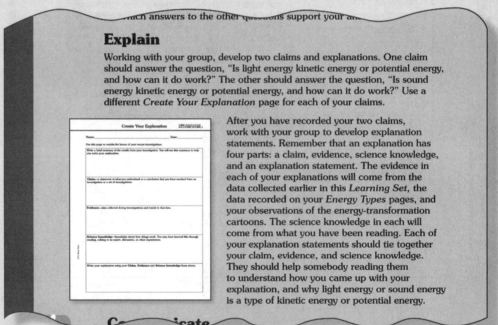

...which answers to the other questions support your an...

Explain

Working with your group, develop two claims and explanations. One claim should answer the question, "Is light energy kinetic energy or potential energy, and how can it do work?" The other should answer the question, "Is sound energy kinetic energy or potential energy, and how can it do work?" Use a different *Create Your Explanation* page for each of your claims.

After you have recorded your two claims, work with your group to develop explanation statements. Remember that an explanation has four parts: a claim, evidence, science knowledge, and an explanation statement. The evidence in each of your explanations will come from the data collected earlier in this *Learning Set*, the data recorded on your *Energy Types* pages, and your observations of the energy-transformation cartoons. The science knowledge in each will come from what you have been reading. Each of your explanation statements should tie together your claim, evidence, and science knowledge. They should help somebody reading them to understand how you came up with your explanation, and why light energy or sound energy is a type of kinetic energy or potential energy.

△ Guide and Assess

Keep students in their groups. Make sure each student has two *Create Your Explanation* pages. Have students work together to develop claims for both light energy and sound energy. Remind them to write one claim on each page. Remind them of the criteria they used to make similar claims for thermal and chemical energy in *Learning Set 3* so they can think about the same criteria to guide their work.

Review the four parts of an explanation with students: a claim, evidence, science knowledge, and an explanation statement. Read through the student text together with the class to emphasize where they should find the information they need to develop the explanations. Visit each group to evaluate their explanations and suggest areas for improvement.

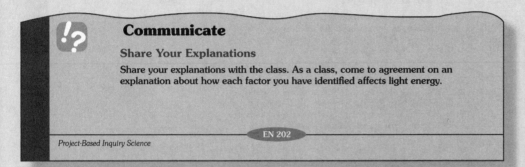

Communicate

Share Your Explanations

Share your explanations with the class. As a class, come to agreement on an explanation about how each factor you have identified affects light energy.

EN 202

Project-Based Inquiry Science

⬡ Get Going

Once groups have come to an agreement on their explanation, have the class take turns sharing. Remind students to listen for the four parts of each group's explanation and encourage them to ask questions if they are unsure of anything. Then guide the discussion to come to an agreement on a class explanation. The class should consider the best points of all the explanations and then compile them into one.

Communicate: Share Your Explanations

15 min

Students present their design sketches to the class.

NOTES

Plan
Your Design

20 min

Students incorporate steps using and producing sound and light energy in their designs.

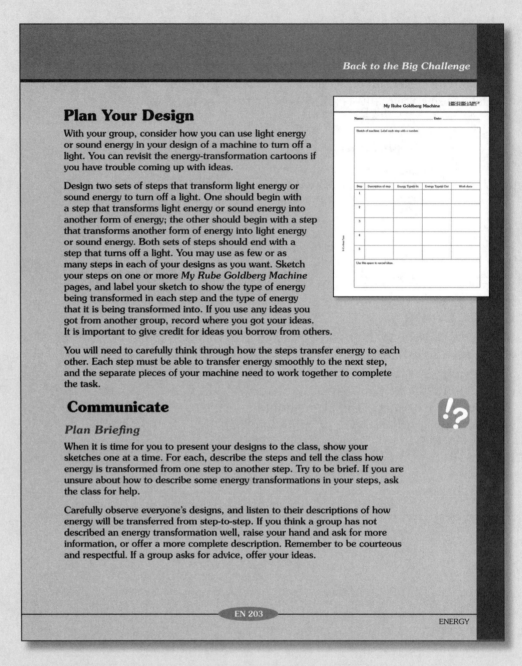

Plan Your Design

With your group, consider how you can use light energy or sound energy in your design of a machine to turn off a light. You can revisit the energy-transformation cartoons if you have trouble coming up with ideas.

Design two sets of steps that transform light energy or sound energy to turn off a light. One should begin with a step that transforms light energy or sound energy into another form of energy; the other should begin with a step that transforms another form of energy into light energy or sound energy. Both sets of steps should end with a step that turns off a light. You may use as few or as many steps in each of your designs as you want. Sketch your steps on one or more *My Rube Goldberg Machine* pages, and label your sketch to show the type of energy being transformed in each step and the type of energy that it is being transformed into. If you use any ideas you got from another group, record where you got your ideas. It is important to give credit for ideas you borrow from others.

You will need to carefully think through how the steps transfer energy to each other. Each step must be able to transfer energy smoothly to the next step, and the separate pieces of your machine need to work together to complete the task.

Communicate

Plan Briefing

When it is time for you to present your designs to the class, show your sketches one at a time. For each, describe the steps and tell the class how energy is transformed from one step to another step. Try to be brief. If you are unsure about how to describe some energy transformations in your steps, ask the class for help.

Carefully observe everyone's designs, and listen to their descriptions of how energy will be transferred from step-to-step. If you think a group has not described an energy transformation well, raise your hand and ask for more information, or offer a more complete description. Remember to be courteous and respectful. If a group asks for advice, offer your ideas.

EN 203

ENERGY

△ Guide

Review with students what they need to do. If needed, use the energy-transformation cartoons to help them think of ideas. Emphasize that they are designing one set of steps that uses each of these forms of energy and one set of steps that produces one of these forms of energy. They should also understand that there is no limit to the amount of steps they include in their design and that they must label each step. If needed, provide students with additional *My Rube Goldberg Machine* pages.

△ Guide and Evaluate

Allow each group to present their sketches to the class. Encourage students to take notes as they listen to each presentation so they can remember the ideas and who presented them.

> **TEACHER TALK**
>
> **"**It is just as important for you to listen to other presentations as it is for you to present your own ideas. Our goal is for all of you to learn from each other. Some groups may have ideas you didn't think about. You may have ideas other groups didn't think about. You can share ideas and build on each other's ideas as long as you give each other credit for what you've presented.**"**

Communicate: *Plan Briefing*

10 min

Students incorporate steps using and producing sound and light energy in their designs.

NOTES

Reflect

10 min

Students work together to review the design ideas presented.

Notice all of the different ideas your classmates have about transforming light energy and sound energy in their machines. You might want to borrow some of those ideas later. Record which group came up with each idea so you can give them credit.

Record ideas you might want to remember the bottom of your *My Rube Goldberg Machine* pages. Remember to record which group presented each idea.

Reflect

Discuss answers to these questions with your group. Be prepared to present your answers to the class.

1. Which two ideas for involving light energy or sound energy transformations in a machine to turn off a light do you like the best? Why? Which type or types of energy does each transform? Which type or types of energy is each transformed into?

2. List two things you know now about addressing the *Big Challenge* that you did not know before these presentations.

3. What else do you need to know about energy and energy transformations to address the *Big Challenge* successfully?

Add the ideas you like best to the class list of favorite steps. For each, record the type or types of energy it transforms, the type or types of energy it is transformed into, and which group suggested the step.

Update the *Project Board*

The *What does it mean for the challenge or question?* column on the *Project Board* is where you should record how learning about light energy and sound energy can help you complete the *Big Challenge.* Share what you know about light energy or sound energy that you think are important to add to the *Project Board* and your evidence for each. As a class, decide what belongs in the *What are we learning?* column. Remember to include evidence in the *What is our evidence?* column. Add any recommendations you have for addressing the *Big Challenge* to the *What does it mean for the challenge or question?* column. You must fit the pieces together to help you address the challenge. Remember to keep a record of what was added to the class *Project Board* on your own *Project Board* page.

EN 204

△ Guide

Ask students to work in their groups to discuss the ideas presented to the class. Have them discuss answers to the questions listed. As you walk around the room, find out if students have correctly identified the types of energy discussed. Then lead a class discussion to list the favorite steps.

△ Guide

Lead a class discussion in which students summarize what they have learned about sound and light energy, and the evidence they have to support their ideas. Ask students to explain how their ideas relate to the *Big Challenge* and what questions they still need answered to accomplish the *Big Challenge*. Record any new information in the appropriate columns of the *Project Board*.

Assessment Options

Targeted Concepts, Skills, and Nature of Science	How do I know if students got it?
Scientists often work together and then share their findings. Sharing findings makes new information available and helps scientists refine their ideas and build on others' ideas. When another person's or group's idea is used, credit needs to be given.	**ASK:** What ideas did you learn by listening to other groups? **LISTEN:** Students should describe any improvements or additions they made to their designs based on the presentations, and they should give credit to the proper students.
Scientific knowledge is developed through observations, recording and analysis of data, and development of explanations based on evidence.	**ASK:** How did your group come to agreement about your explanation? **LISTEN:** Students should describe the process through which they developed their explanation.
Energy exists in different forms and can be changed from one form to another.	**ASK:** What types of energy were present before and after the steps you analyze in the energy-transformation cartoon? **LISTEN:** Students should describe the step they chose, and identify the energy before and after that step occurred.

Update the Project Board

10 min

Students add new information to the Project Board.

ENERGY

Targeted Concepts, Skills, and Nature of Science	How do I know if students got it?
Sound is the transfer of energy as longitudinal waves that cannot travel through a vacuum.	**ASK:** In what way can sound energy be used in your Rube Goldberg design? **LISTEN:** Students should explain how they might use sound energy in their design, such as using sound to make another object vibrate.
Visible light is a small band within the electromagnetic spectrum, which is energy that travels in the form of waves.	**ASK:** In what ways can you use light energy in your design? **LISTEN:** Students may describe turning on a flashlight in an early step of their design that may heat up another object.

Teacher Reflection Questions

- How did you assess students' understanding of how sound and light can carry energy? If you feel your students need more guidance understanding this, what ideas do you have?

- How did students' explanations change after completing this section?

- How did you guide the review of the energy-transformation cartoons? Is there anything you might do differently?

NOTES

....

....

....

....

....

LEARNING SET 5 INTRODUCTION

Learning Set 5

How Do Electricity and Magnetism Provide Energy?

◀ $15\frac{1}{2}$ *class periods*

A class period is considered to be one 40 to 50 minute class.

Students investigate electrical and magnetic energy.

Overview

Students begin the *Learning Set* by building a simple circuit and an electromagnet. They develop early definitions of electrical and magnetic energy, and they examine their energy-transformation cartoons in terms of these new concepts. Students identify indicators of electrical and magnetic energy and look for factors that affect the strength of an electromagnet. The investigations that follow give students a chance to think about controlling electrical energy by turning a bulb on and off, and changing the intensity of light in the bulbs of a circuit. Students then learn the importance of switches in circuits. With a basic knowledge of circuits and current, students build a galvanometer. They relate the galvanometer to the electromagnet and establish an understanding of electromagnetism. Students compare batteries in terms of voltage and then differentiate between series and parallel circuits. Applying everything they have learned, students build a battery and watch a demonstration of a generator being built. They learn how these devices operate, the types of current they produce, and the processes through which current is supplied to homes and businesses.

Targeted Concepts, Skills, and Nature of Science	Section
Scientists often work together and then share their findings. Sharing findings makes new information available and helps scientists refine their ideas and build on others' ideas. When another person's or group's idea is used, credit needs to be given.	5.1, 5.3, 5.4, 5.5, 5.6, 5.7, 5.8
Studying the work of different scientists provides understanding of scientific inquiry and reminds students that science is a human endeavor.	5.2, 5.4, 5.8
Energy is the ability to cause change or do work.	5.1
Electrical energy can flow through circuits.	5.1, 5.3

Targeted Concepts, Skills, and Nature of Science	Section
Electrical energy is the flow of charges through a circuit.	5.3
Like electric charges exert a force of repulsion whereas unlike electric charges exert a force of attraction.	5.3
Electrical energy is used by appliances and equipment.	5.1
Like poles of a magnet repel whereas unlike poles attract.	5.1, 5.2, 5.4
An electric current flowing through a coil of wire can be used to produce an electromagnet.	5.1, 5.2
A galvanometer is used to measure electric current.	5.4, 5.7
Magnetic forces are exerted in the magnetic field around a magnet, with the forces being strongest near the poles.	5.4
Electricity gives rise to magnetism and magnetism gives rise to electricity.	5.4, 5.7
An electric current flowing through a coil of wire can be used to produce an electromagnet.	5.4
The voltage of a battery determines the amount of electric current in a circuit.	5.5
Electric circuits can be wired in series or in parallel.	5.6
A battery converts stored chemical energy into electrical energy.	5.7, 5.8
Conductors allow electric charges to flow through them easily whereas insulators limit the flow of charge through them.	5.8
The amount of current flowing through a circuit depends on voltage and resistance.	5.8
A generator transforms mechanical energy into electrical energy.	5.7, 5.8
Electric current can be direct or alternating.	5.8

Understanding for Teachers

Electricity

All matter is made up of atoms, which consist of protons, neutrons, and electrons. Protons carry a positive electric charge, electrons carry a negative electric charge, and neutrons are neutral. An attractive force is produced between opposite charges, such as a proton and an electron. However, like charges, such as two protons or two electrons, repel each other.

Electrons can be made to flow through some materials, known as conductors. The flow of electric charge is known as electric current. Materials that inhibit the flow of electric charge are known as insulators. The same materials that are good conductors of electricity are also good conductors of heat.

Electric current can flow only through a closed loop, known as an electric circuit. A circuit requires a source of voltage, conducting wire, and a load (resistance). A switch controls the flow of current through a circuit by turning it on and off. If the switch is off, no current can flow and the circuit is said to be an "open circuit."

Electric circuits can be wired in series or in parallel. In a series circuit, current has only one path through which to travel. If the flow of current is interrupted at any point, current cannot flow. In a parallel circuit, current has more than one path through which to flow. If the current is interrupted in one path of a parallel circuit, it can still flow through the other paths.

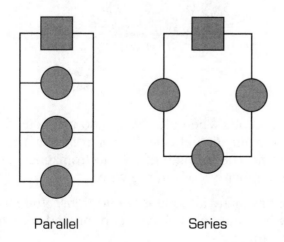

Parallel   Series

The current flowing in a circuit depends on the voltage and the resistance. The greater the voltage, the greater the current. As the resistance increases for the same voltage, the current decreases.

Magnetism

A magnet is an object that has a magnetic field around it. Another magnet will experience a magnetic force in that magnetic field. The force depends on the magnetic poles. Every magnet has a north pole and a south pole. Similar to electricity, like magnetic poles repel each other and unlike poles attract each other.

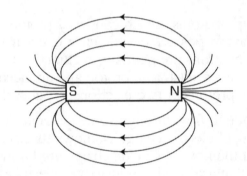

Electromagnetism

Electricity and magnetism are closely related. Moving electrical charges, such as in a closed circuit with an electric current, produce a magnetic field. If the wire carrying the current is bent into a coil, the magnetic effects are increased. The magnetic field produced by a coil of wire is similar to that produced by a bar magnet.

If an iron core is added to the coil, the magnetic field is increased further. The result is known as an electromagnet. An electromagnet is a magnet that

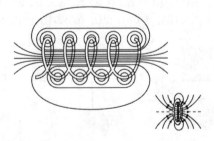

can be turned on and off. When off, there is no magnetic field. In addition, the direction of the magnetic field can be controlled by the direction of the electric current. The strength of the electromagnet can be increased by increasing the number of coils in the wire.

Electromagnetism has many important applications. Students will consider a galvanometer, which measures electric current, and a generator, which produces electric current.

LEARNING SET 5 IMPLEMENTATION

◀ $15\frac{1}{2}$ *class periods**

Learning Set 5

How Do Electricity and Magnetism Provide Energy?

You may have experienced a power failure in your home. If you have, then you know what it is like getting around with the aid of a flashlight, trying to save frozen foods in the freezer and having no heat, computer, or television. If it was a long power failure, you experienced what life was like for humans for most of the past several thousand years on Earth.

Perhaps you have come to take electricity for granted. Do you know how a motor works? Would you be surprised to find out it has magnets inside? Did you know that power plants all over the world use magnetism to generate electrical energy? Would it be strange to hear a power failure called a magnetic power failure?

Electricity will be an important part of your Rube Goldberg machine. In the last step you will turn off a light. You may also have some steps that include magnetism or electricity. In this *Learning Set,* you will be conducting investigations of how electrical energy and magnetic energy are related. You will also explore indicators of electrical and magnetic energy and factors that affect how much of these types of energy are available.

EN 205

ENERGY

Learning Set 5

How Do Electricity and Magnetism Provide Energy?

5 min

Students consider the importance of electricity in their daily lives.

○ Engage

Ask students to think about the last time the power went out in their home and to describe how their routine changed. Perhaps it became very warm or cold inside their home. Maybe they could not see to do their homework, play a video game, or watch television. After students recognize their reliance on electricity, read through the introduction together. Encourage them to consider what electricity has to do with magnets. Lead students to wonder how learning about electricity and magnetism might help them accomplish the *Big Challenge* for this Unit.

*A class period is considered to be one 40 to 50 minute class.

NOTES

5.1 Understand the Question

Think About Electrical and Magnetic Energy

◀ *2 class periods*

A class period is considered to be one 40 to 50 minute class.

Overview

Students investigate how they can use simple materials to build a circuit that will light a bulb. They experiment with permanent magnets and construct an electromagnet. Using paper clips, students compare the electromagnet with a permanent magnet. Students work together to explain their observations, identify indicators of electrical and magnetic energy, and formulate preliminary definitions of electrical and magnetic energy. They revisit the energy-transformation cartoons they observed earlier to look for examples of electrical and magnetic energy and they consider how to relate what they learned to the *Big Challenge*.

Targeted Concepts, Skills, and Nature of Science	Performance Expectations
Scientists often work together and then share their findings. Sharing findings makes new information available and helps scientists refine their ideas and build on others' ideas. When another person's or group's idea is used, credit needs to be given.	Students work together to build a simple circuit and an electromagnet.
Energy is the ability to cause change or do work.	Students identify observable changes as indicators of electrical and magnetic energy.
Electrical energy can flow through circuits.	Students construct a circuit to light a bulb and to produce an electromagnet.
Electrical energy is used by appliances and equipment.	Students observe that electrical energy can cause a bulb to light.

Targeted Concepts, Skills, and Nature of Science	Performance Expectations
Like poles of a magnet repel whereas unlike poles attract.	Students investigate the result of placing two magnets near each other in different arrangements.
An electric current flowing through a coil of wire can be used to produce an electromagnet.	Students construct an electromagnet and compare it to a permanent magnet.

Materials

1 per group	D-cell battery holder D-cell battery Flashlight bulb Flashlight bulb holder Masking tape Iron nail, 4 in.
3 per group	Wires with alligator clips
2 per group	Magnets Wires with alligator clips
20 per group	Steel paper clips
1 per student	*Energy-transformation Cartoon* page *Energy Types* page *Project Board* page
2 per student	*Electricity and Magnetism Observations* page
1 per class	Class *Project Board*

Homework Options

Reflection

- **Science Content:** How can you get two magnets to attract each other? *(Students should describe how they can put two different ends of the magnets near one another.)*

- **Science Content:** Some trains use combinations of permanent magnets and electromagnets to propel a train forward. How might electromagnets in the track be controlled to pull permanent magnets on a train? *(This question is intended to get students thinking about the relationships between magnetic poles and the control of electromagnets. Students may suggest that electromagnets in the track can be reversed so the ends change. This would pull the train forward or push from behind.)*

Preparation for 5.2

- **Science Process:** What indicators did you use to conclude that electricity carries energy? *(Students should cite changes they identified in the circuit, such as the bulb emitting light energy, as indicators that electricity carries energy.)*

NOTES

....

....

....

....

....

....

....

ENERGY

NOTES

SECTION 5.1 IMPLEMENTATION

5.1 Understand the Question

Think About Electrical and Magnetic Energy

When you were very young, you probably played with windup toys. These toys used elastic potential energy. You wound them up, and they moved across the floor, made sounds, or flashed lights. Many of your "toys" today are electronic. You do not have to do any work to power these devices. But think about what happens when you use an electronic device. Eventually the battery runs down. You have to plug it into a charger before you can use it again. The energy needed to recharge (more correctly, reenergize) is provided by the wall outlet.

electromagnet: a magnet that runs on electricity.

You just read that the electrical energy that comes from your outlet required magnets to generate it. You have probably used a magnet to attract a metal, but you probably did not realize that the magnet could be involved in energy transformation. You can use magnets to lift and move things, but they do not run out of energy. Have you ever played with an **electromagnet**? An electromagnet is like a magnet, but it runs on electricity.

In this *Learning Set,* you will explore electrical and magnetic energy and the connection between the two. You will begin by exploring arrangements of batteries, wires, light bulbs, and magnets. Record your observations and indicators on an *Electricity and Magnetism Observations* page.

You need electricity every day to operate devices such as computers.

Project-Based Inquiry Science

5.1 Understand the Question

Think About Electrical and Magnetic Energy

10 min

Students think about what they know about the use of electricity and magnetism.

○ Engage

Ask students to name some common objects and toys they use that require electricity. Have students name the source of electricity, such as plugging the item into an outlet, using batteries, or perhaps using rechargeable batteries. Then ask students about magnets they might use. They may realize they have magnets in their lockers or on their refrigerators. Help students realize that they never need to do anything to the magnets to keep them magnetic.

*A class period is considered to be one 40 to 50 minute class.

Investigation 1: Assembly Required

15 min

Students build a circuit to light a bulb.

META NOTES

It may be tempting to set up a sample circuit for students or tell them what a circuit needs, but give each group time to explore different setups. In this way, they will discover what works and what does not.

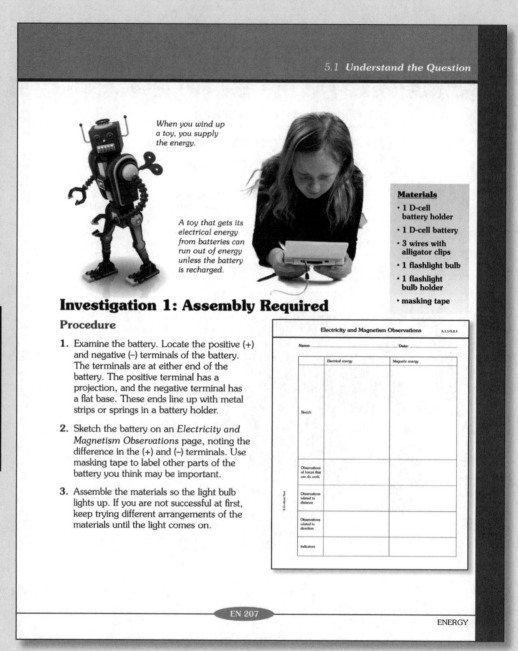

5.1 Understand the Question

When you wind up a toy, you supply the energy.

A toy that gets its electrical energy from batteries can run out of energy unless the battery is recharged.

Materials
- 1 D-cell battery holder
- 1 D-cell battery
- 3 wires with alligator clips
- 1 flashlight bulb
- 1 flashlight bulb holder
- masking tape

Investigation 1: Assembly Required

Procedure

1. Examine the battery. Locate the positive (+) and negative (–) terminals of the battery. The terminals are at either end of the battery. The positive terminal has a projection, and the negative terminal has a flat base. These ends line up with metal strips or springs in a battery holder.

2. Sketch the battery on an *Electricity and Magnetism Observations* page, noting the difference in the (+) and (–) terminals. Use masking tape to label other parts of the battery you think may be important.

3. Assemble the materials so the light bulb lights up. If you are not successful at first, keep trying different arrangements of the materials until the light comes on.

EN 207

ENERGY

⚠ Guide

Show students that the positive (+) terminal of a battery extends out of one end of the battery. Point out that the negative (–) terminal dips into one end of the battery. Demonstrate how an alligator clip works for any students who are unsure. Then allow students to mess about with the materials to try to build a circuit.

PBIS

4. When you succeed in making the light bulb light up, sketch your setup on your *Electricity and Magnetism Observations* page. Label the battery terminals and how the parts are arranged.

5. Record your observations on your *Electricity and Magnetism Observations* page. Then discuss and answer the following questions with your group. Be prepared to share what you are learning with the class.

Stop and Think

1. What is the purpose of the battery in your setup?

2. What is the purpose of the wire in your setup?

3. What indicators of electrical energy did you notice?

4. What indicators of other types of energy besides light energy and electrical energy did you notice?

5. How did you know which battery terminal to connect to each wire?

Project-Based Inquiry Science

△ Guide

Remind students to sketch the battery on their *Electricity and Magnetism Observations* pages, labeling what they think are the important parts. Then tell students that once they light the bulb, they should sketch the setup they used and record their observations.

Stop and Think

5 min

Students analyze the setup they constructed to light a bulb.

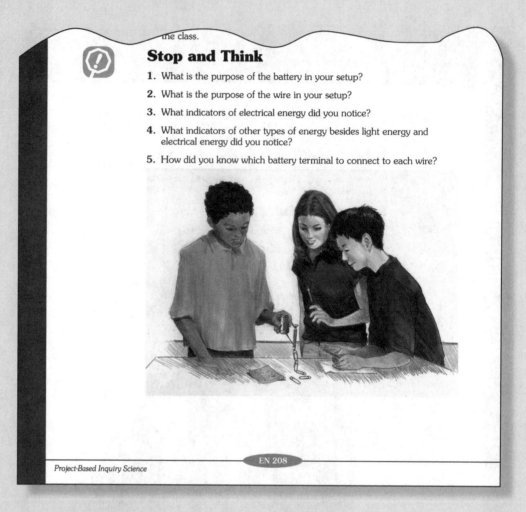

the class.

Stop and Think

1. What is the purpose of the battery in your setup?

2. What is the purpose of the wire in your setup?

3. What indicators of electrical energy did you notice?

4. What indicators of other types of energy besides light energy and electrical energy did you notice?

5. How did you know which battery terminal to connect to each wire?

Project-Based Inquiry Science   EN 208

△ Guide and Assess

Have students work in their groups to answer the questions. As they discuss their answers, listen for the following to assess how well they understand what they just did.

1. Students may suggest that the battery produces electricity (electric current) to light the bulb in the setup.

2. Students should recognize that electricity flows from the battery to the bulb through the wire in the setup.

3. Students should describe the bulb lighting up as an indicator of light energy caused by electrical energy.

4. Students may suggest that they felt the transfer of heat from the bulb, which indicates thermal energy.

5. Students should describe what they observed by changing the direction of the battery. The bulb should light in either arrangement.

Investigation 2: Testing, Testing, 1, 2, 3

Procedure

1. Place one magnet near a second magnet until you can make them repel. To repel means to force away. Use two small pieces of tape to mark the ends of the magnets that are near each other.

2. Push the magnets 1 cm closer together. Record your observations. How does it feel? Let every member of your group have a turn pushing these two ends of the magnet together.

3. Reverse one of the magnets so the unmarked end is near the marked end of the other magnet. Bring the ends of the magnets within 1 cm of each other and let go. Record your observations on another *Electricity and Magnetism Observations* page. Every member of your group should have a chance to do this.

4. Bring the marked end of one magnet near the paper clips. Observe how many paper clips can be lifted.

5. Remove the paper clips and bring the unmarked end of the magnet near the paper clips. Observe any differences.

6. Make an electromagnet by winding one of the wires around the nail. Attach one free end of the wire to the positive (+) battery terminal. Use masking tape to mark this end of the wire. Leave the other end of the wire unattached to make it easy to connect and disconnect to the negative (–) terminal. Use masking tape to mark one end of the iron nail.

7. Mess about with the electromagnet. See what it can do. Sketch what you make it do on the *Electricity and Magnetism Observations* page. Disconnect one wire from the battery when the electromagnet is not in use.

8. Reconnect the electromagnet wires to the battery, but this time, connect the marked wire to the negative (–) terminal. Try using the electromagnet again. How does what it can do now compare to what it could do in *Step 7*?

9. Record your observations on the *Electricity and Magnetism Observations* page. Then discuss and answer the following questions with your group. Be prepared to share your answers with the class.

Materials
- 2 magnets
- 20 steel paper clips
- masking tape
- 1 D-cell battery holder
- 1 D-cell battery
- 2 wires with alligator clips
- 1 iron nail, 4 in.

EN 209

ENERGY

Investigation 2: Testing, Testing, 1, 2, 3

15 min

Students learn properties of permanent magnets and then construct and investigate an electromagnet.

△ Guide

Distribute another *Electricity and Magnetism Observations* page to students and have them complete the first five steps of the procedure to gain familiarity with magnets. Then, tell students they are going to build a device known as an *electromagnet.*

TEACHER TALK

"What do you think an electromagnet is? Think about the parts of the word. The first part, *electro-*, has to do with electricity. The second part, *-magnet,* has to do with magnetism. An electromagnet uses electricity to produce magnetism. You are going to build an electromagnet and compare how it works to a permanent magnet."

○ Get Going

Have students perform Steps 6-9. Electromagnets can be a bit tricky for students to construct. Tell students to wind the wire tightly around the nail. Caution them not to overlap the coils of wire, but to line them up carefully in a row without spaces between them. Students should wind the wire as many times as they can fit to produce an electromagnet with observable results. As students mess about, they should sketch what they do. Also remind them to disconnect one wire from the battery when they are not using the electromagnet.

NOTES

Stop and Think

1. How do the magnets interact with each other? To the paper clips?

2. How does the distance between the magnets affect how they interact with each other?

3. How does the distance between a magnet and the paper clips affect how they interact with each other?

4. What indicators of magnetic energy could you observe?

5. In what ways is the electromagnet like a magnet? In what ways is it different?

6. In what ways does changing the battery terminal connected to the marked wire affect the electromagnet?

Communicate

Share Your Ideas

Each group will present its observations. Show your sketches of a successful light-bulb setup. Then present your sketches of the magnets. List the indicators you found for electrical and magnetic energy. If you disagree with or do not understand another group's presentation, ask questions. Make sure you ask respectfully.

Add any new observations or indicators to your *Electricity and Magnetism Observations* page. Keep a class list on the board of the observations and indicators.

Look at the list on the board. Discuss which you think are indicators of electrical energy and which are indicators of magnetic energy. As a class, come to agreement on at least two indicators for each kind of energy.

Reflect

1. How do you think your battery, wires, and light bulb compare to the operation of a lamp connected to a wall outlet?

2. How do you think you could measure the amount of electrical energy used by the bulb?

3. What do you think electricity is?

EN 210

Project-Based Inquiry Science

Stop and Think

5 min

Students compare the electromagnet they constructed to a permanent magnet.

△ Guide and Assess

Have students answer the *Stop and Think* questions with their groups. Listen for the following in their discussions:

1. Students should describe how the magnets pulled together (attracted) when opposite ends were placed near each other and push apart (repelled) when like ends were placed near each other. They should also describe how the magnets attracted the paper clips no matter what end was placed near the paper clips.

2. Students should recognize that the attraction and repulsion decreased as the distance between the magnets increased.

3. Students should recognize that the attraction for the paper clips decreased as the distance increased.

4. Students may explain that the changes they observed in the movement of the magnets and the paper clips indicated that energy was involved.

5. Students may recognize that the electromagnet acts similar to the bar magnet when the wires are connected to the terminals of the battery. However, the electromagnet can be turned on and off, unlike a permanent magnet.

6. Students who reversed the connections to the battery may have observed that the ends, or poles, of the electromagnet change.

Communicate: Share Your Ideas

10 min

Students share their observations and conclusions.

Communicate

Share Your Ideas

Each group will present its observations. Show your sketches of a successful light-bulb setup. Then present your sketches of the magnets. List the indicators you found for electrical and magnetic energy. If you disagree with or do not understand another group's presentation, ask questions. Make sure you ask respectfully.

Add any new observations or indicators to your *Electricity and Magnetism Observations* page. Keep a class list on the board of the observations and indicators.

Look at the list on the board. Discuss which you think are indicators of electrical energy and which are indicators of magnetic energy. As a class, come to agreement on at least two indicators for each kind of energy.

△ Guide

Have each group share their sketches and ideas about indicators of electrical and magnetic energy. Make sure that groups who could not get their bulbs to light follow the sketches of the circuits. When all the groups have presented, lead a discussion about the indicators of energy.

Remind students to record any new ideas they hear in the presentations. As the class discusses, record a class list of indicators on the board. Then, guide the class to come to an agreement on at least two indicators for each kind of energy.

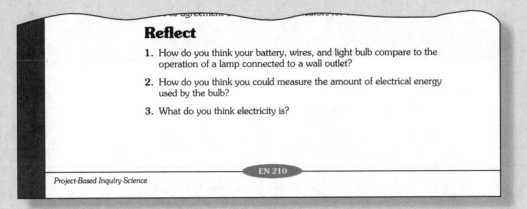

Reflect

1. How do you think your battery, wires, and light bulb compare to the operation of a lamp connected to a wall outlet?

2. How do you think you could measure the amount of electrical energy used by the bulb?

3. What do you think electricity is?

EN 210

Project-Based Inquiry Science

Reflect

5 min

Students answer questions to get them thinking about their real-world knowledge of electricity.

△ Guide and Assess

Allow groups to discuss answers to the *Reflect* questions. Walk around the room to encourage all students to participate in the discussions.

1. Students should recognize that their simple circuit is similar to the operation of a lamp in a household circuit. They probably will not realize that their circuit is direct current while in the home it is alternating current.

2. Students' answers will vary, but some may have seen a voltmeter or ammeter used by a parent.

3. Some students may answer that electricity is the movement of electrons, but many may not know this yet.

4. Students may have difficulty answering this question. Some may say that magnetism is the ability to attract metal or iron.

5. Students may have tested their electromagnet on the paper clip and realize that electricity and magnetism are closely related. Others may remember the discussion of electromagnetic radiation in earlier *Learning Sets* and come to the same conclusion.

What Are the Indicators of Electrical and Magnetic Energy?

20 min

Students read about early discoveries involving electricity and then review some properties of electricity and magnetism.

META NOTES

Students often have difficulty connecting scientific discoveries with the people involved. Spend a few minutes having students discuss how they would feel to explore a new topic in science as Benjamin Franklin did. Mention how Franklin could not look up answers on the Internet. He had to discover them for himself, much as students do when they conduct their investigations.

4. What do you think magnetism is?

5. How do you think electricity and magnetism are related?

What Are the Indicators of Electrical and Magnetic Energy?

The study of electricity dates back to 600 BCE when the Greek philosopher Thales explored the properties of amber. The Greek name for amber was *elektron*. Thales wrote about rubbing wool on amber, a hardened tree sap, and then using the amber to attract feathers. Perhaps you have seen something similar. If you run a plastic comb through your hair, it can attract bits of paper.

If you walk across a room and then touch a doorknob, you sometimes see a spark jump. Early on, scientists recognized a spark as an indicator of electrical energy. They experimented with different ways of making bigger sparks. One German scientist, George Bose, used sparks from a hidden machine to shock his dinner guests! Other indicators of electrical energy they recognized were lightning, a shock from an electric eel, or the movement of a magnetized needle. However, it took quite some time for scientists to realize how these indicators might be related.

In the eighteenth century, scientists began to connect these indicators. One of the most famous achievements was Benjamin Franklin's experiment with a kite, key, and lightning. Franklin wondered if the sparks he could produce in his laboratory were related to lightning. To test this idea, he flew a kite with a key attached to it during a thunderstorm. After the thunderstorm had passed, he moved his hand near the key and received a shock. Despite what many people believe, Franklin did recognize the dangers involved, and he did take safety precautions. He held onto the kite with a length of silk and took cover in a nearby barn.

In your electricity investigation, you found that to light the bulb, it was necessary to have a complete loop with wire connecting the battery to the bulb and back again. The loop in an electric circuit must be made of material that conducts electricity, such as metal wire. A material that can **conduct electricity** allows electricity to flow through it. When two wires correctly connect the battery terminals to the two parts of the base of the bulb, the bulb lights up. You most likely discovered that it does not matter which terminal (+ or –) is connected to each wire.

conduct electricity: allow electricity to flow through a material.

EN 211

ENERGY

○ Engage

Cut or tear tissue paper into small pieces. Run a plastic comb through your hair or the hair of a volunteer several times. Then hold the comb about 1 cm above the tissue paper. Allow students to see the comb attract the pieces of tissue paper. Explain that this observation results from electricity. Once students are engaged, read through the information about early discoveries related to electricity together.

You probably also found that the bulb got hot when it was connected to electricity, and you saw that the electromagnet could do work when both ends of the wire were connected to the battery. Indicators for electrical energy include light, heat released by wires, sparks, and the work done by an electromagnet. Another indicator of electrical energy is that an appliance that is running is connected to a battery or to an electrical outlet.

Indicators of magnetic energy include the ability to do work by lifting steel or iron objects, or by pushing or pulling on other magnets. In an electromagnet, thermal energy (the wires heating up) is an indicator that magnetic energy is being transformed. Another indicator that magnetic energy has been used is a battery running down when an electromagnet has been connected to it for a long time.

Magnets can attract or repel each other, depending on which way each magnet is facing. If two magnets attract, and you turn one to face the opposite way, the magnets will then repel. Both ends of a magnet will attract steel paper clips.

In June, 1752, Benjamin Franklin, along with his son William, experimented with a kite and key to see if lightning was electrical.

Magnets do not attract all metals. For example, they do not attract the copper wires. Magnets can attract through some materials, such as paper or even your finger.

Magnets can do work by lifting an object. There is a limit to how much weight a magnet can lift. This is an indicator that the magnetic energy of a magnet is not unlimited.

An electromagnet can lift paper clips only when the wires are connected to the terminals of the battery. The electromagnet behaves like a magnet because it can repel or attract other magnets. It does not attract the copper wire, and it will attract paper clips. When the wires connecting the electromagnet to the battery are reversed, the marked end changes so that it will now repel the end of a magnet that it had previously attracted.

META NOTES

In addition to the number of coils, the strength of an electromagnet depends on the magnitude of the electric current and the presence of an iron core.

△ Guide

Continue the reading about indicators of magnetic energy. Discuss how these indicators were used in the investigations from the previous section.

TEACHER TALK

❝Do you remember what work is? It is the force exerted on an object multiplied by the distance the object moves. What does that tell you about a magnet that lifts some object, such as a paper clip? It tells you that the magnet does work.❞

△ Guide

Explain that some of the electromagnets students built may have been stronger than others. Tell students that the reason for this is that there are factors that affect the strength of an electromagnet. One factor is the number of coils of wire. The strength of an electromagnet is directly related to the number of coils.

NOTES

....

....

....

....

....

....

....

....

5.1 *Understand the Question*

Reflect

1. In the electrical setup of your investigation, why do you think it was important to have a complete loop with wire connecting the battery to the bulb and back again?

2. What are some indicators of the presence of electrical energy?

3. What are some indicators of the presence of magnetic energy?

4. How is an electromagnet similar to a handheld magnet you might use in your classroom? How is it different?

Conference

With your group, return to the sketch of the energy-transformation cartoon you analyzed before. Look at all of the energy sources and energy transformations. How is electrical energy shown in the cartoon? How is magnetic energy shown?

Make a list of the steps that you think might involve electrical energy or magnetic energy. Describe them on an *Energy-transformation Cartoon* page.

Reflect

1. What indicators have you identified for electrical energy?

2. What factors do you think affect how much electrical energy is available?

3. Do you think electricity is more like potential energy or kinetic energy? Why?

4. What indicators have you identified for magnetic energy?

5. What factors do you think affect how much magnetic energy is available?

6. Do you think magnetic energy is more like potential energy or kinetic energy? Why?

7. Add indicators for electrical energy and magnetic energy to your *Energy Types* page. You might also want to add examples. Do not add factors yet. You will add factors after you know more about what factors affect how much electrical and magnetic energy are available.

EN 213

ENERGY

Reflect

5 min

Students relate the new information they learned to their observations from the investigations earlier in the section.

◇ Evaluate

Have groups discuss answers to the *Reflect* questions. As you visit each group, make sure students provide evidence for each of their answers.

1. Students may realize that there is a reason that a battery has two ends and that the two ends must be connected by wire. Like water, electrons do not flow unless they have somewhere to go.

2. Students should identify some indicators of electrical energy as light, heat, sound, and anything doing work because it is connected to a source of electrical energy.

3. Students should recollect that some indicators of magnetic energy include the ability to attract (or repel) other magnets and to attract objects made of iron and steel.

4. Students should recall that an electromagnet is similar to a permanent magnet in its ability to attract (or repel) other magnets and in its ability to attract iron or steel. It is different because it can be turned on and off, unlike a permanent magnet.

Conference

10 min

Students reexamine their energy-transformation cartoons in terms of electrical and magnetic energy.

Conference

With your group, return to the sketch of the energy-transformation cartoon you analyzed before. Look at all of the energy sources and energy transformations. How is electrical energy shown in the cartoon? How is magnetic energy shown?

Make a list of the steps that you think might involve electrical energy or magnetic energy. Describe them on an *Energy-transformation Cartoon* page.

△ Guide

Have students look at the energy-transformation cartoons they examined previously. Remind students that each time they have looked at the cartoon, they looked for a different type of energy. Tell them that this time they should look for examples of electrical and magnetic energy. Once they have had a chance to come up with ideas, ask them what ideas this gives them for the Rube Goldberg machine they are designing.

Reflect

5 min

Students answer questions to summarize their ideas about electrical and magnetic energy.

◇ Evaluate

Have groups discuss answers to the *Reflect* questions and then share them as a class. Listen to hear that each idea is supported by evidence. Accept all logical responses at this time. Remind students that they will have a chance to revise their ideas as they complete this section.

1. Students' answers will vary depending on which cartoon they selected. Some examples may include that indicators for electrical energy are light energy from a bulb, heat energy from a toaster, or anything that is connected to electricity and is doing work.

2. Students' answers will vary depending upon which cartoon they selected. Some examples of electrical factors are voltage of the source or the number of windings in a generator.

3. Students may decide that electrical energy is more like kinetic energy because it involves the movement of electrons and its presence can be seen.

4. Students will probably list a magnet's ability to attract iron and its ability to generate electricity in a moving coil as indicators of magnetic energy.

5. Students should understand that some of the factors for magnetic energy will include the number of windings in an electromagnet and the size of the magnet itself. Distance is also a factor. The closer to the magnet, the stronger the magnetic field.

6. Students will probably answer that magnetic energy is more like potential energy because it cannot be seen and there are no indicators until something is added to the system. Kinetic energy can always be seen because something will be in motion.

7. Students should add the following indicators for electrical energy to their *Energy Types* pages:

   - attractive or repulsive forces due to static electricity

   - a spark caused by the discharge of electrical energy

   - when current is running through a circuit, thermal energy is an indicator as wires and load generate heat

   - a light on or an appliance running

For magnetic energy, they should identify the following indicators:

   - ability to do work lifting iron objects or by pushing or pulling on other magnets

   - in an electromagnet, thermal energy is an indicator that magnetic energy is being transformed

   - in an electromagnet, a battery running down is an indicator that magnetic energy was being generated

8. Students' answers will vary.

Update the Project Board

5 min

Students add their ideas and questions about electrical and magnetic energy to the Project Board.

8. What else do you need to learn about electrical energy and magnetic energy to be able to include electricity and magnetism in the machine you are designing to turn off a light?

Update the *Project Board*

The question for this *Learning Set* is *How do electricity and magnetism provide energy?* You are just beginning to build your understanding of electrical energy and magnetic energy. Add what you think you know about these types of energy to the *What do we think we know?* column of the *Project Board*. Your class probably has some disagreements about these energy types. You may have identified some things you do not yet understand about electrical and magnetic energy. For example, you might not agree about whether electrical energy can be used to do work if no magnets are used. Add questions you need to answer to resolve those disagreements to the *What do we need to investigate?* column of the *Project Board*. Also, add questions you need to answer to include electricity and magnetic energy in your Rube Goldberg machine to the *What do we need to investigate?* column.

What's the Point?

In your investigations, you explored how electrical energy is transformed to light a bulb or to make an electromagnet. You explored the forces that magnets can exert on each other and materials that contain iron. Electrical energy and magnetic energy seem to be very closely related, but there are some differences. It is very easy to observe a magnet doing work. It is not easy to see work done when a battery is used to light a bulb.

Indicators of electrical energy include light, heat released by the wires or by a light, sparks, and work done by the electromagnet. Indicators of magnetic energy include work done to push or pull other magnets and to attract paperclips, and heating up of wires in the electromagnet.

Indicators of magnetic energy include the ability to do work by lifting steel or iron objects or by pushing or pulling on other magnets. In an electromagnet, thermal energy (the wires heating up) is an indicator that magnetic energy is being transformed. Another indicator that magnetic energy has been transformed is a battery running down when an electromagnet or some appliance has been connected to it for a long time.

△ Guide

Guide a class discussion to fill in the *Project Board*. Ask students to think back to the investigations they performed and determine what they learned from these and the following readings. They should fill in the *What do we think we know?* column with a summary of their understanding of electric and magnetic energy. Anything they do not understand should be added to the *What do we need to investigate?* column.

Assessment Options

Targeted Concepts, Skills, and Nature of Science	How do I know if students got it?
Scientists often work together and then share their findings. Sharing findings makes new information available and helps scientists refine their ideas and build on others' ideas. When another person's or group's idea is used, credit needs to be given.	**ASK:** How did you learn from other students while trying to set up the materials to light the bulb and how did you help others? **LISTEN:** Students should describe the process they used to figure out how to light the bulb.
Energy is the ability to cause change or do work.	**ASK:** What indicator did you use to identify magnetic energy? **LISTEN:** Students may describe changes they observed, such as paper clips moving toward the magnet.
Electrical energy can flow through circuits.	**ASK:** What did you do to cause electricity to reach the bulb in your investigation? **LISTEN:** Students should describe how they used the wires to carry electricity from the battery to the bulb and back to the battery.
Electrical energy is used by appliances and equipment.	**ASK:** What caused the bulb to light in your investigation? **LISTEN:** Students should recognize that electrical energy was converted into light energy.
Like poles of a magnet repel whereas unlike poles attract.	**ASK:** How can you push a magnet using a second magnet? **LISTEN:** Students may suggest placing the end of a second magnet near the same end of another magnet.

Targeted Concepts, Skills, and Nature of Science	How do I know if students got it?
An electric current flowing through a coil of wire can be used to produce an electromagnet.	**ASK:** Why do you think an electromagnet is useful? **LISTEN:** Students may suggest that unlike a permanent magnet, the electromagnet can be turned on and off.

Teacher Reflection Questions

- What difficulties did students encounter when trying to construct their circuits? How might you guide them next time?

- How were you able to involve all students in the investigations and the discussions? What might you do next time to encourage greater participation?

- How well were students able to use the same basic processes of identifying indicators to newly introduced forms of energy? What can you do to help them develop these skills?

NOTES

5.2 Explore

What Factors Allow You To Control Electrical Energy?

◄ **3 class periods**

A class period is considered to be one 40 to 50 minute class.

Overview

In this section, students have an opportunity to explore the control of electrical energy. In their first investigation, students work to design a circuit in which they can control the intensity of light from a bulb. They go on to investigate ways to turn a light on and off. Then students read to learn about electric current and how current can flow through an electric circuit. Students find out why the switches they used were able to turn the light on and off, and how electrical force is related to voltage.

Targeted Concepts, Skills, and Nature of Science	Performance Expectations
Scientists often work together and then share their findings. Sharing findings makes new information available and helps scientists refine their ideas and build on others' ideas. When another person's or group's idea is used, credit needs to be given.	Students work together to construct circuits to control the operation of a light bulb.
Like electric charges exert a force of repulsion whereas unlike electric charges exert a force of attraction.	Students relate the electric force to voltage.
Electrical energy can flow through circuits.	Students discover that an electric current can flow only through a closed circuit.
Electrical energy is the flow of charges through a circuit.	Students learn that an electric current consists of a flow of electric charges.

Materials	
1 per group	Flashlight bulb Flashlight bulb holder Switch, SPST Iron nail, 4 in.
2 per group	D-cell battery holders D-cell batteries Rubber bands Magnets
3 per group	Wires with alligator clips
1 per student	*Electricity and Magnetism Observations* page
1 per class (optional)	Set of marbles Tubing or section of plastic car track

Homework Options

Reflection

- **Science Content:** Describe the reasons for keeping an accurate record of what setups you tried and their results? *(Students' answers should point out the need to rule out setups that did not have the desired results so information can be learned from them.)*

Preparation for 5.3

- **Science Process:** How did you compare amounts of electrical energy in the electric circuit you constructed? *(Students should describe how they compared the intensity of light by seeing how bright or dim the light was, or if the bulb was lit at all.)*

SECTION 5.2 IMPLEMENTATION

5.2 Explore

What Factors Allow You To Control Electrical Energy?

One great advantage of electricity is that it enables you to precisely control devices. When you turn the volume knob on a radio to very low, you know the music will not wake a baby in the next room.

When you turn the volume knob on a radio to very low, you know the music will not wake a baby in the next room.

You may know exactly how many seconds to set the microwave for to perfectly warm a mug of cocoa. In this section, you will start to explore ways that you can control electrical energy in your Rube Goldberg machine. For your machine to function properly, you may need to carefully control the amount of electrical energy transformed in some step. You also might want to find ways to start or stop the transformation of electrical energy. The better you understand factors that affect electrical energy, the better you will be able to control it.

You may know exactly how many seconds to set the microwave for to perfectly warm a mug of cocoa.

EN 215

ENERGY

5.2 Explore

What Factors Allow You to Control Electrical Energy?

10 min

Students consider how they control energy in their daily lives.

○ Engage

Ask students if they use an alarm clock to wake up. Ask a student to describe how to "set" an alarm clock so that it makes a certain sound at a particular time. Emphasize that the alarm is set to turn on and then turn off as the student wishes. Tell students that they are going to conduct an investigation to find out how they can use devices to control electrical energy.

*A class period is considered to be one 40 to 50 minute class.

Investigation 1: More Intense Light

20 min

Students try to control the brightness of a light in a circuit.

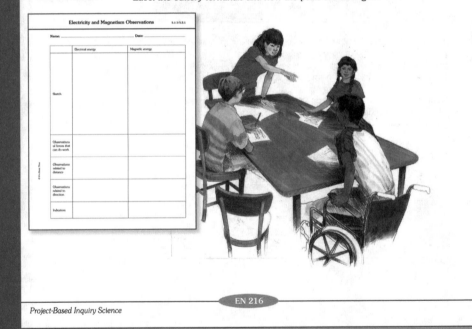

Investigation 1: More Intense Light

Now you will try to make the light from a light bulb more intense. You may use any of the materials you have been given. You may have some left over and unused when you are finished. Record your observations on a new *Electricity and Magnetism Observations* page.

Materials

- 2 D-cell battery holders
- 2 D-cell batteries
- 3 wires with alligator clips
- 1 flashlight bulb
- 1 flashlight bulb holder
- 1 switch, SPST
- 3 steel paper clips
- 2 rubber bands
- 2 magnets
- 1 iron nail, 4 in.

Procedure

1. Look at your successful sketch of a working battery and light-bulb setup from the previous investigation. Assemble the materials again the same way so the bulb lights up.

2. Now consider how your materials list is different here than it was for the earlier investigation. Then explore ways to make the light more intense. You may not be successful at first, but keep trying until you succeed.

3. When you succeed in making the light more intense, sketch a diagram of your setup on your *Electricity and Magnetism Observations* page. Label the battery terminals and how the parts are arranged.

△ Guide

Distribute the materials to groups. Let them know that they do not have to use all of the materials in their investigation. Students will already be familiar with the materials from their work in *Section 5.1* and should apply what they learned of the materials to this investigation. Point out that they should refer to their sketches from *Section 5.1*.

Encourage students to make as many attempts as they need to control the intensity of the light. For example, you may see students try using a combination of batteries rather than just one or a combination of more than one bulb. When they are satisfied with the intensity of the light, they should sketch the setup that produced it on their *Electricity and Magnetism Observations* pages.

NOTES

Stop and Think

5 min

Students answer questions about how electrical energy was used in the investigation.

5.2 **Explore**

Stop and Think

Discuss and answer the following questions with your group. Be prepared to share answers with the class.

1. Why do you think the bulb is emitting more light energy this time?

2. What indicators of other types of energy besides light energy and electrical energy did you notice?

3. How does the arrangement of the battery terminals make a difference?

4. What factor affects the available amount of electrical energy?

5. How do you think you can wire the light and battery so that you can easily turn the light on and off? Why?

Investigation 2: Take Charge

Now you will try to turn the light on and off. You may use any of the materials you were given in *Investigation 1*. You may have some left over and unused when you are finished with this investigation. Record your observations on an *Electricity and Magnetism Observations* page.

Procedure

1. Reassemble your simplest battery and light setup so the bulb lights up. This will be the setup you used at the beginning of the previous investigation and earlier in the *Learning Set*.

2. Examine the materials you have available. Add items that allow you to turn the light on and off. If you are not successful at first, keep trying until you succeed.

3. Sketch a diagram of your successful setup on your *Electricity and Magnetism Observations* page. Label the battery terminals and how the parts are arranged.

4. Now disconnect your setup and try a different setup in which you use an electromagnet to turn the light on and off. If you are not successful at first, keep trying. (Hint: You might have the iron nail attract a paper clip into an "on" position. When the electromagnet is disconnected, a rubber band could return the paper clip to the "off" position.)

EN 217

ENERGY

Guide and Assess

Have students answer the questions in their groups. Listen to make sure they can relate the setup they used to the indicators they observed to the conclusions they reached. Then make sure they make a prediction about turning a light on and off.

1. Students should understand that by using two batteries instead of one, they have doubled the electrical energy, making the light from the bulb brighter.

2. Students may have noticed that the bulb became hot, therefore emitting thermal energy.

3. Students should recognize that the batteries had to be placed in series (positive terminal to negative terminal) to get the bulb to light.

4. Students should understand that the number of batteries available determines the amount of electrical energy available.

5. Answers may vary, but students may respond that they could put an on-off switch in the circuit to turn the light off. When the circuit is open, the electrons cannot move and there is no light.

△ Guide

Have groups reassemble the simplest setup that worked for them. Guide them to use this as a base starting point for this investigation. When they have the bulb lit, challenge students to alter the setups to turn a light on and off.

Students might try any of the following:

- insert a switch in series into the circuit

- add a wire and two free ends (alligator clips) together to turn the light on, and pull the clips apart to turn the light off

- make an electromagnet that pulls on a paper clip to open the circuit. The rubber band can then snap the paper clip back into place when they close the circuit.

- have the iron nail complete the circuit by attracting a paper clip to it. A rubber band could return the paper clip to the "off" position.

Investigation 2: Take Charge

20 min

Students mess about to try to turn a light on and off.

NOTES

....

....

....

....

....

Stop and Think

5 min

Students answer questions about how they turn a light on and off.

Stop and Think

Discuss and answer these questions with your group. Be prepared to share your answers with the class.

1. You have made a light switch. What other places have you seen switches being used?

2. What other ways might there be to make a light switch?

3. A pile driver is a machine that is used to hammer piles, or long pieces of wood, steel, or concrete, vertically into soil. To do this, a heavy rod is raised and then held in place. When the gravitational potential energy is needed, the rod is released and dropped on the head of the pile to do work. How is this similar to a light switch that stops the flow of electrical energy? What does the operation of a light switch tell you about whether electrical energy can be considered to be a type of kinetic energy or a type of potential energy?

A pile driver does work by transforming gravitational potential energy.

Communicate

Share Your Ideas

Share with the class the way you made your light bulb glow more intensely in the first investigation. Notice how many different ways your classmates came up with for making a bulb glow more intensely. Make a class list of factors that seem to affect the intensity of light emitted by the light bulb.

Share your switches with the class. Show how your electrical switch operates and describe how your electromagnetic switch operates. Discuss your ideas about what happens when you use the switch. Share what you think about whether electrical energy is a type of kinetic energy or potential energy and why.

EN 218

△ Guide and Assess

You may need to give students a few examples of switches to get the discussion started. For example, you might mention switches on hair dryers, video game devices, copy machines, and televisions. They should be able to list many examples. Allow students to be creative in describing types of switches. Tell them to think back to the Rube Goldberg cartoons they saw earlier. Students may suggest that a switch stops the motion of something, making electrical energy a form of kinetic energy.

1. Students' answers will vary. Almost every electrical device has an on-off switch.

2. Students' answers will vary.

3. Students may answer that when the pile driver is lifting the rod, it is doing work and creating potential energy that can return the work. When the pile driver drops the rod, it is like turning on a light switch. The potential energy becomes kinetic energy and does work. Students should see that electrical energy is like the dropping rod, full of kinetic energy.

△ Guide

Allow each group to demonstrate how they used a switch in their setup. Students should describe how they understand the switch to work. Once all groups have presented, discuss factors that they think affect the intensity of light from the bulbs they used.

Communicate: Share Your Ideas

5 min

Students share their switches with the class.

NOTES

....

....

....

....

....

....

....

....

....

Reflect

5 min

Students answer questions about different kinds of switches.

Reflect

1. In your home, you may have a light with a "dimmer" switch. This allows you to make the light brighter or dimmer. How do you think this switch operates?

2. In your home or at school, you may have turned on a light that has two switches, one at either end of a room. This light can be turned on or off from either switch. How could you put another switch in a third location that will also turn the light on and off?

What Is Electricity?

Electrical energy is the energy associated with charged particles such as electrons. In certain materials, usually metals, charged particles are free to move from one place to another. The flow of charged particles is called an **electric current**.

Electricity for a house flows from a power plant along electrical wires, through insulators and transformers, and into the house.

A current in a wire exists only if charged particles can move freely in a complete path. This pathway is called an **electric circuit**. An electric circuit is a closed path through which charged particles may flow. The circuit you built used wires to provide a path along which the charged particles could move. Any break in a circuit, no matter where it is located, will stop the flow of charged particles. If the charged particles cannot move around the path, the light bulb does not emit light.

Electric current comes into a room through the electrical wires to an electrical outlet.

electric current: the flow of charged particles.

electric circuit: a pathway where charged particles can move freely in a complete path.

ENERGY

△ Guide and Assess

Describe the operation of a dimmer switch for students unfamiliar with them. Then have groups discuss ideas about how a dimmer switch works based on their investigations. If your classroom has more than one switch for the same lights, demonstrate the switches for the class. Then have students think about how two or three switches might be used to operate the same device.

1. Students might know that a dimmer switch works by controlling the amount of electrical energy, the voltage, going to the light bulb.

2. Some students might have a general idea about how this could be done. This is called a *three-way switch* and the circuit is wired to allow the two switches to toggle between two circuits.

○ Engage

To get students started thinking about flow of electrons, consider performing a demonstration model. If possible, allow marbles to flow through a piece of tubing or along a section of plastic car track. Liken the marbles to the flow of electrons. If marbles are not available, describe water flowing through a hose. Then define electric current.

What Is Electricity?

20 min

Students read about electric currents and circuits.

META NOTES

Be careful to avoid misconceptions when describing switches. Students may associate "closed" with "off" and "open" with "on." Help students recognize that when the switch is closed, the circuit is complete, so the light is on. When the switch is open, the circuit is not complete so the light is off.

NOTES

....

....

....

....

....

....

....

....

....

....

....

ENERGY

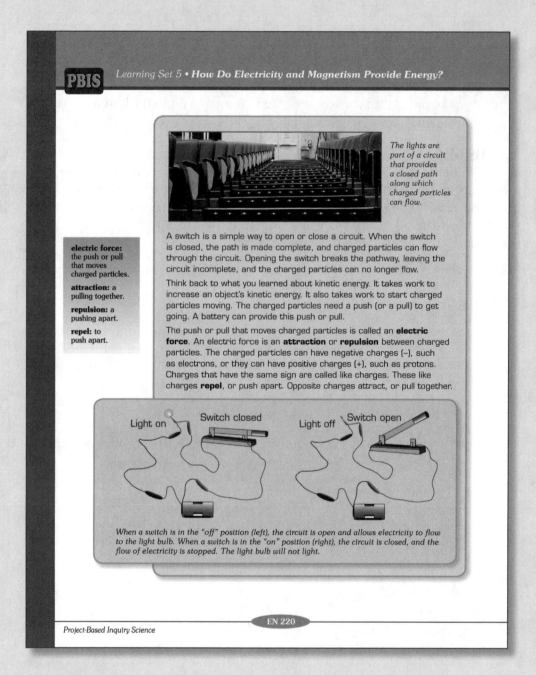

The lights are part of a circuit that provides a closed path along which charged particles can flow.

electric force: the push or pull that moves charged particles.

attraction: a pulling together.

repulsion: a pushing apart.

repel: to push apart.

A switch is a simple way to open or close a circuit. When the switch is closed, the path is made complete, and charged particles can flow through the circuit. Opening the switch breaks the pathway, leaving the circuit incomplete, and the charged particles can no longer flow.

Think back to what you learned about kinetic energy. It takes work to increase an object's kinetic energy. It also takes work to start charged particles moving. The charged particles need a push (or a pull) to get going. A battery can provide this push or pull.

The push or pull that moves charged particles is called an **electric force**. An electric force is an **attraction** or **repulsion** between charged particles. The charged particles can have negative charges (–), such as electrons, or they can have positive charges (+), such as protons. Charges that have the same sign are called like charges. These like charges **repel**, or push apart. Opposite charges attract, or pull together.

Light on   Switch closed   Light off   Switch open

When a switch is in the "off" position (left), the circuit is open and allows electricity to flow to the light bulb. When a switch is in the "on" position (right), the circuit is closed, and the flow of electricity is stopped. The light bulb will not light.

EN 220

Project-Based Inquiry Science

△ Guide

Ask students to think back to the setups they experimented with in *Section 5.1*. Ask students if anyone tried to light the bulb without a complete loop. Help students realize that electric current can only flow through a complete pathway known as an electric circuit.

Use the diagrams to explain how a switch works. Help students relate these examples to the switches they used. Clarify any misunderstandings about how students thought their switches worked before they read about them.

Think back to Thales and his exploration of amber. The amber attracted the feathers. This could happen only if the charges in the amber were opposite to the charges in the feathers. One had to be positive and the other negative. A battery provides electric force in a similar way. In a battery, you can think of the positive terminal as attracting, or pulling on, the negatively charged particles. The negative terminal is repelling, or pushing away, the negatively charged particles. This is how a battery supplies the push and pull to move electric charges in a circuit.

You may have observed a number on each battery followed by a "V." This number is the **voltage**. Voltage is a measure of how much electrical energy is supplied to each charged particle. As an electric charge moves around a circuit, it picks up energy at the battery and loses or "drops" its energy at devices like light bulbs. You can compare this to eating food to obtain the energy you need to use your muscles. Just like blood carries energy to your muscles, an electric charge carries energy in a circuit. Also, note that the blood does not get used up, only the energy. In an electric circuit, the electric charge does not get used up, only its energy.

voltage: a measure of the energy for an amount of charge.

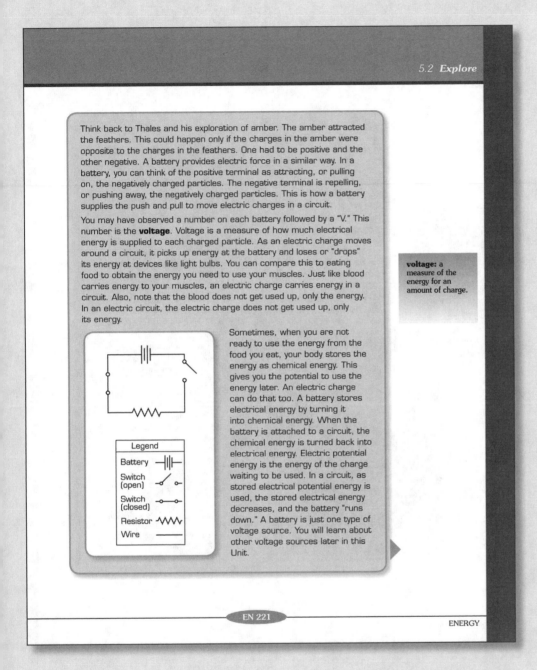

Legend	
Battery	⊣⊢⊣⊢
Switch (open)	⟋
Switch (closed)	—
Resistor	⋀⋀⋀
Wire	—

Sometimes, when you are not ready to use the energy from the food you eat, your body stores the energy as chemical energy. This gives you the potential to use the energy later. An electric charge can do that too. A battery stores electrical energy by turning it into chemical energy. When the battery is attached to a circuit, the chemical energy is turned back into electrical energy. Electric potential energy is the energy of the charge waiting to be used. In a circuit, as stored electrical potential energy is used, the stored electrical energy decreases, and the battery "runs down." A battery is just one type of voltage source. You will learn about other voltage sources later in this Unit.

Describe to students how voltage is similar to water in a plumbing system. Ask them to suppose they are using a hose attached to a pressurized water tank. If they increase the pressure of the tank, more water will come out of the hose in much the same way that increasing the voltage will cause more current to flow in a circuit.

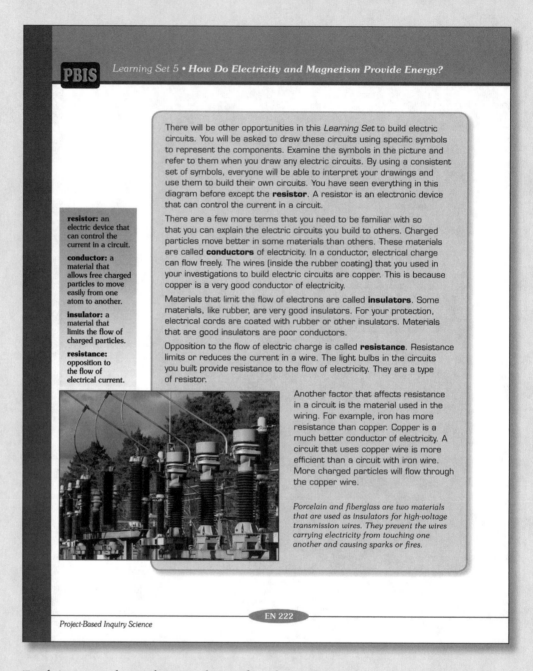

There will be other opportunities in this *Learning Set* to build electric circuits. You will be asked to draw these circuits using specific symbols to represent the components. Examine the symbols in the picture and refer to them when you draw any electric circuits. By using a consistent set of symbols, everyone will be able to interpret your drawings and use them to build their own circuits. You have seen everything in this diagram before except the **resistor**. A resistor is an electronic device that can control the current in a circuit.

There are a few more terms that you need to be familiar with so that you can explain the electric circuits you build to others. Charged particles move better in some materials than others. These materials are called **conductors** of electricity. In a conductor, electrical charge can flow freely. The wires (inside the rubber coating) that you used in your investigations to build electric circuits are copper. This is because copper is a very good conductor of electricity.

Materials that limit the flow of electrons are called **insulators**. Some materials, like rubber, are very good insulators. For your protection, electrical cords are coated with rubber or other insulators. Materials that are good insulators are poor conductors.

Opposition to the flow of electric charge is called **resistance**. Resistance limits or reduces the current in a wire. The light bulbs in the circuits you built provide resistance to the flow of electricity. They are a type of resistor.

resistor: an electric device that can control the current in a circuit.

conductor: a material that allows free charged particles to move easily from one atom to another.

insulator: a material that limits the flow of charged particles.

resistance: opposition to the flow of electrical current.

Another factor that affects resistance in a circuit is the material used in the wiring. For example, iron has more resistance than copper. Copper is a much better conductor of electricity. A circuit that uses copper wire is more efficient than a circuit with iron wire. More charged particles will flow through the copper wire.

Porcelain and fiberglass are two materials that are used as insulators for high-voltage transmission wires. They prevent the wires carrying electricity from touching one another and causing sparks or fires.

EN 222

Project-Based Inquiry Science

Explain to students that insulators for electricity and insulation for a home are similar. Both prevent the flow of something. Insulation around a wire prevents the flow of electrons outside the wire. Insulation in the walls of a house prevent the flow of heat energy. Also, conductors for electrical energy and heat are often the same substance—metals.

5.2 Explore

Stop and Think

1. What is the relationship between an electric current and an electric circuit?

2. How does a switch affect the flow of charged particles in an electric circuit?

3. What is the relationship between batteries and voltage?

4. Why are copper wires in an electrical circuit often coated with rubber? Use the terms "conductor" and "insulator" in your answer.

Reflect

1. What additional indicators have you identified for electrical energy?

2. What additional factors do you think might be used to control electrical energy?

3. In what ways are electric charges similar to the opposite ends of magnets? In what ways are they different?

4. How do you think a circuit could be used to turn another circuit on and off?

Update the *Project Board*

Record what you know about electric circuits in the *What are we learning?* column of the *Project Board*. Record evidence that supports what you have learned in the *What is our evidence?* column. Record what you think about the factors that might be used to control electrical energy in the *What do we think we know?* column. If you have more questions about electrical energy, record them in the *What do we need to investigate?* column.

What's the Point?

In this section, you set up an electric circuit that allowed electricity to flow through a battery, wires, and light bulb, and back to the battery. You found that as long as the circuit is complete, or closed, the light bulb would light. The battery provided the energy for the electric charges to move in the circuit and light the bulb. The measure of the energy for a given amount of charge is called voltage. When the circuit was opened by a switch, the flow of electrical charges was interrupted, and the light bulb did not light.

EN 223

ENERGY

Stop and Think

5 min

Students answer questions to summarize their understanding of electric current and circuits.

Guide and Assess

Remind students that when they answer these questions, they should use their knowledge of what they learned in the experiments and what they learned from the previous reading.

Use the following guidelines to assess students' answers:

1. Students should explain that an electric current is a flow of charges that can travel through a closed electric circuit.

2. Students should describe how a switch opens a circuit and stops the flow of electrons.

3. Students should recognize that a battery is a source of voltage in a circuit. Batteries can be of various sizes and voltages.

4. Students should understand that wires are conductors of electrical energy and usually are covered with rubber as insulator so that the electrical energy reaches its intended endpoint. Otherwise it could be "short-circuited" and blow a circuit-breaker, if not cause a fire.

Reflect

5 min

Students relate what they have learned about electric circuits to earlier observations and additional tasks.

Reflect

1. What additional indicators have you identified for electrical energy?

2. What additional factors do you think might be used to control electrical energy?

3. In what ways are electric charges similar to the opposite ends of magnets? In what ways are they different?

4. How do you think a circuit could be used to turn another circuit on and off?

◇ Evaluate

Have students discuss answers to the *Reflect* questions. Tell them to record their answers and note any disagreements.

1. Students' answers will vary and depend upon which indicators they identified earlier. Their list should include light energy, thermal energy, kinetic energy of appliances, and sounds of audio systems.

2. Students' answers will vary and depend upon which factors they identified earlier. Their list should include voltage source, resistors, switches, windings in a generator, and strength of magnetic field in a generator.

3. Students should remember that electric charges are like the ends of a permanent magnet because like charges repel, just as like magnetic poles repel. Opposite charges attract, just as opposite poles attract one another. They are different in that electrical charges move to do work while magnetic fields do not move.

4. Most students will not know the answer. However, a few students may suggest ways in which a circuit could be used to turn another circuit on and off. For example, a circuit with a battery in it could run a motor which opened a switch in the circuit, turning off the power to the motor.

Update the *Project Board*

Record what you know about electric circuits in the *What are we learning?* column of the *Project Board*. Record evidence that supports what you have learned in the *What is our evidence?* column. Record what you think about the factors that might be used to control electrical energy in the *What do we think we know?* column. If you have more questions about electrical energy, record them in the *What do we need to investigate?* column.

△ Guide

Remind students of some of the indicators and factors they have already noted on the *Project Board*. Then have them summarize ideas they have about indicators and factors related to electrical energy. Record these ideas on the *Project Board* along with evidence to support them. Identify any questions that have already been answered and record any new questions that students have formulated.

Update the Project Board

5 min

Students record ideas and questions from what they have done in the section on the Project Board.

Assessment Options

Targeted Concepts, Skills, and Nature of Science	How do I know if students got it?
Scientists often work together and then share their findings. Sharing findings makes new information available and helps scientists refine their ideas and build on others' ideas. When another person's or group's idea is used, credit needs to be given.	**ASK:** How did your group work together to find a way to turn a light on and off? **LISTEN:** Students should describe the process they used to determine a setup that would work.
Like electric charges exert a force of repulsion whereas unlike electric charges exert a force of attraction.	**ASK:** What type of electric force would be produced by two negative charges brought together? **LISTEN:** Students should know that like charges exert a force of repulsion on one another.
Electrical energy can flow through circuits.	**ASK:** What indicators did you use to determine changes in the amount of electrical energy flowing through your circuit? **LISTEN:** Students should describe changes in the intensity of the light, including no light at all.

Targeted Concepts, Skills, and Nature of Science	How do I know if students got it?
Electrical energy is the flow of charges through a circuit.	**ASK:** How does a switch control the electric current in a circuit?
	LISTEN: Students should explain that an open switch stops the flow of electric charges in a circuit.

Teacher Reflection Questions

- In what ways were students intimidated by the challenges of the investigations? How were you able to guide them through the procedure?

- How did students show that they grasped the concept of using indicators to recognize energy?

- How were you able to help students understand their observations in terms of electric current, circuits, and voltage? What would you do differently next time?

NOTES

....

....

....

....

....

....

5.3 Explore

How Can You Measure Electrical Energy?

◀ *2 class periods*

A class period is considered to be one 40 to 50 minute class.

Overview

Students begin the section by reading about the first galvanometer. Then, they build one of their own. Students work together to relate the galvanometer to the electromagnet they built in *Section 5.1*. They read about magnetic forces, magnetic poles, and magnetic fields. Students learn that the relationship between electricity and magnetism is named electromagnetism. The section concludes with an opportunity for students to think about using electromagnetism to open and close a circuit in a way that might be applied to the *Big Challenge*.

Targeted Concepts, Skills, and Nature of Science	Performance Expectations
Scientists often work together and then share their findings. Sharing findings makes new information available and helps scientists refine their ideas and build on others' ideas. When another person's or group's idea is used, credit needs to be given.	Students work together to build a galvanometer and explain how it works.
Studying the work of different scientists provides understanding of scientific inquiry and reminds students that science is a human endeavor.	Students learn about the contributions of Hans Oersted to the knowledge of electromagnetism.
A galvanometer is used to measure electric current.	Students use a galvanometer to detect electric current.
Magnetic forces are exerted in the magnetic field around a magnet, with the forces being strongest near the poles.	Students observe iron filings aligned with the magnetic field around a bar magnet.

Targeted Concepts, Skills, and Nature of Science	Performance Expectations
Like poles of a magnet repel whereas unlike poles attract.	Students read about the magnetic forces produced between magnetic poles.
Electricity gives rise to magnetism and magnetism gives rise to electricity.	Students read about electromagnetism.
An electric current flowing through a coil of wire can be used to produce an electromagnet.	Students relate the galvanometer they build to the electromagnet they already built.

Materials

1 per group	Magnetic compass D-cell battery D-cell battery holder Spool of copper magnet wire, #24, enamel coated (4 m) SPST switch Masking Tape, 4 pieces, 10 cm Sandpaper
3 per group	Wires with alligator clips
1 per class	Iron filings Plastic sheet Magnet

NOTES

....

....

....

....

Homework Options

Reflection

- **Science Content:** How can a galvanometer be used to identify a change in the direction of electric current? *(Students should relate the direction of the current to the direction in which the needle is deflected, recognizing that a change in the direction of current will result in a change in the direction of deflection.)*

- **Science Process:** Why do you use a compass to build a galvanometer? *(Students should describe how the needle of a compass aligns with a nearby magnetic field. Because the electric current in the coil of wire creates a magnetic field, the compass can detect the presence of the magnetic field and thus the electric current.)*

NOTES

....

....

....

....

....

....

....

....

....

....

ENERGY

NOTES

SECTION 5.3 IMPLEMENTATION

5.3 Explore

How Can You Measure Electrical Energy?

In the last section, you read about several factors that can be used to control an electric current: whether a circuit is complete and the voltage. You could see whether electrical energy was being transformed by observing indicators, such as whether or not the light bulb was lit. You could estimate the amount of electrical energy present by observing the intensity of light emitted by the bulb. However, you do not know yet how to measure electrical energy.

A galvanometer measures small electric currents.

galvanometer: a device for detecting or measuring small electric currents.

Electric current is another factor that determines the amount of electrical energy present. For a given circuit, the greater the electric current, the greater the electrical energy present.

You can measure electric current using another indicator of electrical energy that was discovered in 1819 by the Danish scientist Hans Oersted. While teaching his students about electricity, Oersted observed that a current in a wire caused a nearby compass needle to move. Within months, the first **galvanometer** was built. A galvanometer is a device used to measure small electric currents. If you insert a galvanometer into an electric circuit, you can measure the electric current in the circuit. You will be building on the work of other scientists as you build and use a simple galvanometer.

Build Your Own Galvanometer

You will build a simple galvanometer and test it in an electric circuit.

Procedure

1. Take a 4-m length of #24 copper magnet wire and sand the two ends to remove any coating of paint or varnish.

EN 224

Project-Based Inquiry Science

5.3 Explore

How Can You Measure Electrical Energy?

5 min

Students are introduced to the galvanometer.

○ Engage

Ask students how drivers know how fast they are moving. Students may suggest using a speedometer. Use this to begin a discussion about how different types of meters measure some quantity. Tell students that they will build a type of meter known as a galvanometer. Then read through the introduction to describe Oersted's discovery and the first galvanometer.

*A class period is considered to be one 40 to 50 minute class.

If time allows, recreate Oersted's demonstration by building a simple series circuit. Place compasses around the circuit. Then have students watch the compasses as you open and close the switch. The compasses should align with the circuit when you close the switch.

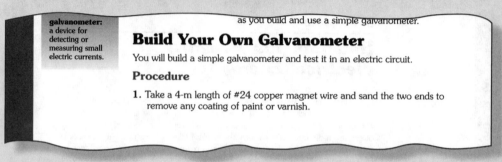

galvanometer: a device for detecting or measuring small electric currents.

as you build and use a simple galvanometer.

Build Your Own Galvanometer

You will build a simple galvanometer and test it in an electric circuit.

Procedure

1. Take a 4-m length of #24 copper magnet wire and sand the two ends to remove any coating of paint or varnish.

Build Your Own Galvanometer

20 min

Students build a simple galvanometer.

META NOTES

As students work on their galvanometers, it may be necessary to review how switches work. Remind students of the terminology describing switches as open and closed.

△ Guide

Before starting the activity, review the *Procedure* with students. Distribute materials to each group to observe to gain a better understanding of what they will be building.

Point out the diagrams to help students visualize what they are building. They should use this to guide their constructions. Allow them to build the galvanometer. If students have difficulty, help them check each connection to make sure the electric current has a complete circuit through which to flow.

NOTES

2. Tape the wire about 15 cm from one end to the back of the compass.

3. While holding the compass with one hand, wrap the wire around the compass face over and over until you have about 30 turns of wire. Leave about 15 cm of the wire free at both ends.

4. Secure the other end of the wire to the back of the compass with a second piece of tape.

5. Build a circuit using the switch, battery and battery holder, wires with alligator clips, and the wires wrapped around the compass. Leave the switch open.

Materials
- 1 magnetic compass
- 1 D-cell battery
- 1 D-cell battery holder
- spool of copper magnet wire, #24, enamel-coated (4 m)
- 1 SPST switch
- 3 wires with alligator clips
- masking tape, 4 pieces, 10 cm
- 1 piece sandpaper

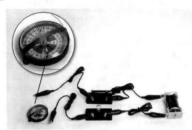

6. Turn the compass so that the 30 turns of wire are in line with the compass needle.

7. Close the switch and observe the compass needle. Record your observations and sketch the compass as it looks before and after the switch is closed. If the needle fails to move, it is likely that the circuit is open. Check all connections to make sure they are secure.

EN 225

ENERGY

NOTES

....

....

Stop and Think

5 min

Students analyze their observations.

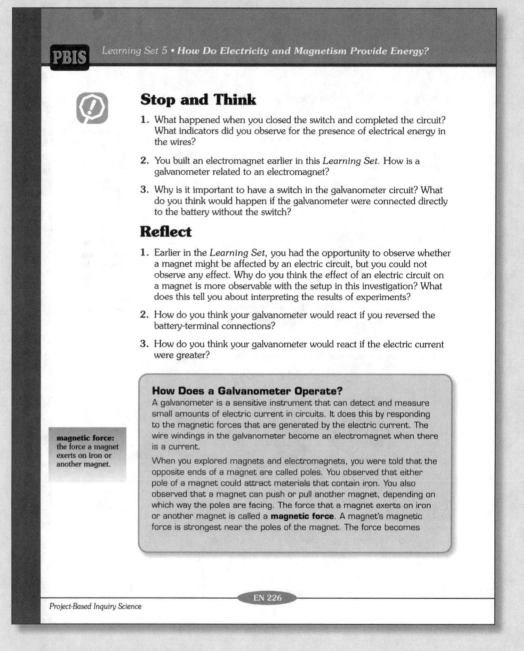

Stop and Think

1. What happened when you closed the switch and completed the circuit? What indicators did you observe for the presence of electrical energy in the wires?

2. You built an electromagnet earlier in this *Learning Set*. How is a galvanometer related to an electromagnet?

3. Why is it important to have a switch in the galvanometer circuit? What do you think would happen if the galvanometer were connected directly to the battery without the switch?

Reflect

1. Earlier in the *Learning Set*, you had the opportunity to observe whether a magnet might be affected by an electric circuit, but you could not observe any effect. Why do you think the effect of an electric circuit on a magnet is more observable with the setup in this investigation? What does this tell you about interpreting the results of experiments?

2. How do you think your galvanometer would react if you reversed the battery-terminal connections?

3. How do you think your galvanometer would react if the electric current were greater?

magnetic force: the force a magnet exerts on iron or another magnet.

How Does a Galvanometer Operate?

A galvanometer is a sensitive instrument that can detect and measure small amounts of electric current in circuits. It does this by responding to the magnetic forces that are generated by the electric current. The wire windings in the galvanometer become an electromagnet when there is a current.

When you explored magnets and electromagnets, you were told that the opposite ends of a magnet are called poles. You observed that either pole of a magnet could attract materials that contain iron. You also observed that a magnet can push or pull another magnet, depending on which way the poles are facing. The force that a magnet exerts on iron or another magnet is called a **magnetic force**. A magnet's magnetic force is strongest near the poles of the magnet. The force becomes

EN 226

Project-Based Inquiry Science

△ Guide and Assess

Have students discuss the *Stop and Think* questions in their groups. Listen to check that students identify an indicator. Make sure that comparisons to the electromagnet are logical and that students recognize the importance of the switch.

1. Students should have observed that the needle on the compass galvanometer moved when the switch was closed. This is one more indicator of electric energy and magnetic energy.

2. Students should remember that they used electric energy to create a magnetic field in their electromagnet. The galvanometer does the same thing.

3. Students should understand that the electric energy of the battery is being used as long as the circuit is closed. The battery would "go dead" quickly if the switch were left closed.

to the battery without the switch.

Reflect

1. Earlier in the *Learning Set,* you had the opportunity to observe whether a magnet might be affected by an electric circuit, but you could not observe any effect. Why do you think the effect of an electric circuit on a magnet is more observable with the setup in this investigation? What does this tell you about interpreting the results of experiments?

2. How do you think your galvanometer would react if you reversed the battery-terminal connections?

3. How do you think your galvanometer would react if the electric current were greater?

Reflect

5 min

Students use their observations of a galvanometer to make predictions.

△ Guide and Assess

Have students discuss the *Reflect* questions in their groups. Listen to discussions.

1. Students may realize that the needle of the compass has little mass or friction and it would take much less force to make it move. Here is a place to return to the idea that technology works hand in hand with science to make observations that might not have been possible with equipment used in earlier investigations.

2. Students should recognize that if the battery terminal connections were switched, the electric current would be reversed. This would cause the needle of the compass galvanometer to deflect in the opposite direction.

3. Students may correctly predict that a greater electric current would cause the needle to deflect by a greater amount.

NOTES

....

....

....

How Does a Galvanometer Operate?

30 min

Students learn explanations for their observations of the galvanometer.

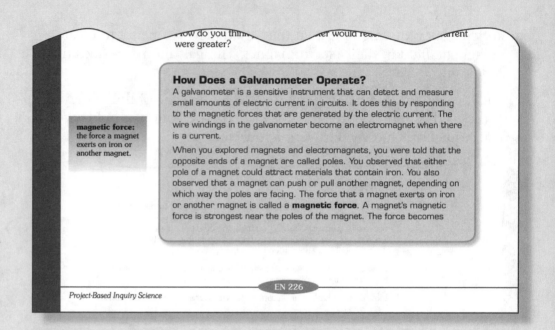

How do you think ...ter would rea... ...rrent were greater?

How Does a Galvanometer Operate?

A galvanometer is a sensitive instrument that can detect and measure small amounts of electric current in circuits. It does this by responding to the magnetic forces that are generated by the electric current. The wire windings in the galvanometer become an electromagnet when there is a current.

When you explored magnets and electromagnets, you were told that the opposite ends of a magnet are called poles. You observed that either pole of a magnet could attract materials that contain iron. You also observed that a magnet can push or pull another magnet, depending on which way the poles are facing. The force that a magnet exerts on iron or another magnet is called a **magnetic force**. A magnet's magnetic force is strongest near the poles of the magnet. The force becomes

magnetic force: the force a magnet exerts on iron or another magnet.

△ Guide

Remind students about their investigations with magnets. Then read through the text to introduce the magnetic force. Ask students to think about the wire windings in the galvanometer they explored. Point out that they are made of copper, which is not magnetic like iron can be. This means that the magnetic force must be caused by the electric current rather than the metal itself.

NOTES

....

....

....

....

....

weaker as you move away from the poles and is weakest near the middle of the magnet.

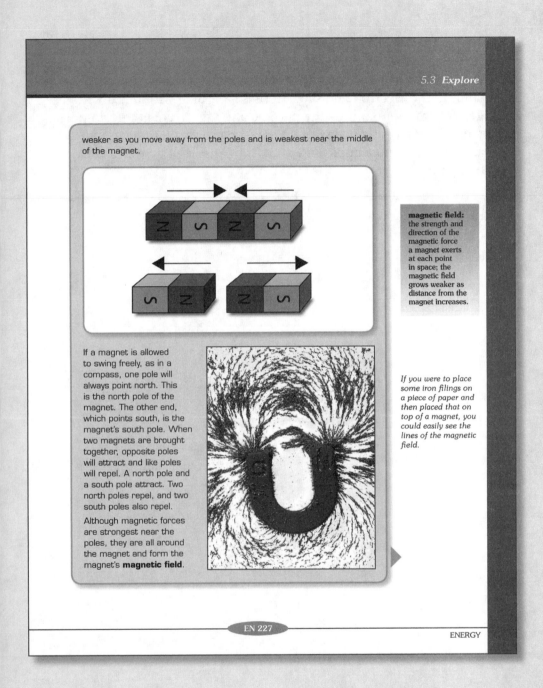

magnetic field: the strength and direction of the magnetic force a magnet exerts at each point in space; the magnetic field grows weaker as distance from the magnet increases.

If a magnet is allowed to swing freely, as in a compass, one pole will always point north. This is the north pole of the magnet. The other end, which points south, is the magnet's south pole. When two magnets are brought together, opposite poles will attract and like poles will repel. A north pole and a south pole attract. Two north poles repel, and two south poles also repel.

Although magnetic forces are strongest near the poles, they are all around the magnet and form the magnet's **magnetic field**.

If you were to place some iron filings on a piece of paper and then placed that on top of a magnet, you could easily see the lines of the magnetic field.

EN 227

ENERGY

◯ **Engage**

To introduce the concept of a magnetic field, spread iron filings on a thin sheet of plastic. Place a bar magnet under the plastic. Then gently tap the plastic so that the iron filings can align with the magnetic field. Show students the pattern formed by the iron filings. Then read the information about magnetic fields, using the photograph to explain the concept.

TEACHER TALK

❝One big difference between electricity and magnetism is that we can point to the electron and say, "Here is a particle with negative charge." We cannot point to any particle and say, "Here is a north-pole particle." You can cut a magnet into smaller and smaller pieces and it will always have a north pole and a south pole. Magnetic poles always come in pairs.❞

NOTES

....

....

....

....

....

....

....

....

....

....

....

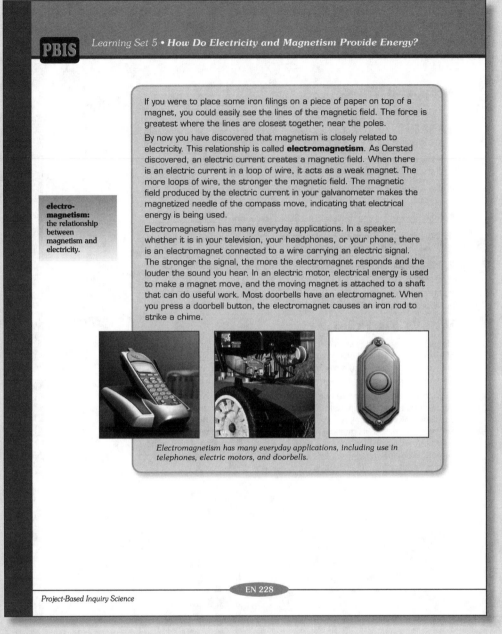

If you were to place some iron filings on a piece of paper on top of a magnet, you could easily see the lines of the magnetic field. The force is greatest where the lines are closest together, near the poles.

By now you have discovered that magnetism is closely related to electricity. This relationship is called **electromagnetism**. As Oersted discovered, an electric current creates a magnetic field. When there is an electric current in a loop of wire, it acts as a weak magnet. The more loops of wire, the stronger the magnetic field. The magnetic field produced by the electric current in your galvanometer makes the magnetized needle of the compass move, indicating that electrical energy is being used.

Electromagnetism has many everyday applications. In a speaker, whether it is in your television, your headphones, or your phone, there is an electromagnet connected to a wire carrying an electric signal. The stronger the signal, the more the electromagnet responds and the louder the sound you hear. In an electric motor, electrical energy is used to make a magnet move, and the moving magnet is attached to a shaft that can do useful work. Most doorbells have an electromagnet. When you press a doorbell button, the electromagnet causes an iron rod to strike a chime.

electro-magnetism: the relationship between magnetism and electricity.

Electromagnetism has many everyday applications, including use in telephones, electric motors, and doorbells.

META NOTES

Students may relate a compass to direction only. A compass consists of a needle that is free to spin. The needle is magnetized, so it aligns with nearby magnetic fields. A compass can detect the magnetic field near a wire, but it can also detect Earth's magnetic field. Earth is surrounded by a magnetic field as if it had a bar magnet running along its axis.

△ Guide

Lead a discussion about the relationship between electricity and magnetism. Remind students of what they observed when they built an electromagnet. Then relate the information to the galvanometer.

Stop and Think

5 min

Students answer questions to focus their learning about electricity and magnetism.

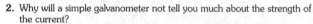

Stop and Think

1. What is the role of a magnetic force in a galvanometer?

2. Why will a simple galvanometer not tell you much about the strength of the current?

3 How does electromagnetism help you understand the relationship between electricity and magnetism?

4. What additional indicators, if any, do you now know for magnetic energy?

5. What factors do you think might be used to control magnetic energy?

6. In what ways are magnetic poles similar to electric charges? In what ways are they different?

7. How do you think an electromagnet could be used to open and close a circuit?

8. What are some ways that you might use an electromagnet in a Rube Goldberg machine?

What's the Point?

Magnetic forces are similar to electric forces in many ways. Opposite poles of a magnet attract, and like poles of a magnet repel. The strength of the magnetic force exerted by a magnet decreases as distance from the magnet increases. You can observe this magnetic field by using iron filings.

The movement of the needle of a magnet by an electric current is an indicator that magnetic energy is being transformed. In building and using your own galvanometer, you experienced the relationship between electricity and magnetism. The magnetic field produced by the electric current in the galvanometer caused the compass needle to move. The ability of an electric current to produce a magnetic field is an important concept and has many practical applications in everyday life.

EN 229

ENERGY

△ Guide and Assess

Have students answer the *Stop and Think* questions in their groups. Listen to confirm that students are identifying indicators of magnetic energy and factors that might control magnetic energy. Make sure students recognize that a magnetic force exists between magnetic poles and an electric force exists between electric charges. Use the pictures of electromagnets to help students consider ways that an electromagnet might be used to open and close a circuit, such as in the Rube Goldberg machine they are designing.

1. Students should describe how a galvanometer measures electric current by the strength of the magnetic field created through its copper windings.

2. Students may realize that a simple compass galvanometer is too crude to accurately measure current.

3. Students may say that knowing about electromagnetism helps them to understand how light energy can have both an electric and magnetic component.

4. Students' answers will vary. However, their list should include the following indicators for magnetic energy: attraction (or repulsion) to (or from) another magnetic field, attraction to iron or steel, and the ability to generate electric current when a wire coil passes through it.

5. Students may suggest that the strength of a magnetic field can be controlled by the strength of, or number of, magnets selected for use. Also, distance from the magnetic field is a way to increase or decrease its strength. If one is making an electromagnet, its field can be controlled by the number of windings in the coil or by the speed the coil turns while in the magnetic field.

6. Students should understand that magnetic poles and electric charges are similar in that like poles repel, as do like charges. Also, opposite poles attract one another, as do opposite charges. They differ in that electric energy can be turned on and off, but magnetic energy cannot. This is because electric energy is carried by particles which move. Magnetic energy is stationary and is not associated with a particle. **NOTE:** An electromagnet can be shut on or off by switching its power source, electric energy, on or off.

7. Students' answers will vary, but they may find it difficult to figure out how to use an electromagnet to open and close a circuit. You can refresh their thinking by reviewing the following points:

   • An electric current flowing through the coil of wire creates a magnetic field.

   • A magnetic field can be used to move any material containing iron, such as steel.

8. Student answers will be similar to those for Question 7, but more specific. Students may suggest using an electromagnet to lift a piece of metal to unbalance a beam, causing kinetic energy to begin, such as balls to roll. Or, they may suggest using it to move a steel switch. It could also be used to repel another magnet, causing something else to happen in the next step.

Assessment Options

Targeted Concepts, Skills, and Nature of Science	How do I know if students got it?
Scientists often work together and then share their findings. Sharing findings makes new information available and helps scientists refine their ideas and build on others' ideas. When another person's or group's idea is used, credit needs to be given.	**ASK:** What ideas did other students have about the galvanometer with which you disagreed? **LISTEN:** Students should identify disagreements along with their reasoning.
Studying the work of different scientists provides understanding of scientific inquiry and reminds students that science is a human endeavor.	**ASK:** How did Hans Oersted contribute to the current knowledge of electromagnetism? **LISTEN:** Students should recognize that Oersted first discovered that an electric current gives rises to a magnetic field.
A galvanometer is used to measure electric current.	**ASK:** What was the purpose of building a galvanometer? **LISTEN:** Students should discuss using the galvanometer to identify an electric current.
Magnetic forces are exerted in the magnetic field around a magnet, with the forces being strongest near the poles.	**ASK:** How do the magnetic forces around a magnet vary? **LISTEN:** Students might describe that the magnetic forces are strongest near the poles.

Targeted Concepts, Skills, and Nature of Science	How do I know if students got it?
Like poles of a magnet repel whereas unlike poles attract.	**ASK:** If the north end of a compass needle is attracted to the end of a magnet, what pole of the magnet must it be? **LISTEN:** Students should explain that it must be the south pole of the magnet because opposite poles attract one another.
Electricity gives rise to magnetism and magnetism gives rise to electricity.	**ASK:** Why is a compass deflected when placed next to a wire carrying electric current? **LISTEN:** Students should explain that an electric current produces a magnetic field.
An electric current flowing through a coil of wire can be used to produce an electromagnet.	**ASK:** How is the galvanometer like the electromagnet? **LISTEN:** Students might recognize that both involve the use of a magnetic field produced by an electric current.

Teacher Reflection Questions

- What difficulties did students have constructing the galvanometer? What did you do to assist them?

- How were you able to help students understand and visualize a magnetic field? How might you change your approach in the future?

- How have you kept students engaged in class discussions? What else can you do to engage students?

NOTES

5.4 Investigate

Which Battery Provides More Electrical Energy?

◀ 2 class periods

A class period is considered to be one 40 to 50 minute class.

Overview

Students begin the section thinking about batteries and what happens to batteries with use. They build a circuit to compare a D-cell battery with a 6-V dry-cell battery. Students discover that the voltage of the battery is related to the amount of electric current, as measured by the deflection of a compass needle. After making these observations, students read about voltage and how it is related to electric current.

Targeted Concepts, Skills, and Nature of Science	Performance Expectations
Scientists often work together and then share their findings. Sharing findings makes new information available and helps scientists refine their ideas and build on others' ideas. When another person's or group's idea is used, credit needs to be given.	Students work together to compare batteries with different voltage.
The voltage of a battery determines the amount of electric current in a circuit.	Students discover that a battery with a higher voltage produces a greater electric current than a battery with a lower voltage.

Materials

1 per group	Galvanometer
	D-cell battery
	D-cell battery holder
	6-V dry-cell battery
	SPST switch
	15 ohm, 10-W resistor

Materials	
1 per group	Galvanometer
	D-cell battery
	D-cell battery holder
	6-V dry-cell battery
	SPST switch
	15ohm, 10-W resistor
4 per group	Wires with alligator clips

Homework Options

Reflection

- **Science Content:** How did you use evidence to support your claims? *(Students should describe how they used their observations and their drawings to identify factors and compare batteries.)*

- **Science Content:** Some electric circuits include several batteries connected together. How do you think adding batteries will affect the amount of electric current in a circuit? *(Students should answer that adding batteries effectively increases the voltage, thereby increasing the electric current.)*

Preparation for 5.5

- **Science Process:** In what ways do you think you could change a circuit to do more work? *(This question is intended to get students thinking about building more complex circuits with additional light bulbs or pathways.)*

NOTES

....

....

....

SECTION 5.4 IMPLEMENTATION

5.4 Investigate

Which Battery Provides More Electrical Energy?

You probably use batteries every day, and you may decide to use batteries in your Rube Goldberg machine. AAA, AA, C, D, and 9-V—these are only a few of the types of batteries you can find in a store. TV remotes, game controllers, alarm clocks, cell phones, flashlights, toys, and many other electronic devices all require different sizes of batteries. You might wonder why different devices need different batteries and what the differences are among all of these types of batteries.

Remember that batteries are a type of voltage source that gives charged particles the push they need to move through a circuit. You will now have an opportunity to use the galvanometer you made in the last section to test whether different batteries with different voltages provide different amounts of electrical energy. Your observations will help you identify some factors that determine the amount of electrical energy available from a voltage source. Knowing this will help you include electricity in your Rube Goldberg machine.

Batteries come in a variety of sizes, from tiny hearing-aid batteries to large car batteries.

Project-Based Inquiry Science

5.4 Investigate

Which Battery Provides More Electrical Energy?

5 min

Students think about different types of batteries.

○ Engage

Show students different batteries, or refer to the photograph of batteries. Ask students to name devices they might know that use each type of battery. For example, a television remote control might use AA batteries and a portable radio might use D batteries.

*A class period is considered to be one 40 to 50 minute class.

Predict

5 min

Students predict which type of battery provides the greatest amount of electrical energy.

Predict

Observe both of the batteries in the picture. Think about what might determine how much electrical energy a battery uses to do work on electrons in the wire. Which battery do you think will provide more electrical energy? Why?

Procedure

1. Assemble a circuit that includes your galvanometer, the D-cell battery, the resistor, and a switch. Leave the switch in the open ("off") position.

2. Move the compass so that the wire windings of the galvanometer line up in the same direction as the compass needle (in the north–south direction).

3. Close the switch to the "on" position. Record your observations of the movement of the compass needle. Make a drawing of the galvanometer showing how far the needle moved. Label the drawing as "1.5-V D-cell battery." Open the switch to the "off" position after 30 seconds because the resistor becomes hot.

4. Remove the D-cell battery from the circuit and replace it with the 6-V dry-cell battery. Leave the switch in the open ("off") position.

5. Check that the wire windings of the galvanometer line up in the same direction as the compass needle (in the north–south direction).

6. Close the switch to the "on" position. Record your observations of the needle in the galvanometer. Make a drawing of the galvanometer showing how far the needle moved. Label the drawing as "6-V dry-cell battery." Open the switch to the "off" position after 30 seconds because the resistor becomes hot.

⚠️ Do not touch the resistor. It can become hot.

Materials
- galvanometer
- D-cell battery
- D-cell battery holder
- 6-V dry-cell battery
- SPST switch
- 4 wires with alligator clips
- 15 ohm, 10-W resistor

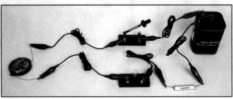

EN 231

ENERGY

⚠ Guide

Remind students of what a battery does. Make sure students remember that a battery converts stored chemical energy into electrical energy. Then have students predict whether a D-cell battery or a 6-V dry-cell battery provides more energy. Ask students to record and defend their predictions.

◯ Get Going

Have students meet with their groups and review the procedure. Answer any questions about what students are going to do. Then distribute materials to groups. They should have their galvanometer, the D-cell battery, the resistor, and a switch to start. Allow students to build their circuits and record their results. Make sure they understand that they should sketch their galvanometers to show how the needle moved and label their drawings.

As students work through the procedure, make sure that the placement of the wires are correct. Emphasize that they should line up with the compass needle, in the north-south direction.

Procedure

20 min

Students compare batteries in a circuit to determine which provides more electrical energy.

NOTES

....

....

....

....

....

....

....

....

....

....

Analyze Your Results

10 min

Students discuss their observations about a D-cell battery and 6-V dry-cell battery.

Analyze Your Results

Use the observations you recorded and your drawings to answer the following questions with your group. Also, read the information recorded on each battery. That information will help you answer some of these questions.

1. Which battery caused the greater movement of the compass needle?

2. Which characteristic(s) of the batteries do think are responsible for the movement of the needle in the galvanometer? Why do you think these characteristic(s) are important?

3. What one characteristic do you think is responsible for one battery causing the needle to move more than the other?

4. What other factors in the circuit may be important?

Communicate

Investigation Expo

Share the results of your investigation with the class. Everyone did the same investigation, so you will only discuss your results rather than presenting them with a poster. It will be important to make sure that all groups observed the same results. If any groups have results that conflict with yours, you should ask questions about their procedures. Make sure you ask respectfully. Discuss the reasons why their results might be different.

After sharing results, discuss the different features of each type of battery. Share the characteristics that your group thought might be responsible for the difference in how far the compass needle moved.

Each group should then contribute one characteristic they think is a factor that affects the current in a circuit. Record on the board each group's contribution.

△ Guide and Assess

Allow groups to discuss answers to the questions. Listen to hear that students observed a greater deflection from the 6-V dry-cell battery. Make sure students recognize different characteristics of the batteries, such as how the wires are connected to the terminals, the size of the battery, and the voltage of the battery. Students should recognize that the voltage of the battery determines the deflection of the compass needle. If students have difficulty thinking about factors of the circuit, ask them to consider whether the circuit includes devices, such as bulbs, or whether the current has more than one path through which to travel. Have students compare their observations with their predictions.

1. Students should report that the larger, 6-V dry-cell battery caused the greater deflection in the compass galvanometer.

2. Students should understand that the higher voltage produces greater electric current and moves the needle more. More current can do more work, such as light a brighter light bulb, or move a needle more.

3. Students may answer that the voltage is most responsible for moving the needle more.

4. Students may suggest that the size of the resistor or the number of windings around the compass galvanometer are also important factors to the circuit.

△ Guide

Have each group present their results and discuss their answers to the questions. Note any disagreements among groups. Work as a class to come to a consensus. Record the results so that you can return to them later after students read about voltage sources.

Communicate: Investigation Expo

10 min

Students share their observations and analyses with the class.

META NOTES

Students should present their ideas, knowing that they will read more about batteries and will later have a chance to revise their ideas.

NOTES

How Does a Voltage Source Store and Provide Energy?

5 min

Students read about voltage sources.

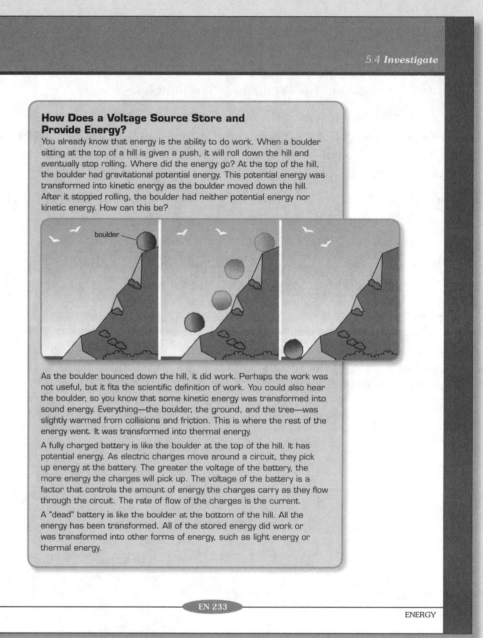

How Does a Voltage Source Store and Provide Energy?

You already know that energy is the ability to do work. When a boulder sitting at the top of a hill is given a push, it will roll down the hill and eventually stop rolling. Where did the energy go? At the top of the hill, the boulder had gravitational potential energy. This potential energy was transformed into kinetic energy as the boulder moved down the hill. After it stopped rolling, the boulder had neither potential energy nor kinetic energy. How can this be?

boulder

As the boulder bounced down the hill, it did work. Perhaps the work was not useful, but it fits the scientific definition of work. You could also hear the boulder, so you know that some kinetic energy was transformed into sound energy. Everything—the boulder, the ground, and the tree—was slightly warmed from collisions and friction. This is where the rest of the energy went. It was transformed into thermal energy.

A fully charged battery is like the boulder at the top of the hill. It has potential energy. As electric charges move around a circuit, they pick up energy at the battery. The greater the voltage of the battery, the more energy the charges will pick up. The voltage of the battery is a factor that controls the amount of energy the charges carry as they flow through the circuit. The rate of flow of the charges is the current.

A "dead" battery is like the boulder at the bottom of the hill. All the energy has been transformed. All of the stored energy did work or was transformed into other forms of energy, such as light energy or thermal energy.

EN 233

ENERGY

○ Engage

Ask students what happens to the batteries in a toy after they use it for some time. Lead students to recognize that the batteries need to be replaced because they no longer work. The batteries are said to be "dead." Read through the information together that likens a battery to a boulder rolling down a hill.

△ Guide

If students have difficulty with the concept, consider using another analogy. Describe to students how electric current is sometimes like water flowing through a pipe. If the pipe is slightly tilted, the water flows slowly through the pipe. If one end of the pipe is held higher, the water flows at a faster rate. The tilt of the pipe is like the voltage of a battery. The greater the voltage, the greater the electric current.

NOTES

Stop and Think

5 min

Students check their understanding of batteries.

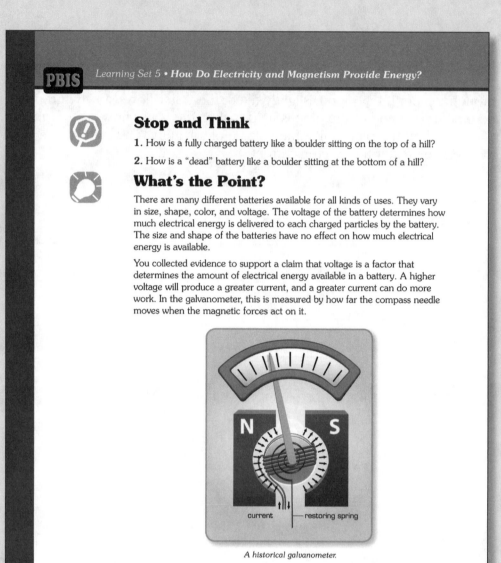

Stop and Think

1. How is a fully charged battery like a boulder sitting on the top of a hill?

2. How is a "dead" battery like a boulder sitting at the bottom of a hill?

What's the Point?

There are many different batteries available for all kinds of uses. They vary in size, shape, color, and voltage. The voltage of the battery determines how much electrical energy is delivered to each charged particles by the battery. The size and shape of the batteries have no effect on how much electrical energy is available.

You collected evidence to support a claim that voltage is a factor that determines the amount of electrical energy available in a battery. A higher voltage will produce a greater current, and a greater current can do more work. In the galvanometer, this is measured by how far the compass needle moves when the magnetic forces act on it.

current — restoring spring

A historical galvanometer.

EN 234

Project-Based Inquiry Science

Guide and Assess

Ask all students to answer the questions. Then invite volunteers to share their answers. Lead a brief class discussion about the answers and clarify any misconceptions.

1. Students should answer that a fully-charged battery has its maximum potential electric energy and a boulder on top of a hill has its maximum potential gravitational energy.

2. Students should understand that a "dead" battery has no potential energy left, just as a boulder at the bottom of a hill has exhausted its potential energy.

Assessment Options

Targeted Concepts, Skills, and Nature of Science	How do I know if students got it?
Scientists often work together and then share their findings. Sharing findings makes new information available and helps scientists refine their ideas and build on others' ideas. When another person's or group's idea is used, credit needs to be given.	**ASK:** What did you learn by listening to other groups? **LISTEN:** Students should describe any observations they have overlooked, ideas they had not considered, or disagreements they had.
The voltage of a battery determines the amount of electric current in a circuit.	**ASK:** What did you discover about the relationship between voltage and electric current? **LISTEN:** Students should describe how they used a compass to discover that the amount of electric current depends on the voltage of a battery.

Teacher Reflection Questions

- What evidence do you have that students are accepting the relationship between electricity and magnetism? What conceptual difficulties do you need to address to make this clear?

- What evidence do you have that students understand the importance of sharing their observations and building on each other's ideas?

- How did you choose which students would present from each group? How do you plan to choose students to represent their groups next time?

NOTES

5.5 Explore

How Can One Voltage Source Light More Than One Light Bulb?

◀ *2 class periods*

A class period is considered to be one 40 to 50 minute class.

Overview

Students work together to find a way to build a circuit that can light two bulbs. Once they have built the circuit, students remove one bulb to find out if affects the other bulb. Students read about series and parallel circuits. They not only learn about the characteristics of each, but they figure out which type of circuit they built.

Targeted Concepts, Skills, and Nature of Science	Performance Expectations
Scientists often work together and then share their findings. Sharing findings makes new information available and helps scientists refine their ideas and build on others' ideas. When another person's or group's idea is used, credit needs to be given.	Students work together to build a circuit to light two bulbs at the same time.
Electric circuits can be wired in series or in parallel.	Students learn about the advantages and disadvantages of series and parallel circuits.

Materials	
2 per group	D-cell batteries
	D-cell battery holders
	Small light bulbs
	Light bulb holders
1 per group	SPST switch
5 per group	Wires with alligator clips

Materials	
1 per student	*Energy Types* page *Project Board* page
1 per class	Class *Project Board*

Homework Options

Reflection

- **Science Content:** Suppose you built a series circuit with two bulbs. How would adding a third bulb to the circuit affect the brightness of the bulbs? *(Students should predict that all of the bulbs would be less bright than they would be if they were alone in the circuit.)*

- **Science Content:** Why is a parallel circuit useful for wiring appliances in a kitchen? *(Students may suggest that if one appliance breaks the flow of current, the other appliances will continue to work.)*

Preparation for 5.6

- **Science Content:** How are electric circuits in your home different from the circuits you built? *(This question is intended to get students to think about sources of electrical energy other than batteries.)*

NOTES

....

....

....

....

....

SECTION 5.5 IMPLEMENTATION

5.5 Explore

How Can One Voltage Source Light More Than One Light Bulb?

At the beginning of this *Learning Set,* you assembled an electric circuit. You were able to produce a flow of charged particles from one terminal of a battery, through the wires and the light, and back to the opposite terminal of the battery. This worked just fine for you. But what if you had to light a whole string of lights? They would look quite unattractive if every bulb had to have its own battery! In this section, you will investigate how to light a whole set of devices from one source of energy. When you can do this, you will understand something about how electricity is used in buildings. A source of electrical energy is brought to the building, and it is used to operate everything in the building. This may be useful in building your Rube Goldberg machine.

It would not be very efficient if every light on this bridge had to have its own source of energy!

ENERGY

5.5 Explore

How Can One Voltage Source Light More Than One Light Bulb?

5 min

Students think about building a circuit with more than one light bulb.

○ Engage

Ask students to think about strings of lights, such as holiday lights, lights on a restaurant, or lights at a theater. Ask students if they think each light has its own battery or plug. After students recognize that they do not, read through the introductory text together.

*A class period is considered to be one 40 to 50 minute class.

Predict

5 min

Students sketch how to build a circuit with more than one light bulb.

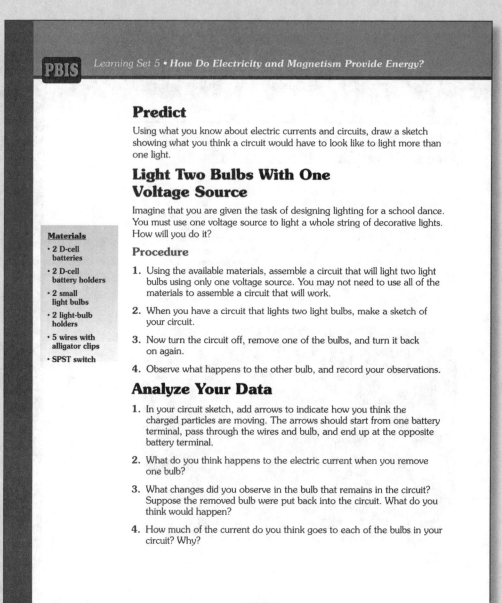

Predict

Using what you know about electric currents and circuits, draw a sketch showing what you think a circuit would have to look like to light more than one light.

Light Two Bulbs With One Voltage Source

Imagine that you are given the task of designing lighting for a school dance. You must use one voltage source to light a whole string of decorative lights. How will you do it?

Materials
- 2 D-cell batteries
- 2 D-cell battery holders
- 2 small light bulbs
- 2 light-bulb holders
- 5 wires with alligator clips
- SPST switch

Procedure

1. Using the available materials, assemble a circuit that will light two light bulbs using only one voltage source. You may not need to use all of the materials to assemble a circuit that will work.

2. When you have a circuit that lights two light bulbs, make a sketch of your circuit.

3. Now turn the circuit off, remove one of the bulbs, and turn it back on again.

4. Observe what happens to the other bulb, and record your observations.

Analyze Your Data

1. In your circuit sketch, add arrows to indicate how you think the charged particles are moving. The arrows should start from one battery terminal, pass through the wires and bulb, and end up at the opposite battery terminal.

2. What do you think happens to the electric current when you remove one bulb?

3. What changes did you observe in the bulb that remains in the circuit? Suppose the removed bulb were put back into the circuit. What do you think would happen?

4. How much of the current do you think goes to each of the bulbs in your circuit? Why?

EN 236

Project-Based Inquiry Science

⬡ Get Going

Remind students about the parts of the circuits they have already built. Then tell students to use what they have learned already to draw their sketches. Have students keep the sketches nearby so they can compare them to the circuits they build.

◯ Get Going

Have students read the procedure. Answer any questions students may have about what they need to do. Make sure students understand that when they remove the bulb, they are not removing the bulb holder. They are only unscrewing the bulb from the holder. Otherwise, they would be changing the circuit itself. Remind students that they do not need to use all of the materials they have.

△ Guide and Assess

Have students discuss answers to the questions in their groups. The analysis will depend on the type of circuit the students constructed. If students are having difficulty, tell them to think back to the role of a switch in controlling the flow of electric charges. Guide them to understand that if removing the bulb caused the other bulb to turn off, then removing the bulb acted like opening a switch. If removing the bulb did not cause the other bulb to turn off, then removing the bulb did not act like a switch. When students are finished with the discussion, have them compare their final circuits to their predicted circuits. Ask them how they are similar and different from what they expected.

1. Students should understand how to follow the directions for the series circuit. For the parallel circuit, they may make some mistakes. Be sure to point out that electrons move from the negative terminal to the positive terminal of the battery.

2. Students who made a series circuit should understand that they have created an open circuit and that the current has stopped. Students who made the parallel circuit may not notice much difference, although the remaining bulb should get brighter.

3. Students who made the series circuit should report that the remaining bulb went out. Students who made the parallel circuit may notice that the remaining bulb got brighter.

4. Students may guess that each bulb will receive half the current.

NOTES

....

....

Light Two Bulbs With One Voltage Source

25 min

Students build a circuit that will light two bulbs.

Analyze Your Data

5 min

Students discuss their circuits and observations.

ENERGY

Communicate: Investigation Expo

20 min

Students present their circuits to the class.

META NOTES

Students may have difficulty relating their observations to everyday applications. Suggest they think about replacing the light bulbs with other devices that use electricity in their homes. This will help them consider the consequences of having devices wired together.

5.5 Explore

Communicate

Investigation Expo

When it is your group's turn, demonstrate the circuit you assembled. Then describe how you assembled the circuit and the path of the electric current. Your sketches should make this easy to show.

Make sure you answer all the following questions in your presentation:

1. How would you describe the circuit you built?

2. What are some advantages to using your circuit? What are some disadvantages?

3. How might your circuit be useful in an everyday application?

As you are watching the presentations, notice the intensity of the lights. How many types of circuits has the class built? How is the intensity of the lights different in each type of circuit?

Reflect

1. How many different types of circuits did the groups build? Sketch each one. Draw arrows to show how the current moves through each one. You might want to construct the types of circuits you did not construct previously.

2 For each type of circuit, what are its advantages and disadvantages?

3. How might each be useful in different everyday applications?

4. Why do you think the intensity of the lights differs in each type of circuit? The arrows you sketched for each one might help you answer this question.

EN 237

ENERGY

⬡ Get Going

Give groups some time to prepare a presentation of their circuit. Let them know that in their presentations, they will demonstrate their circuit and share how it was assembled and the path of the electric current. To guide students' presentations, point out they should answer all of the questions in the student text. Also point out that as the class is listening to the other groups, they should be listening for the answers.

Once all groups have shared their circuits, have a class discussion to identify differences between circuits and the results that were observed.

△ Guide and Assess

Have students discuss answers to the *Reflect* questions in their groups. Then discuss them as a class. Encourage students to share all ideas at this point. They will soon read about different types of circuits.

1. Students' answers will vary, but only two types of circuits can be built—either series or parallel.

2. Students should answer that the series circuit has the disadvantage of losing both lights when one light is removed (or burned out). The parallel circuit has the advantage of maintaining one light even when one light burns out. The parallel circuit also has the advantage of providing brighter lights, and bulbs in the series circuit are somewhat dimmer.

3. Students' answers will vary, but should reflect the advantages and disadvantages of each. The series circuit would be useful in situations where only one device needs to be powered because it is a simpler, cheaper circuit. The parallel circuit would be useful in most other applications where the loss of one branch would not hurt the other parallel branches.

4. Students may find this a difficult question to answer. A correct answer would reflect the fact that, in a series circuit, each of the two bulbs gets half the voltage. Bulbs in the parallel circuit get more than half the voltage and are, therefore, brighter.

META NOTES

If all groups build series circuits, you may consider building a parallel circuit to show them another option. This will give them ideas to think about as they analyze their circuits and compare alternatives.

Reflect

5 min

Students answer questions about different types of circuits.

NOTES

....

....

....

....

Series and Parallel Circuits

20 min

Students read about the characteristics of series and parallel circuits.

META NOTES

If needed, review the term *parallel* with students by drawing sets of parallel lines on the board.

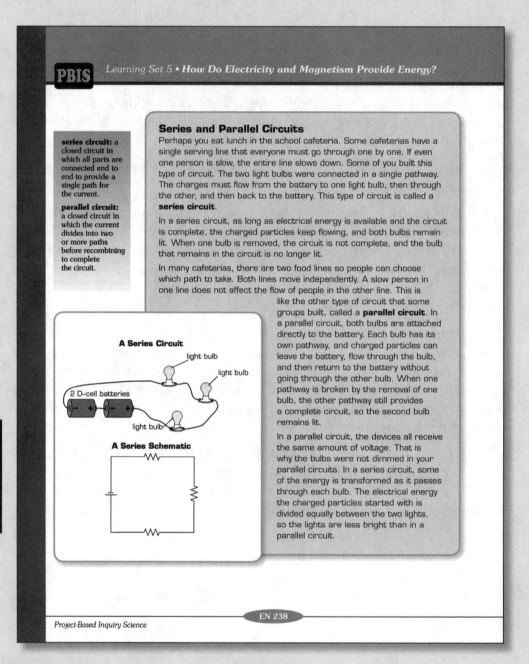

series circuit: a closed circuit in which all parts are connected end to end to provide a single path for the current.

parallel circuit: a closed circuit in which the current divides into two or more paths before recombining to complete the circuit.

Series and Parallel Circuits

Perhaps you eat lunch in the school cafeteria. Some cafeterias have a single serving line that everyone must go through one by one. If even one person is slow, the entire line slows down. Some of you built this type of circuit. The two light bulbs were connected in a single pathway. The charges must flow from the battery to one light bulb, then through the other, and then back to the battery. This type of circuit is called a **series circuit**.

In a series circuit, as long as electrical energy is available and the circuit is complete, the charged particles keep flowing, and both bulbs remain lit. When one bulb is removed, the circuit is not complete, and the bulb that remains in the circuit is no longer lit.

In many cafeterias, there are two food lines so people can choose which path to take. Both lines move independently. A slow person in one line does not affect the flow of people in the other line. This is like the other type of circuit that some groups built, called a **parallel circuit**. In a parallel circuit, both bulbs are attached directly to the battery. Each bulb has its own pathway, and charged particles can leave the battery, flow through the bulb, and then return to the battery without going through the other bulb. When one pathway is broken by the removal of one bulb, the other pathway still provides a complete circuit, so the second bulb remains lit.

In a parallel circuit, the devices all receive the same amount of voltage. That is why the bulbs were not dimmed in your parallel circuits. In a series circuit, some of the energy is transformed as it passes through each bulb. The electrical energy the charged particles started with is divided equally between the two lights, so the lights are less bright than in a parallel circuit.

A Series Circuit

light bulb

light bulb

2 D–cell batteries

light bulb

A Series Schematic

△ Guide

Read through the information in the text together. Use the diagrams to make sure students understand the differences between the circuits. Then ask students to classify the type of circuit they built. Make sure they now understand their observations in terms of the characteristics of each circuit. The most important point to make is that parallel circuits provide more dependable electricity but are more complex and more expensive than a serial circuit. The only advantage to a series circuit is that it is simpler.

In nearly all homes, offices, and schools, the electric outlets and lights are connected in parallel circuits. This way, outlets that are not being used will not break the path for charged particles flowing to outlets that are in use.

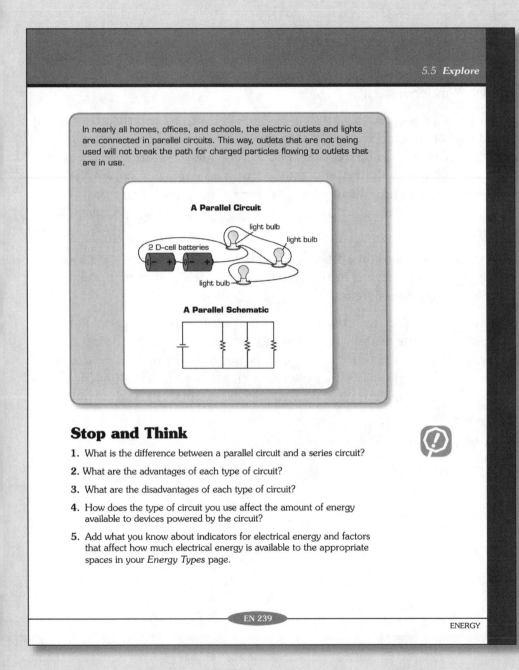

A Parallel Circuit

light bulb

light bulb

2 D–cell batteries

light bulb

A Parallel Schematic

Stop and Think

1. What is the difference between a parallel circuit and a series circuit?

2. What are the advantages of each type of circuit?

3. What are the disadvantages of each type of circuit?

4. How does the type of circuit you use affect the amount of energy available to devices powered by the circuit?

5. Add what you know about indicators for electrical energy and factors that affect how much electrical energy is available to the appropriate spaces in your *Energy Types* page.

EN 239

ENERGY

Stop and Think

5 min

Students answer questions to evaluate their understanding of series and parallel circuits.

△ Guide and Assess

Have each group discuss and answer the *Stop and Think* questions. Listen to make sure they correctly understand the characteristics of each type of circuit.

1. Students should respond that a series circuit has all of the elements—batteries, switch, bulbs—in one circuit and each element affects all the others. In a parallel circuit, each bulb has its own circuit and is minimally affected by the other circuits.

2. Students should answer that there is little advantage to a series circuit, unless only one device is to be powered. Then it is a simpler, cheaper circuit to build. The parallel circuit can power several devices independently.

3. Students should recognize that a series circuit has the disadvantages that each powered device is dependent on any other devices in the circuit. If one bulb burns out, they all go out. Also, in a series circuit, all the voltage is shared and the function of each device will be affected by the functioning of all others. The parallel circuit has only the disadvantage of being more complex and somewhat more expensive.

4. Students should realize that the parallel circuit will provide more energy to each device in the circuit. The series circuit requires that the total voltage is shared among the devices.

5. Students will add the new information about series and parallel circuits as being ways to control the amount of electrical energy to a device. Parallel circuits are more dependable and provide a constant amount of electricity. Series circuits will fail when one light burns out. Also, a series circuit will provide less voltage to each appliance in the circuit.

6. Students' answers will vary.

NOTES

....

....

....

....

....

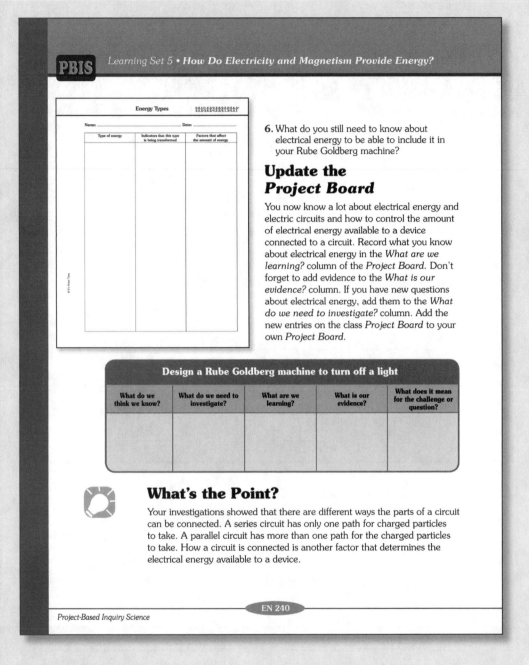

6. What do you still need to know about electrical energy to be able to include it in your Rube Goldberg machine?

Update the Project Board

You now know a lot about electrical energy and electric circuits and how to control the amount of electrical energy available to a device connected to a circuit. Record what you know about electrical energy in the *What are we learning?* column of the *Project Board*. Don't forget to add evidence to the *What is our evidence?* column. If you have new questions about electrical energy, add them to the *What do we need to investigate?* column. Add the new entries on the class *Project Board* to your own *Project Board*.

Design a Rube Goldberg machine to turn off a light

What do we think we know?	What do we need to investigate?	What are we learning?	What is our evidence?	What does it mean for the challenge or question?

What's the Point?

Your investigations showed that there are different ways the parts of a circuit can be connected. A series circuit has only one path for charged particles to take. A parallel circuit has more than one path for the charged particles to take. How a circuit is connected is another factor that determines the electrical energy available to a device.

EN 240

Update the Project Board

5 min

Students add ideas and evidence to the Project Board.

△ Guide

Lead a discussion in which students review new information they have learned about circuits. Add this information to the Project Board. Be sure to include the evidence they cite.

Assessment Options

Targeted Concepts, Skills, and Nature of Science	How do I know if students got it?
Scientists often work together and then share their findings. Sharing findings makes new information available and helps scientists refine their ideas and build on others' ideas. When another person's or group's idea is used, credit needs to be given.	**ASK:** How did your group come up with the idea for the circuit you used? **LISTEN:** Students should describe the process through which they arrived at either a series or a parallel circuit.
Electric circuits can be wired in series or in parallel.	**ASK:** Why do all the bulbs in a parallel circuit shine with the same intensity? **LISTEN:** Students should recognize that the same voltage is applied to each bulb wired in parallel.

Teacher Reflection Questions

- How did building the circuit help students to grasp the concept of series and parallel circuits? What could you do differently to make sure the groups build different kinds of circuits?

- What issues came up when groups presented their circuits in the *Investigation Expo?* How can you help make the process go more smoothly in the future?

- How do you expect students to apply what they learned to the *Big Challenge?* What specific concepts do you think will be the most useful for the challenge?

SECTION 5.6 INTRODUCTION

5.6 Explore

How Is Electrical Energy Produced?

◀ *3 class periods*

A class period is considered to be one 40 to 50 minute class.

Overview

Students begin the section by considering the use of batteries and generators. Groups are challenged to build a battery using a lemon. Then the class observes a demonstration involving a generator. They watch the construction of the generator from a cardboard box and then observe how it spins. After the demonstration, students compare batteries and generators using what they have learned in the two activities. They read about batteries and generators and work together to further compare the two devices.

Targeted Concepts, Skills, and Nature of Science	Performance Expectations
Scientists often work together and then share their findings. Sharing findings makes new information available and helps scientists refine their ideas and build on others' ideas. When another person's or group's idea is used, credit needs to be given.	Students work together to construct a battery to analyze its operation.
A battery converts stored chemical energy into electrical energy.	Students use a lemon to produce an electrical current.
Electricity gives rise to magnetism and magnetism gives rise to electricity.	Students move magnets to produce an electric current.
A generator transforms mechanical energy into electrical energy.	Students observe that mechanical energy can produce an electric current.
A galvanometer is used to measure electric current.	Students observe that a galvanometer can detect electric current produced by a generator.

Materials	
1 per group	Galvanometer Pair of stereo headphones Plastic knife
2 per group	Large, fresh lemons Galvanized nails, 2 in. Pennies
3 per group	Wires with alligator clips
1 per student	Safety goggles
1 per class	Small, open-ended cardboard box, 13 cm x 9 cm Large iron nail, about 10 cm (4 in.) Compass galvanometer 300 ft enamel-coated magnet wire, #30 Student galvanometer, +/- 500 μA
8 per class	Alnico magnets
2 per class (optional)	Alligator clips
1 per class	*Lemon Battery and Generator Exploration* page

Homework Options

Reflection

- **Science Content:** How is the energy transformation in a battery different from in a generator? *(Students should explain that batteries and generators both produce electrical energy. However, the battery uses stored chemical energy and the generator uses mechanical energy.)*

- **Science Content:** Earlier in this Unit, you read about hydroelectric power plants. What is the source of mechanical energy for the generators in these power plants? *(Students should recall that hydroelectric power plants use the mechanical energy of falling water to turn a turbine that operates a generator.)*

SECTION 5.6 IMPLEMENTATION

5.6 Explore

How Is Electrical Energy Produced?

It can be frustrating to be talking on a cell phone, listening to your favorite song, or playing a fun game when your battery goes dead. Think about what that means. It means that the battery runs out of energy. That might make you think about how the battery gets energy in the first place.

When batteries run out, usually there is another voltage source you can use to operate your electronic gadget, or you might have a device you can use to recharge (reenergize) the battery. Either of these requires an AC adapter that can be plugged into an electrical outlet. You know that an electric outlet can be counted on to deliver all the energy you need to run your gadget or reenergize its batteries. But where does the energy in an electric outlet come from, and what happens to this energy when there is a power failure?

Electricity in the electrical outlets in your home and other buildings is produced by a **generator**. A generator transforms mechanical energy into electrical energy, using the motion of a magnet inside a coil of wire. Both the electric outlet in a wall and a battery are sources of voltage. You already know that the amount of voltage in a voltage source determines how much electrical energy is available. To help you better understand voltage sources, your group will make a battery. Then you will observe a demonstration showing the construction and operation of a simple generator.

generator: a device that converts mechanical energy into electrical energy using the motion of a magnet inside a coil of wire.

Wires come into your house and into an electric outlet.

EN 241

ENERGY

5.6 Explore

How Is Electrical Energy Produced?

5 min

Students are introduced to electrical generators.

○ Engage

Have students list a few devices that use rechargeable batteries or that do not use batteries at all. Ask students where these batteries or devices get their electrical energy. Lead students to recognize that they plug them into an electrical outlet. Guide students to think about what an electrical outlet is. Then read the introductory text and introduce the term *generator*.

*A class period is considered to be one 40 to 50 minute class.

Build a Battery

10 min

Students build batteries using lemons.

Build a Battery

You will make your battery from lemons and two different metals. Then you will test the battery with a galvanometer and with headphones. One metal you will use is copper. The other is a galvanized nail. A galvanized nail is a steel nail coated with the metal zinc.

Materials

- 2 large, fresh lemons
- 2 galvanized nails, 2 in.
- 2 pennies
- 1 galvanometer
- 1 set stereo headphones
- 3 wires with alligator clips
- 1 plastic knife
- safety glasses

Procedure

1. Put on your safety glasses. Using the plastic knife, make two slits in one of the lemons, about 2.5 cm (about 1 in.) apart.

2. Push a galvanized nail about halfway into one of the slits. Insert the penny into the other slit, about halfway in. It is very important that the nail and the coin do not touch.

   Insert the zinc nail in this slit | Insert the penny in this slit

3. To test your lemon battery, you will use the galvanometer that you built earlier. Using the alligator clip wires, connect one wire from the galvanometer to the penny. Connect the other galvanometer wire to the galvanized nail. Observe and record the movement of the needle in the galvanometer. Then disconnect the galvanometer. Record your observation.

4. Put on the headphones. Using the two wires with alligator clips, connect the headphone plug to the lemon battery. Typically, there are three sections on the plug. Try various combinations until you hear a click through the headphones. This click indicates the presence of electrical energy. Once you hear the click, remove the headphones from the circuit.

5. Increase the voltage of your circuit by using two lemons, two coins, and two nails. Connect the first lemon battery in series with the second lemon. Test this two-battery combination with your galvanometer. Observe how much the needle in the galvanometer moves. Then disconnect the galvanometer, and record this observation.

EN 242

⬡ Get Going

Assign the experiment to each group in the class and have students review the procedure. Use the diagram and photograph to help them understand what they are going to do. Then distribute the materials to each group. Make sure students put on their safety glasses before they begin. Then have students build their battery.

5.6 Explore

Stop and Think

1. What indicators of the presence of electrical energy did you observe?

2. What do you think would happen if you used two nails to make the battery instead of a nail and a penny? Why do you think this?

3. How did the galvanometer move when you connected the two lemon batteries in series as compared to when you used only one lemon battery?

4. What factors affected the amount of electrical energy available?

5. What do you predict would happen if you connected the two lemon batteries in a parallel circuit rather than in a series circuit? Why do you think this? If you have time, you may try this out.

Demonstration: Build a Generator

A generator transforms mechanical energy into electrical energy. You can make a generator by moving a wire through a magnetic field. Electric current will be generated from work done by kinetic energy. Your teacher will build a generator in class. As you observe the generator being built and what it does, think about the purpose of the magnet-wire coil.

Observe

Note the parts and placement of parts as your teacher builds a simple generator.

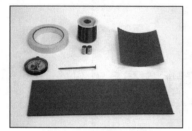

Materials

- 1 small, open-ended cardboard box, 13 cm x 9 cm
- 8 Alnico magnets
- 1 large iron nail, about 10 cm (4 in.)
- sandpaper
- masking tape
- 1 compass galvanometer
- 300 ft enamel-coated magnet wire, #30
- optional: 2 alligator clips
- 1 student galvanometer, +/- 500 μA

Stop and Think

5 min

Students review the concepts involved in the lemon-batteries they built.

△ Guide and Assess

Have groups discuss possible answers to the questions. Encourage students to provide all explanations and predictions, even if they are unsure about the answers, as long as they provide evidence to support their ideas.

1. Students should respond that they observed a "click" in the headphones and also movement in the galvanometer as indicators of electrical energy.

2. Students may realize that they would not be able to make a battery using two identical metals and that a battery requires two different metals. Students may not know why this is so.

3. Students should report that they observed more movement in the galvanometer when they used two lemons in place of one lemon.

4. Students may respond that the number of lemons or the number of batteries affected the amount of electrical energy available.

5. Students' answers will vary, but they may realize that with only one device being powered by the lemon batteries, they may get the same galvanometer deflection as with only one battery.

Demonstration: Build a Generator

10 min

Students observe a generator being built.

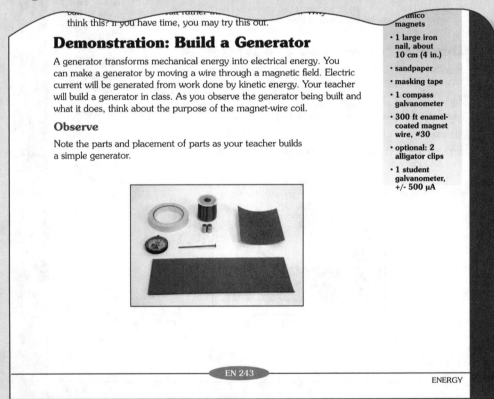

think this? If you have time, you may try this out.

Demonstration: Build a Generator

A generator transforms mechanical energy into electrical energy. You can make a generator by moving a wire through a magnetic field. Electric current will be generated from work done by kinetic energy. Your teacher will build a generator in class. As you observe the generator being built and what it does, think about the purpose of the magnet-wire coil.

Observe

Note the parts and placement of parts as your teacher builds a simple generator.

Alnico magnets

• 1 large iron nail, about 10 cm (4 in.)
• sandpaper
• masking tape
• 1 compass galvanometer
• 300 ft enamel-coated magnet wire, #30
• optional: 2 alligator clips
• 1 student galvanometer, +/- 500 µA

EN 243

ENERGY

◯ Engage

Point out to students that the electricity coming to their electrical outlets does not come from a lemon. Explain that, instead, it is produced by a generator at a power plant. Tell students that you are going to build a simple generator for them to observe.

Procedure

Review the procedure with students. The steps are a bit more complex than the previous setups, so make sure students understand what you are going to do. Build the generator slowly and explain each step. Remind them to record their observations and to think about the magnet-wire coil.

Overview

When completed, this simple generator will produce electricity by moving a magnetic field through a stationary coil of wire. There are three variables which control how much electricity is produced—the strength of the magnetic field, the number of wire loops, and the speed that the magnetic field moves. Point out to the students that either the magnets or the coil of wire can move—both will produce electricity. In a commercial power plant, the magnets are stationary and it is the coils of wire that move. The movement of the turbine which drives the turning coil is driven by water, wind, steam, or tidal motion.

1. Show the students the parts you will use to build the generator:

   - 1-rectangle of corrugated pasteboard (cardboard): dimensions 3.5 in x 12 in

   - a compass galvanometer

   - 1-4 in nail

   - 8-Alnico magnets (2 stacks of 4)

   - 300 ft-enamel-coated magnet wire (#30), sandpaper

   - ½ masking tape

   - sandpaper

   - 1-student galvanometer (if available)

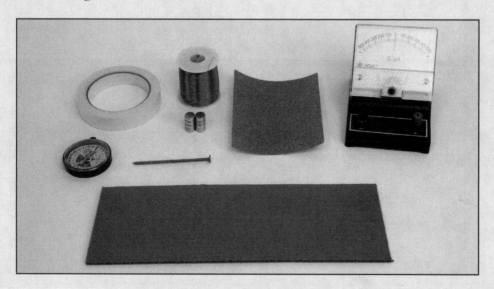

2. Draw lines on the cardboard at 3.5 in., 4.5 in., 7.5 in., and 8.5 in. These lines should be perpendicular to the longer edge, as shown. Using a good straight edge, such as a wooden ruler, crease each line so that it is flexible. You can save class time by having previously drawn the lines and creased the cardboard.

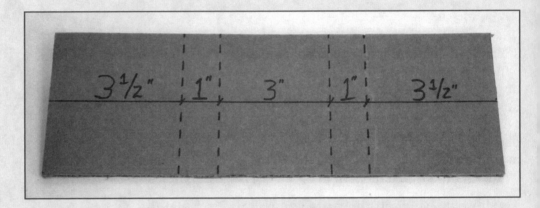

3. Fold the cardboard to form an open-ended box that is approximately 3.5 in. x 3.5 in. and with about a 3/4 in. internal gap between the two wider sides. Tape the loose edge with masking tape to hold the box together.

4. Draw a large X from corner to corner on the two wider sides of the box. In the center of one X push the nail through and then through the center of the other X. It should go completely through the box, passing through three layers of cardboard. Wiggle the nail around to make the hole slightly larger so the nail can turn freely. Hold the nail and spin the box. The box should spin easily.

5. With the nail in the box, stack four magnets and attach them magnetically to the nail inside the box. Attach the other four stacked magnets in the same way on the exact opposite side of the nail. The eight magnets should form a straight line and not touch the box. Hold the box and spin the nail with the magnets on it. The magnets should not touch the box.

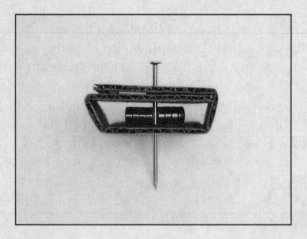

6. Leaving a 1-m wire lead, tape one end of the magnet wire to the outside of the box. Wind the remainder of the wire (about 200 turns) around the center of the box as shown, leaving a 1-m length hanging. Tape this loose end to the box also. You will have about 200 turns of wire with two 1-m leads hanging off. The nail with magnets should still turn freely inside the box. This completes the construction of the generator.

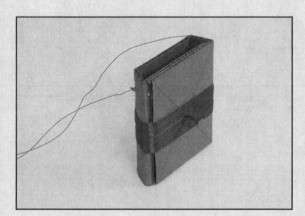 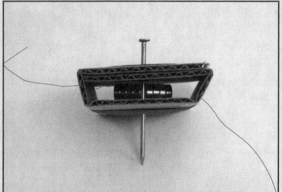

7. To test the generator, sand about ½ in. of enamel coating from each end of the wire leads. Attach the two leads from the generator to the two leads of the compass galvanometer by twisting them together. Since the magnets could affect the compass if too close, leave about 1 meter between the generator and the compass galvanometer.

8. If electricity is being generated, it will pass through the wire leads and through the coil on the compass galvanometer. This will create a magnetic field around the compass and the needle will move. Spin the nail by hand so that the magnets are moving. Spin the nail fast and then slow. Allow the students to observe the movement of the compass needle.

Test the generator with both the compass galvanometer and the student galvanometer, if available. The voltage produced will be alternating current and the needle may pulsate back and forth. You might try spinning it very slowly compared to spinning it fast so that they can see the difference.

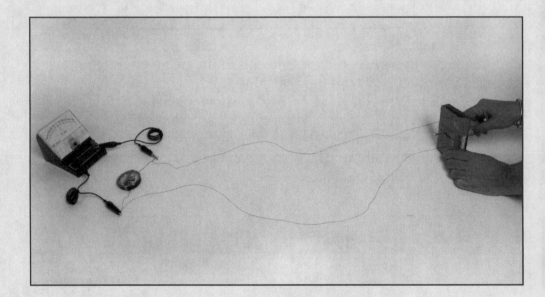

NOTES

....

....

....

Procedure

1. The generator will be housed in a small cardboard box. Draw a large "X" from corner to corner on the two wider sides of the cardboard box. In the center of one "X," push the nail through the box and through the center of the other "X." It should go completely through the box, passing through two walls. Wiggle the nail around to make the hole slightly bigger. Hold the nail and spin the box. The box should be able to spin freely around the nail.

2. With the nail through the box, stack four magnets and attach them magnetically to the nail inside the box. Attach the other four magnets in the same way on the exact opposite side of the nail. The eight magnets should form a straight line and should be as close as possible to the inside walls of the box without touching the box.

3. Spin the nail with the magnets on it. The nail and magnets should be able to spin freely without the magnets hitting the walls of the box. Keep the nail and magnets inside the box during the next step.

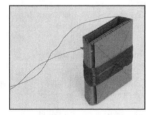 

NOTES

....

....

....

4. Leaving a 1-m wire lead, tape one end of the magnet wire to the outside of the box. Wind the remainder of the magnet wire (about 200 turns) around the center of the box, leaving a 1-m length hanging. Tape this end to the box also. You will have about 200 turns of wire with two 1-m leads hanging off. The nail with magnets should still turn freely inside the box.

5. Sand about ½ in. on both ends of the magnet wire to remove the enamel coating. Attach the two leads from the generator to the two leads from the compass galvanometer by twisting them together. The distance between the generator and the galvanometer must be at least 3 ft so the magnets do not affect the compass galvanometer.

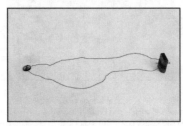

6. Spin the nail so the magnets are moving. Spin the nail fast and then slow. Observe and record the movement of the needle in the galvanometer.

7. As an option, a student galvanometer may be introduced to the circuit, using two alligator clip leads. This tool will provide a more sensitive and more accurate measuring device.

8. When the generator is completed, it will be connected to a galvanometer like the one you built and spun slowly. Record your observations on paper.

9. Next, the generator will be spun very fast. Record your observations on paper.

10. The generator will then be connected to a compass galvanometer. As the generator is spun slowly, record your observations on paper.

11. The generator will be spun fast. Record your observations on paper.

NOTES

....

....

....

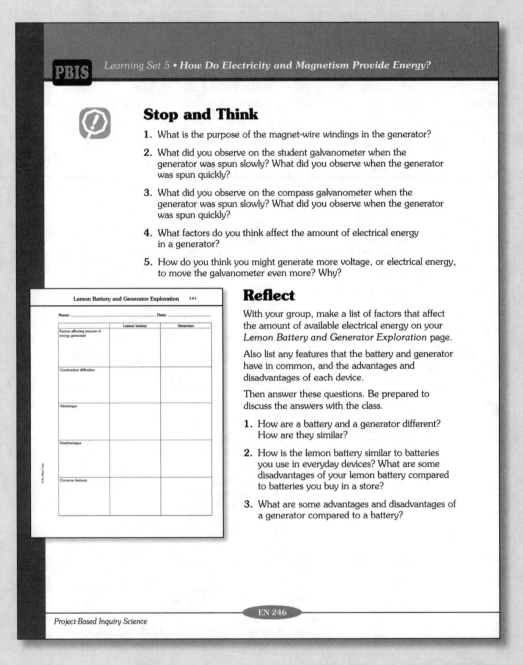

Stop and Think

1. What is the purpose of the magnet-wire windings in the generator?

2. What did you observe on the student galvanometer when the generator was spun slowly? What did you observe when the generator was spun quickly?

3. What did you observe on the compass galvanometer when the generator was spun slowly? What did you observe when the generator was spun quickly?

4. What factors do you think affect the amount of electrical energy in a generator?

5. How do you think you might generate more voltage, or electrical energy, to move the galvanometer even more? Why?

Lemon Battery and Generator Exploration   5.6.1

Name: _____   Date: _____

	Lemon battery	Generator
Factors affecting amount of energy generated		
Construction difficulties		
Advantages		
Disadvantages		
Common features		

Reflect

With your group, make a list of factors that affect the amount of available electrical energy on your *Lemon Battery and Generator Exploration* page.

Also list any features that the battery and generator have in common, and the advantages and disadvantages of each device.

Then answer these questions. Be prepared to discuss the answers with the class.

1. How are a battery and a generator different? How are they similar?

2. How is the lemon battery similar to batteries you use in everyday devices? What are some disadvantages of your lemon battery compared to batteries you buy in a store?

3. What are some advantages and disadvantages of a generator compared to a battery?

Stop and Think

5 min

Students consider the generators they observed being built and operated.

Guide and Assess

Remind students that they have observed that an electric current gives rise to a magnetic field. In this experiment, they used a moving magnetic field to create an electric current. The magnetic field is moving if the magnets move or if a coil of wire is moved through the magnets. Now, have students answer the questions provided.

1. Students' answers will vary. They should mention that the moving magnets produce electric energy in the coil.

2. Students may report that they observed a deflection of the galvanometer when the generator was spun slowly. When the generator was spun quickly, the deflection was greater because more electric energy was generated. **NOTE:** Because the electricity generated is alternating current, the galvanometer needle will try to go back and forth. It may look like the needle is not moving, but only quivering.

3. Students will probably report that the compass galvanometer moved less than the student galvanometer but that the same effects were seen.

4. Students should respond that the factors affecting the amount of electrical energy from the generator might be: the number of windings in the coil, the strength of the magnetic field (or the number of magnets), and the speed at which the generator turns.

5. Students should recognize that they could increase the amount of electrical energy by increasing the number of windings in the coil, by increasing the number of magnets, or by spinning the generator faster.

Reflect

5 min

Students compare the characteristics of the lemon battery with those of the generator.

to move the galvanometer even more? Why?

Reflect

With your group, make a list of factors that affect the amount of available electrical energy on your *Lemon Battery and Generator Exploration* page.

Also list any features that the battery and generator have in common, and the advantages and disadvantages of each device.

Then answer these questions. Be prepared to discuss the answers with the class.

1. How are a battery and a generator different? How are they similar?

2. How is the lemon battery similar to batteries you use in everyday devices? What are some disadvantages of your lemon battery compared to batteries you buy in a store?

3. What are some advantages and disadvantages of a generator compared to a battery?

△ Guide and Assess

Have students complete their *Lemon Battery and Generator Exploration* pages, describing the exploration they conducted. Then have each group present their results. Tell students to fill in the other column of the chart by listening to the presentations.

1. Students should recognize that both devices provide electrical energy. However, the battery is portable whereas a real generator can be difficult to transport. In addition, the battery will eventually run out whereas the generator will not.

2. Students may describe that the lemon battery provides a source of small amounts of energy that can be used to power electrical devices. Unlike a store-bought battery, the lemon battery is difficult to transport and cannot be placed into electrical equipment, but its waste is biodegradable.

3. Students may list a variety of suggestions. Lead them to recognize that, despite initial construction and cost, a generator can produce more power for a longer period of time than a battery.

NOTES

....

....

....

....

....

....

....

....

....

....

....

ENERGY

How Do Batteries and Generators Compare?

5 min

Students learn more about batteries and generators, including the concepts of direct current and alternating current.

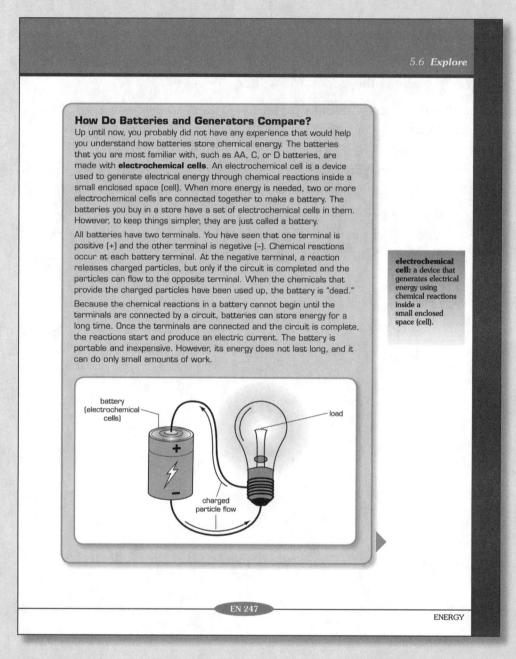

How Do Batteries and Generators Compare?

Up until now, you probably did not have any experience that would help you understand how batteries store chemical energy. The batteries that you are most familiar with, such as AA, C, or D batteries, are made with **electrochemical cells**. An electrochemical cell is a device used to generate electrical energy through chemical reactions inside a small enclosed space (cell). When more energy is needed, two or more electrochemical cells are connected together to make a battery. The batteries you buy in a store have a set of electrochemical cells in them. However, to keep things simpler, they are just called a battery.

All batteries have two terminals. You have seen that one terminal is positive (+) and the other terminal is negative (–). Chemical reactions occur at each battery terminal. At the negative terminal, a reaction releases charged particles, but only if the circuit is completed and the particles can flow to the opposite terminal. When the chemicals that provide the charged particles have been used up, the battery is "dead."

Because the chemical reactions in a battery cannot begin until the terminals are connected by a circuit, batteries can store energy for a long time. Once the terminals are connected and the circuit is complete, the reactions start and produce an electric current. The battery is portable and inexpensive. However, its energy does not last long, and it can do only small amounts of work.

electrochemical cell: a device that generates electrical energy using chemical reactions inside a small enclosed space (cell).

battery (electrochemical cells)

load

charged particle flow

○ Engage

Ask students whether they would rather use a battery to run their cell phone, or a generator. Then, ask them "Why?" and discuss their reasons. If they decide a generator would save them the trouble of recharging the batteries, ask them what the source of energy for their mini-generator would be.

direct current (DC): an electric current that flows in only one direction.

alternating current (AC): an electric current that reverses direction at a regular rate.

Direct and Alternating Current

Batteries work well for many purposes, but they are not the most efficient means of producing electric current. Batteries produce electrical current that moves in only one direction, from the negative (–) terminal to the positive (+) terminal. This is called **direct current (DC)**. Most portable electrical equipment operates on direct current. Generators can produce direct current or **alternating current (AC)**, depending on how they are designed. In an alternating current, the current constantly reverses direction. Describing how an alternating current is produced is fairly complicated. You will learn more about this in later science courses, or you may wish to read about it on your own. The type of current in the wall outlets of homes in the United States is AC.

Direct current is not different electrically from alternating current, other than it flows in the same direction all the time. Appliances can be designed to run on either direct or alternating current. The big advantage of alternating current is that it is easy to change the voltage. This makes it easier for power companies to transmit large amounts of electrical energy over long distances. You can read about how this is done in the *More to Learn, Bringing Power to the Neighborhood.*

Stop and Think

1. How do electrochemical cells function within a battery?

2. What is the importance of the positive terminal on a battery? What about the negative terminal?

3. How do alternating current and direct current differ?

4. Where in your house might you find alternating current? List three places.

5. Where in your house might you find direct current? List three places.

Reflect

1. Do you think electric energy is more like potential energy or kinetic energy? Why?

⬡ Get Going

Have students read about the differences between batteries and generators in the *How Do Batteries and Generators Compare?* section. Point out the arrows showing the direction of the current in a DC circuit. Emphasize that chemical reactions can produce only a few volts for each cell and to provide large voltages, many cells would be required. This would add to the cost and the weight.

Stop and Think

5 min

Students consolidate their understanding of batteries and electric current from the reading.

Stop and Think

1. How do electrochemical cells function within a battery?
2. What is the importance of the positive terminal on a battery? What about the negative terminal?
3. How do alternating current and direct current differ?
4. Where in your house might you find alternating current? List three places.
5. Where in your house might you find direct current? List three places.

△ Guide and Assess

Remind students that an electrochemical cell changes chemical potential energy into electrical energy. Help them understand that a battery contains a set of cells connected in series to boost the voltage. For example, a 9-V battery contains 6 cells that are 1.5-V each.

1. Students should answer that when the terminals of a battery are connected in a closed circuit, electrochemical cells produce electrical energy from chemical reactions.

2. Students should know that the positive terminal on a battery is the place that electrons go after they complete the circuit. The negative terminal is where the electrons come from as they begin their journey through the circuit.

3. Students should understand that alternating current changes direction periodically, and direct current goes in only one direction (from the negative terminal to the positive terminal).

4. Students should recognize that alternating current is found in every wall socket in their home. It is also found in every light fixture and appliance.

5. Students may remember that direct current is found wherever there are batteries in the house. This includes flashlights, some radios, cameras, hearing aids, and some smoke detectors.

Reflect

5 min

Students extend their understanding of electric energy and magnetic energy.

Reflect

1. Do you think electric energy is more like potential energy or kinetic energy? Why?

△ Guide and Assess

Have students answer the questions individually and then share them with their group before returning to their *Energy Types* pages.

1. Students should answer that electric energy is more like kinetic energy because the electrons are moving particles.

2. Do you think magnetic energy is more like potential energy or kinetic energy? Why?

3. Go back to your *Energy Types* page and record what you now know about the indicators for electric and magnetic energy, the factors that affect how much of each is available, examples, and your decision about whether each is a type of potential energy or a type of kinetic energy.

Update the *Project Board*

You now know a lot about how to generate and store electric energy, and what affects the amount of electrical energy that is available. You also know a lot about how magnetic energy is used to produce electric energy and how electric energy can produce magnetic energy. Add what you now know to the *What are we learning?* column of the *Project Board*. Do not forget to add evidence for each of your entries to the *What is our evidence?* column. If you have more questions for the *What do we need to investigate?* column, add them now. Make sure your personal *Project Board* matches the class *Project Board*.

What's the Point?

You observed two types of voltage sources—a battery and a generator. Each type of source has advantages and disadvantages. Large generators provide much more energy than batteries. The biggest disadvantage of a generator, however, is the cost of building one and the need for a reliable source of energy to spin the generator.

A battery produces direct current (DC), which flows in only one direction. Generators can produce either direct current or alternating current (AC). An alternating current reverses direction. This is the type of current available through the electrical outlets in most homes in North America.

It is important to remember that both a battery and a generator operate by transforming one type of energy into another. The electrical energy produced by a battery comes from chemical potential energy. When this chemical energy is transformed, charged particles can move through a circuit to do work. In a generator, the kinetic energy of spinning the magnets you observed is transformed into electrical energy. You will learn more about energy transformations in the next *Learning Set*. Energy transformations will be important in the Rube Goldberg machine you are designing.

2. Students should answer that magnetic energy is more like potential energy because its energy is due to its position, either with respect to a moving coil or with respect to another magnet.

3. Student answers will vary, but should contain the following components:

- Indicators for electric energy: light, heat, sound, magnetic field in an electromagnet, any device's operation that depends on electricity, such as a fan or computer.

- Factors for controlling electric energy: size of generator, number of windings in a generator, size or strength of a magnet in a generator, speed of turning of a generator, size of DC source, number of cells in a battery, resistance in load, choice of parallel or series circuit.

- Indicators for magnetic energy: movement of galvanometer, generation of electric energy in a moving coil, effect on iron or steel, attraction or repulsion of another magnet.

- Factors for magnetic energy: size of magnet, number of coils of wire in an electromagnet, distance from magnet, size of current through an electromagnet.

Update the Project Board

5 min

Students add ideas and evidence to the Project Board.

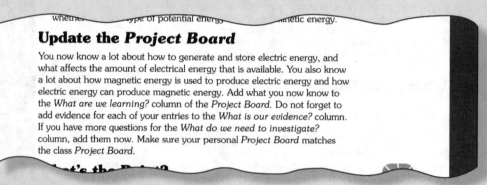

whether ___ ype of potential energy ___ netic energy.

Update the *Project Board*

You now know a lot about how to generate and store electric energy, and what affects the amount of electrical energy that is available. You also know a lot about how magnetic energy is used to produce electric energy and how electric energy can produce magnetic energy. Add what you now know to the *What are we learning?* column of the *Project Board*. Do not forget to add evidence for each of your entries to the *What is our evidence?* column. If you have more questions for the *What do we need to investigate?* column, add them now. Make sure your personal *Project Board* matches the class *Project Board*.

△ Guide

Lead a discussion in which students review new information they have learned electric energy and magnetic energy. Add this information to the *Project Board*. Be sure they include the evidence for their information.

NOTES

....

....

....

....

....

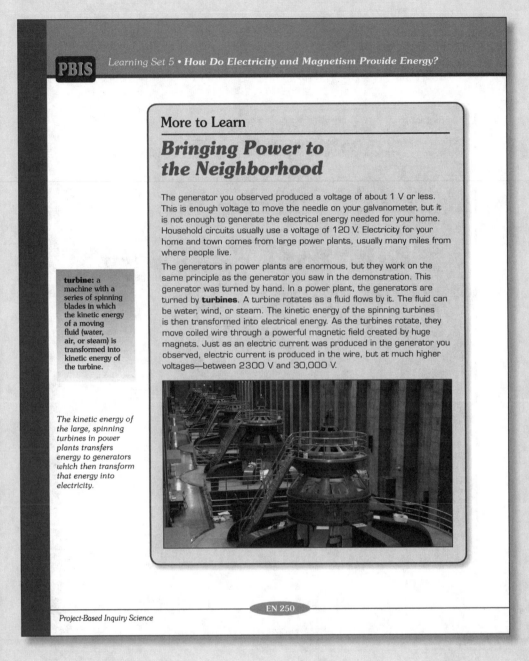

More to Learn

Bringing Power to the Neighborhood

The generator you observed produced a voltage of about 1 V or less. This is enough voltage to move the needle on your galvanometer, but it is not enough to generate the electrical energy needed for your home. Household circuits usually use a voltage of 120 V. Electricity for your home and town comes from large power plants, usually many miles from where people live.

The generators in power plants are enormous, but they work on the same principle as the generator you saw in the demonstration. This generator was turned by hand. In a power plant, the generators are turned by **turbines**. A turbine rotates as a fluid flows by it. The fluid can be water, wind, or steam. The kinetic energy of the spinning turbines is then transformed into electrical energy. As the turbines rotate, they move coiled wire through a powerful magnetic field created by huge magnets. Just as an electric current was produced in the generator you observed, electric current is produced in the wire, but at much higher voltages—between 2300 V and 30,000 V.

turbine: a machine with a series of spinning blades in which the kinetic energy of a moving fluid (water, air, or steam) is transformed into kinetic energy of the turbine.

The kinetic energy of the large, spinning turbines in power plants transfers energy to generators which then transform that energy into electricity.

More to Learn: *Bringing Power to the Neighborhood*

5 min

Students read how turbines supply electricity to homes.

○ Engage

Ask students if there is a power plant nearby and if they know how electric energy gets into their homes. Discuss where the nearest power plant is and how far the energy has to travel. Then read through the selection with them, stopping to make certain they understand the meaning of the new words: turbines, transformers, and circuit breakers.

The electric current produced by generators leaves the power plant through power lines. As the current leaves the power plant, its voltage is increased by **transformers** to between 120,000 V and 500,000 V. A transformer can increase or decrease the voltage of an AC current.

The high voltages in power lines are dangerous, but necessary, so that electric current can be transmitted long distances with very little energy loss. If you see a sign that says, "High Voltage—Keep Away," do not attempt to go near it. The voltage really is very high and very dangerous. When the electric current reaches communities, the voltage is decreased by transformers. It is lowered even more, to 120 V, as it enters your home.

transformer: an electric device by which alternating current of one voltage is changed to another voltage, either greater or smaller.

circuit breaker: a switch that opens a circuit when electric current reaches an unsafe level.

Electricity from power plants first travels through transformers on power poles before it enters your house. The wires in a circuit breaker box send electricity to different parts of your house.

Electricity coming into your home goes through a meter that measures how much energy you use. From the meter, the wire leads into a **circuit breaker** box. Several separate circuits leave from this point, branching out to different areas of the building. One circuit may run to your kitchen. The wires making up this circuit go to wall outlets and light switches. These parallel circuits make it possible to leave an appliance off, or an outlet unused, without breaking the path of charged particles going to other outlets and appliances.

However, circuits can become overloaded. If the appliances on a circuit require more current than the circuit can handle, the wires will heat

EN 251

ENERGY

Find out from students if they have experienced the loss of power. Ask questions to determine if they know why the electricity stopped flowing. Tell them that sometimes it is a local event, such as a thunderstorm with wind and lightning causing a shutdown. Occasionally, it will be a power grid failure where large sections of the country are without power. Power grid failure is usually due to there being too much demand for power and the electric company has to shut down the grid to avoid extensive damage to equipment.

power distribution grid (power grid): a system of high-tension cables by which electrical energy is distributed throughout a region.

blackout: a temporary cutoff of electrical energy in a region.

up. This can be a fire hazard, because heated wires can ignite building materials in the walls. This is what the circuit breaker is for. When the current in the wires is too high, the circuit breaker automatically opens the circuit so that charged particles cannot flow. Power to that circuit is discontinued until the circuit breaker is reset.

As you can imagine, delivering electrical energy to large populations can be complex. Power is delivered over large areas through **power distribution grids**. Sometimes these grids can become overloaded and shut down, resulting in a widespread **blackout**. This happens at times of peak energy usage, for example during a heat wave when many people have their air conditioners on all day.

Both direct current and alternating current can be used to operate electrical equipment. The equipment just needs to be designed to run on the current available. Alternating current was chosen in North America, because when large power companies were being established in the early twentieth century, AC systems were more reliable than DC systems. The problems in delivering direct current to widespread areas have been corrected. However, North American power companies continue to supply AC because the systems are already in place. In most of Europe, the current that is supplied to homes is DC.

Stop and Think

1. How do turbines in power plants work?

2. How do transformers and circuit breakers affect the electricity you use in your house?

3. What causes a blackout of power?

Stop and Think

5 min

Students consolidate their understanding of the transmission of electricity from the power plant to their homes.

People take electricity for granted until there is a blackout. During the blackout of August, 2003, the lights went out across the Northeast. The picture on the left was taken by satellite 20 h before the blackout. The picture on the right was 7 h after the blackout.

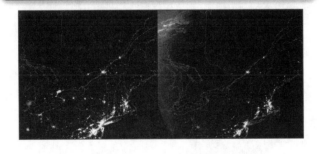

△ Guide and Assess

Have students discuss answers to the *Stop and Think* questions in their groups. Then discuss them as a class. Encourage students to share all ideas at this point.

1. Students should describe how a source of mechanical energy (water, wind, steam) is used to turn a coil of wire in a magnetic field to generate electricity in a power plant. The turbine is the device that converts the mechanical energy to a rotating kinetic energy to spin the coil of wire.

2. Students should describe how a transformer decreases the voltage to a safer level as it enters the home. Circuit breakers protect people and property by shutting off the electric current when it exceeds a certain value.

3. Students should know that a blackout of power can occur when a power distribution grid becomes overloaded and shuts down.

Assessment Options

Targeted Concepts, Skills, and Nature of Science	How do I know if students got it?
Scientists often work together and then share their findings. Sharing findings makes new information available and helps scientists refine their ideas and build on others' ideas. When another person's or group's idea is used, credit needs to be given.	**ASK:** What difficulties, if any, did your group overcome when building the battery? **LISTEN:** Students should discuss any problems they encountered and describe how they worked together to solve them.
A battery converts stored chemical energy into electrical energy.	**ASK:** What was the source of chemical energy in the batteries that were built? **LISTEN:** Students should recognize that the lemon and metals provided chemical energy.
Electricity gives rise to magnetism and magnetism gives rise to electricity.	**ASK:** Why were magnets used to produce electrical current in the generator? **LISTEN:** Students should recognize that moving magnets produced an electrical current in a wire coil.

Targeted Concepts, Skills, and Nature of Science	How do I know if students got it?
A generator transforms mechanical energy into electrical energy.	**ASK:** What was the source of mechanical energy in the generator? **LISTEN:** Students should recognize that the motion of the teacher's hand spinning the nail provided mechanical energy.
A galvanometer is used to measure electric current.	**ASK:** How was the galvanometer used in the generator demonstration? **LISTEN:** Students should explain that the galvanometer was used to indicate the production of electric current.

Teacher Reflection Questions

- What concepts in this section do you think students had the most difficulty with? What ideas do you have to help students understand these concepts?

- What can you do to lead students into the explanation of energy transformation in the next section?

- How did you manage the battery-building among the different groups? What ideas do you have to help them share their results next time?

NOTES

NOTES

Back to the Big Challenge

Design a Rube Goldberg Machine to Turn Off a Light

◀ $1\frac{1}{2}$ *class periods*

A class period is considered to be one 40 to 50 minute class.

Overview

Students return to their energy-transformation cartoons once more to look for indicators of electric and magnetic energy. They then develop claims and explanations about electric and magnetic energy in terms of whether they represent kinetic or potential energy. Students use their explanations to design steps for their own Rube Goldberg machines that use and produce electric and magnetic energy. Students share their ideas and interact to learn from each other's designs, and they relate what they learn to the *Big Challenge*.

Targeted Concepts, Skills, and Nature of Science	Performance Expectations
Scientists often work together and then share their findings. Sharing findings makes new information available and helps scientists refine their ideas and build on others' ideas. When another person's or group's idea is used, credit needs to be given.	Students share their ideas about electric and magnetic energy, and how they can be related to designing a Rube Goldberg machine.
Scientific knowledge is developed through observations, recording and analysis of data, and development of explanations based on evidence.	Students develop explanations about electric and magnetic energy.
Energy exists in different forms and can be changed from one form to another.	Students look for forms of energy that exist before and after a step in their energy-transformation cartoons.
Electrical energy is used by appliances and equipment.	Students design a step for their Rube Goldberg machines that uses or produces electrical energy.

ENERGY

Targeted Concepts, Skills, and Nature of Science	Performance Expectations
Magnetic forces are exerted in the magnetic field around a magnet, with the forces being strongest near the poles.	Students design a step for their Rube Goldberg machines that uses or produces magnetic energy.

Materials	
1 per student	*Create Your Explanation* page *My Rube Goldberg Machine* page *Project Board* page
1 per class	Class *Project Board*

Homework Options

Reflection

- **Science Content:** How can you use a magnet to move objects closer or farther away? *(Students should explain how they can rearrange the poles of a magnet to attract or repel another magnet. This question may help students to recognize ways to use magnets in their Rube Goldberg designs.)*

- **Science Content:** What can you include in your design to control the production of electrical energy? *(Students should describe their ideas, including adding a switch to a circuit.)*

BACK TO THE BIG CHALLENGE IMPLEMENTATION

Learning Set 5

Back to the Big Challenge

Design a Rube Goldberg Machine to Turn Off a Light

The *Big Challenge* you are working on for this Unit is *Design a Rube Goldberg machine to turn off a light.* You have designed many different sequences of steps to turn off a light. Most likely, none of your steps involved electricity or magnetism. You now know enough about electrical energy and magnetic energy to imagine how these might be transformed in your machine. However, before doing that, you will think once more about whether electrical energy and magnetic energy are kinetic energy or potential energy and how these types of energy can be transformed to do work.

The electromagnet used in a railway yard to lift heavy iron rails transforms both electrical and magnetic energy.

Reflect

To help you think about electrical energy and magnetic energy, you will examine the energy-transformation cartoons again from the Unit *Introduction.* Identify the steps that involve electrical energy or magnetic energy in your group's cartoon. Then, for each, answer these questions. Be prepared to share your answers with the class.

1. How do you know the step involves electrical energy or magnetic energy? What are the indicators? (You may have to search carefully to find indicators of magnetic energy.)

2. How does the step transform electrical energy or magnetic energy?

3. What are the effects of each step, and what kind of energy is produced by each step?

EN 253

ENERGY

Learning Set 5

Back to the Big Challenge

5 min

Students revisit the goal of the Big Challenge *by summarizing what have learned about electric and magnetic energy.*

○ **Engage**

Ask students if they have used a magnet today. They may not realize that they use a magnet to keep their refrigerator closed, hang papers in their lockers, or keep a diary sealed. Get students to start thinking about how they can use magnetic energy or electric energy in their Rube Goldberg designs.

*A class period is considered to be one 40 to 50 minute class.

Reflect

10 min

Students review the energy-transformation cartoons in terms of electric and magnetic energy.

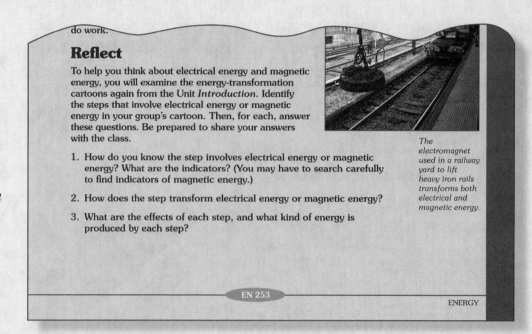

do work.

Reflect

To help you think about electrical energy and magnetic energy, you will examine the energy-transformation cartoons again from the Unit *Introduction*. Identify the steps that involve electrical energy or magnetic energy in your group's cartoon. Then, for each, answer these questions. Be prepared to share your answers with the class.

1. How do you know the step involves electrical energy or magnetic energy? What are the indicators? (You may have to search carefully to find indicators of magnetic energy.)

2. How does the step transform electrical energy or magnetic energy?

3. What are the effects of each step, and what kind of energy is produced by each step?

The electromagnet used in a railway yard to lift heavy iron rails transforms both electrical and magnetic energy.

EN 253

ENERGY

△ Guide

Have students work in their groups to review the energy-transformation cartoons. Ask them to discuss answers to the questions listed. Tell students to narrow their search to either electric energy or magnetic energy. Encourage students to suggest their best possible answers based on what they know.

1. Students' answers will vary depending on which cartoon they are analyzing. Examples of indicators for electric energy are the presence of a battery causing a change in the next step, a switch, wires, timers, amplifiers. Magnetic energy is indicated by a motor, such as in a hair dryer, or the generation of electricity by a U-shaped piece of metal with two poles.

2. Students' answers will vary. One example for electric energy is the generation of heat in setting fire to a pile of steel wool. The fire is used to set fire to a rope which releases a spring. Magnetic energy is seen in a step where a coil of wire is spun in a magnetic field to generate electricity. The electricity is used to run a toy train.

3. Students' answers will vary. In the example in the answer to Question 2, the electrical energy of a 9-V battery is used to generate thermal energy and then to release a spring's potential energy. In another example, the electricity generated from a magnet is used to give kinetic energy to a toy train.

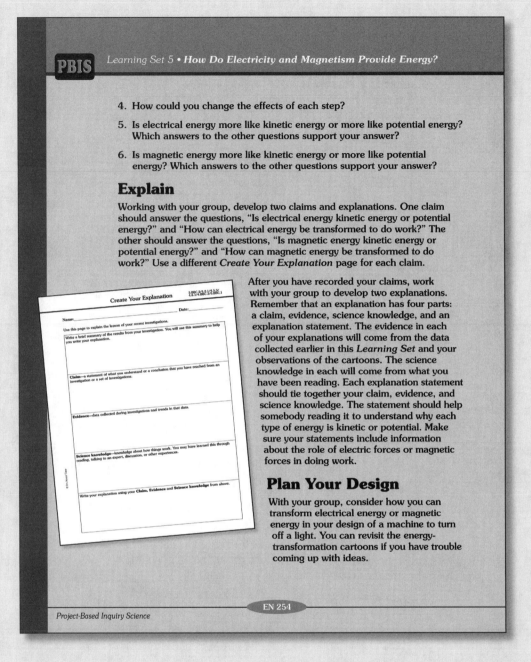

4. How could you change the effects of each step?

5. Is electrical energy more like kinetic energy or more like potential energy? Which answers to the other questions support your answer?

6. Is magnetic energy more like kinetic energy or more like potential energy? Which answers to the other questions support your answer?

Explain

Working with your group, develop two claims and explanations. One claim should answer the questions, "Is electrical energy kinetic energy or potential energy?" and "How can electrical energy be transformed to do work?" The other should answer the questions, "Is magnetic energy kinetic energy or potential energy?" and "How can magnetic energy be transformed to do work?" Use a different *Create Your Explanation* page for each claim.

After you have recorded your claims, work with your group to develop two explanations. Remember that an explanation has four parts: a claim, evidence, science knowledge, and an explanation statement. The evidence in each of your explanations will come from the data collected earlier in this *Learning Set* and your observations of the cartoons. The science knowledge in each will come from what you have been reading. Each explanation statement should tie together your claim, evidence, and science knowledge. The statement should help somebody reading it to understand why each type of energy is kinetic or potential. Make sure your statements include information about the role of electric forces or magnetic forces in doing work.

Plan Your Design

With your group, consider how you can transform electrical energy or magnetic energy in your design of a machine to turn off a light. You can revisit the energy-transformation cartoons if you have trouble coming up with ideas.

EN 254

4. Students' answers will vary but in every case, students should alter a control factor to produce more or less energy (electric or magnetic).

5. Students will likely respond that electrical energy is more like kinetic energy. Supporting answers will vary for this question.

6. Students will likely respond that magnetic energy is more like potential energy. Supporting answers will vary for this question.

Explain

10 min

Students work together to develop a claim and an explanation.

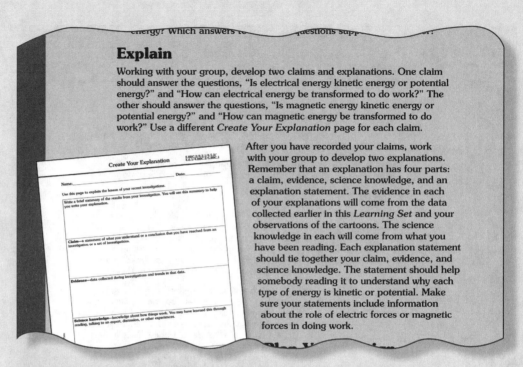

Explain

Working with your group, develop two claims and explanations. One claim should answer the questions, "Is electrical energy kinetic energy or potential energy?" and "How can electrical energy be transformed to do work?" The other should answer the questions, "Is magnetic energy kinetic energy or potential energy?" and "How can magnetic energy be transformed to do work?" Use a different *Create Your Explanation* page for each claim.

After you have recorded your claims, work with your group to develop two explanations. Remember that an explanation has four parts: a claim, evidence, science knowledge, and an explanation statement. The evidence in each of your explanations will come from the data collected earlier in this *Learning Set* and your observations of the cartoons. The science knowledge in each will come from what you have been reading. Each explanation statement should tie together your claim, evidence, and science knowledge. The statement should help somebody reading it to understand why each type of energy is kinetic or potential. Make sure your statements include information about the role of electric forces or magnetic forces in doing work.

△ Guide and Assess

Keep students in their groups. Make sure each group has two *Create Your Explanation* pages. Have students work together to develop the two claims described. Remind them to write one claim on each page. Ask them to think about what criteria they used to make similar claims for thermal and chemical energy in *Learning Set 3* and sound and light energy in *Learning Set 4* so they can think about the same criteria now.

Review the four parts of an explanation with students. Read through the paragraph together to make sure students know where to find the information they need to develop the explanations. Visit each group to evaluate their explanations and suggest areas for improvement.

Plan Your Design

20 min

Students incorporate steps using and producing electric and magnetic energy in their designs.

Plan Your Design

With your group, consider how you can transform electrical energy or magnetic energy in your design of a machine to turn off a light. You can revisit the energy-transformation cartoons if you have trouble coming up with ideas.

△ Guide

Review with students what they need to do. Make sure they understand that they should design two sets of steps in their Rube Goldberg machine that will turn off a light. Use the energy-transformation cartoons to help them think of ideas. Make sure they understand that they are designing one step that uses of these forms of energy and one step that produces one of these forms of energy.

My Rube Goldberg Machine

Name: _____ Date: _____

Sketch of machine. Label each step with a number.

Step	Description of step	Energy Type(s) In	Energy Type(s) Out	Work done
1				
2				
3				
4				
5				

Use this space to record ideas.

Design two sets of steps that transform electrical energy or magnetic energy in a machine that turns off a light. One should begin with a step that transforms electrical energy or magnetic energy; the other should begin with a step that produces electrical energy or magnetic energy. Both sets of steps should end with a step that turns off a light. Your machine needs to have at least three steps in it. You may also want to include a circuit connected to a source of electrical energy. It would be good if you can power two steps of your machine with the same source of electrical energy.

Sketch your steps, and label your sketch to show the type of energy being transformed in each step and the type of energy that it is transformed into. If you borrowed some of your ideas from other groups, record where you got your ideas. It is important to give credit when you borrow ideas from others.

You will need to carefully think through how the steps transfer energy to each other. Each step must be able to transfer energy smoothly to the next step, and the separate pieces of your machine need to work together to complete the task.

Communicate

Plan Briefing

When it is time for you to present your designs to the class, show your sketches one at a time. For each, describe the steps, and tell the class how energy is transferred from one step to another. Try to be brief. If you are unsure about how to describe some energy transformations in your steps, ask the class for help.

Observe everyone's designs carefully, and listen to their descriptions of how energy will be transferred from step to step. If you think a group has not described an energy transformation well, raise your hand and ask for more information or offer a more complete description. Remember to be courteous and respectful. If a group asks for advice, offer your ideas.

Remind students to label their sketches on *My Rube Goldberg Machine* pages and let them begin. As students work, emphasize the importance of procedure. They should keep in mind that each step they design must coordinate with the previous or next.

Communicate: Plan Briefing

10 min

Students present their design sketches to the class.

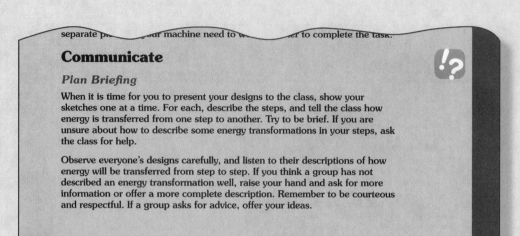

separate p... ...ur machine need to w... ...er to complete the task.

Communicate

Plan Briefing

When it is time for you to present your designs to the class, show your sketches one at a time. For each, describe the steps, and tell the class how energy is transferred from one step to another. Try to be brief. If you are unsure about how to describe some energy transformations in your steps, ask the class for help.

Observe everyone's designs carefully, and listen to their descriptions of how energy will be transferred from step to step. If you think a group has not described an energy transformation well, raise your hand and ask for more information or offer a more complete description. Remember to be courteous and respectful. If a group asks for advice, offer your ideas.

△ Guide and Evaluate

Allow each group to present their sketches to the class. Guide students to include descriptions of each step and descriptions of how the energy in each step transfers to the next in their presentations.

NOTES

Notice all of the different ideas your classmates have about transforming energy and about including electrical energy and magnetic energy in their machines. You might want to borrow some of those ideas later. Record which group came up with each idea so you can give them credit.

Record ideas you might want to remember on the bottom of your *My Rube Goldberg Machine* page. Remember to record which group presented each idea.

Reflect

Discuss answers to these questions with your group. Be prepared to share your answers with the class.

1. Which two ideas for transforming electrical energy or magnetic energy do you like the best? Why? Which type or types of energy does each transform? Which type or types of energy does each transform into?

2. List two things you know now about addressing the *Big Challenge* that you did not know before these presentations.

3. What else do you need to know about energy and energy transformations to address the *Big Challenge* successfully?

Add the ideas you like best to the class list of favorite steps. For each, record the type or types of energy it transforms, the type or types of energy it transforms into, and which group suggested the step.

Update the *Project Board*

The *What does it mean for the challenge or question?* column on the *Project Board* is where you should record how learning about electricity and magnetism can help you complete the *Big Challenge*. Share what you know about electrical energy and magnetic energy that you think are important to add to the *Project Board* and your evidence for each. As a class, decide what belongs in the *What are we learning?* column. Remember to include evidence in the *What is our evidence?* column. You must fit the pieces together of what was added to the class *Project Board* on your own *Project Board* page. Add any recommendations you have for addressing the *Big Challenge* to the *What does it mean for the challenge or question?* column.

Encourage students to take notes as they listen to each presentation so they can remember the ideas and who presented them. If they are unclear about a group's design they should ask for more information from the group. Help students to identify changes in energy, or energy transformations.

Reflect

10 min

Students work together to review the design ideas presented.

Reflect

Discuss answers to these questions with your group. Be prepared to share your answers with the class.

1. Which two ideas for transforming electrical energy or magnetic energy do you like the best? Why? Which type or types of energy does each transform? Which type or types of energy does each transform into?

2. List two things you know now about addressing the *Big Challenge* that you did not know before these presentations.

3. What else do you need to know about energy and energy transformations to address the *Big Challenge* successfully?

Add the ideas you like best to the class list of favorite steps. For each, record the type or types of energy it transforms, the type or types of energy it transforms into, and which group suggested the step.

Update the *Project Board*

△ Guide

Ask students to work in their groups to discuss the ideas presented. Have them discuss answers to the questions listed. As you walk around the room, find out if students correctly identify the types of energy discussed. Then lead a class discussion to list the favorite steps.

Update the *Project Board*

10 min

Students add new information to the Project Board.

Update the *Project Board*

The *What does it mean for the challenge or question?* column on the *Project Board* is where you should record how learning about electricity and magnetism can help you complete the *Big Challenge.* Share what you know about electrical energy and magnetic energy that you think are important to add to the *Project Board* and your evidence for each. As a class, decide what belongs in the *What are we learning?* column. Remember to include evidence in the *What is our evidence?* column. You must fit the pieces together of what was added to the class *Project Board* on your own *Project Board* page. Add any recommendations you have for addressing the *Big Challenge* to the *What does it mean for the challenge or question?* column.

△ Guide

Lead a class discussion in which students summarize what they have learned about electric and magnetic energy, and the evidence they have to support their ideas. Ask students to explain how their ideas relate to the *Big Challenge,* and what questions they still need answered to accomplish the *Big Challenge.* Record any new information in the appropriate columns of the *Project Board.*

Assessment Options

Targeted Concepts, Skills, and Nature of Science	How do I know if students got it?
Scientists often work together and then share their findings. Sharing findings makes new information available and helps scientists refine their ideas and build on others' ideas. When another person's or group's idea is used, credit needs to be given.	**ASK:** What ideas did you learn by listening to other groups? **LISTEN:** Students should describe any improvements or additions they made to their designs based on the presentations, and they should give credit to the proper students.
Scientific knowledge is developed through observations, recording and analysis of data, and development of explanations based on evidence.	**ASK:** How did your group come to agreement about your explanation? **LISTEN:** Students should describe the process through which they developed their explanation and the information they used.
Energy exists in different forms and can be changed from one form to another.	**ASK:** What types of energy were present before and after the steps you analyze in the energy-transformation cartoon? **LISTEN:** Students should describe the step they chose, and identify the energy before and after that step occurred.
Electrical energy is used by appliances and equipment.	**ASK:** In what way can electrical energy be used in your Rube Goldberg design? **LISTEN:** Students should explain how they might use electrical energy in their design, such as including a battery in a circuit.

Targeted Concepts, Skills, and Nature of Science	How do I know if students got it?
Magnetic forces are exerted in the magnetic field around a magnet, with the forces being strongest near the poles.	**ASK:** In what ways can you use magnetic energy in your design? **LISTEN:** Students may describe building an electromagnet to attract an object.

Teacher Reflection Questions

- What concepts from earlier *Learning Sets* did students use when they explained their designs in the *Plan Briefing?* What evidence do you have that they are synthesizing all of the information they have been learning?

- What kinds of questions were students asking during the *Plan Briefing?* What can you do to get students actively thinking about what they can learn from the *Plan Briefing?*

- What issues came up in the discussions of the *Plan Briefing?* How can you keep students engaged in accomplishing the *Big Challenge?*

NOTES

....

....

....

....

....

LEARNING SET 6 INTRODUCTION

Learning Set 6

How Is Energy Transformed?

◄ $8\frac{1}{2}$ *class periods*

A class period is
considered to be one
40 to 50 minute class.

Students investigate energy transformations.

Overview

Students begin the *Learning Set* by working together to identify types
of energy that exist before and after changes in common devices. In so
doing, students begin to think about what happens to energy during
a transformation. They go on to conduct investigations in which they
observe changes in the mechanical energy of an object. Through these
investigations, students start to develop an understanding of systems which
they then use to explain what happens to lost energy. Students learn that
the total amount of energy in a system is conserved even though some
energy is transformed into a form that is not usable. The pros and cons of
different energy resources are then explored, and students compare the
use of energy resources to produce electricity. Finally, students use what
they learn about energy resources to recommend a power plant to a small
seaside community.

Targeted Concepts, Skills, and Nature of Science	Section
Scientists often work together and then share their findings. Sharing findings makes new information available and helps scientists refine their ideas and build on others' ideas. When another person's or group's idea is used, credit needs to be given.	6.1, 6.2, 6.3
Scientists make claims (conclusions) based on evidence (trends in data) from reliable investigations.	6.2, 6.3
Energy is the ability to cause change or do work.	6.1
Energy exists in different forms and can be changed from one form to another.	6.1, 6.2, 6.3, 6.4, 6.6
Studying the work of different scientists provides understanding of scientific inquiry and reminds students that science is a human endeavor.	6.4

Targeted Concepts, Skills, and Nature of Science	Section
Kinetic energy is associated with the motion of an object.	6.2
Potential energy is stored energy associated with position or condition.	6.2
Energy is neither created nor destroyed in ordinary processes.	6.3, 6.4
Some energy resources are renewable, such as wind energy, hydroelectric energy, solar energy, biomass energy, geothermal energy, and tidal energy whereas others are nonrenewable, such as fossil fuel energy and nuclear energy.	6.5, 6.6
Nuclear reactions include fission during large nuclei are split apart, and fusion during which smaller nuclei are joined together.	6.5
During nuclear reactions, small amounts of mass are converted into large amounts of energy.	6.5

Students' Initial Conceptions and Capabilities

- Even when students are aware of the energy conservation principle and are able to use it to explain phenomena, it seems that most of them do not choose to use it when given a free choice. (Duit, 1981)

- Students interpret the idea that *Energy is not created or destroyed* to mean that energy us stored up in the system and can even be released again to its original form. (Black and Solomon, 1983)

NOTES

....

....

....

....

....

Understanding for Teachers

In this *Learning Set,* students learn about a variety of energy transformations. Energy is the ability to do work or cause change. Energy exists in several different forms, including electrical, magnetic, chemical, mechanical, light, sound, and nuclear energy. Each form of energy can be transformed into another form of energy. During any transformation, some energy becomes usable energy that can do work. Some energy is changed into thermal energy that is "lost" to the system as heat.

Energy that is said to be lost is not destroyed. According to the law of conservation of energy, energy is neither created nor destroyed in ordinary processes. The exception to this is during nuclear reactions, including fission and fusion. In these processes, the total amount of energy and mass is conserved.

Energy resources are sources of energy that can be used to produce electricity. Each energy resource has advantages and disadvantages that include how easy it is to obtain, whether or not it will run out, how much it costs, and what impact it has on the environment.

NOTES

NOTES

LEARNING SET 6 IMPLEMENTATION

◀ $8\frac{1}{2}$ *class periods* *

Learning Set 6

How Is Energy Transformed?

Energy transformations are important in your daily life. For example, think about the energy transformations involved in blow-drying your hair. Electrical energy has been transported a long distance from a power plant to your home, and its voltage has been transformed several times along the way. The hair dryer transforms electrical energy to produce heat and the motion of air. The hair dryer has a fan that moves air. The fan's motor uses magnets to transform electrical energy into kinetic energy of the fan blades. The blades of the fan exert a force that does work to increase the kinetic energy of the air. The electrical energy to run the hair dryer travels from the outlet through wires into the dryer.

The electrical energy to operate your hair dryer was generated at a power plant, perhaps one that burns coal as fuel. In a coal-burning power plant, coal is burned to produce heat. The coal's chemical energy is potential energy. It takes some thermal energy to start coal burning. (You know this if you have ever started a charcoal fire for a barbecue.) Once the coal is burning, it releases thermal energy, which is used to heat water. As the water's thermal energy increases, its particles move faster, and the water turns to steam. The steam expands, which means it can do work to turn a turbine. The kinetic energy of the turbine is transferred to wire coils that spin in a magnetic field inside a generator. The generator transforms the kinetic energy of the turbine into electrical energy that is sent to your home.

The electrical energy you use in your house is generated in a power plant.

EN 257

ENERGY

Learning Set 6

How Is Energy Transformed?

5 min

○ **Engage**

Have students think about the Rube Goldberg machines they examined earlier. Remind them that the machine involved a series of steps to perform a task. Tell students that a series of steps, though not as unusual as the Rube Goldberg machine, make it possible for them to use everyday devices such as a hair dryer.

*A class period is considered to be one 40 to 50 minute class.

If you wanted to trace the energy back even farther, you would start with the Sun. Photons have been traveling through empty space from the Sun to Earth for billions of years. The photons struck the leaves of plants, and their energy was transformed in a chemical reaction to make sugars and starches, which store chemical energy. Over millions of years, the remains of plants were converted by heat and pressure into coal, which is a more concentrated form of chemical energy.

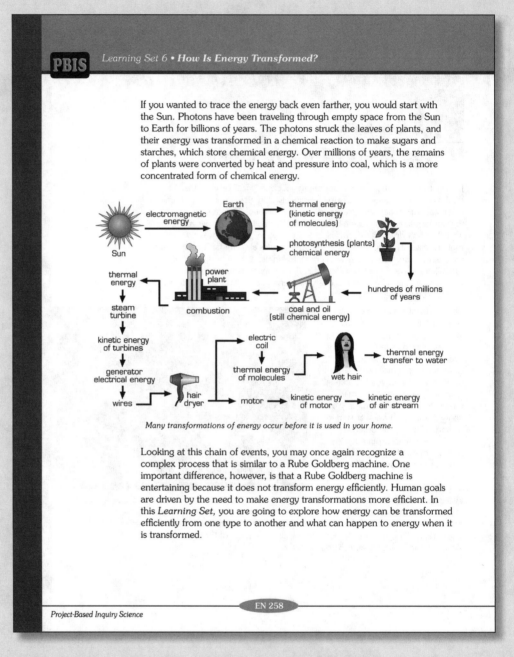

Many transformations of energy occur before it is used in your home.

Looking at this chain of events, you may once again recognize a complex process that is similar to a Rube Goldberg machine. One important difference, however, is that a Rube Goldberg machine is entertaining because it does not transform energy efficiently. Human goals are driven by the need to make energy transformations more efficient. In this *Learning Set,* you are going to explore how energy can be transformed efficiently from one type to another and what can happen to energy when it is transformed.

EN 258

Read through the introductory text together so students can consider several examples. Focus the discussion on the changes in energy described in each example. Tell students that they are going to learn about many energy transformations and how they can be used to perform tasks.

6.1 Understand the Question

Think About Energy Transformation

◀ *1 class period*

A class period is considered to be one 40 to 50 minute class.

Overview

Students are reminded of an energy transformation they considered earlier—a stretched rubber band. They go on to consider other types of everyday energy transformations. Then each group is assigned a common device to identify types of energy before and after some change occurs. Students are asked to consider what happens to a type of energy that no longer appears after a change so they begin to recognize that one type of energy changes into another.

Targeted Concepts, Skills, and Nature of Science	Performance Expectations
Scientists often work together and then share their findings. Sharing findings makes new information available and helps scientists refine their ideas and build on others' ideas. When another person's or group's idea is used, credit needs to be given.	Students work together to identify energy transformations.
Energy is the ability to cause change or do work.	Students use changes that occur as indicators of energy.
Energy exists in different forms and can be changed from one form to another.	Students identify the types of energy that exist before and after a change occurs.

Materials	
1 per student	*Project Board* page
1 per class	Class *Project Board*

Homework Options

Reflection

- **Science Content:** Chemical energy is stored in the battery of a flashlight until the flashlight is turned on. What happens to the chemical energy? *(Students may suggest that the chemical energy is transformed into electrical energy.)*

- **Science Content:** Tapping a xylophone causes it to make sound. What type of energy is transformed into sound? *(Students should describe tapping as a form of kinetic energy.)*

Preparation for 6.2

- **Science Content:** Potential energy is stored in the compressed spring of a toaster until the spring "pops." What happens to the potential energy? *(Students may suggest that the potential energy is transformed into kinetic energy.)*

NOTES

....

....

....

....

....

....

....

....

....

....

SECTION 6.1 IMPLEMENTATION

6.1 Understand the Question

Think About Energy Transformation

When you stretch a rubber band, it has elastic potential energy. You know this because of the indicators you can observe. The material is elastic and is deformed as it is stretched. As long as you hold the rubber band in this position, it has elastic potential energy. As soon as it is released, you see motion, an indicator of kinetic energy. The potential energy in the stretched rubber band is transformed into kinetic energy when you let go of one side of the band.

Energy transformations constantly happen all around you. They occur in your body every time you transform energy from food to take a breath or play sports. Sometimes one type of energy is transformed into more than one other type of energy. When you strike a match, for example, chemical energy is transformed into light energy, sound energy, and thermal energy.

To help you understand energy transformations better, you are going to take a closer look at some familiar examples of energy transformations. You will identify the type(s) of energy before the transformation and the types of energy after the transformation.

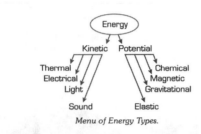

Menu of Energy Types.

When a match is lit, how many types of energy are transformed, and how many are they transformed into?

ENERGY

6.1 Understand the Question

Think About Energy Transformation

5 min

Students think about changes from one form of energy to another.

△ Guide

Remind students that they considered changes between kinetic and potential energy earlier in the Unit. Refer back to the diagram in *Section 2.4* of the bouncing ball that used bars to compare kinetic and potential energy. Use the photograph to extend the concept by making sure students realize that energy transformations are occurring all around them. Point out that they have observed many energy transformations throughout the Unit.

*A class period is considered to be one 40 to 50 minute class.

ENERGY

Get Started

15 min

Students analyze objects to identify energy transformations.

META NOTES

Before students begin, it may be helpful to have their notes about each item available from previous sections.

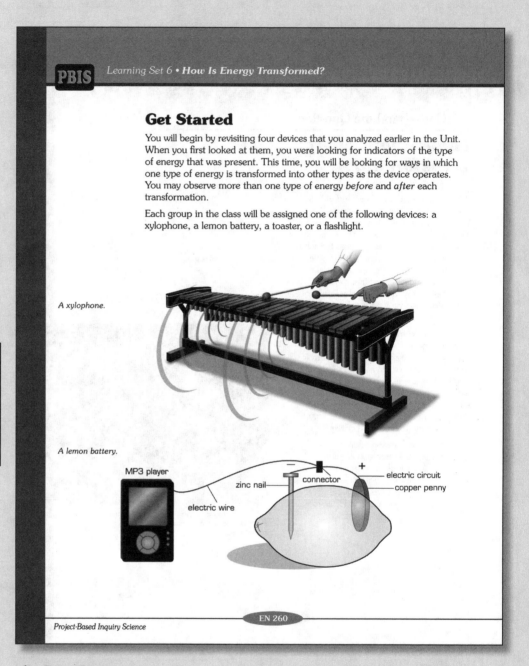

Get Started

You will begin by revisiting four devices that you analyzed earlier in the Unit. When you first looked at them, you were looking for indicators of the type of energy that was present. This time, you will be looking for ways in which one type of energy is transformed into other types as the device operates. You may observe more than one type of energy *before* and *after* each transformation.

Each group in the class will be assigned one of the following devices: a xylophone, a lemon battery, a toaster, or a flashlight.

A xylophone.

A lemon battery.

MP3 player

electric wire

zinc nail

connector

electric circuit

copper penny

EN 260

Project-Based Inquiry Science

⬡ Get Going

Assign one item to each group. Have groups discuss what they know about the object and how it operates. Then tell students to complete the chart by identifying the energy transformations involved. Point out that there may be more than one transformation, and they may occur in different parts of the device. Help students focus on one part of the device at a time. For

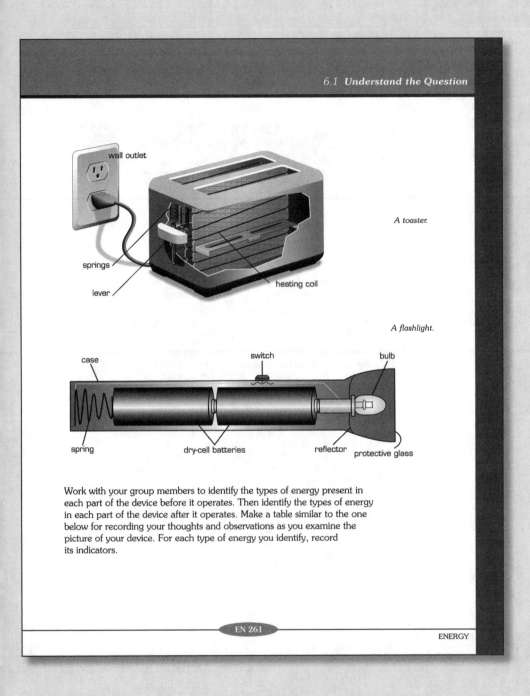

wall outlet

A toaster.

springs

lever

heating coil

A *flashlight.*

case

switch

bulb

spring

dry-cell batteries

reflector

protective glass

Work with your group members to identify the types of energy present in each part of the device before it operates. Then identify the types of energy in each part of the device after it operates. Make a table similar to the one below for recording your thoughts and observations as you examine the picture of your device. For each type of energy you identify, record its indicators.

EN 261

ENERGY

example, students might consider the spring in the toaster before and after it pops. They might consider the coils before and after they heat up. Guide them to avoid comparing the before and after of different parts such as the spring and the hot coils.

Analyze
Your Data

5 min

*Students analyze the
energy transformations
they considered.*

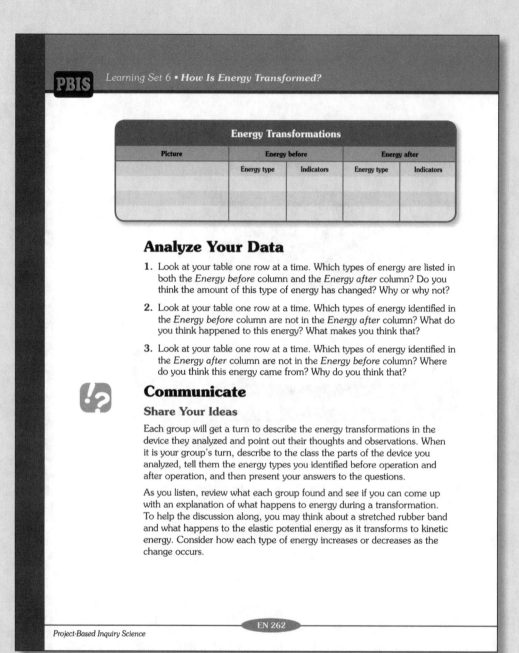

Energy Transformations				
Picture	Energy before		Energy after	
	Energy type	Indicators	Energy type	Indicators

Analyze Your Data

1. Look at your table one row at a time. Which types of energy are listed in both the *Energy before* column and the *Energy after* column? Do you think the amount of this type of energy has changed? Why or why not?

2. Look at your table one row at a time. Which types of energy identified in the *Energy before* column are not in the *Energy after* column? What do you think happened to this energy? What makes you think that?

3. Look at your table one row at a time. Which types of energy identified in the *Energy after* column are not in the *Energy before* column? Where do you think this energy came from? Why do you think that?

Communicate

Share Your Ideas

Each group will get a turn to describe the energy transformations in the device they analyzed and point out their thoughts and observations. When it is your group's turn, describe to the class the parts of the device you analyzed, tell them the energy types you identified before operation and after operation, and then present your answers to the questions.

As you listen, review what each group found and see if you can come up with an explanation of what happens to energy during a transformation. To help the discussion along, you may think about a stretched rubber band and what happens to the elastic potential energy as it transforms to kinetic energy. Consider how each type of energy increases or decreases as the change occurs.

EN 262

Project-Based Inquiry Science

△ Guide and Assess

Have students discuss answers to the *Analyze Your Data* questions in their groups. Remind students to provide evidence for their answers. Encourage students to propose their best answers based on what they know at this time. Tell students that they will continue to learn about energy transformations and can revise their ideas later.

1. Students' answers will depend upon the device that they analyzed. For example, analysis of the lemon battery shows that chemical energy was present both *before* and *after.* However, since some of it was used to make electricity, there is less of it *after.* Chemical energy was changed either to light or heat or both.

2. Students' answers will depend upon the device that they analyzed. For example, analysis of the toaster shows that potential elastic energy was present *before,* but not *after.* It was changed into kinetic energy when the toast popped up. It probably turned into thermal energy.

3. Students' answers will depend upon the device that they analyzed. For example, analysis of the xylophone shows that sound energy was present after but not before. It was produced by the kinetic energy of the sticks when they struck the xylophone bars.

△ Guide

Have each group present their completed charts and their answers to the *Analyze Your Data* questions. Encourage all students to take part in the presentation by displaying the object, showing the chart, and discussing the questions. After all the groups have shared, guide a class discussion of the factors that affect the type of energy before and after the transformations.

Communicate: Share Your Ideas

10 min

Students share their ideas about energy transformations in the devices they observed.

NOTES

After all groups have presented, discuss the factors that influence how much of each type of energy is present *before* and *after*. What do you think are the factors that affect the amount of sound energy? Which factors do you think affect the amount of chemical energy? Thermal energy? Electrical energy?

Reflect

1. List three things you think you know about energy transformations.

2. List three questions you need answered to better understand the energy transformations that have just been presented.

Update the *Project Board*

Although you have observed energy transformations throughout the Unit, this is the first time you are focusing on what happens to energy before and after an energy transformation. Based on your experience, there may be some things you think you know about how energy transforms and what happens to energy after a transformation. These should be added to the *What do we think we know?* column of the *Project Board*.

In the *What do we need to investigate?* column, list the class's questions about energy transformation. If the class had disagreements during the presentations, record questions in this column that you could answer to resolve the disagreements.

What's the Point?

You have reviewed and observed several different types of energy transformations. A list of these, with indicators and factors, will be useful in achieving the *Big Challenge*. However, you do not know exactly what factors control energy transformations. You may have questions, such as, "How do I know if an energy transformation will occur?" or, "How much of the total energy will be transformed?" In the rest of this *Learning Set,* you will be investigating questions such as these.

ENERGY

Reflect

5 min

Students consider what they know and need to know about energy transformations.

◇ **Evaluate**

Have students discuss the ideas and questions described. Tell them to base what they think they know on the devices they observed, the presentations they watched, and the experiments they have performed throughout the Unit.

1. Students' answers will vary. They should include a mention of the law of conservation of energy.

2. Students' answers will vary. They might wonder why thermal energy is sometimes considered useful and sometimes not.

△ Guide

By completing the *Reflect* task, students gathered their thoughts and questions about energy transformations. Form a class list, and record the information on the *Project Board*.

Assessment Options

Targeted Concepts, Skills, and Nature of Science	How do I know if students got it?
Scientists often work together and then share their findings. Sharing findings makes new information available and helps scientists refine their ideas and build on others' ideas. When another person's or group's idea is used, credit needs to be given.	**ASK:** How did your group come to agreement about the types of energy you observed in each part of the device? **LISTEN:** Students should describe the process they used, and any disagreements they had.
Energy is the ability to cause change or do work.	**ASK:** How did you determine which indicators to use? **LISTEN:** Students should identify changes they observed as the device operated.
Energy exists in different forms and can be changed from one form to another.	**ASK:** What happens to energy if it exists before, but not after, a change? **LISTEN:** Students should recognize that the energy is transformed into another type of energy.

Update the *Project Board*

5 min

Students add their ideas and questions to the Project Board.

Teacher Reflection Questions

- What difficulties did students have isolating parts of the devices they observed? What might you do differently next time?

- What evidence do you have to convince you that students grasp the idea that energy can change form? How might you help them to understand this concept better?

- What did you do to make sure that all students actively participated in the group discussions? What might you do to encourage participation from all students?

NOTES

SECTION 6.2 INTRODUCTION

6.2 Explore

What Happens to Mechanical Energy During Its Transformations?

◀ *2 class periods*

A class period is considered to be one 40 to 50 minute class.

Overview

Students conduct two investigations involving changes between kinetic and potential energy. In one investigation, students measure the height to which a ball bounces during successive bounces. In the other investigation, students measure the height to which a marble rolls during successive rolls. Students analyze their data to identify trends in the mechanical energy of each object. Students then read about a device that is being developed to convert the mechanical energy of dancers into electrical energy, and they relate this example to the investigations.

Targeted Concepts, Skills, and Nature of Science	Performance Expectations
Scientists often work together and then share their findings. Sharing findings makes new information available and helps scientists refine their ideas and build on others' ideas. When another person's or group's idea is used, credit needs to be given.	Students work together to analyze the motion of a bouncing ball or a rolling marble.
Scientists make claims (conclusions) based on evidence (trends in data) from reliable investigations.	Students graph their data and make claims based on trends they observe.
Energy exists in different forms and can be changed from one form to another.	Students identify changes in mechanical energy.
Kinetic energy is associated with the motion of an object.	Students recognize that a moving object has kinetic energy.

Targeted Concepts, Skills, and Nature of Science	Performance Expectations
Potential energy is stored energy associated with position or condition.	Students recognize that an object can gain potential energy as it rises.

Materials	
1 per group	Marking pen Larger sheet of poster paper Bouncy ball Meter stick Marble, 2-cm diameter Track for marbles, 100-cm long
1 per student	*Energy-transformation Cartoon* page *Project Board* page
1 per class	Class *Project Board*

NOTES

....

....

....

....

....

....

....

....

Activity Setup and Preparation

The activities in this section require groups to perform their investigation at stations, and then rotate to another station. To save time, you may want to set up the stations before class. Use the descriptions and diagram in the student text to guide your assembly of the stations. Also, have a plan ready for the rotation of groups between stations. Stations 1 and 2 share the same setup and procedure. Stations 3 and 4 share the same setup and procedure. When groups rotate, those at Stations 1 and 2 will move to Stations 3 and 4, and vice-versa.

Homework Options

Reflection

- **Science Content:** : How did the mechanical energy of the objects change over time? How do you know? *(Students should recognize that the mechanical energy decreased over time as indicated by decreases in the peak heights of each.)*

- **Science Process:** What was the dependent variable in each investigation? *(Students should identify the peak height of the object as the dependent variable.)*

Preparation for 6.3

- **Science Content:** Was the total amount of energy of each object (ball or marble) conserved? *(This question is intended to focus students on the decrease in mechanical energy and the idea that the energy must have been transformed into another type of energy.)*

NOTES

....

....

....

....

....

....

NOTES

SECTION 6.2 IMPLEMENTATION

6.2 Explore

What Happens to Mechanical Energy During Its Transformations?

Now you will focus your attention on what happens to mechanical energy during a transformation. You read earlier that mechanical energy is the sum of the kinetic energy, gravitational potential energy, and elastic potential energy in a system. You will collect data to determine what occurs during mechanical energy transformations. As you do that, you will see how it is possible to measure the decrease and increase in mechanical energy as energy transformations take place.

Your group will be assigned to one of four stations set up around the classroom. You might have to wait for a station. When you are finished at your station and are waiting for another station, use the time to read about the dancer-powered dance floor in the box, *Dancers Powering a Generator*. As you do, think about the energy transformations that are happening in that example.

At one point, the bowling ball is motionless with potential energy. Then it is moving with kinetic energy down the bowling alley toward the bowling pins.

When the arrow is drawn back on the stretched bow, the arrow is motionless with potential energy. Then the arrow is moving fast with kinetic energy toward the target.

EN 264

Project-Based Inquiry Science

6.2 Explore

What Happens to Mechanical Energy During Its Transformations?

5 min

Students recall what they learned about mechanical energy.

⃝ Engage

Have a class discussion describing a boulder rolling down a hill. Remind students that the boulder has gravitational potential energy at the top of the hill and it has kinetic energy as it moves down the hill. Explain that the amount of potential energy and kinetic energy constantly changes as the boulder moves downhill. However, remind students that the total amount of kinetic and potential energy—the mechanical energy—stays the same.

*A class period is considered to be one 40 to 50 minute class.

Stations 1 and 2— Energy Transformations in a Bouncing Ball

20 min

Students observe the mechanical energy of a bouncing ball.

LOOKING AHEAD

You may need to review the process of graphing. For the first two stations, make sure students understand that they are relating the number of bounces to the height of the bounce. For the second two stations, students are relating the rolls of the marble to the peak height. It may be useful to describe the variable on the *x*-axis as the manipulated variable and the variable on the *y*-axis as the dependent variable.

6.2 Explore

Stations 1 and 2—Energy Transformations in a Bouncing Ball

Procedure

1. Tape the sheet of poster paper to the wall. The paper should touch the floor.

2. One person should hold the ball 50 cm above the floor in front of the poster paper and drop it. Observe the ball as it bounces up and down. Identify the energy transformations that are happening as the ball bounces up and down.

3. Draw a diagram of the energy transformations you observed in the bouncing ball. Note where the ball has the most gravitational potential energy and where it has the most kinetic energy.

4. Repeat *Step 2*, but this time one group member should mark on the poster paper the peak height of the ball after each bounce. Continue recording peak heights until the peak height is less than 5 cm.

5. Measure the peak height of each bounce, using the meter stick. Record your measurements and plot them on a graph. The horizontal (*x*-axis) should be the bounce number from 0 to 10 (or more). The vertical (*y*-axis) should be the peak height in cm, beginning with 50 cm at 0 bounces.

Materials
- marking pen
- large sheet of poster paper
- bouncy ball
- meter stick

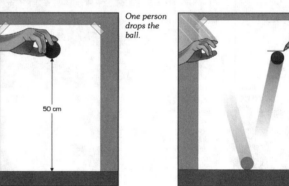

One person drops the ball.

50 cm

A second person marks the peak height of each bounce.

EN 265

ENERGY

○ Get Going

Have groups assigned to this investigation meet at Stations 1 and 2. Keep in mind that groups at these stations will perform the same investigations simultaneously. Have groups read through the procedure before starting. Tell students they may need to practice a few times to become comfortable with the process of marking the height of each bounce. Emphasize to students that they should be looking for energy transformations as they observe the ball bouncing so they may draw labeled diagrams of their observations.

In their procedure, they should let the ball bounce again, after the initial bounce that they diagramed. They should mark its peak heights, until it starts to bounce to less than 5 cm. Then they should measure the marks and plot their data on graphs. Offer assistance to groups as needed.

Have students begin the investigation. If a group has finished the activity and has graphed its data before the rest of the class, guide the group to move ahead and read *Dancers Powering a Generator* in the student text. Otherwise, let the group move to the setups of Stations 3 and 4.

NOTES

Stations 3 and 4— Energy Transformations in a Rolling Marble

20 min

Students observe the mechanical energy of a rolling marble.

Stations 3 and 4—Energy Transformations in a Rolling Marble

Procedure

Materials
- marking pen
- large sheet of poster paper
- marble, 2 cm in diameter
- track for marbles, 100 cm long
- meter stick

1. Position the flexible track so the top of each end of the 100-cm length is 40 cm above the floor. The lowest point of the track should be on the floor. Tape the paper to the wall behind the track. The paper should touch the floor.

2. From the top of the track at one end, release the marble and observe the behavior of the marble as it rolls down one side of the track and up the other side. Identify the energy transformations as the marble rolls back and forth.

3. Draw a diagram of the energy transformations you observed in the rolling marble. Note where the marble has the most gravitational potential energy and where it has the most kinetic energy.

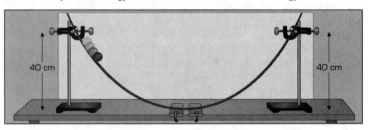

4. Repeat *Step 2*, but this time one group member should mark the height of the marble each time it reaches a peak, just before it reverses direction and rolls down the ramp again. Continue recording peak heights until the peak height is less than 5 cm.

5. Measure the peak heights using a meterstick. Record your measurements and plot a graph. The horizontal (*x*-axis) should be the successive rolls of the marble from 0 to 10 (or more). The vertical (*y*-axis) should be the peak height in cm, beginning with 40 cm at 0 rolls.

EN 266

Project-Based Inquiry Science

⬡ Get Going

When it is the group's turn to perform this investigation, have them meet at Stations 3 and 4 and read through the procedure. Once they understand what they will be doing, tell them to check that the station is set up correctly. Tell students they may need to practice a few times to become comfortable with the process of marking the height of the marble.

Let students know that these investigations also require them to watch for energy transformations as the marble rolls so that they can draw a labeled diagram of their observations. Then they should let the marble roll again, marking its peak heights, until it starts to rise to less than 5 cm. Then they should measure the marks and plot their data. Offer assistance to groups as needed.

If groups finish at the station before the rest of the class, have them move ahead to the *Dancers Powering a Generator* reading in the student text.

NOTES

....

....

....

....

....

....

....

....

....

....

....

....

Analyze Your Data

10 min

Students analyze the data they recorded from the four stations.

Analyze Your Data

1. How does the peak height of the ball or marble change as it continues bouncing or rolling?

2. Looking at the graph you made, what is the trend of the peak heights the ball or marble reached? How does the peak height compare to the original height?

3. If the ball or marble never gets back to the height at which it started, this means that some gravitational potential energy in the ball or marble is not transformed into kinetic energy. It may also mean that some kinetic energy is not transformed into gravitational potential energy. What evidence do you have that supports these statements?

4. What do you think might have happened to the "lost" energy? What evidence, if any, do you have that supports your answer?

5. How many bounces or rolls did you observe before the peak height was too small to measure?

Communicate

Share Your Results

When it is time for your group to present, begin by having one or two group members demonstrate what you did and how you took your measurements. Others in your group should then present your energy transformation diagram, your data, and your interpretation of the data. Make sure you address each of the *Analyze Your Data* questions as part of your presentation.

As you listen to other groups, notice the similarities and differences between their data and yours. Decide if you agree with their answers, but do not ask questions yet. Wait until everybody has presented before having a discussion.

After all the groups have made their presentations, look at the whole set of graphs. Discuss what you think happens to the original gravitational potential energy of the balls and marbles. See if you can come to agreement about what happened to the gravitational potential energy that caused the ball to stop bouncing or the marble to stop rolling. Support your ideas with evidence from the investigations.

EN 267

ENERGY

△ Guide and Assess

Have students discuss their data in their groups. Students' data will vary. However, listen to make sure students observe that the peak height of the ball or marble decreases as it continues to bounce or roll. The graphs should show the decrease in height from left to right across the *x*-axis. Students should propose explanations for the data based on what they have learned about energy so far.

1. Students should have observed that the height of the ball and the marble became less and less with each bounce or roll-return.

2. Students should recognize that the trend of the peak heights is to diminish with time. The peak height is always less than the original height.

3. Students should understand that as the peak height decreases, energy is lost. This continues until the ball stops bouncing or the marble stops rolling.

4. Some students may have an understanding of friction and conclude that the "lost" energy was due to friction in the system. Evidence for this will probably be hard to come by.

5. Students' responses will vary. It should take 4-5 bounces or rolls before the peak height is too small to measure.

△ Guide

Give groups some time to prepare their presentations. They should have their diagrams and graphs ready to show the class and they should decide which group members will demonstrate how they conducted their investigations. Point out that their presentations should also be guided by their answers to the *Analyze Your Data* questions.

After the groups have presented their work, lead a discussion to compare the results. Make sure the class can see all the graphs. Identify similarities and differences among the groups' data. Invite students to share their ideas based on evidence.

Communicate: Share Your Results

10 min

Students share their procedures, measurements, and data analysis with the class.

NOTES

....

....

....

....

....

Reflect

10 min

Students answer questions to analyze their results.

LOOKING AHEAD

Students will learn what happens to "lost" energy in the next section. At this point, focus only on the fact that mechanical energy is decreasing. Students should think about what happens to the "missing" energy, but they should not try to explain it just yet.

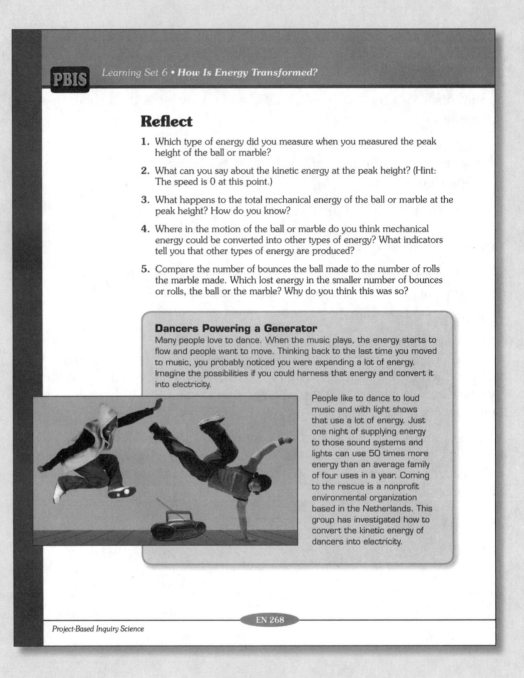

Reflect

1. Which type of energy did you measure when you measured the peak height of the ball or marble?

2. What can you say about the kinetic energy at the peak height? (Hint: The speed is 0 at this point.)

3. What happens to the total mechanical energy of the ball or marble at the peak height? How do you know?

4. Where in the motion of the ball or marble do you think mechanical energy could be converted into other types of energy? What indicators tell you that other types of energy are produced?

5. Compare the number of bounces the ball made to the number of rolls the marble made. Which lost energy in the smaller number of bounces or rolls, the ball or the marble? Why do you think this was so?

Dancers Powering a Generator
Many people love to dance. When the music plays, the energy starts to flow and people want to move. Thinking back to the last time you moved to music, you probably noticed you were expending a lot of energy. Imagine the possibilities if you could harness that energy and convert it into electricity.

People like to dance to loud music and with light shows that use a lot of energy. Just one night of supplying energy to those sound systems and lights can use 50 times more energy than an average family of four uses in a year. Coming to the rescue is a nonprofit environmental organization based in the Netherlands. This group has investigated how to convert the kinetic energy of dancers into electricity.

EN 268

Project-Based Inquiry Science

◇ Evaluate

Have students discuss answers to the *Reflect* questions.

1. Students should recognize that at the peak height, the ball or marble had 100 percent potential energy and no kinetic energy.

2. Students should explain that the kinetic energy of the ball or marble is 0 J at the peak height because the object stops moving at this point.

3. Students should describe that ideally, the total mechanical energy is conserved. However, they may recognize that because the peak height is decreasing, some mechanical energy is being "lost."

4. Students should suggest possible ideas, such as sound or thermal energy. They should describe indicators such as the fact that they can hear the ball bounce.

5. Students should use the graphs to determine which object lost energy faster. It will be the object for which the peak height decreased at the faster rate.

△ Guide

Have students read the information about piezoelectric devices under a dance floor. Challenge students to identify energy transformations. Record them as a flow chart on the board. For example, chemical energy stored in food that dancers eat is transformed into mechanical energy of motion. Mechanical energy is then transformed into electrical energy. Electrical energy is transformed into sound energy and light energy.

Dancers Powering a Generator

10 min

Students read about a dance floor that uses dancers' energy to power lights and music.

NOTES

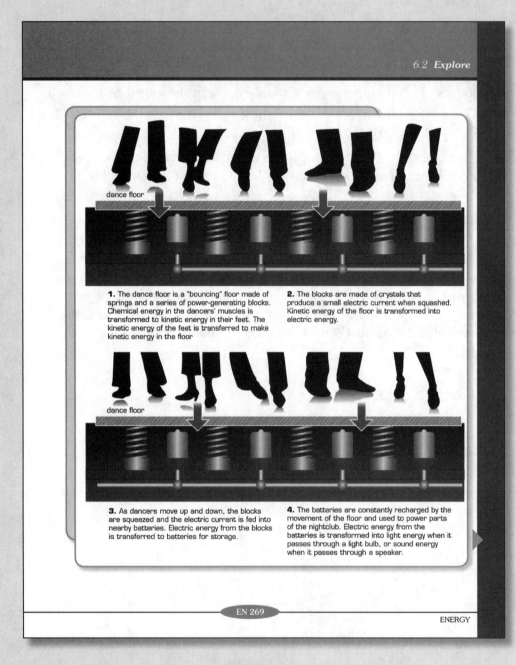

dance floor

1. The dance floor is a "bouncing" floor made of springs and a series of power-generating blocks. Chemical energy in the dancers' muscles is transformed to kinetic energy in their feet. The kinetic energy of the feet is transferred to make kinetic energy in the floor

2. The blocks are made of crystals that produce a small electric current when squashed. Kinetic energy of the floor is transformed into electric energy.

dance floor

3. As dancers move up and down, the blocks are squeezed and the electric current is fed into nearby batteries. Electric energy from the blocks is transferred to batteries for storage.

4. The batteries are constantly recharged by the movement of the floor and used to power parts of the nightclub. Electric energy from the batteries is transformed into light energy when it passes through a light bulb, or sound energy when it passes through a speaker.

EN 269

ENERGY

Discuss with students the benefits of using dancers' energy to power lights and music. Focus the discussion on how this type of dance floor would conserve limited natural resources and reduce pollution.

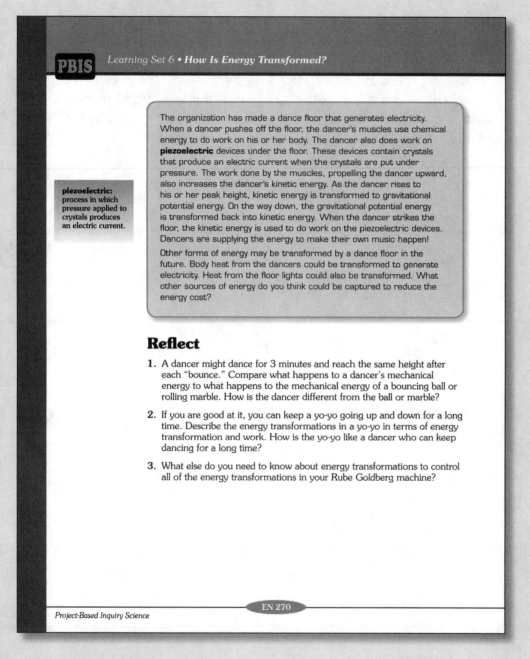

The organization has made a dance floor that generates electricity. When a dancer pushes off the floor, the dancer's muscles use chemical energy to do work on his or her body. The dancer also does work on **piezoelectric** devices under the floor. These devices contain crystals that produce an electric current when the crystals are put under pressure. The work done by the muscles, propelling the dancer upward, also increases the dancer's kinetic energy. As the dancer rises to his or her peak height, kinetic energy is transformed to gravitational potential energy. On the way down, the gravitational potential energy is transformed back into kinetic energy. When the dancer strikes the floor, the kinetic energy is used to do work on the piezoelectric devices. Dancers are supplying the energy to make their own music happen!

Other forms of energy may be transformed by a dance floor in the future. Body heat from the dancers could be transformed to generate electricity. Heat from the floor lights could also be transformed. What other sources of energy do you think could be captured to reduce the energy cost?

piezoelectric: process in which pressure applied to crystals produces an electric current.

Reflect

1. A dancer might dance for 3 minutes and reach the same height after each "bounce." Compare what happens to a dancer's mechanical energy to what happens to the mechanical energy of a bouncing ball or rolling marble. How is the dancer different from the ball or marble?

2. If you are good at it, you can keep a yo-yo going up and down for a long time. Describe the energy transformations in a yo-yo in terms of energy transformation and work. How is the yo-yo like a dancer who can keep dancing for a long time?

3. What else do you need to know about energy transformations to control all of the energy transformations in your Rube Goldberg machine?

EN 270

Project-Based Inquiry Science

Reflect

5 min

Students compare the energy of the dancers to other examples.

△ Guide and Assess

Have students discuss possible answers to the *Reflect* questions.

1. Students may suggest that unlike the ball or marble, the dancer can supply more energy until getting too tired to dance.

2. Students may explain that as in the example of the dance floor, a person can keep supplying energy to keep the yo-yo's motion the same. On the downward path, the yo-yo uses kinetic energy of the wrist and potential gravitational energy to spin. At the end of the string, the yo-yo rewinds the string and travels upward using the kinetic energy of its spin and a little extra kinetic energy supplied by the wrist.

3. Student answers will vary.

NOTES

6.2 Explore

Update the Project Board

Record what you think you know about energy transformations in the *What do we think we know?* column of the *Project Board*. You may have had disagreements with classmates about the investigation results. Put questions in the *What do we need to investigate?* column of the *Project Board* that will help you resolve those disagreements. Also add the questions you need to answer to control all of the energy transformations in the Rube Goldberg machine you are designing.

You can keep a yo-yo going up and down for a long time.

What's the Point?

The investigations with the ball and marble allowed you to measure what happens to mechanical energy during a series of transformations. The graphs of your data show a downward trend. This suggests that some of the energy the ball and marble started with was "lost." You might wonder what happened to that "lost" energy.

EN 271

ENERGY

Update the Project Board

5 min

Students add ideas about energy transformations to the Project Board.

△ Guide

Lead a discussion in which students share what they have learned about energy transformations and what evidence they have to support their ideas. Record their ideas on the *Project Board*.

Assessment Options

Targeted Concepts, Skills, and Nature of Science	How do I know if students got it?
Scientists often work together and then share their findings. Sharing findings makes new information available and helps scientists refine their ideas and build on others' ideas. When another person's or group's idea is used, credit needs to be given.	**ASK:** What observations did you have in common with the other groups, and what observations were different? **LISTEN:** Students should describe how their results compared with those of the other groups.
Scientists make claims (conclusions) based on evidence (trends in data) from reliable investigations.	**ASK:** What trends did you observe in the data you graphed? **LISTEN:** Students should describe how the peak height decreased with each successive bounce or roll.
Energy exists in different forms and can be changed from one form to another.	**ASK:** What happened to the kinetic and potential energy of the object you observed? **LISTEN:** Students should describe that the kinetic energy changed to potential energy as the object rose, and potential energy changed to kinetic energy as the object fell.
Kinetic energy is associated with the motion of an object.	**ASK:** Why didn't the object have kinetic energy at its peak height? **LISTEN:** Students should explain that at the peak, the object came to a stop and changed direction. Because kinetic energy is energy of motion, the object does not have kinetic energy when it is stopped.

Targeted Concepts, Skills, and Nature of Science	How do I know if students got it?
Potential energy is stored energy associated with position or condition.	**ASK:** How could you tell that the potential energy of the object changed over time? **LISTEN:** Students should recognize that potential energy is related to the peak height of the object, and because the peak height decreased, the potential energy must have decreased.

Teacher Reflection Questions

- What challenges did students face in completing the investigations? What might you do differently next time?

- How well were students able to compare the two different investigations? What might you do to help them make the comparison?

- What evidence do you have to suggest that students were able to extend the concept of energy transformations to the reading about the dancers? What can you do to clarify any misunderstandings?

NOTES

NOTES

6.3 Explore

What Happens to the "Lost" Energy?

◀ *1 class period*

A class period is considered to be one 40 to 50 minute class.

Overview

Students observe a demonstration, which is an extension of the investigations they conducted in *Section 6.2*. This time, however, students focus on forms of energy in addition to kinetic and potential energy. They not only look for changes in height, but they listen for sounds and feel for heat. After making their observations, students read about usable energy and efficiency. They then use what they have learned to analyze the energy-transformation cartoons in terms of usable energy and efficiency.

Targeted Concepts, Skills, and Nature of Science	Performance Expectations
Scientists often work together and then share their findings. Sharing findings makes new information available and helps scientists refine their ideas and build on others' ideas. When another person's or group's idea is used, credit needs to be given.	Students share ideas about energy transformations in the cartoons they have been examining.
Scientists make claims (conclusions) based on evidence (trends in data) from reliable investigations.	Students relate their observations from the demonstration to the investigations they performed earlier.
Energy exists in different forms and can be changed from one form to another.	Students identify energy transformations to look for usable energy.
Energy is neither created nor destroyed in ordinary processes.	Students recognize that if the total mechanical energy decreased, the "lost" energy was changed into other forms of energy.

Materials	
1 per class	Bouncy ball
	Class *Project Board*
2 per class	Marbles
	Tracks
	Ringstands
	Track assemblies
	C-clamps
	Right-angle holders
	Cross arms
1 per student	*Energy-transformation Cartoon* page
	Project Board page

Activity Setup and Preparation

The demonstration in this section uses the same track assembly from Stations 3 and 4 in *Section 6.2*. Keep one of these assembled so that it is ready to use in this section.

Homework Options

Reflection

- **Science Content:** Friction is a force that opposes the motion of an object. How does friction affect the amount of energy lost as heat? *(Students should recognize that friction is directly related to the amount of energy lost as heat. Decreasing friction increases the efficiency of any device.)*

- **Science Process:** How are graphs useful for identifying changes over time in energy? *(Students should describe how they used their graphs to identify trends, such as decreases in the peak height of a bouncing ball or rolling marble. This made it possible to recognize a trend in the total amount of mechanical energy, and therefore the amount of energy lost to the system.)*

Preparation for 6.4

- **Science Content:** In *Learning Set 2,* you learned that energy is conserved. Now you learned that the total amount of mechanical energy can be decreased. What might this suggest about all types of energy? *(This question is intended to get students to think about the idea that all types of energy are conserved.)*

NOTES

....

....

....

....

....

....

....

....

....

....

....

....

....

NOTES

SECTION 6.3 IMPLEMENTATION

6.3 Explore

What Happens to the "Lost" Energy?

When you were carrying out the investigation with the bouncing ball and the rolling marble, you were focused on observing transformations between gravitational potential energy and kinetic energy. So it is not surprising that you may not have noticed other energy transformations that were happening. You will now have the opportunity to watch a demonstration that will give you clues about other energy transformations that were happening when you bounced your ball or rolled your marble. As you watch the demonstration, look for evidence of all the different types of energy that are present. After the demonstration, you may be able to figure out what happened to the energy that seemed to be "lost."

Chemical energy changes into light, sound, and thermal energy when fireworks explode. However, because the light and sound are so impressive, most people don't think about the thermal energy.

EN 272

Project-Based Inquiry Science

6.3 Explore

What Happens to the "Lost" Energy?

5 min

Students are asked to think about why the mechanical energy of the objects in Section 6.2 decreased.

○ Engage

Refer students back to the graphs they made in *Section 6.2*. Ask them to summarize what happened to the overall potential energy and kinetic energy in each situation. Help students to recognize that the overall amount, which is the mechanical energy, decreased. Then let them know that they are going to investigate this "loss" of energy further.

*A class period is considered to be one 40 to 50 minute class.

Demonstration

10 min

*Students observe
a demonstration
to consider energy
transformations.*

Demonstration

Observe

Your teacher will bounce a ball and then roll a marble down a ramp. Watch
and listen carefully. As you observe each, try to find evidence of other
energy types in addition to kinetic energy and gravitational potential energy.
Record your observations. Besides kinetic energy and gravitational potential
energy, what other energy types are you able to detect?

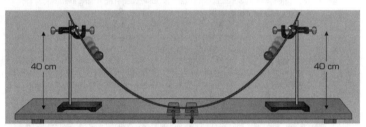

*What kinds of energy transformations occur when two balls run down the track toward each
other? What does this demonstration tell you about "lost" energy?*

After observing the ball and the marble, you will observe a collision between
two marbles as they roll down opposite sides of the track. Besides kinetic
energy and gravitational potential energy, what other energy types are you
able to detect? Record your observations.

Analyze Your Data

1. What do you think happened to the total amount of mechanical energy
   the ball had before the teacher dropped it? What do you think happened
   to the total amount of mechanical energy each of the marbles had at the
   top of the ramp? You may want to draw diagrams to help you identify all
   the energy changes you observed.

2. Examine the graphs you made in your investigation of the bouncing balls
   and rolling marbles. Describe any differences in the patterns found on
   the graphs. For example, one graph might show a steeper decline than
   the other graph. Use what you just experienced to explain why.

EN 273

ENERGY

◯ Get Going

Begin the demonstration by bouncing a ball. Tell students to use their
senses to gather information about the ball. Then roll a marble down a ramp
by itself and then roll two marbles from opposite sides of a track. Again tell
students to use their senses to gather information about the ball. Repeat as
necessary to be sure students make their observations.

△ Guide and Assess

Have students discuss answers to the questions. Students should recognize that the total amount of mechanical energy decreased in each case. Listen as students compare the graphs. Help them relate the conditions of each trial to the resulting trends. For example, a ball released from a greater height will result in a slightly different graph than a ball released from a lower height.

1. Students may suggest that all the mechanical energy was potential energy before the teacher dropped the ball. When dropped, the potential gravitational energy transformed into kinetic energy. With each bounce, the kinetic energy transformed into elastic potential energy. Students may know that mechanical energy is lost due to friction. The situation with the marbles is the same. Diagrams should show gravitational potential energy, kinetic energy, and elastic potential energy.

2. Students' answers will vary depending on the results. Mechanical energy is lost on the way down as the ball (or marbles) pushes aside molecules of air. The marble also loses energy due to friction with the track. When the ball hits the floor, some of the kinetic energy is lost to sound energy and friction. The ball is not perfectly elastic. More energy is lost on the way back up.

Analyze Your Data

10 min

Students discuss their observations from the demonstration.

NOTES

....

....

....

....

....

....

ENERGY

Energy Transformation and Energy Losses

10 min

Students read about usable energy.

META NOTES

Avoid the misconception that energy is actually lost. Use the reading to explain that the term *lost* is generally used to describe energy that is not available to do useful work. The energy itself is not destroyed, nor is its whereabouts unknown.

META NOTES

Mention that some "lost" energy might be directed toward other applications. Heat produced by a car's engine, for example, is used to warm the interior of a car.

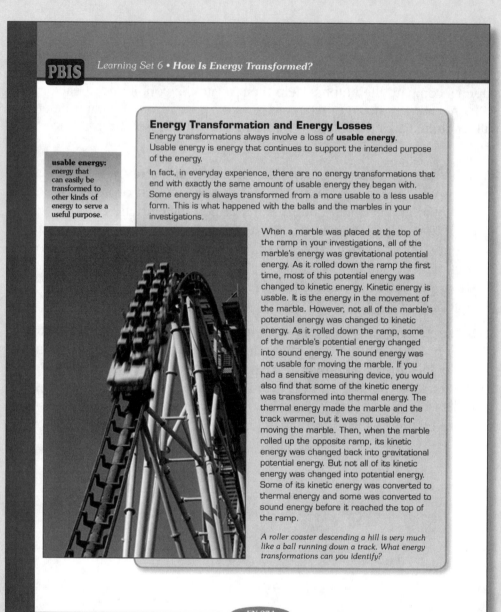

Energy Transformation and Energy Losses

Energy transformations always involve a loss of **usable energy**. Usable energy is energy that continues to support the intended purpose of the energy.

In fact, in everyday experience, there are no energy transformations that end with exactly the same amount of usable energy they began with. Some energy is always transformed from a more usable to a less usable form. This is what happened with the balls and the marbles in your investigations.

usable energy: energy that can easily be transformed to other kinds of energy to serve a useful purpose.

When a marble was placed at the top of the ramp in your investigations, all of the marble's energy was gravitational potential energy. As it rolled down the ramp the first time, most of this potential energy was changed to kinetic energy. Kinetic energy is usable. It is the energy in the movement of the marble. However, not all of the marble's potential energy was changed to kinetic energy. As it rolled down the ramp, some of the marble's potential energy changed into sound energy. The sound energy was not usable for moving the marble. If you had a sensitive measuring device, you would also find that some of the kinetic energy was transformed into thermal energy. The thermal energy made the marble and the track warmer, but it was not usable for moving the marble. Then, when the marble rolled up the opposite ramp, its kinetic energy was changed back into gravitational potential energy. But not all of its kinetic energy was changed into potential energy. Some of its kinetic energy was converted to thermal energy and some was converted to sound energy before it reached the top of the ramp.

A roller coaster descending a hill is very much like a ball running down a track. What energy transformations can you identify?

△ Guide

Have students read the information about energy transformations and energy losses. Explain that usable energy can be thought of as the energy available to do work. Describe additional examples to help students understand the concept:

- In a car engine, gasoline is burned, producing very fast combustion, inside a cylinder. In this way, the stored chemical energy is transformed into other forms. Some energy becomes mechanical energy that moves the car. Some energy becomes electrical energy that powers the radio and other devices in the car. Much of the energy becomes thermal energy that is released into the environment as heat. The thermal energy does not do useful work in the car, so it is not considered usable energy. This energy is said to be "lost."

- In an ecosystem, plants store chemical energy in food. They use some of that energy for their own life processes, and they store the rest in their tissues. When an animal eats a plant, it takes in that stored energy. Only about 10 percent of the energy from the plant is passed on to the animal. Much of that energy is converted into thermal energy that is "lost" to the environment as heat.

Discuss how energy efficiency is the energy transferred by the device divided by the total energy supplied to the device. Suppose, for example, 100 kilojoules (kJ) are stored in a sample of gasoline. If the engine produces 40 kJ that can be used to produce movement, the engine is said to be 40 percent fuel efficient. The other 60 kJ are lost as heat through the exhaust and radiator.

Make sure students recognize that some amount of energy is lost as heat in every energy transformation.

NOTES

....

....

....

....

....

ENERGY

On each successive roll up and down the ramp, the marble continued to lose usable energy. The "lost" energy was transferred into the track, into the ball, and into the air.

The same thing happened with the bouncing balls. With each successive bounce, some of the usable energy changed into sound energy and thermal energy. Neither of these is usable in keeping the ball moving.

Your body behaves in a similar way. It transforms the chemical energy in the food you eat into other forms of energy that your body needs to move, grow, and sustain itself. But a lot of the energy used by your body is lost as thermal energy. When you work out or play hard or dance, you notice how much heat your body gives off. As your body changes some of its chemical energy into kinetic energy, some of its chemical energy is also changed into thermal energy. The thermal energy makes you warm, but it does not contribute to your movement.

The amount of usable energy you get from a system is called its **energy efficiency**. If, after transformation, 90 percent of the energy is still usable, the transformation is said to be 90 percent efficient. Your body is a lot less than 90 percent efficient. But even an energy transformation that is not efficient does not lose energy. It just turns some of the energy into a form that is not usable for whatever work the system is doing.

energy efficiency: the degree to which a process produces a usable energy output for a given energy input.

Appliances are rated for their energy efficiency. You can find this information on a tag, which helps you make a better decision of which appliance to buy.

NOTES

....

....

....

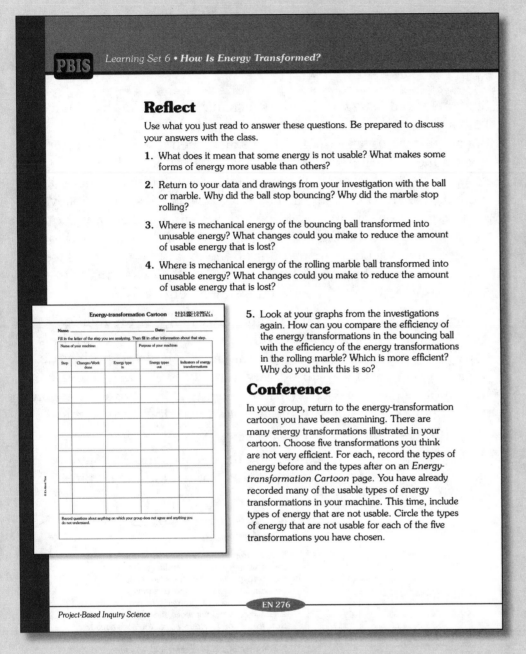

Reflect

Use what you just read to answer these questions. Be prepared to discuss your answers with the class.

1. What does it mean that some energy is not usable? What makes some forms of energy more usable than others?

2. Return to your data and drawings from your investigation with the ball or marble. Why did the ball stop bouncing? Why did the marble stop rolling?

3. Where is mechanical energy of the bouncing ball transformed into unusable energy? What changes could you make to reduce the amount of usable energy that is lost?

4. Where is mechanical energy of the rolling marble ball transformed into unusable energy? What changes could you make to reduce the amount of usable energy that is lost?

5. Look at your graphs from the investigations again. How can you compare the efficiency of the energy transformations in the bouncing ball with the efficiency of the energy transformations in the rolling marble? Which is more efficient? Why do you think this is so?

Conference

In your group, return to the energy-transformation cartoon you have been examining. There are many energy transformations illustrated in your cartoon. Choose five transformations you think are not very efficient. For each, record the types of energy before and the types after on an *Energy-transformation Cartoon* page. You have already recorded many of the usable types of energy transformations in your machine. This time, include types of energy that are not usable. Circle the types of energy that are not usable for each of the five transformations you have chosen.

Reflect

5 min

Students propose answers to questions about usable energy and efficiency.

△ Guide and Assess

Have students discuss answers to the questions in their groups. Encourage students to tie together everything they have learned and observed about energy transformations.

1. Students should answer that the term usable energy means that the energy is available to do work. All energy eventually ends up as thermal energy and is lost for any useful purpose because it cannot be used to do work.

2. Students will realize that the ball stopped bouncing and the marble stopped rolling because all of the mechanical energy had been transformed into sound and heat. Or just heat, as sound ends up as heat.

3. Students should suggest that the mechanical energy of the bouncing ball is transformed into unusable energy on the way down to the floor as it pushes aside molecules of air. When it strikes the floor, it loses mechanical energy when it makes a sound and when it compresses (as it transforms energy into elastic potential energy). As the ball returns to its original shape, it loses more energy. Finally, as the kinetic energy moves it upward, it again loses energy due to the work it does pushing aside air molecules. If the ball was to be bounced in a vacuum, the amount of energy lost could be reduced. Also, if the type of material used to make the ball were made from a more elastic material, it would reduce the energy loss.

4. Students may suggest that the mechanical energy of the rolling marble is transformed into unusable energy as it travels down the track in two ways. It takes a small amount of energy to push aside the air molecules in its path but larger amounts of energy are used by friction with the track. Also, some energy is transformed to sound energy all along the track. If the marble rolled down a frictionless track in a vacuum, there would be no loss of energy to heat.

5. Student answers will depend on the results from the exploration. Students may guess that the object—ball or marble—that comes to rest first is the least efficient.

Conference

5 min

Students analyze their energy-transformation cartoons in terms of usable energy and efficiency.

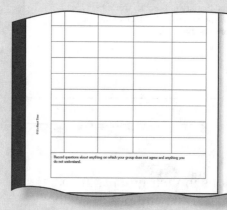

Conference

In your group, return to the energy-transformation cartoon you have been examining. There are many energy transformations illustrated in your cartoon. Choose five transformations you think are not very efficient. For each, record the types of energy before and the types after on an *Energy-transformation Cartoon* page. You have already recorded many of the usable types of energy transformations in your machine. This time, include types of energy that are not usable. Circle the types of energy that are not usable for each of the five transformations you have chosen.

△ Guide

Have groups refer back to the energy-transformation cartoons. Tell them to have all their previous analyses of the cartoons available for reference. Ask students to find examples of usable energy as described, and then answer the questions listed.

Then answer these questions. Be prepared to share your answers with the class.

1. What types of energy in your cartoon are not transformed in the next step? How could this unusable energy have been transformed if the step was different?

2. Based on what you have learned about energy efficiency, describe why you think the machine in the cartoon you have been examining is efficient or not efficient.

3. How could you increase the efficiency of one step in the machine?

4. Which step in the machine do you think is the most efficient? Why do you think this?

Communicate

Share Your Ideas

When it is your group's turn to present, remind the group which Rube Goldberg machine you were examining. Then present two of the inefficient energy transformations you identified. For each of the inefficient energy transformations, tell the class what type of energy was transformed into what other types, which types were unusable, and what happened to that unusable energy. Then tell the class how you think that step of the machine could be changed to be more efficient.

Also present the step you think is most efficient. Tell the class what makes the step you chose more efficient than other steps in the machine. End your presentation by telling the class whether you think the machine in the cartoon is efficient or not efficient and why.

As you are listening, pay attention to the energy transformations, and make sure you understand each one and agree with the presenters. If you do not understand or do not agree, raise your hand and ask a question. Remember to be respectful.

After everyone has presented, discuss how efficient you think each of the four energy-transformation cartoon machines is. Do you think one of them is a lot more efficient than the others? If so, why? Do you think one is a lot less efficient than the others? If so, why?

1. Students' answers will vary depending upon the cartoon they are analyzing and the steps they have selected. Students should describe the step and the energy transformations that are occurring in it. They should then point out the unusable energy. As an example, in the *Can Picker* cartoon, the first step uses a rocket to knock a ball out of a glove. The rocket has a great deal of kinetic energy from the chemical energy it started with. The glove needs very little kinetic energy to simply flip the ball a few feet and so there is a lot of unused energy. This will be in the form of heat and work done as

the rocket continues well past the baseball glove, perhaps hitting the ceiling and causing damage (work). This step could be made more efficient by using a smaller rocket with less chemicals.

2. Students should understand that the Rube Goldberg cartoons are very inefficient because often tremendous amounts of energy are used to cause a very simple effect. In general, the more steps, the less efficient.

3. Students' answers will vary depending on the cartoon and the step selected. As an example, in the *Breakfast Server* cartoon, the machine makes tea by condensing steam on a wooden paddle wheel. If a steel paddle wheel were used, more of the steam would condense and the tea cup would fill more quickly and the tea would be hotter.

4. Students' answers will vary depending on the cartoon and the step selected. Generally, the steps which transform gravitational potential energy to kinetic energy are going to be the most efficient. As an example, in the *Trash-to-Stereo Server* cartoon, the first step, where falling garbage strikes a paddle wheel to turn a fan, is high in efficiency. It could be made more efficient by increasing the size of the paddles so that more of the garbage hits them.

Communicate

15 min

Students share their ideas on inefficient and efficient steps.

Communicate

Share Your Ideas

When it is your group's turn to present, remind the group which Rube Goldberg machine you were examining. Then present two of the inefficient energy transformations you identified. For each of the inefficient energy transformations, tell the class what type of energy was transformed into what other types, which types were unusable, and what happened to that unusable energy. Then tell the class how you think that step of the machine could be changed to be more efficient.

Also present the step you think is most efficient. Tell the class what makes the step you chose more efficient than other steps in the machine. End your presentation by telling the class whether you think the machine in the cartoon is efficient or not efficient and why.

As you are listening, pay attention to the energy transformations, and make sure you understand each one and agree with the presenters. If you do not understand or do not agree, raise your hand and ask a question. Remember to be respectful.

After everyone has presented, discuss how efficient you think each of the four energy-transformation cartoon machines is. Do you think one of them is a lot more efficient than the others? If so, why? Do you think one is a lot less efficient than the others? If so, why?

△ Guide

Choose the order in which groups present their work. It may be helpful to have groups analyzing the same cartoon present at the same time since the other students will be more familiar with the cartoon the second time it is analyzed. Make sure that each student in the group participates in some way.

Update the *Project Board*

Record what you now know about energy transformations in the *What are we learning?* column of the *Project Board*. Record your evidence in the *What is our evidence?* column. If you still have questions about energy transformations, record those in the *What do we need to investigate?* column.

What's the Point?

The demonstrations with the ball and the marbles colliding provided you with some evidence that energy is not lost in energy transformations. In addition to the kinetic energy observed as the two marbles rolled down the ramps, you also observed evidence of sound energy. This sound energy flowed into the surrounding air. You might have also observed evidence of thermal energy, if you had a sensitive measuring device. The thermal energy warmed the marbles and the ramp. The potential and kinetic energy that changed into sound energy and thermal energy were no longer available to help the marbles move. While none of the potential energy of the marbles and balls disappeared, some of it was changed into forms that were not usable to do the work of moving the marbles or bouncing the ball. The more an energy transformation changes energy into a usable form, the more efficient the energy transformation is.

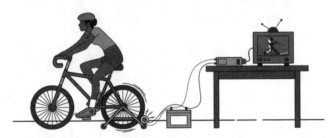

This bicycle provides electricity to a television. Some energy may appear to be lost in the energy transformations. What do you think happens to that "lost" energy?

Update the *Project Board*

5 min

Students add ideas about energy transformations to the Project Board.

△ Guide

Work with students to summarize the new ideas they have learned about energy transformations and usable energy. Ask them to describe any confusion they may have and what questions they would like to have answered. Record this new information in the appropriate columns of the *Project Board.*

Assessment Options

Targeted Concepts, Skills, and Nature of Science	How do I know if students got it?
Scientists often work together and then share their findings. Sharing findings makes new information available and helps scientists refine their ideas and build on others' ideas. When another person's or group's idea is used, credit needs to be given.	**ASK:** How did your group decide which energy transformations in the cartoon were not efficient? **LISTEN:** Students should describe the process the group used and the criteria they identified.
Scientists make claims (conclusions) based on evidence (trends in data) from reliable investigations.	**ASK:** What claim can you make if you know the total mechanical energy of an object is decreasing? **LISTEN:** Students may suggest that they can claim some of the energy is being changed into other forms.
Energy exists in different forms and can be changed from one form to another.	**ASK:** What form of energy is some energy being transformed to during every energy transformation? **LISTEN:** Students should recognize that some energy is always transformed to thermal energy, which is lost as heat.
Energy is neither created nor destroyed in ordinary processes.	**ASK:** Why isn't lost energy really lost? **LISTEN:** Students should explain that energy is not destroyed, but rather changed to another form that may not be usable.

Teacher Reflection Questions

- What misconceptions did students have about lost energy? How were you able to clarify any misunderstandings?

- What difficulties did students have relating the demonstration to the investigations from *Section 6.2?* What did you do to make the comparison clear?

- How were you able to engage students in analyzing the energy-transformation cartoons again? What might you do next time?

NOTES

NOTES

6.4 Read

The Law of Conservation of Energy

◄ $\frac{1}{2}$ *class period*

A class period is considered to be one 40 to 50 minute class.

Overview

Students learn that the law of conservation of energy states that energy is neither created nor destroyed. Students read a passage written by Richard Feynman as an analogy. They then use their reading to come up with their own definition of a system.

Targeted Concepts, Skills, and Nature of Science	Performance Expectations
Scientists often work together and then share their findings. Sharing findings makes new information available and helps scientists refine their ideas and build on others' ideas. When another person's or group's idea is used, credit needs to be given.	Students read a story written by Richard Feynman to learn about conservation of energy.
Energy exists in different forms and can be changed from one form to another.	Students recall observing one form of energy change into another in the investigations and demonstration from the previous sections.
Energy is neither created nor destroyed in ordinary processes.	Students learn about the law of conservation of energy.

Materials	
1 per student	*Project Board* page
1 per class	Class *Project Board*

ENERGY

Homework Options

Reflection

- **Science Content:** What happens to the potential energy of a boulder that is pushed over a cliff? *(Students should describe how the potential energy is converted to other forms of energy, such as the kinetic energy of motion, the sound energy that can be heard, and the heat energy that is released into the environment.)*

Preparation for 6.5

- **Science Content:** In what ways can people use energy transformations to do useful work? *(This question is intended to get students thinking about controlling energy transformations, as is accomplished in power plants.)*

NOTES

....

....

....

....

....

....

....

....

....

SECTION 6.4 IMPLEMENTATION

◀ $\frac{1}{2}$ *class period**

6.4 Read

The Law of Conservation of Energy

The data gathered in your explorations show that mechanical energy decreased steadily in the bouncing ball and rolling marble. It appeared that the ball and the marble "lost" energy every time they traveled up or down. However, when you observed the demonstrations of the ball and the colliding marbles, you were able to hear the sound of the ball bouncing and moving through the air. You could also hear the sound of the marbles moving down the track. The energy that changed into sound energy was not useable for doing the work of moving the ball and the marbles. However, none of the energy disappeared.

The **law of conservation of energy** states that energy cannot be created or destroyed, but can only change form. The total amounts of energy before and after any energy transformation are equal. It is sometimes hard to know what happened to some of the energy. But energy is not destroyed. Instead, it is often transformed into some type of energy that may not be usable for the intended purpose.

law of conservation of energy: a law of physics that states that energy cannot be created or destroyed; it can only change form.

Energy of a system may decrease. If so, the system has lost energy, but that energy can be found in the environment around the system. Energy of a system also may increase. If so, the system has gained energy, so the energy of the surrounding environment must have decreased.

The story on the next page may help you better understand the idea of conservation of energy. This story comes from Richard Feynman, one of the greatest American physicists of the twentieth century.

Richard Feynman (1918–1988) was an American physicist and a member of the Manhattan Project team during WW II. In addition to winning a Nobel Prize for his work in quantum electrodynamics, he was a free spirit known for his pranks, painting, and bongo playing.

EN 279

ENERGY

6.4 Read

The Law of Conservation of Energy

10 min

Students read about conservation of energy.

> **META NOTES**
>
> Avoid the misconception that this law has to do with preserving natural resources. Students may be familiar with the idea of cutting back on their use of electricity to reduce their use of fossil fuels. While important, make sure they know that this is a very different concept.

△ Guide

Remind students of the ball and marble explorations they participated in earlier. Ask the class to think about what appeared to happen as the ball bounced and the marble rolled. They should think of the "lost" energy that they discussed in *Section 6.3*.

*A class period is considered to be one 40 to 50 minute class.

META NOTES

The exception to the law of conservation of energy occurs in nuclear reactions during which mass is changed into energy. In this case, the total amount of mass and energy is conserved. This occurs only in stars and nuclear reactors.

Help students understand that in ordinary process, energy is neither created nor destroyed. Point out that in the demonstration in *Section 6.3,* the ball and marble made a sound when they hit each other. Tell them that the energy that they thought to be "lost" never disappeared and was changed into sound energy. Remind them of the concept of a system as being composed of several related parts. Energy lost from one part of the system may be transferred to another part of the system. The overall amount of energy in the system remains the same, but the amount at any one specific part of the system may vary.

NOTES

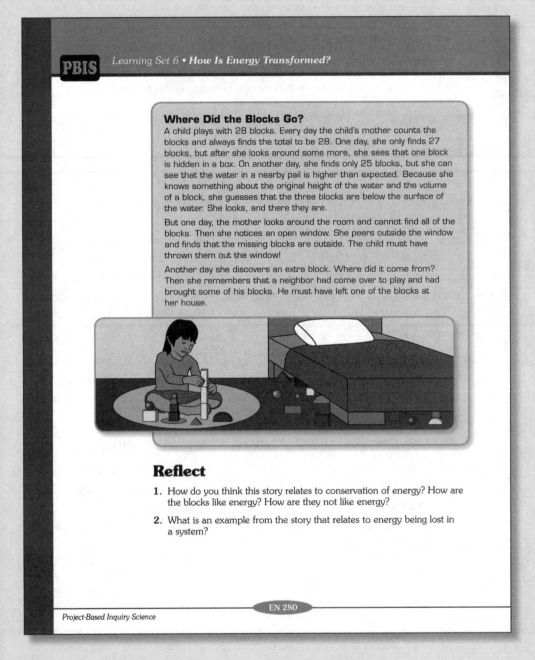

Where Did the Blocks Go?

A child plays with 28 blocks. Every day the child's mother counts the blocks and always finds the total to be 28. One day, she only finds 27 blocks, but after she looks around some more, she sees that one block is hidden in a box. On another day, she finds only 25 blocks, but she can see that the water in a nearby pail is higher than expected. Because she knows something about the original height of the water and the volume of a block, she guesses that the three blocks are below the surface of the water. She looks, and there they are.

But one day, the mother looks around the room and cannot find all of the blocks. Then she notices an open window. She peers outside the window and finds that the missing blocks are outside. The child must have thrown them out the window!

Another day she discovers an extra block. Where did it come from? Then she remembers that a neighbor had come over to play and had brought some of his blocks. He must have left one of the blocks at her house.

Reflect

1. How do you think this story relates to conservation of energy? How are the blocks like energy? How are they not like energy?

2. What is an example from the story that relates to energy being lost in a system?

Where Did the Blocks Go?

5 min

Students read a story by Richard Feynman to further understand the law of conservation of energy through examples.

Get Going

Have students read the student text with their groups. Once they have finished, tell them they should move on to answer the *Reflect* questions, applying their knowledge of the law of conservation of energy to the example in the story.

Reflect

10 min

Students consider what they have learned about conservation of energy and apply it to the story of the blocks.

Reflect

1. How do you think this story relates to conservation of energy? How are the blocks like energy? How are they not like energy?

2. What is an example from the story that relates to energy being lost in a system?

△ Guide and Assess

Have students discuss answers to the *Reflect* questions.

1. Students should apply the law of conservation of energy to the story by stating that the total number of blocks remains the same, but they can be transferred to different parts of the room just as the total amount of energy remains the same but it can be transferred to different parts of a system. The blocks are not like energy in that they have a physical form with mass and volume. This makes them easy to see and to count. Energy can be dispersed and transformed in very small amounts and cannot be seen.

2. Students may suggest that blocks being hidden in a box or sunken in a bucket of water can be likened to energy being lost from one part of a system. Just as the blocks still exist, so does the missing energy.

3. Students should recall that the mother found an extra block one day and that would be like having energy added to a system.

4. Students' answers will vary. Their explanation should include the concept that a system is defined and can always be made larger or smaller. Students were introduced to the concept of a system in *Section 2.4*. They should now revise their ideas about systems based on this new information.

NOTES

....

....

....

....

3. What is an example from the story that relates to energy being added to a system?

4. Based on the story of the blocks, what do you think a *system* is? Describe what happens to energy in a system. Write a statement you think describes how energy could enter or leave a system.

Update the *Project Board*

Add what you have learned about the law of conservation of energy to the *What are we learning?* column. Do not forget to add evidence to the *What is our evidence?* column. In the *What do we need to investigate?* column, record any new questions you have about energy transformations and the law of conservation of energy.

What's the Point?

The law of conservation of energy states that energy cannot be created or destroyed but can only change form. Although it sometimes seems that energy is lost during an energy transformation, it is not lost, but rather, it is changed into a less easily observed type of energy, like sound energy or thermal energy.

It is not always easy to observe all the changes that are happening during an energy transformation. It is important to remember that sometimes things are not exactly as they appear. When you bounced the ball or rolled the marble back and forth on a ramp, it looked like energy was lost. However, that energy was not lost. It was changed into sound energy and thermal energy. Some of this energy may have left the system. If you had relied solely on the results of your investigation, it would have been easy to support a claim that energy was lost. However, when you investigated further, you found that if the energy of the system decreased, the energy of the surrounding environment must have increased.

Update the Project Board

5 min

Students add ideas about conservation of energy to the Project Board.

think describes how energy could enter or leave a system.

Update the *Project Board*

Add what you have learned about the law of conservation of energy to the *What are we learning?* column. Do not forget to add evidence to the *What is our evidence?* column. In the *What do we need to investigate?* column, record any new questions you have about energy transformations and the law of conservation of energy.

What's the Point?

△ Guide

Discuss with students what they have learned about conservation of energy. Ask students to relate this new information to what they observed in the previous two sections when investigating mechanical energy. Summarize any ideas about what has been learned with evidence to support it. Welcome any ideas about what still needs to be investigated. Record the summary on the *Project Board*.

NOTES

Assessment Options

Targeted Concepts, Skills, and Nature of Science	How do I know if students got it?
Scientists often work together and then share their findings. Sharing findings makes new information available and helps scientists refine their ideas and build on others' ideas. When another person's or group's idea is used, credit needs to be given.	**ASK:** What did you learn by reading the story from Richard Feynman? **LISTEN:** Students should relate the analogy of blocks to energy in systems.
Energy exists in different forms and can be changed from one form to another.	**ASK:** What must happen to the mechanical energy that is lost by a bouncing ball? **LISTEN:** Students should explain that the energy is converted to other forms within the system, such as sound and thermal energy.
Energy is neither created nor destroyed in ordinary processes.	**ASK:** What is the significance of the law of conservation of energy? **LISTEN:** Students should explain that energy is neither created nor destroyed in ordinary processes.

Teacher Reflection Questions

- How did students relate the law of conservation of energy to the data they obtained from their investigations? How were you able to help them relate the concepts?

- What difficulties did students have differentiating between the energy of an object and the energy of a system? What can you do to help them understand the relationship?

- How were you able to keep students engaged in the reading? What might you do differently to appreciate the significance of the material?

NOTES

6.5 Read

The Energy Resources That Provide Electricity

◄ *2 class periods*

A class period is considered to be one 40 to 50 minute class.

Overview

Students are introduced to several energy resources used to produce electricity. They then work together in groups to conduct research to identify the pros and cons of each energy resource. As a class, students work together to compare energy resource in terms of environmental impact, sustainability, and cost. Finally, students read about nuclear energy and its possibilities as an energy resource.

Targeted Concepts, Skills, and Nature of Science	Performance Expectations
Scientists often work together and then share their findings. Sharing findings makes new information available and helps scientists refine their ideas and build on others' ideas. When another person's or group's idea is used, credit needs to be given.	Students learn about the pros and cons of different energy resources.
Nuclear reactions include fission during which large nuclei are split apart, and fusion during which smaller nuclei are joined together.	Students differentiate between nuclear fusion and nuclear fission.
During nuclear reactions, small amounts of mass are converted into large amounts of energy.	Students learn that during nuclear reactions, mass and energy are conserved.

NOTES

....

....

....

Materials	
1 per student	*Energy Resources Pros and Cons* page
	Transforming My Energy Resource page
1 per class (optional)	Toy pinwheel

Homework Options

Reflection

- **Science Content:** Why are energy resources used even if they produce pollution? *(Students might recognize that cost plays a role in the decision to use an energy resource.)*

- **Science Content:** How is steam common to electricity production by different energy resources? *(Students should describe those energy sources that produce heat either through burning, such as is true for fossil fuels, biomass, and geothermal energy, or by nuclear reactions, such as is true for nuclear fission.)*

NOTES

....

....

....

....

....

....

....

....

SECTION 6.5 IMPLEMENTATION

6.5 Explore

The Energy Resources That Provide Electricity

The photograph below shows a satellite image of North America at night. The lights you see are powered by electricity. Lighting each of those lights requires energy transformations similar to the energy transformations needed to light one bulb. However, in the satellite image, you are seeing the light of billions of light bulbs. Thousands of electrical power plants around the world are generating the electrical energy needed to keep all of the world's bulbs lit.

Power plants that generate electricity transform some energy resource into electrical energy. Each power plant has huge generators that produce the electricity. These generators must turn constantly to provide a uniform source of power. Turning the generators is the job of giant turbines. Just like the spinning magnets in the generator you observed, the turbines need a source of energy to keep them in motion. Turbines can be powered by steam, water, wind, or other available sources of kinetic energy. Steam-powered power plants use some other energy resource to generate steam. Some power plants use the chemical energy in coal or oil. Some use nuclear energy. Some use the kinetic energy of moving water or wind, or the light energy of the Sun.

The lights you see in a satellite image of North America at night come from billions of light bulbs.

In this section, you will read about the different energy resources transformed into electrical energy. In the next section, you will have a chance to analyze the efficiency of these resources and the efficiency of the energy transformations that bring electrical energy to your home.

EN 282

Project-Based Inquiry Science

6.5 Read

The Energy Resources That Provide Electricity

5 min

Students begin to think about how electricity is produced.

○ Engage

Plug an electric device, such as a radio, into a wall outlet. Ask students if they know where the electrical energy comes from to power the device. Describe your nearest power plant. Then explain that there are several different types of power plants, and tell students they are going to read about each type.

*A class period is considered to be one 40 to 50 minute class.

Throughout the Unit, students have been introduced to the concept of power plants several times. However, here they use what they have learned about energy transformations and conservation of energy to consider each type of energy resource.

NOTES

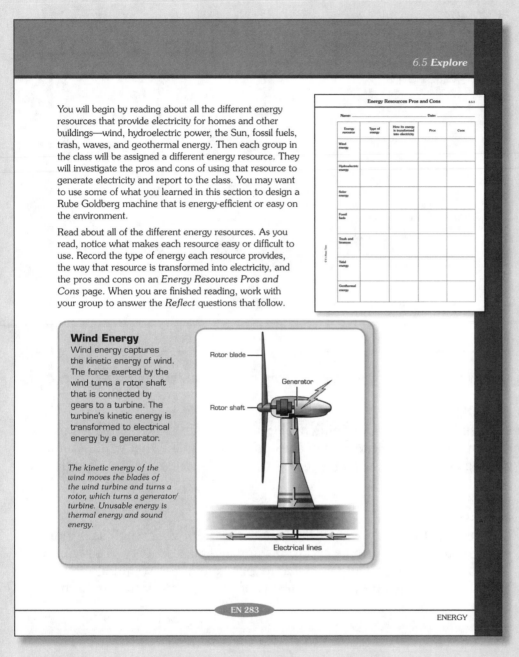

6.5 Explore

You will begin by reading about all the different energy resources that provide electricity for homes and other buildings—wind, hydroelectric power, the Sun, fossil fuels, trash, waves, and geothermal energy. Then each group in the class will be assigned a different energy resource. They will investigate the pros and cons of using that resource to generate electricity and report to the class. You may want to use some of what you learned in this section to design a Rube Goldberg machine that is energy-efficient or easy on the environment.

Read about all of the different energy resources. As you read, notice what makes each resource easy or difficult to use. Record the type of energy each resource provides, the way that resource is transformed into electricity, and the pros and cons on an *Energy Resources Pros and Cons* page. When you are finished reading, work with your group to answer the *Reflect* questions that follow.

Wind Energy
Wind energy captures the kinetic energy of wind. The force exerted by the wind turns a rotor shaft that is connected by gears to a turbine. The turbine's kinetic energy is transformed to electrical energy by a generator.

The kinetic energy of the wind moves the blades of the wind turbine and turns a rotor, which turns a generator/turbine. Unusable energy is thermal energy and sound energy.

Rotor blade

Generator

Rotor shaft

Electrical lines

EN 283

ENERGY

△ Guide

Distribute the *Energy Resources Pros and Cons* pages to students. Tell them that they will be filling in these pages as they are introduced to the energy resources in the following readings. Then each group will be assigned one of the sources to further research and then share their findings with the class.

Wind Energy

10 min

Students read about wind energy and decide the pros and cons of using it as an energy resource.

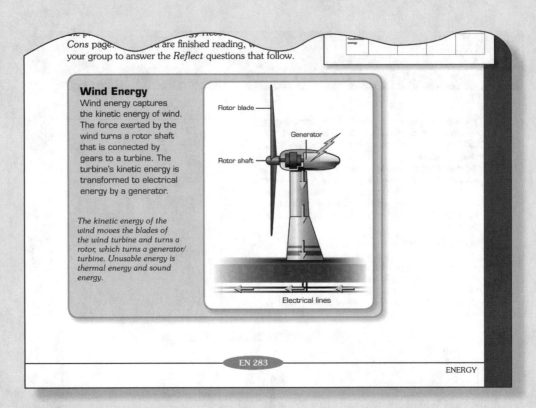

the p... ...gy Res...
Cons page. ...d are finished reading, w...
your group to answer the *Reflect* questions that follow.

Wind Energy
Wind energy captures the kinetic energy of wind. The force exerted by the wind turns a rotor shaft that is connected by gears to a turbine. The turbine's kinetic energy is transformed to electrical energy by a generator.

The kinetic energy of the wind moves the blades of the wind turbine and turns a rotor, which turns a generator/turbine. Unusable energy is thermal energy and sound energy.

Rotor blade

Generator

Rotor shaft

Electrical lines

EN 283

ENERGY

○ Engage

If possible, blow on a toy pinwheel. Show students how the blades of the pinwheel move when air pushes on them. Explain that wind is simply moving air. On a much larger scale, wind can be used to turn a windmill or a wind turbine.

△ Guide

Tell students that early windmills were used to do work, such as grinding grain. Modern wind turbines convert the mechanical energy of moving wind into electrical energy. Help students recognize that the sound along with any thermal energy are unusable forms of energy produced during the use of wind turbines.

NOTES

....

....

....

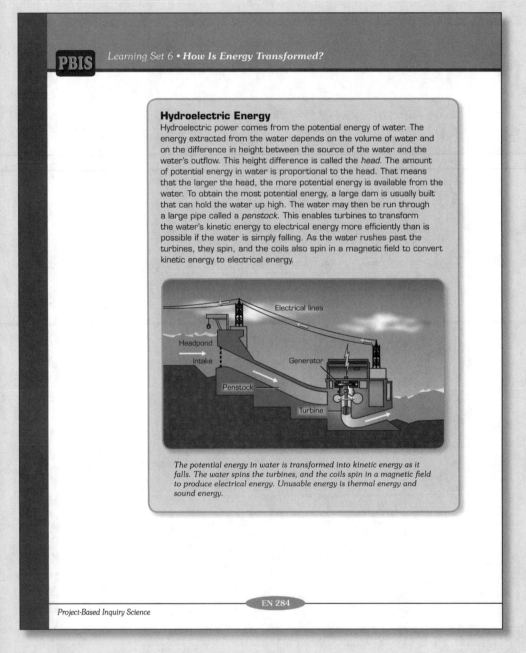

Hydroelectric Energy

Hydroelectric power comes from the potential energy of water. The energy extracted from the water depends on the volume of water and on the difference in height between the source of the water and the water's outflow. This height difference is called the *head*. The amount of potential energy in water is proportional to the head. That means that the larger the head, the more potential energy is available from the water. To obtain the most potential energy, a large dam is usually built that can hold the water up high. The water may then be run through a large pipe called a *penstock*. This enables turbines to transform the water's kinetic energy to electrical energy more efficiently than is possible if the water is simply falling. As the water rushes past the turbines, they spin, and the coils also spin in a magnetic field to convert kinetic energy to electrical energy.

Electrical lines

Headpond

Intake

Generator

Penstock

Turbine

The potential energy in water is transformed into kinetic energy as it falls. The water spins the turbines, and the coils spin in a magnetic field to produce electrical energy. Unusable energy is thermal energy and sound energy.

EN 284

Project-Based Inquiry Science

Hydroelectric Energy

10 min

Students read about hydroelectric energy and decide the pros and cons of using it as an energy resource.

△ Guide

Remind students that they were introduced to hydroelectric energy earlier in the Unit. They learned that the potential energy of the water at the top of the dam is converted into the kinetic energy of the falling water. That mechanical energy then turns a turbine to produce electrical energy. As in the case of wind turbines, some energy is lost as sound and thermal energy.

Solar Energy

10 min

Students read about solar energy and decide the pros and cons of using it as an energy resource.

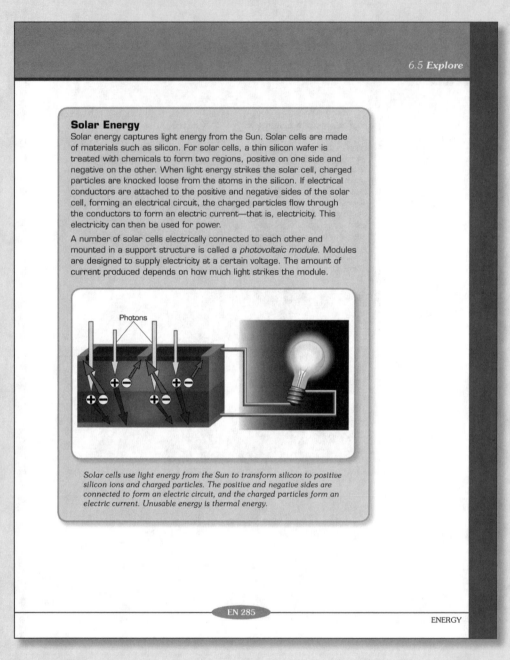

Solar Energy

Solar energy captures light energy from the Sun. Solar cells are made of materials such as silicon. For solar cells, a thin silicon wafer is treated with chemicals to form two regions, positive on one side and negative on the other. When light energy strikes the solar cell, charged particles are knocked loose from the atoms in the silicon. If electrical conductors are attached to the positive and negative sides of the solar cell, forming an electrical circuit, the charged particles flow through the conductors to form an electric current—that is, electricity. This electricity can then be used for power.

A number of solar cells electrically connected to each other and mounted in a support structure is called a *photovoltaic module*. Modules are designed to supply electricity at a certain voltage. The amount of current produced depends on how much light strikes the module.

Photons

Solar cells use light energy from the Sun to transform silicon to positive silicon ions and charged particles. The positive and negative sides are connected to form an electric circuit, and the charged particles form an electric current. Unusable energy is thermal energy.

EN 285

ENERGY

△ Guide

Remind students that energy from the Sun is known as solar energy. Show students a solar-powered device, such as a calculator. Explain the solar energy is converted directly to electricity in the photovoltaic cell of the device.

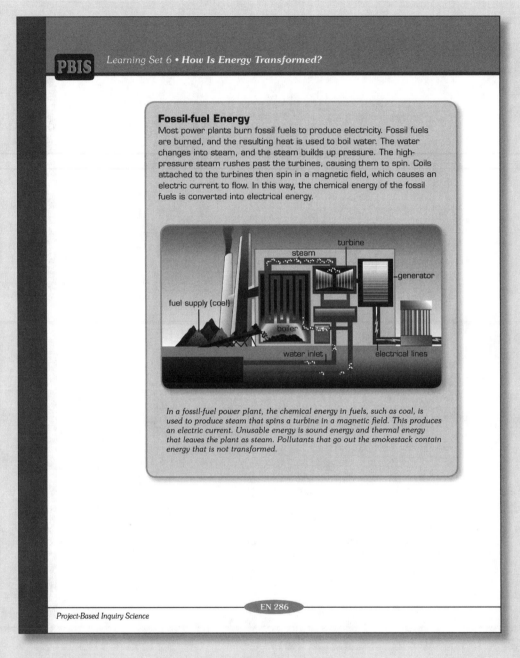

Fossil-fuel Energy

Most power plants burn fossil fuels to produce electricity. Fossil fuels are burned, and the resulting heat is used to boil water. The water changes into steam, and the steam builds up pressure. The high-pressure steam rushes past the turbines, causing them to spin. Coils attached to the turbines then spin in a magnetic field, which causes an electric current to flow. In this way, the chemical energy of the fossil fuels is converted into electrical energy.

turbine

steam

generator

fuel supply (coal)

boiler

water inlet

electrical lines

In a fossil-fuel power plant, the chemical energy in fuels, such as coal, is used to produce steam that spins a turbine in a magnetic field. This produces an electric current. Unusable energy is sound energy and thermal energy that leaves the plant as steam. Pollutants that go out the smokestack contain energy that is not transformed.

Fossil-fuel Energy

10 min

Students read about fossil-fuel energy and decide the pros and cons of using it as an energy resource.

△ Guide

Remind students that fossil fuels include coal, natural gas, and petroleum. These fuels were formed over millions of years from the remains of ancient plants and animals. These fuels store the chemical energy once stored in living organisms. Tell students that when the fuels are burned, that chemical energy is transformed into thermal energy that can boil water to form steam. The pressure of the resulting steam can turn a turbine.

Trash and Biomass Energy

10 min

Students read about trash and biomass energy and decide the pros and cons of using it as an energy resource.

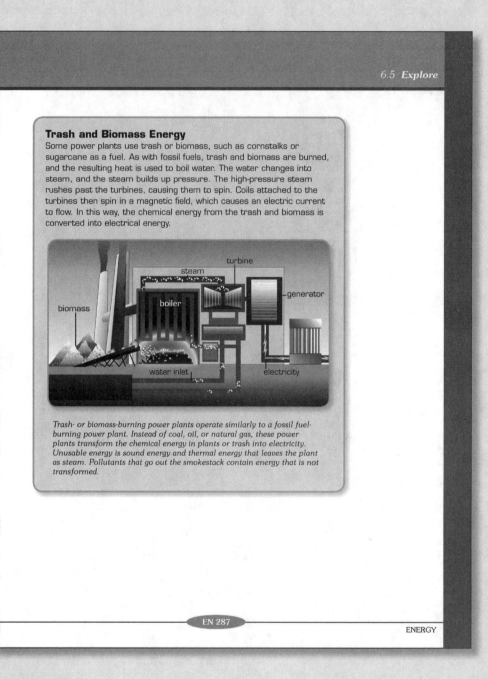

Trash and Biomass Energy

Some power plants use trash or biomass, such as cornstalks or sugarcane as a fuel. As with fossil fuels, trash and biomass are burned, and the resulting heat is used to boil water. The water changes into steam, and the steam builds up pressure. The high-pressure steam rushes past the turbines, causing them to spin. Coils attached to the turbines then spin in a magnetic field, which causes an electric current to flow. In this way, the chemical energy from the trash and biomass is converted into electrical energy.

Trash- or biomass-burning power plants operate similarly to a fossil fuel-burning power plant. Instead of coal, oil, or natural gas, these power plants transform the chemical energy in plants or trash into electricity. Unusable energy is sound energy and thermal energy that leaves the plant as steam. Pollutants that go out the smokestack contain energy that is not transformed.

EN 287

ENERGY

△ Guide

Explain to students that biomass is material from living, or recently living, organisms. Examples include food wastes, crops, and wood. Tell students that trash and biomass can be burned much like fossil fuels can. An important difference is that biomass does not take millions of years to form. It can be managed in such a way that it is renewable. When biomass is burned, some energy is converted into unusable forms, such as light, sound, and waste heat.

Wave Energy

Wave energy captures the energy of the ocean or of very large lakes. Wave-energy devices called *attenuators* are oriented parallel to the direction of the waves. One example is a series of long, cylindrical, floating devices connected to each other with hinges and anchored to the seabed. The cylindrical parts drive *hydraulic rams* in the connecting sections, and those in turn drive an electric generator. The devices send the electricity through cables (very thick wires) to the sea floor where it then travels through a cable to shore.

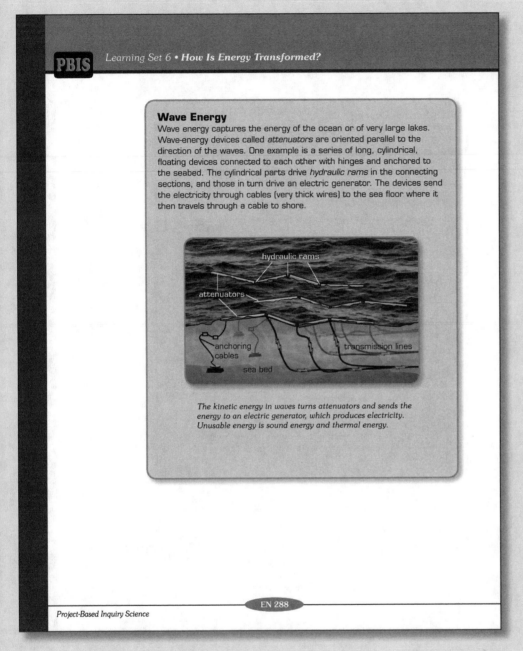

The kinetic energy in waves turns attenuators and sends the energy to an electric generator, which produces electricity. Unusable energy is sound energy and thermal energy.

Wave Energy

10 min

Students read about wave energy and decide the pros and cons of using it as an energy resource.

△ Guide

Explain to students that the oceans and very large lakes have waves generated by the wind. The kinetic energy of these waves can be captured by devices engineered to take this energy and transform it into electric energy. Point out that the movement of the water is mechanical energy. Like other energy resources, wave power installations lose some energy as waste heat and some as sound.

Geothermal Energy

10 min

Students read about geothermal energy and decide the pros and cons of using it as an energy resource.

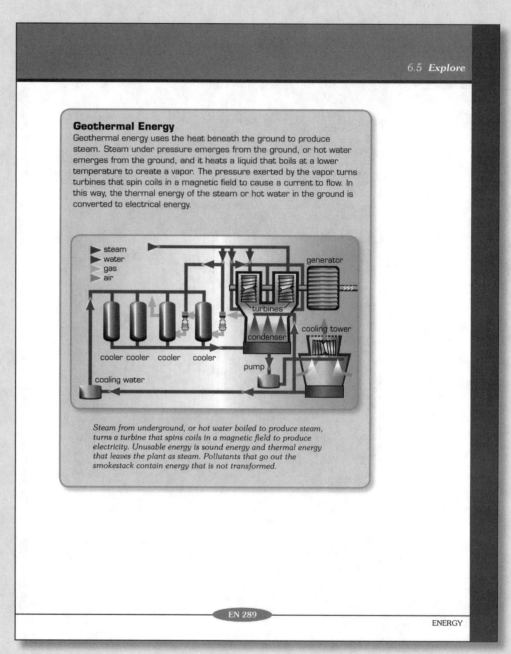

Geothermal Energy

Geothermal energy uses the heat beneath the ground to produce steam. Steam under pressure emerges from the ground, or hot water emerges from the ground, and it heats a liquid that boils at a lower temperature to create a vapor. The pressure exerted by the vapor turns turbines that spin coils in a magnetic field to cause a current to flow. In this way, the thermal energy of the steam or hot water in the ground is converted to electrical energy.

steam
water
gas
air

generator

turbines

cooling tower

condenser

cooler cooler cooler cooler

pump

cooling water

Steam from underground, or hot water boiled to produce steam, turns a turbine that spins coils in a magnetic field to produce electricity. Unusable energy is sound energy and thermal energy that leaves the plant as steam. Pollutants that go out the smokestack contain energy that is not transformed.

EN 289

ENERGY

△ Guide

Tell students that there is high heat and pressure beneath Earth's surface. The conditions are so intense that solid rock can melt into molten magma. In some locations, the heat causes water near the surface to boil. The resulting steam can be used to turn a turbine and produce electricity. These types of power plants lose some energy as sound and some as waste heat.

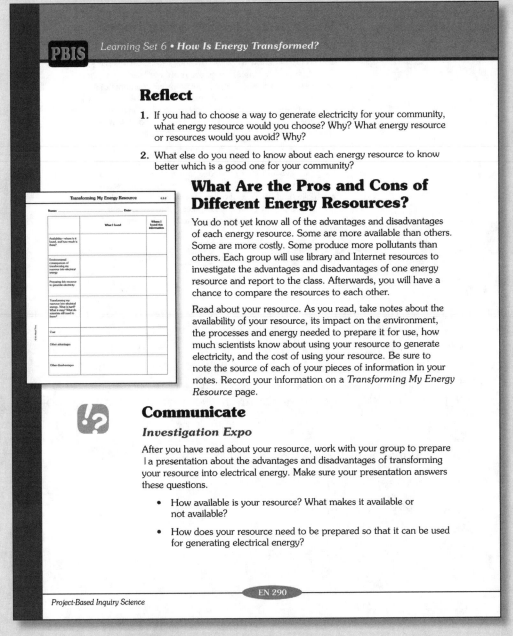

Reflect

1. If you had to choose a way to generate electricity for your community, what energy resource would you choose? Why? What energy resource or resources would you avoid? Why?

2. What else do you need to know about each energy resource to know better which is a good one for your community?

What Are the Pros and Cons of Different Energy Resources?

You do not yet know all of the advantages and disadvantages of each energy resource. Some are more available than others. Some are more costly. Some produce more pollutants than others. Each group will use library and Internet resources to investigate the advantages and disadvantages of one energy resource and report to the class. Afterwards, you will have a chance to compare the resources to each other.

Read about your resource. As you read, take notes about the availability of your resource, its impact on the environment, the processes and energy needed to prepare it for use, how much scientists know about using your resource to generate electricity, and the cost of using your resource. Be sure to note the source of each of your pieces of information in your notes. Record your information on a *Transforming My Energy Resource* page.

Communicate

Investigation Expo

After you have read about your resource, work with your group to prepare a presentation about the advantages and disadvantages of transforming your resource into electrical energy. Make sure your presentation answers these questions.

- How available is your resource? What makes it available or not available?

- How does your resource need to be prepared so that it can be used for generating electrical energy?

Reflect

5 min

Students use what they learned about energy resources to answer the Reflect questions.

△ Guide and Assess

Have students discuss the *Reflect* questions with their groups. Encourage students to consider the geographical conditions of the region in which they live and the energy needs of the population.

1. Students' answers will vary. Their answers should reflect renewable energy resources that are available nearby. They should avoid choosing nonrenewable resources that pollute the land, air, and water.

2. Students' answers will vary.

PBIS

What Are the Pros and Cons of Different Energy Resources?

20 min

Students research the pros and cons of each energy resource.

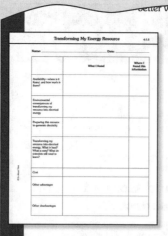

What Are the Pros and Cons of Different Energy Resources?

You do not yet know all of the advantages and disadvantages of each energy resource. Some are more available than others. Some are more costly. Some produce more pollutants than others. Each group will use library and Internet resources to investigate the advantages and disadvantages of one energy resource and report to the class. Afterwards, you will have a chance to compare the resources to each other.

Read about your resource. As you read, take notes about the availability of your resource, its impact on the environment, the processes and energy needed to prepare it for use, how much scientists know about using your resource to generate electricity, and the cost of using your resource. Be sure to note the source of each of your pieces of information in your notes. Record your information on a *Transforming My Energy Resource* page.

▲ Guide

Distribute the *Transforming My Energy Resource* pages to students and let them know they will fill in answers based on their energy resources. Give students an opportunity to research their energy resource. Tell students to focus on the questions provided, but to include additional information that they find appropriate. Emphasize that the *Transforming My Energy Resource* page should be used to guide their focus on the following points:

- availability of the resource
- the resource's impact on the environment
- the processes and energy needed to prepare it for use
- how much scientists know about using the resource to generate electricity
- the cost of using the resource

NOTES

....

....

....

....

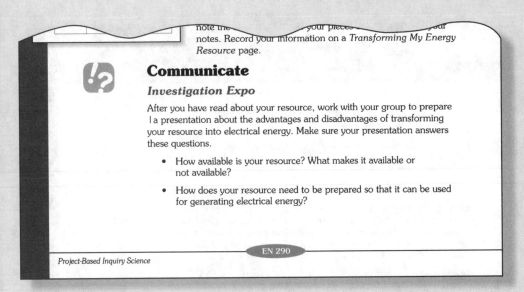

Communicate

Investigation Expo

After you have read about your resource, work with your group to prepare a presentation about the advantages and disadvantages of transforming your resource into electrical energy. Make sure your presentation answers these questions.

- How available is your resource? What makes it available or not available?

- How does your resource need to be prepared so that it can be used for generating electrical energy?

EN 290

Project-Based Inquiry Science

Communicate: Investigation Expo

10 min

Students share their findings on their energy resource with the class and the class gains a more in-depth understanding of the resources they were introduced to earlier.

△ Guide

Describe the nature of this activity and point out that they will be learning from one another, just as scientists do. Tell students that they will teach each other about energy resources. Let them know they will make a presentation about the resource they focused on, informing the rest of the class, and then learn more about the other resources they were only introduced to from other students.

Give groups time to prepare their presentations. Remind them to use the *Energy Resources Pros and Cons* pages and the *Transforming My Energy Resources* pages they filled in earlier. Also, point out the bulleted questions in the student text. Let them know that their presentations should answer these questions.

NOTES

- What are the environmental consequences of transforming your energy resource into electrical energy?

- What do scientists know about transforming your resource into electrical energy? What is hard about transforming it? What is easy? What do scientists still need to find out?

- What is the cost of transforming your resource into electrical energy?

When it is your group's turn to present, make a presentation to the class about your energy resource. Make sure each member of your group has a chance to speak. As you are listening, notice the similarities and differences between your resource and other resources. Take notes on your *Energy Resources Pros and Cons* page.

Reflect

Work with your group to answer these questions. Be prepared to share your answers with the class.

1. Which resources have a large impact on the environment? What are the pros and cons of transforming these energy resources into electrical energy?

2. Which resources have less impact on the environment? What are the pros and cons of these "friendly" energy resources?

3. How does the cost of transforming your energy resource compare to the cost of transforming other resources?

4. If you had to choose a way to generate electricity for your community, what energy resources would you choose? Why? What energy resource or resources would you avoid? Why?

What's the Point?

There are many energy resources that can be transformed into electricity. These resources include fossil fuels, wind, sunlight, biomass, running water, and waves. Some of these resources took hundreds of millions of years to produce and are in such great demand that they cannot be replaced and are not renewable. Others seem to be in endless supply. Each of these resources has different environmental and economic impacts. This is why people must make wise choices about what resources they use.

EN 291

ENERGY

☐ Assess

Have groups present their resource to the class. As the class listens, remind them to take notes of the other resources on their *Energy Resources Pros and Cons* pages. Emphasize that they should be listening for the similarities and differences between the resources.

As groups present, the following information should be shared for each resource. Make sure the class is recording information about the resources they did not research.

Energy Resource	Pros	Cons
Wind	• renewable resource • does not generate much pollution, except, possibly, noise	• limited to locations with steady wind • can produce loud noise • unattractive appearance • can be damaged by lightning
Hydroelectric	• renewable resource that is replenished by water cycle • reservoirs also provide recreational activities • inexpensive repairs and maintenance • does not produce pollution	• requires flooding entire valleys disrupts natural changes in rivers and ecosystems • expensive to build • limited by droughts • can cause massive floods if badly damaged
Solar	• renewable resource that is replenished by nuclear reactions in the Sun • does not produce pollution • does not produce noise	• initial cost is high • can generate electricity only during daylight hours • can be affected by weather, such as cloud cover • large scale electricity production requires covering large areas of land with solar cells
Fossil fuels	• relatively inexpensive form of energy	• extraction involves damaging impact to the environment • burning releases greenhouse gases into the atmosphere • limited nonrenewable resources will eventually run out
Trash and biomass	• produced at minimum cost • renewable resource	• requires a large area of land • burns organic matter that might be better returned to the soil • produces pollutants from materials in the trash
Waves	• does not produce pollution • renewable resource	• limited to certain coastal locations • can damage local seabed • not proven on a commercial scale
Geothermal	• renewable resource • relatively low cost • does not produce pollution	• suitable locations are limited

Reflect

5 min

Students compare energy resources based on their research.

Reflect

Work with your group to answer these questions. Be prepared to share your answers with the class.

1. Which resources have a large impact on the environment? What are the pros and cons of transforming these energy resources into electrical energy?

2. Which resources have less impact on the environment? What are the pros and cons of these "friendly" energy resources?

3. How does the cost of transforming your energy resource compare to the cost of transforming other resources?

4. If you had to choose a way to generate electricity for your community, what energy resources would you choose? Why? What energy resource or resources would you avoid? Why?

△ Guide and Assess

Have students discuss answers to the *Reflect* questions with their groups. They should refer to their notes from the *Investigation Expo* to guide their answers. Help students compare the energy resources in different ways: impact on the environment, renewable resources, and cost. Then have them reconsider the question of what type of energy resource to use in their community.

1. Students will probably say that the hydropower, fossil fuels, and trash/biomass options have the largest impact on the environment. Hydropower is renewable, but requires the interruption of the natural flow of a river. Fossil fuels cause all kinds of pollution— carbon dioxide, VOC's, mercury, acid rain—and they are a limited resource. Burning trash and biomass are renewable, but have some of the same problems that burning fossil fuels have.

2. Students may answer that wind, solar, waves, and geothermal energy have the least impact on the environment. All are "friendly" and unlimited in quantity. Wind requires large amounts of land where the wind blows constantly, but there can be a problem with sound pollution. Solar energy also requires large areas to provide a large proportion of current usage and is expensive. Solar energy requires a storage system, such as batteries, to deliver power at night or on cloudy days. Waves and geothermal energy can only be found in localized specific places.

3. Students' answers will vary. Initial costs are high for every type of energy source, unless a fossil fuel power plant is already nearby.

4. Students' answers will vary. They should select renewable, cheap, nonpolluting, and local energy sources. They should avoid nonrenewable, expensive, polluting, and distant energy sources.

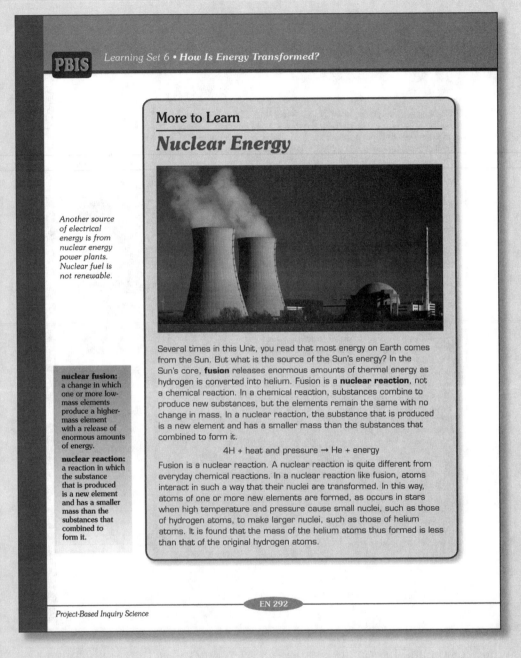

More to Learn

Nuclear Energy

Another source of electrical energy is from nuclear energy power plants. Nuclear fuel is not renewable.

nuclear fusion: a change in which one or more low-mass elements produce a higher-mass element with a release of enormous amounts of energy.

nuclear reaction: a reaction in which the substance that is produced is a new element and has a smaller mass than the substances that combined to form it.

Several times in this Unit, you read that most energy on Earth comes from the Sun. But what is the source of the Sun's energy? In the Sun's core, **fusion** releases enormous amounts of thermal energy as hydrogen is converted into helium. Fusion is a **nuclear reaction**, not a chemical reaction. In a chemical reaction, substances combine to produce new substances, but the elements remain the same with no change in mass. In a nuclear reaction, the substance that is produced is a new element and has a smaller mass than the substances that combined to form it.

4H + heat and pressure → He + energy

Fusion is a nuclear reaction. A nuclear reaction is quite different from everyday chemical reactions. In a nuclear reaction like fusion, atoms interact in such a way that their nuclei are transformed. In this way, atoms of one or more new elements are formed, as occurs in stars when high temperature and pressure cause small nuclei, such as those of hydrogen atoms, to make larger nuclei, such as those of helium atoms. It is found that the mass of the helium atoms thus formed is less than that of the original hydrogen atoms.

More to Learn: *Nuclear Energy*

20 min

Students learn about another source of electricity—nuclear energy.

△ Guide

Read the information about nuclear energy together. Make sure students distinguish between fusion and fission. Emphasize to students that using nuclear fission to produce electricity is similar to other energy resources in that thermal energy is used to produce steam, which can turn a turbine. The difference is that this resource produces radioactive waste that is dangerous for thousands of years to come. Scientists are working to recycle spent fuel, thereby cutting down on the resulting waste.

This is quite different from everyday chemical reactions. In chemical reactions, the substances formed are measured to have the same mass as the substances that originally reacted. Now that you have been reading about "missing energy," you might be wondering about what happens to the missing mass.

You may have learned in chemistry about the *law of conservation of mass*. This law is very similar to the *law of conservation of energy*, but it applies to mass. It states that mass is not created or destroyed through ordinary chemical reactions. So what happens to the missing mass in a nuclear reaction? Albert Einstein, a German physicist, realized that mass could be converted into energy, and energy could be converted into mass. So when mass appears to be missing, it has really been transformed into energy. Einstein stated that mass is a form of energy. These ideas, called the law of conservation of mass and energy, explain the enormous energy released in fusion reactions. Einstein formulated his famous equation $E = mc^2$ (energy equals mass times the speed of light squared) to explain what happens to this "missing mass." The energy released in a nuclear reaction like fusion is called **nuclear energy**.

Fusion is the same process that releases energy in a hydrogen bomb. However, fusion reactions have never been used to generate electricity efficiently. In a power plant on Earth, it is very hard to recreate conditions of high temperature and pressure similar to those found inside the Sun. Thus far, on Earth, it has always taken more energy to make fusion happen than the energy produced by a fusion reaction. However, there is another nuclear energy process that has been used successfully to generate energy—**nuclear fission**. In nuclear fission, large atoms are split to make smaller atoms. Again, there is a tiny difference in mass, and this mass is converted into large amounts of energy.

Nuclear fission provides yet another way to make electricity by boiling water to make steam. In this process, the nuclei of uranium split into smaller atoms, releasing energy. This energy is used to heat water and create steam. The steam turns a turbine to produce electricity, just as in a coal-fired power plant.

Albert Einstein was one of the most famous scientists to study energy and energy transformations.

nuclear energy: energy released from a reaction in which atomic nuclei interact to form new nuclei that have a lower combined mass.

nuclear fission: a change in which one high-mass element produces two or more low-mass elements, with a release of enormous amounts of energy.

EN 293

ENERGY

While fusion and fission are almost opposite processes, they both convert tiny amounts of mass into huge amounts of energy. Fusion of hydrogen atoms to form helium atoms and energy is not commercially feasible yet and will not be available for years.

Help the students understand that the radiation products of fission are not that foreign to us and make up a part of background radiation. Exposure to large amounts, of course, can be very dangerous. α-rays are simply high energy electrons, β-rays are helium nuclei, and most gamma radiation comes from outer space when we are.

α-rays: radiation emitted during nuclear reactions; a helium nucleus with a positive charge.

β-rays: radiation emitted during nuclear reactions; an electron with a negative charge.

gamma rays: high energy electromagnetic radiation with no mass or charge.

condenser: a device that changes gases to liquid or solid form.

Because it emits none of the pollutants associated with coal, nuclear energy is considered by many people to be clean energy, but there are three problems. The first problem arises when the uranium ore is mined. There is pollution left from mining uranium that can damage the environment, and the miners who work in the mines can develop cancer from the radiation in the uranium. Radiation is the release of sub-atomic particles, **α-rays** and **β-rays**, or the release of energy in the form of **gamma rays**. All of these forms of radiation are dangerous and cause damage to tissues and genetic material.

The second problem is disposal of the nuclear fuel after it has been used. The term "spent fuel" refers to the nuclear fuel that has been used and can no longer be easily used in nuclear reactions. Spent fuel from a nuclear power plant is even more radioactive than the original uranium, and scientists are still seeking a way to store it for a hundred thousand years or more, far away from people. The third problem is the water that is used to keep the circulating water from the power plant's **condenser** cool. Usually, this water is taken from a lake or river and brought into the power plant to cool the condenser. Once it has been heated up, it is no longer useful for cooling and must be returned to the lake or river. Unless great care is taken, this heated water can damage the environment. This can also be a problem with electricity generated from steam in other ways.

The uranium that is used as a source of nuclear energy was formed in a star that exploded in the far, far, distant past. When our solar system formed from the remnants of an exploded star, the uranium was deposited on Earth, along with all of the other elements. That means that uranium is nonrenewable and therefore not a long-term solution to the problem of generating electricity on Earth. However, there is plenty of uranium available right now.

Reflect

1. How does a nuclear power plant generate electricity?

2. What are the advantages and disadvantages of a nuclear power plant?

3. Would you want a nuclear power plant near where you live? Why or why not?

Reflect

5 min

Students integrate the science content from the reading by answering questions.

△ Guide and Assess

Once groups have had time to answer the *Reflect* questions, lead a class discussion of their answers. Encourage students to ask questions about each other's answers and to make comments respectfully.

1. Students should respond that the heat from nuclear reactions is used to produce steam from water. As in a coal-fired power plant, the steam is used to turn a turbine connected to a generator, creating electricity. The nuclear reaction is called fission whereby uranium is split into smaller atoms in a chain reaction, creating heat.

2. Students should explain that the major advantage of a nuclear power plant is in the type of pollution generated. There is no "global-warming" carbon dioxide produced, nor any acid rain or particulate matter. However, to produce the fuel for such a plant does require some local pollution at the mine sites, in the processing plants, and in the waste disposal. The heating of cooling water must be closely monitored so that its release does not harm the environment.

3. Students' answers will vary. They should know that the operation of a nuclear power plant is quite safe, that radioactive pollutants are not generally released at the site, and that there have been very few disastrous accidents. However, any accidents do have the potential for massive damage to the local environment and the plants require constant monitoring.

Assessment Options

Targeted Concepts, Skills, and Nature of Science	How do I know if students got it?
Scientists often work together and then share their findings. Sharing findings makes new information available and helps scientists refine their ideas and build on others' ideas. When another person's or group's idea is used, credit needs to be given.	**ASK:** What type of unusable energy is produced from all energy resources? **LISTEN:** Students should recognize that some waste heat is always produced.
Nuclear reactions include fission during large nuclei are split apart, and fusion during which smaller nuclei are joined together.	**ASK:** Which type of nuclear reaction is controlled in nuclear power plants? **LISTEN:** Students should identify the process as nuclear fission.

Targeted Concepts, Skills, and Nature of Science	How do I know if students got it?
During nuclear reactions, small amounts of mass are converted into large amounts of energy.	**ASK:** Why don't nuclear reactions violate the law of conservation of energy?
	LISTEN: Students should explain that they are a special case in which the total mass and energy are conserved. According to Einstein's famous equation, $E = mc^2$, the mass and energy are interconvertable.

Teacher Reflection Questions

- Did students have any difficulties with the introduction to the energy resources? Would you present the information differently next time?

- Did the groups encounter any problems conducting their research together? How were you able to guide them in this process?

- How were you able to keep students focused on energy transformations? What might you do differently?

NOTES

NOTES

6.6 Explore

Energy Transformations and Conservation of Resources

◀ *2 class periods*

A class period is considered to be one 40 to 50 minute class.

Overview

In this section, students compare energy resources in terms of the processes through which they are used to produce electricity. Students first trace the pathway from the energy resource to its conversion to electricity. Then they trace the pathway of electric energy transmission from the power plant to its use in a light bulb at home. Students use what they have learned about the different energy resources to complete diagrams representing the various energy transformations. Afterward, students work together to recommend an energy resource to a small community.

Targeted Concepts, Skills, and Nature of Science	Performance Expectations
Scientists often work together and then share their findings. Sharing findings makes new information available and helps scientists refine their ideas and build on others' ideas. When another person's or group's idea is used, credit needs to be given.	Students work together to find similarities and differences between energy resources.
Energy exists in different forms and can be changed from one form to another.	Students trace the energy transformations that take place during the production of electricity from different sources.

Materials	
1 per student	*Energy Pathways* page *Project Board* page
1 per class	Class *Project Board*

Homework Options

Reflection

- **Science Content:** How is the energy pathway from solar energy different from the other energy resources? *(Students may describe that solar energy is converted directly into electrical energy whereas other resources undergo several transformations along the way.)*

NOTES

....

....

....

....

....

....

....

....

....

....

....

SECTION 6.6 IMPLEMENTATION

6.6 Explore

Energy Transformations and Conservation of Resources

As you have read, most power plants are fueled by the chemical energy in fossil fuels. Turbines can also be powered by water, wind, solar, or nuclear energy. Other energy transformations happen as the electricity generated in the power plants is transported over power grids to the places where the power is needed.

Each of these energy transformations results in a loss of usable energy. In this section, you will explore what it takes to supply you, your neighborhood, and your nation with the power needed to turn on the lights and to run everything people use that is powered by electricity. You have read about many of the advantages and disadvantages of the different energy sources. However, you have not read yet about the efficiency of each of these resources as a source of electrical energy. You will use what you know about energy transformations and energy efficiency to figure out how efficient each of these sources of electrical energy is.

Where Does Energy Needed to Light a Bulb Come From?

You have read about how your energy resource is used to generate electricity. Now you will complete a chain of energy transformations connecting your resource to an electrical outlet in a home where electrical energy can light a bulb. You will complete your chain of energy transformations using the *Energy Resource* images and *Energy Transmission* images shown on the pages following the *Procedure*. Your chain of transformations might be very long. The instructions below will help you complete your chain.

Use an *Energy Pathways* page to organize your ideas about the ways energy is transformed from one of the energy sources to the light bulb.

EN 295

ENERGY

6.6 Explore

Energy Transformations and Conservation of Resources

10 min

Students are introduced to the idea that usable energy is lost in the process of producing electricity.

◯ Engage

Bring together the concepts that students have been learning—that energy is transformed, that power plants produce electricity, and that usable energy is lost during each transformation.

*A class period is considered to be one 40 to 50 minute class.

ENERGY

Where Does Energy Needed to Light a Bulb Come From?

5 min

Students trace the production of energy to its source.

TEACHER TALK

❝Think about the electricity you use in your home. Now think about all the homes on your street. Consider all the homes in your community, in your city, and in your state. Supplying electricity to all the homes, businesses, and schools in a region requires a lot of energy. You are going to investigate that energy.**❞**

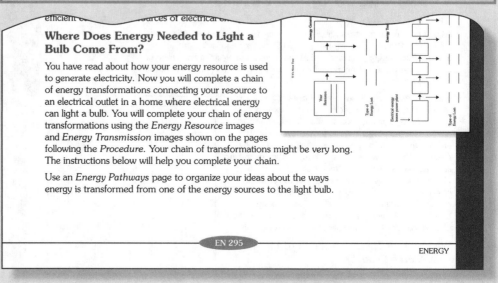

efficient ... sources of electrical ...

Where Does Energy Needed to Light a Bulb Come From?

You have read about how your energy resource is used to generate electricity. Now you will complete a chain of energy transformations connecting your resource to an electrical outlet in a home where electrical energy can light a bulb. You will complete your chain of energy transformations using the *Energy Resource* images and *Energy Transmission* images shown on the pages following the *Procedure*. Your chain of transformations might be very long. The instructions below will help you complete your chain.

Use an *Energy Pathways* page to organize your ideas about the ways energy is transformed from one of the energy sources to the light bulb.

EN 295

ENERGY

○ Get Going

Groups in this activity will focus on the energy resources they looked at in *Section 6.5*. Because the class learned about all the resources in the *Investigation Expo,* there are options for assigning groups. You may want to keep groups together and have them continue to work on the same resource, or you may want to have groups investigate another resource.

Once the class has been divided, distribute the *Energy Pathways* pages to students and go through the procedure and diagrams so that students understand what to do.

NOTES

....

....

....

....

Energy Resources: Procedure

1. Read again about how the energy resource you have been assigned is transformed into electrical energy. As you read, keep notes about all of the different actions and energy transformations that have to happen to generate electrical energy from your resource.

2. Share your list with your group and come to agreement about the sequence through which your energy resource is transformed into electrical energy.

3. Select *Energy Resource* images that show this sequence of energy transformations. List the images in the correct order so they show how your energy resource is transformed into electrical energy.

4. Write the numbers of the images and a description in the boxes of the *Energy Generation Pathway* diagram on an *Energy Pathways* page. In the first box, record the type of energy in your resource. In the other boxes, record the transformations that transform your resource's energy into electrical energy. Depending on the resource you were assigned, you might have blank boxes.

5. The boxes in your diagram show energy transformations that produce usable energy. Below the diagram, record the types of unusable energy that are produced in each step of the pathway.

6. Do your best to make an estimate of how efficient it is to use your energy resource to light a bulb. To do this, list other energy resources you think will be *more* efficient. Then list other energy resources you think will be *less* efficient.

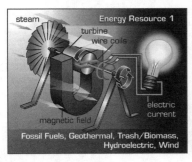

Project-Based Inquiry Science

Energy Resources: Procedure

15 min

Students complete an Energy Generation Pathway *diagram.*

◯ Get Going

To begin, have students review what they learned and researched about each energy resource. Have students identify the actions and energy transformations of their energy resource that produce electricity. With their groups, have students decide on a sequence for these transformations and have students pick the *Energy Resources* to complete their diagrams. Remind them to record the type of energy, the type of energy transformations, and to identify the usable energy produced at each step.

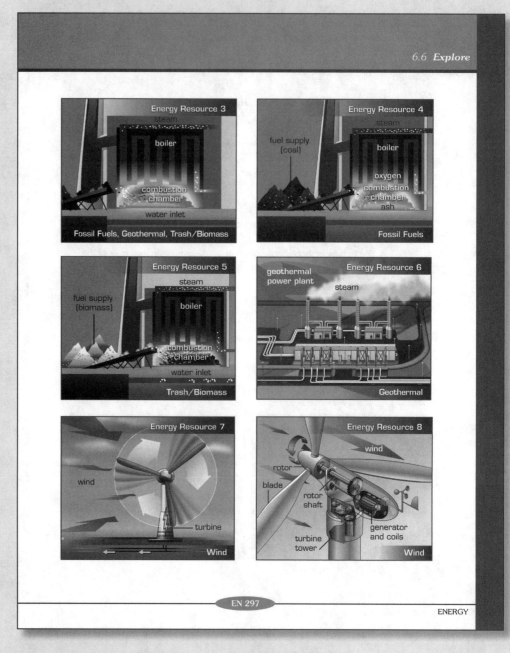

EN 297

ENERGY

Guide them to consider how efficiently their resource works by describing how they should make their choice by comparison.

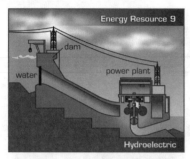

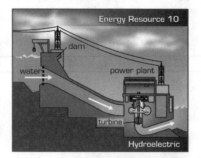

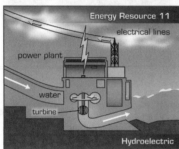

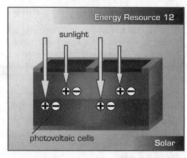

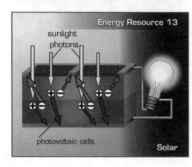

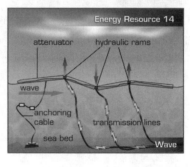

EN 298

Project-Based Inquiry Science

NOTES

....

....

....

Energy Transmission: Procedure

15 min

Students complete an Energy Transmission Pathway *diagram.*

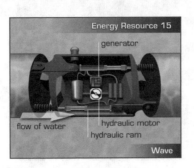

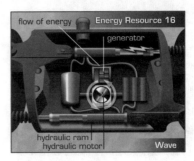

Energy Transmission: Procedure

1. Now identify the energy transformations needed to transmit the electrical energy to an outlet in a home and into a light bulb. To figure this out, you may want to reread *Energy From a Generator* in *Learning Set 5*. It describes how electrical energy generated in a power plant is transported to a home and through the wiring in a home to an outlet.

2. List the *Energy Transmission* images into a sequence of energy transformations that shows how electrical energy is brought to a light bulb in a home. Make sure your list is in the correct order.

3. When you think you have the correct sequence, fill in the empty boxes in the bottom *Energy Transformation Pathway* diagram on your *Energy Pathways* page.

4. The boxes in your diagram show energy transformations that produce usable energy. Below the diagram, record the types of unusable energy that are produced in each step of the pathway.

5. Make a list of the types of unusable energy generated along the whole pathway.

EN 299

ENERGY

⬡ Get Going

Before students begin, have them reread the *Energy From a Generator* in *Section 5.6*. Just as they did before, they will choose the sequence that they think correctly shows how electrical energy is transferred to an outlet in a home to a light bulb. Have students complete the diagram on their *Energy Pathways* pages, reminding them to identify the usable and unusable energy produced.

Energy Transmission A

Electrical energy is transmitted through low-power voltage lines such as those in neighborhoods.

Energy Transmission B

Electricity goes through a meter that measures how much electricity you use.

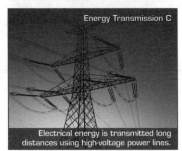

Energy Transmission C

Electrical energy is transmitted long distances using high-voltage power lines.

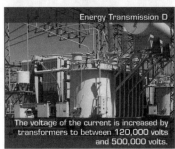

Energy Transmission D

The voltage of the current is increased by transformers to between 120,000 volts and 500,000 volts.

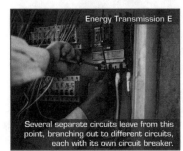

Energy Transmission E

Several separate circuits leave from this point, branching out to different circuits, each with its own circuit breaker.

Energy Transmission F

From the meter, the wire leads into a circuit breaker box.

EN 300

Project-Based Inquiry Science

NOTES

....

....

Communicate: *Investigation Expo*

10 min

Students share their diagrams from the investigations.

Energy Transmission G

The electric current is reduced to 120 volts.

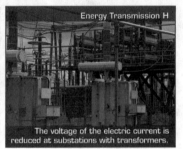
Energy Transmission H

The voltage of the electric current is reduced at substations with transformers.

Energy Transmission I

The electric current leaves the generators through power lines.

Communicate

Investigation Expo

Each group in the class is expert on one energy resource. It is time now to report to the class about your resource so everyone will know about how to generate electricity from each resource, how each is transformed to light a bulb, and the efficiency of each of the energy resources. Spend time preparing your report. You might want to make a poster. Or you might want to make a computer presentation. Your report should include the following:

• The type(s) of energy in your energy resource.

EN 301

ENERGY

△ Guide and Assess

Point out to students that, once again, they will be learning about different energy resources from one another. Have each group review the bulleted list of items to include in their presentation and give them time to organize their information and decide how they want to present it.

- A description of the way your type of energy is transformed into electrical energy. Show the class the sequences on the *Energy Pathways* page. For each step in the sequence, describe the types of energy before the energy transformation, the actions or devices that transform energy from one type to another, and the types of energy after the energy transformation. Include both the usable energy and unusable energy that is generated.

- A description of the transformations needed to transport generated energy to the light bulb.

- A list of the "lost" energy for each step in these sequences.

When it is your group's turn to present, one group member should clearly present the transformations that transform your resource into electrical energy. Another group member should clearly present the transformations that transform electrical energy into light energy. The other group members should present what you know about the unusable energy that is generated and the efficiency of the energy transformations.

As you listen, notice similarities and differences in the energy transformation pathways being presented by the different groups. Notice which sources of energy are more efficient than others for generating electricity and turning on a light. As always, ask questions if you do not understand what a group is reporting or if you think they have not reported the processes accurately. However, save your comments about similarities and differences until all of the presentations are completed. Remember to be respectful.

When all of the presentations have been made, work as a class to put the resources into categories. Some are very much like one another. Some are a little like others. Some are different from all the others. Then discuss the answers to these questions as a class.

Reflect

1. For each category of resources, what is similar about the energy transformation pathways? For each, what is different?

2. Rank the sources of energy for their overall efficiency in lighting a bulb. Which is most efficient? Which is least efficient? What makes each more or less efficient?

Once groups have prepared their presentations, choose the order in which groups present to the class. Encourage students to ask questions about what they have seen. Guide a class discussion about the similarities and differences between presentations. Then work together as a class to categorize the energy resources.

Reflect

5 min

Students compare and contrast the energy resources using what they learned in the Investigation Expo.

answers to these questions as a class.

Reflect

1. For each category of resources, what is similar about the energy transformation pathways? For each, what is different?

2. Rank the sources of energy for their overall efficiency in lighting a bulb. Which is most efficient? Which is least efficient? What makes each more or less efficient?

Guide and Assess

Have students describe the categories of energy resources in their own words. Students should explain how energy transformation pathways are similar or different.

1. Students' answers will vary, but all should mention that using fossil fuels, biomass, or nuclear energy all produce steam. After that, the energy pathways are the same. Geothermal energy uses steam directly to generate electricity. Solar energy is directly converted to electric energy, which makes it unique. Wind energy and wave energy are produced by using the natural resource to turn a generator for electricity.

2. Students' answers will vary. Usually, the fewer steps in a process, the more efficient it is.

3. Students' answers will vary based on location. Answers should be based on closeness of the resource, amount of pollution, cost, and renewability.

NOTES

....

....

....

....

....

....

....

3. Knowing what you know now about each of these sources of energy, which would you choose for your community? Why? Which would you want your community to avoid? Why?

Conference

Suppose a small community, located at the seashore far from any big city, is developing plans for an electric power plant. The citizens would like to consider all of the alternative types of energy sources before deciding what type they should use to run their plant. What resource do you think they should use to generate electricity? Consider these issues as you decide on your recommendation:

1. How readily available is the resource to the seashore?

2. How abundant is the resource?

3. How expensive is the resource?

4. What are the possible environmental concerns that may come from using this resource?

5. How appropriate is this resource for the location of the community?

6. Will this resource be available far into the future, or is there a probability that it may run out?

When you have decided on a recommendation, prepare a 3-part poster that describes the energy resource you have chosen. On one panel of the poster, list the advantages of the energy resource. On another panel, list the disadvantages. On the third panel, make a final recommendation about your energy resource for this community. State why you think it is the right resource.

Communicate

Share Your Ideas

When it is your group's turn to present, present your recommendation. Discuss the desirable and undesirable qualities of your energy resource, making sure you address each of the issues you discussed from the questions in your group conference.

EN 303

ENERGY

Conference

20 min

Students work together to propose an energy plan for a small, fictitious community.

⬡ Get Going

Read the situation together. Point out the details provided, such as that the community is small and is located by an ocean. Have groups work together to consider the questions posed. Remind students to use what they have learned about each type of energy resource to make their decisions.

Review the requirements of the poster with students. Remind students to include information to support their recommendations.

Communicate: Share Your Ideas

20 min

Students share their energy recommendations with the class.

Communicate

Share Your Ideas

When it is your group's turn to present, present your recommendation. Discuss the desirable and undesirable qualities of your energy resource, making sure you address each of the issues you discussed from the questions in your group conference.

△ Guide

Allow each group to present their posters. Have each member of the group describe a different part of the poster. After the presentations, identify similarities and differences among the ideas. Lead a discussion to bring the class to some consensus about their ideas. Then decide on the best recommendation.

NOTES

....

....

....

....

....

....

....

....

....

....

After all of the groups have had a chance to present, decide as a class which energy resource would work best for this community, and give good reasons for your choice.

Update the *Project Board*

You have investigated the energy transformations that occur as energy resources are transformed to generate electricity for your home. You have also had an introduction to several different energy resources. Return to the *Project Board* and add your understanding of these ideas to the *What are we learning?* column. Make sure to include a description of the different stages in the chain of energy transformations that connect an energy resource with electricity in a home. Put your evidence, either from your energy transformation diagrams or your reading, in the *What is our evidence?* column.

What's the Point?

People who live near a power plant often do not like having it there because of how it lessens their enjoyment of their local environment. Fossil-fuel plants pollute the air with pollutants that can make it hard to breathe. Hydroelectric dams widen rivers and flood areas behind the dam, sometimes displacing people from their homes. They also affect fish that swim up and down the river past the dams. People who oppose wind and solar farms do not want new transmission lines built in the sparsely populated areas where wind and solar facilities are often placed, or they don't want to look at the wind farms. Wind farms also affect flying birds. But not everyone agrees, because there are always tradeoffs with any energy resource.

How do you think this small, seashore community gets their electricity?

Project-Based Inquiry Science

Update the *Project Board*

5 min

Students add new information about energy transformations involved in electricity production to the Project Board.

△ Guide

Invite the class to describe new information they have learned about energy transformations and energy resources. Add the ideas and evidence to the *Project Board*. Review the questions listed on the board, and discuss any questions that have been answered since they were asked.

Assessment Options

Targeted Concepts, Skills, and Nature of Science	How do I know if students got it?
Some energy resources are renewable, such as wind energy, hydroelectric energy, solar energy, biomass energy, geothermal energy, and tidal energy whereas others are nonrenewable, such as fossil fuel energy and nuclear energy.	**ASK:** What information did you use to make your recommendation for an energy resource to the small community? **LISTEN:** Students should explain their reasoning, such as they chose tidal energy because the community is quite small and is located along the sea.
Energy exists in different forms and can be changed from one form to another.	**ASK:** What were the many different forms of energy you identified in your energy transmission diagram? **LISTEN:** Students should summarize the energy transformations they included.

Teacher Reflection Questions

- What difficulties did students have in identifying the pathway from their energy resources to electricity? How were you able to help them?

- What evidence do you have to show that students recognize that some energy is transformed into heat that is not usable during every energy transformation? What else can you do to reinforce this concept?

- How were you able to get the class to agree on one recommendation for the community? What might you do differently?

Back to the Big Challenge

Design a Rube Goldberg Machine to Turn Off a Light

◀ $1\frac{1}{2}$ *class periods*

A class period is considered to be one 40 to 50 minute class.

Overview

Students relate what they have learned about the law of conservation of energy to efficiency. They think about the steps in a Rube Goldberg machine in terms of efficiency and energy. They then work together to review the steps they have proposed throughout the Unit. This time, however, they compare the steps not only in terms of the types of energy they involve but also in terms of the amount of usable energy they produce. Students then share their ideas and suggestions as a class.

Targeted Concepts, Skills, and Nature of Science	Performance Expectations
Scientists often work together and then share their findings. Sharing findings makes new information available and helps scientists refine their ideas and build on others' ideas. When another person's or group's idea is used, credit needs to be given.	Students work together to decide upon a sequence of steps for their Rube Goldberg machine designs.
Energy exists in different forms and can be changed from one form to another.	Students identify the usable and unusable energy that results from each step in their designs.
Energy is neither created nor destroyed in ordinary processes.	Students apply the law of conservation of energy to evaluate efficiency.

Materials	
1 per student	*My Rube Goldberg Machine* page
	Project Board page

Materials	
1 per class	Class *Project Board*

Homework Options

Reflection

- **Science Content:** Which form of unusable energy was produced in every step of the design? *(Students should recognize that some thermal energy is lost as waste heat in every energy transformation.)*

- **Science Content:** What is the advantage of increasing efficiency? *(Students should explain that increasing efficiency cuts down on the loss of unusable energy, and therefore means that less energy is required at the beginning of the process.)*

NOTES

....

....

....

....

....

....

....

....

....

....

Learning Set 6

Back to the Big Challenge

Design a Rube Goldberg Machine to Turn Off a Light

In *Learning Set 6*, you discovered an important concept. Whenever energy of a particular type seems to disappear, it actually reappears as a different type of energy. The total amount of energy you have at the beginning is the same as the total amount you have at the end. However, some of the energy may not be available to do what you want it to do. This is summarized in the *law of conservation of energy*: Energy cannot be created or destroyed. It can only change form. One of the criteria of the *Big Challenge* is that it should be as energy efficient as possible. To help you think about how to keep your machine energy efficient, you will first think about how you can identify energy efficiency in a Rube Goldberg machine. Then you will analyze the machines you have been designing to identify their efficiency.

Reflect

1. What would it mean for a Rube Goldberg machine to transform energy efficiently? Why?

2. How do you think you can determine how efficient a step in a Rube Goldberg machine is?

3. How do you think you can determine how efficient a whole Rube Goldberg machine is?

Analyze Your Ideas

You are getting close to achieving the criteria of the challenge and designing a machine to turn off a light. You have identified many steps and sequences of steps that can achieve parts of the challenge. Your challenge is to design a machine with at least five steps and at least three energy transformations. In addition, your machine should be as efficient as you can make it. To prepare you for designing a machine that transforms energy efficiently, you will analyze the sequences you have designed up to now and determine the efficiency of each one.

EN 305

ENERGY

Learning Set 6

Back to the Big Challenge

5 min

Students think about the law of conservation of energy.

⭘ **Engage**

Ask students to think about what happens when a light is turned on. Students should recognize that the bulb produces light that they can use to see. Help students to recognize that the bulb also produces thermal energy that is released as heat.

Ask students what they use the heat for. Use this question to make sure students understand that the thermal energy is lost to the environment as "waste" heat. It is not used for a purpose when the light is turned on.

Ask students how the light bulb example shows them something about the law of conservation of energy. Make sure they understand that the electric energy that travels to the light bulb is changed to other forms. No energy is destroyed, even though not all of the energy is changed to a useful form.

Reflect

5 min

Students consider efficiency in terms of a Rube Goldberg machine.

Reflect

1. What would it mean for a Rube Goldberg machine to transform energy efficiently? Why?

2. How do you think you can determine how efficient a step in a Rube Goldberg machine is?

3. How do you think you can determine how efficient a whole Rube Goldberg machine is?

△ Guide and Assess

Have students discuss the *Reflect* questions in their groups. Make sure they recognize that efficiency in a Rube Goldberg machine relates to the amount of energy that is converted to a usable form. The more energy that is converted to a form that is not used to do work, the lower the efficiency of the step is.

1. Students should respond that to use energy efficiently means that wasted energy is minimal. When energy is used efficiently, less is required to accomplish work.

2. Students' answers will vary. They should explain how an efficient step uses nearly 100 percent of the energy available at the beginning of the step.

3. Students should understand that the overall efficiency of the machine is determined by adding up the efficiency of each step. Fewer steps usually means greater efficiency.

Analyze Your Ideas

10 min

Students review all of their ideas for designing a Rube Goldberg machine.

Analyze Your Ideas

You are getting close to achieving the criteria of the challenge and designing a machine to turn off a light. You have identified many steps and sequences of steps that can achieve parts of the challenge. Your challenge is to design a machine with at least five steps and at least three energy transformations. In addition, your machine should be as efficient as you can make it. To prepare you for designing a machine that transforms energy efficiently, you will analyze the sequences you have designed up to now and determine the efficiency of each one.

△ Guide

Tell students to take out their design plans from the Unit. Have them work together in groups to combine the steps and to choose their sequences.

Gather all of the sequences of steps you designed earlier in the Unit. You should have two sequences that involve thermal energy or chemical energy, two sequences that involve light energy or sound energy, and two sequences that involve electrical energy or magnetic energy. Of these, choose two sequences you think you are most likely to use as part of your final design.

1. Analyze each step of each sequence. Record your answers on an *Analysis of Steps* page.

   a) What type or types of energy go into the step? There may be some you have not yet listed.

   b) Where does the energy come from—the previous step of the sequence or somewhere else?

   c) How is energy transformed during the step?

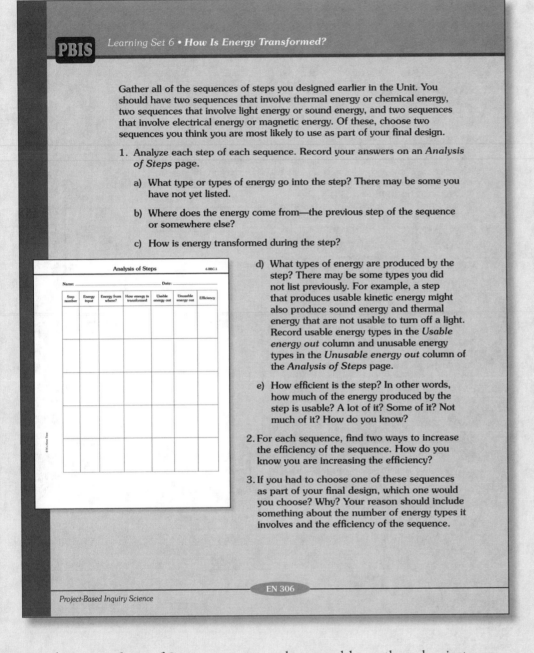

   d) What types of energy are produced by the step? There may be some types you did not list previously. For example, a step that produces usable kinetic energy might also produce sound energy and thermal energy that are not usable to turn off a light. Record usable energy types in the *Usable energy out* column and unusable energy types in the *Unusable energy out* column of the *Analysis of Steps* page.

   e) How efficient is the step? In other words, how much of the energy produced by the step is usable? A lot of it? Some of it? Not much of it? How do you know?

2. For each sequence, find two ways to increase the efficiency of the sequence. How do you know you are increasing the efficiency?

3. If you had to choose one of these sequences as part of your final design, which one would you choose? Why? Your reason should include something about the number of energy types it involves and the efficiency of the sequence.

EN 306

Distribute *Analysis of Steps* pages to students and have them begin to consider the steps of their Rube Goldberg machine. They should use the questions in the student text to guide their analyses and choose what to record on their *Analysis of Steps* pages.

Communicate: Plan Briefing

10 min

Students discuss their proposed sequences for their Rube Goldberg designs with the class.

Communicate

Plan Briefing

When it is your group's turn, present to the class the sequence you chose in *Question 3* of *Analyze Your Ideas*. Show the class your drawing of the sequence of steps. Then present the analysis you did of the steps. Say what type or types of energy go into each step, how they are transformed, what types of energy are produced by each step, and how efficient the step is. Then tell the class your two ways of making the sequence more efficient. Finally, show the class the sequence you did not choose in *Question 3*, and very briefly describe it and say why you chose the other sequence.

As you listen, notice whether you agree with the analyses presented by other groups. If you think they have not been clear enough about the energy transformations that are happening in each step, or if you think they forgot some type of energy, raise your hand and ask a question or offer your advice. Remember to be respectful, even when you are disagreeing.

Record ideas you might want to remember on the bottom of a *My Rube Goldberg Machine* page. Remember to record which group presented each idea. You will want to give credit if you use an idea presented by another group.

Reflect

Answer these questions with your group. Be prepared to discuss the answers with the class.

1. Which two sequences do you think are the most energy efficient? Why?

2. List two things you know about addressing the *Big Challenge* that you did not know before these presentations.

3. Which two steps do you definitely want in your final design? Why?

4. Which steps do you want to avoid in your final design? Why?

ENERGY

△ Guide

Choose the order in which groups will present their ideas. Make sure that each student in the group participates in the presentation. Remind the rest of the class to listen closely so that they can identify flaws or get ideas to help with their own designs.

△ Guide

Ask students to work in their groups to discuss the ideas presented. Have them discuss answers to the questions listed. As you walk around the room, find out if students provide logical reasons for their decisions.

1. Student answers will vary depending on the presentation.

2. Student answers will vary.

3. Student answers will vary depending on their choices. They should be looking for efficiency.

4. Students should want to avoid inefficient steps.

Reflect

10 min

Students work together to review the design ideas presented.

NOTES

Update the Project Board

10 min

Students examine the information on the Project Board.

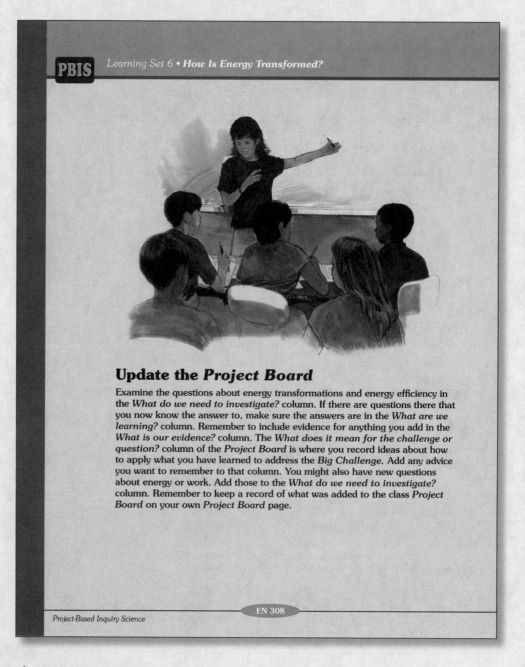

Update the *Project Board*

Examine the questions about energy transformations and energy efficiency in the *What do we need to investigate?* column. If there are questions there that you now know the answer to, make sure the answers are in the *What are we learning?* column. Remember to include evidence for anything you add in the *What is our evidence?* column. The *What does it mean for the challenge or question?* column of the *Project Board* is where you record ideas about how to apply what you have learned to address the *Big Challenge*. Add any advice you want to remember to that column. You might also have new questions about energy or work. Add those to the *What do we need to investigate?* column. Remember to keep a record of what was added to the class *Project Board* on your own *Project Board* page.

Project-Based Inquiry Science   EN 308

△ Guide

Use the *Project Board* to point out that students have come a long way since they first began learning about energy. As a class, discuss any remaining ideas, evidence, and questions and record them in the appropriate columns. Work to tie together the ideas with the *Big Challenge*.

Assessment Options

Targeted Concepts, Skills, and Nature of Science	How do I know if students got it?
Scientists often work together and then share their findings. Sharing findings makes new information available and helps scientists refine their ideas and build on others' ideas. When another person's or group's idea is used, credit needs to be given.	**ASK:** In what ways did you help other students with their designs? **LISTEN:** Students should describe if they identified any flaws or offered any useful suggestions to other groups.
Energy exists in different forms and can be changed from one form to another.	**ASK:** How did you identify the usable energy produced in each step? **LISTEN:** Students should describe identifying the energy that would be used to cause some change in the following step.
Energy is neither created nor destroyed in ordinary processes.	**ASK:** Why were some steps more efficient than others? **LISTEN:** Students should explain that some steps changed more of the original energy into useful energy whereas other steps changed energy into forms that would not be used to do work.

Teacher Reflection Questions

- What evidence do you have that students are synthesizing all of the information they have been learning?

- What evidence do you have that students have a sense of the purpose of the Unit's *Big Challenge?*

- What management issues arose during this section? What ideas do you have for handling them next time?

NOTES

Address the Big Challenge

Design a Rube Goldberg Machine to Turn Off a Light

◀ *2 class periods*

A class period is considered to be one 40 to 50 minute class.

Overview

Students review the goal of the *Big Challenge* and revise the criteria and constraints based on what they have learned throughout the Unit. They pull together the many pieces of the design that they have proposed to develop a final sequence of steps that will result in turning off a light. They share their designs with the class, accept input from other students, and then revise their designs one final time. With all of their evidence in place, students then present their final Rube Goldberg machine designs.

Targeted Concepts, Skills, and Nature of Science	Performance Expectations
Scientists often work together and then share their findings. Sharing findings makes new information available and helps scientists refine their ideas and build on others' ideas. When another person's or group's idea is used, credit needs to be given.	Students review and critique each other's designs to offer suggestions and identify flaws.
Scientific knowledge is developed through observations, recording and analysis of data, and development of explanations based on evidence.	Students use the notes and plans they have been developing throughout the Unit to develop a final design for the *Big Challenge*.
Criteria and constraints are important in determining effective scientific procedures and answering scientific questions.	Students revise the criteria and constraints for the *Big Challenge*, and adjust their final designs accordingly.

Materials	
1 per student	*My Rube Goldberg Machine* page *Project Board* page
1 per class	Class *Project Board*

Homework Options

Reflection

- **Science Process:** How is it possible that different groups came up with different final designs? *(Students should discuss that energy can be transformed in many different ways. As long as the students used the transformations to achieve the same goal—turning off a light—they can use many different designs.)*

- **Science Process:** What changes did you make to your list of criteria and constraints? Upon what did you base the changes? *(Students should describe incorporating new ideas from the readings and the Plan Briefings into their criteria and constraints.)*

NOTES

Address the Big Challenge

Design a Rube Goldberg Machine to Turn Off a Light

You now know enough about energy and energy transformations to design your own Rube Goldberg machine. Like Rube Goldberg's machines, yours will involve a series of complicated steps to do something very simple. Your machine will pull a cord or flip a switch to turn off a light. You have already identified several possible last steps for your machine and the types of energy that might be transformed to power each of those last steps. You have also generated a lot of ideas about sequences of steps that can be used to turn off a light. However, you have not yet designed a sequence of steps that can fulfill all of the criteria and constraints of the challenge. It is now time to design the sequence of steps that can fulfill these criteria and constraints.

Remember that the challenge has several criteria and constraints. Because you will be working with sketches and not really building the machine, there is no limitation on the costs or types of materials you can select. However, each individual step in your machine must be logical, be capable of working, and must initiate the next step. Your machine must have at least five steps, and it must transform at least three different types of energy. You must also report on the efficiency of your machine. The less energy it needs to do its work, the better. There is one more thing. Your machine cannot be dangerous. For example, it can use fire in some steps, as long as the fire is contained. However, it cannot blow anything up. Your machine must be designed so that you would be willing to stand in the same room with it if it were built.

A solar calculator transforms several different types of energy to do the work of calculating math problems.

EN 309

ENERGY

Address the Big Challenge

Design a Rube Goldberg Machine to Turn Off a Light

5 min

Students prepare to complete their final Rube Goldberg designs.

⚠ Guide

Let students know that they will now develop their final designs. They will use all of the ideas they have proposed, interpret them in terms of the criteria and constraints, and decide upon a final design.

*A class period is considered to be one 40 to 50 minute class.

727

Revise the Criteria and Constraints

10 min

Students identify the criteria and constraints of the Big Challenge.

PBIS

You will have a chance to work on two *iterations* of your design. An iteration is the repetition of a process in order to make something better over time. You will present the first iteration to the class. The class may give you ideas about how to make your design better. Then you will have time for a second iteration. Your design will have to fulfill the criteria and constraints, and you will also need to describe to the class how your machine transforms energy and how efficient it is.

Revise the Criteria and Constraints

Before you get started on your final design, restate the challenge in your own words. Then review the criteria and constraints you identified earlier in the Unit. If they need to be revised, do that now. Remember that criteria are conditions that must be satisfied to achieve the challenge, and that constraints are factors that limit how you can solve the problem. Below is a chart with some of the criteria and constraints filled in. Work together as a class to complete the chart.

Criteria	Constraints
Machine must have at least five steps.	Machine must not be dangerous.
Machine must use at least three types of energy.	
Machine must turn off a light.	

Plan Your Design

Throughout this Unit, you have been doing some planning for your design. Each time you learned about a new type of energy, you gave thought to how it might be transformed in your machine. Learning about energy transformations gave you the chance to think about how different energy types might be transformed, how much of each might be available before and after an energy transformation, and how this could work in the design of your machine.

△ Guide

Have students work in their groups to describe the criteria and constraints in their own words. They should begin by going over the list of criteria and constraints they already identified and revising them as necessary. They have learned a lot since they first identified criteria and constraints, and they may need to add criteria and constraints to their lists. Then work together as a class to complete the chart provided.

△ Guide

When student groups have completed their lists of criteria and constraints, let them know that they will now begin planning designs to accomplish the *Big Challenge.* Go over the questions with the class, emphasizing that these questions will help them develop their ideas. Emphasize that students should use their drawings, other notes, earlier designs, and their books to answer the questions.

Plan Your Design

20 min

Students develop their final designs.

NOTES

You have many resources you can use for ideas. You have *Energy Types* pages and *Energy-transformation Cartoon* pages. You also have *My Rube Goldberg Machine* pages. All of these have ideas about energy transformations you might use in your design. Your class has also created a class list of possible steps and their energy transformations. And in the last *Learning Set*, you identified steps and sequences of steps you might want to use in your design. You also have notes from each of the *Plan Briefings*.

It is now time to pull together all that you have done in the earlier planning stages of your design. Work as a group to design a sequence of steps that achieves the criteria of the *Big Challenge* without violating the constraints. Use your *Energy Types* pages, *Energy-transformation Cartoon* pages, *My Rube Goldberg Machine* pages, and *Analysis of Steps* page from *Learning Set 6* to help you.

When you have a sequence of steps you like, sketch your proposed machine on a *My Rube Goldberg Machine* page, and mark each step with the following information.

- What work does the step do?

- What energy does the step transform? If there is any energy that does not come from the previous step, be sure to mark it in.

- How does the step transform its energy, and what types of energy does it produce?

- Show unusable energy from each step flowing out of the machine. Show usable energy from each step flowing into the next step.

- Where do you anticipate any problems occurring?

Now analyze your machine. See if there are steps where you can adjust something to make the step work more efficiently or more accurately. You may see a place where another energy transformation could be added. If so, now is the time to put it in. You will have one more opportunity to make revisions to your machine, and if something does not work logically, it can be changed. However, it will be much harder to add something later than to add it now.

☐ Assess

As groups discuss the questions, monitor their progress. Ask them what ideas they have discussed and whether they have considered alternatives.

PBIS

Revise your sketch and the labels on each step if you change anything. Then analyze your machine again. Which steps do you have questions about? Which energy transformations do you have questions about? You will soon be presenting to the class, and when you do, you will have a chance to ask the class for advice. It would be a good idea, too, to make sure your sketch is neat and clear enough for others to be able to follow what you are proposing. Put your sketch on poster paper so it can be displayed to the class.

Communicate

Plan Briefing

When you are planning a design, the expertise of others can be helpful. The purpose of this *Plan Briefing* is to get advice from your classmates about how to make your machine even better. This means you must present it well enough so your classmates can understand your ideas. As a presenter, you will learn the most from this *Plan Briefing* if you can be specific about your design plans and about why you made your design decisions.

Groups will take turns making presentations. When it is your turn, show your sketch, and make sure to answer the following questions:

- What are the steps in your machine?

- Where does each step get its energy? What type or types of energy does the step transform? What energy transformations will occur in each step? What types of energy does each step produce?

- How do the different parts of the machine work together to achieve the criteria?

- What have you done to increase the efficiency of your machine, and what else do you think you might do to increase its efficiency?

- Are there any problems you think might occur with this design?

- What do you predict will happen when you use the machine to turn off a light?

- What, if anything, do you need help with?

EN 312

Project-Based Inquiry Science

Communicate:
Plan Briefing

20 min

Students present their designs in the Plan Briefings.

⚠ Guide

Explain to students that they will be presenting their designs to get feedback from other students. Ask groups to review the list of questions provided. Tell them that they need to address all of these questions in their presentations. Once they are ready, have each group present their design. Encourage students who are listening to ask questions, provide suggestions, and identify any flaws in the design. Model the kinds of questions they should be asking.

Revise Your Design

20 min

Students revise their designs.

As a listener, you will provide the best help if you ask probing questions about things you do not understand. Be polite when you point out errors and misconceptions in the reasoning of others. These kinds of conversations will allow other listeners to learn, as well. For each presentation, if you are not sure you understand the answers to the *Plan-Briefing* questions, make sure to question your classmates. When you ask them to clarify what they are telling you, you can learn more. They can learn, too, by trying to be more precise. Also, be generous with your advice. Do the best you can to help other groups design a smooth-working, energy-efficient machine.

Use another *My Rube Goldberg Machine* page to record any ideas you want to remember from the presentations.

Revise Your Design

Remember that an iteration is the repetition of a process in order to make something better over time. Designers use iterations to improve their designs. Each time they test a design, they usually find a way to make it better. Each change and the resulting new design are called an iteration.

You may still have ideas about how to make your design better, or your classmates may have asked you questions that tell you that you have more work to do.

EN 313

ENERGY

△ Guide

Give students an opportunity to work in their groups to revise their designs based on the feedback they received or ideas they may have developed by listening to other groups. Emphasize that the sketch and labels should be as detailed as possible. Point out that the materials list must also be descriptive.

PBIS

Revise your design so you are satisfied that it could turn off a light if you built it. Use any ideas you received from the class in the *Plan Briefing* to improve on or to add more steps to your design.

Sketch your revised design on a new *My Rube Goldberg Machine* page. Do your best to make high-quality sketches that clearly show how your machine will work.

Label your sketch the way you labeled the previous version. Then develop a materials list to go with your finished design.

Communicate Your Design

Plan Showcase

You will present your final design to the class in a *Plan Showcase*. Because this is your final product, you will not be asking for help. Instead, you will be presenting a summary of your plan for turning off a light and telling the class how you arrived at this plan. You will also describe why you think this is a good design. Use the science you have learned to support why you designed your machine the way you did. This will help you better understand the science of energy.

To make an interesting and informative presentation, create a poster to showcase your plan. Your poster should include the following information.

- a clear sketch of your machine
- labels for each step of the machine that show:
  - the energy types and the energy transformations involved,
  - energy that is produced by each step, including which types are usable and which are not,
  - indicators for each type of energy you transform,
  - factors that affect each type of energy you transform, and
  - steps where energy is lost or seems to disappear, and where it goes.

EN 314

Communicate Your Design: *Plan Showcase*

20 min

Students present their designs in a Plan Showcase.

△ Guide

Once students have finished revising their designs, let them know they will present their final designs to the class by making a poster. Highlight the information the *Plan Showcase* should convey about the design itself, the process they used, and the students involved in the group.

- a chart that shows how you arrived at your final design. Include, for example, answers to these questions. What problems or questions did you have earlier? What did you do to address those questions? Why did you do those things? How did understanding the science of energy help you make your design better?

Use the following guidelines to help you in your presentation.

- Include the names of your group members.

- Briefly describe the challenge and how you chose the last step in your machine to turn off a light.

- Show your sketch, and walk the class through each step. Help the class understand the energy transformations in each step and how energy from each step flows into the next step. Tell them the factors that affect how much energy each step produces and how you controlled those factors.

- Consider the efficiency of your machine. Which step is the most efficient in transferring energy? Which step is the least efficient? Why? Discuss the overall efficiency of your machine.

- Report the science you used to make your machine more efficient or to control the energy in each step.

Listening to the presentations of others will provide you with chances to see different ways machines can use a series of energy transformations to perform a simple task. Make sure you understand how each machine works and the reasoning behind each design. How did other groups use energy transformations the same way your group did? How did other groups use energy transformations differently than your group did? Which energy transformations were most popular in the class? Why?

Reflect

1. Select one good idea from another group's machine design. What are the advantages of this design idea? What is the difference between how this group included energy transformations and how your group did?

2. Looking overall at the machines the class designed, are there any that are energy efficient? Do you think a Rube Goldberg machine can be energy efficient? Why or why not?

EN 315

ENERGY

◯ Get Going

Once groups have prepared their posters, have each group briefly make their presentation. Remind students to review all of the information they are presenting and make sure it addresses all of the questions provided. The other students have now seen the designs in earlier stages, so each group may want to point out any recent changes they've made and explain their reasoning.

☐ Assess

Assess students' skill in sharing ideas, asking questions, and responding to peers. Look for whether you can easily follow the design and whether students support their designs with evidence.

⬡ Get Going

Have students meet back with their groups to discuss the presentations. Tell them to answer the questions with their group, focusing on the advantages of another group's design and the differences between their design, and the energy efficiency of the Rube Goldberg machines.

Reflect

5 min

Students discuss the Rube Goldberg machine designs of other groups.

NOTES

Update the Project Board

5 min

Students add new information to the Project Board.

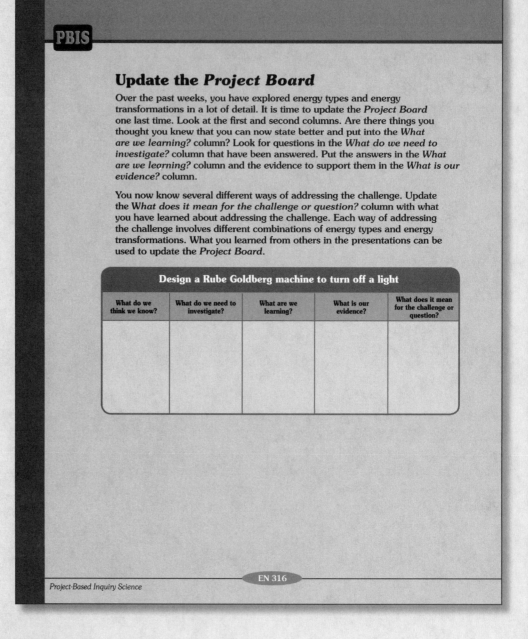

PBIS

Update the *Project Board*

Over the past weeks, you have explored energy types and energy transformations in a lot of detail. It is time to update the *Project Board* one last time. Look at the first and second columns. Are there things you thought you knew that you can now state better and put into the *What are we learning?* column? Look for questions in the *What do we need to investigate?* column that have been answered. Put the answers in the *What are we learning?* column and the evidence to support them in the *What is our evidence?* column.

You now know several different ways of addressing the challenge. Update the *What does it mean for the challenge or question?* column with what you have learned about addressing the challenge. Each way of addressing the challenge involves different combinations of energy types and energy transformations. What you learned from others in the presentations can be used to update the *Project Board*.

Design a Rube Goldberg machine to turn off a light				
What do we think we know?	What do we need to investigate?	What are we learning?	What is our evidence?	What does it mean for the challenge or question?

△ Guide

Review the information on the *Project Board*. Work as a class to change any ideas that have been corrected or replaced. Identify all questions that have been answered or topics that have been investigated. Identify information that was shared among students in the class.

Assessment Options

Targeted Concepts, Skills, and Nature of Science	How do I know if students got it?
Scientists often work together and then share their findings. Sharing findings makes new information available and helps scientists refine their ideas and build on others' ideas. When another person's or group's idea is used, credit needs to be given.	**ASK:** How did you find it helpful to present your preliminary designs to the class? **LISTEN:** Students should describe that it gave them opportunities to figure out if they needed to add more detail, change a step, or provide additional evidence.
Scientific knowledge is developed through observations, recording and analysis of data, and development of explanations based on evidence.	**ASK:** How was it important to keep clear records of preliminary designs and ideas? **LISTEN:** Students should describe how they used their ideas from the previous sections to develop their final design, and it was important that they be able to understand what they had done already.
Criteria and constraints are important in determining effective scientific procedures and answering scientific questions.	**ASK:** In what ways did the criteria and constraints affect your final design? **LISTEN:** Students may describe steps they had to eliminate because they did not adhere to the criteria and constraints.

Teacher Reflection Questions

- What difficulties did students have synthesizing all of the ideas they learned in this Unit in developing their final design? What could you do to make this easier next time?

- How were you able to help students improve their final designs? What can you do to help them in the future?

- How were you able to engage students in asking questions and discussing groups' *Plan Briefings?* What might you try next time?

NOTES

ENERGY

Blackline Masters

Energy Blackline Masters

* Number indicates Learning Set.section.sequence within section

Energy Types

0.0.1/1.2.2/2.5.2/2.6.2/
3.2.2/3.6.2/4.5.2/5.1.3/5.5.1

Name: _____ Date: _____

Type of energy	Indicators that this type is being transformed	Factors that affect the amount of energy

Name: _____ **Date:** _____

As you watch the videos, identify all the different ways energy is transformed.

Video #1: Record your observations of when and where you see evidence of energy and any work being done.

Video #2: Record your observations of when and where you see evidence of energy transformations and any work being done.

Energy-transformation Cartoon

0.0.3/1.BBC.1/3.BBC.1/
4.1.2/4.BBC.1/5.1.2/6.3.1

Name: _____ **Date:** _____

Fill in the letter of the step you are analyzing. Then fill in other information about that step.

Name of your machine:		Purpose of your machine:		
Step	Changes/Work done	Energy type in	Energy types out	Indicators of energy transformations

Record questions about anything on which your group does not agree and anything you do not understand.

Name: _____ Date: _____

Conditions	Observations	Causes

Conditions in or near the radiometer	Predictions	Observations
1. Flashlight is held very close to the radiometer and shined on it for 1 min.		
2. Flashlight is held 2 m from the radiometer and shined on it for 1 min.		
3. Flashlight is held 2 m from the radiometer then moved toward the radiometer and back again.		

Energy Observations

1.2.1/2.1.1

Name: _____ Date: _____

Object	Observation of how the object works	Indicator	Type(s) of energy

My Rube Goldberg Machine

Name: _____ Date: _____

Sketch of machine. Label each step with a number.

Step	Description of step	Energy Type(s) In	Energy Type(s) Out	Work done
1				
2				
3				
4				
5				

Use this space to record ideas.

Name: _____ **Date:** _____

Run #	Mass of cart and weight	Speed of cart	Predicted smoosh	Actual smoosh
1	250 g	4 km/hr		
Question 1	What does the dent produced in the ball of clay mean?			
Question 2	How do you think the dent in a ball of clay can be used to measure the kinetic energy of the cart?			
Question 3	How do you think you might be able to change the kinetic energy of the cart?			
2	750 g	4 km/hr		
3	250 g	12 km/hr		

Name: _____ **Date:** _____

Your question:

Your prediction:

Your independent (manipulated) variable:

Your dependent (resulting) variable:

Instructions for how to conduct the experiment:

Elastic Energy Explorations

Name: _____ **Date:** _____

Set 1 Items transforming elastic energy	Indicator	Factors	Set 2 Items not transforming elastic energy	Indicator
1.			1.	
2.			2.	
3.			3.	
4.			4.	
5.			5.	
6.			6.	

Thermal Energy in Water

Name: _____ Date: _____

	Beaker A or C Bag A or C	Beaker B or D Bag B or D	Unlabeled bag
Prediction			
Volume			
Initial temperature			
Time to melt			
Temperature after 5 min			
Temperature after 10 min			
Temperature after 15 min			

Name: _____ **Date:** _____

For Your Group:			
	= Your tablet size ($\frac{1}{4}$, $\frac{1}{2}$, $\frac{3}{4}$, or 1 tablet)		
	Height	Distance	Your prediction:
Trial 1			
Trial 2			
Trial 3			
Trial 4			
Trial 5			

For your Class:

Film Canister Launches (Average Data)

	($\frac{1}{4}$ tablet)		($\frac{1}{2}$ tablet)		($\frac{3}{4}$ tablet)		(1 tablet)	
	Height	Distance	Height	Distance	Height	Distance	Height	Distance
Group 1								
Group 2								
Group 3								
Group 4								
Group 5								
Group 6								
Group 7								
Group 8								
Class average								

Name:_____ Date:_____

Use this page to explain the lesson of your recent investigations.

Write a brief summary of the results from your investigation. You will use this summary to help you write your explanation.

Claim—a statement of what you understand or a conclusion that you have reached from an investigation or a set of investigations.

Evidence—data collected during investigations and trends in that data.

Science knowledge—knowledge about how things work. You may have learned this through reading, talking to an expert, discussion, or other experiences.

Write your explanation using your Claim, Evidence and Science knowledge from above.

Name: _____ Date: _____

	Sound Energy	Light Energy
Examples of sound energy and light energy		
Indicators that energy is present		
Factors that affect how much energy an object possesses		
What I am not sure about		

Name: _____ **Date:** _____

Race data				
Race Number	Winner	Winning time	Factors changed	Other observations
1				
2				
3				
4				
5				
6				
7				
8				

Summary of observations

Wave speed	Wave reflection

Effect of Distance and Source Brightness on Light Intensity

Name: _____ **Date:** _____

Light source	Distance to wall (cm)	Area illuminated at wall (cm²)	Intensity rating (scale of 1 to 10)
25–W bulb	25		
	50		
	100		
60–W bulb	25		
	50		
	100		
flashlight	25		
	50		
	100		

Electricity and Magnetism Observations

Name: _____ Date: _____

	Electrical energy	Magnetic energy
Sketch		
Observations of forces that can do work		
Observations related to distance		
Observations related to direction		
Indicators		

Name: _____ Date: _____

	Lemon battery	Generator
Factors affecting amount of energy generated		
Construction difficulties		
Advantages		
Disadvantages		
Common features		

Energy Resources Pros and Cons

Name: _____ Date: _____

Energy resource	Type of energy	How its energy is transformed into electricity	Pros	Cons
Wind energy				
Hydroelectric energy				
Solar energy				
Fossil fuels				
Trash and biomass				
Tidal energy				
Geothermal energy				

Transforming My Energy Resource

Name: _____ **Date:** _____

	What I found	Where I found this information
Availability—where is it found, and how much is there?		
Environmental consequences of transforming my resource into electrical energy		
Preparing this resource to generate electricity		
Transforming my resource into electrical energy. What is hard? What is easy? What do scientists still need to learn?		
Cost		
Other advantages		
Other disadvantages		

Name: _____ Date: _____

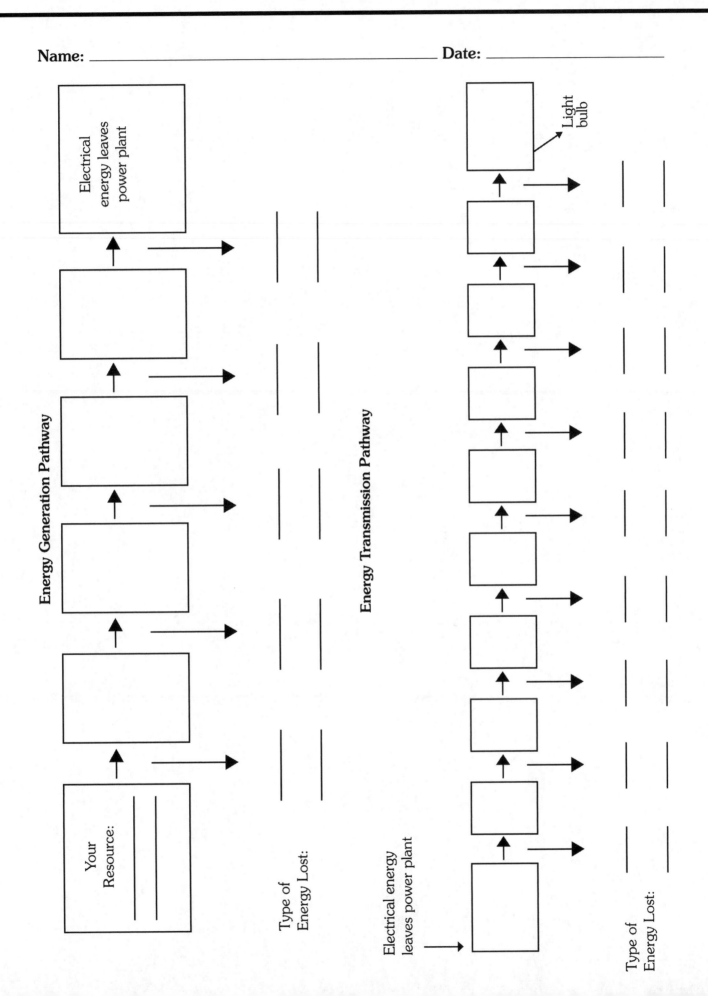

Name: _____ **Date:** _____

Step number	Energy input	Energy from where?	How energy is transformed	Usable energy out	Unusable energy out	Efficiency

Project Board

Name: _____ Date: _____

What do we think we know?	**What do we need to investigate?**	**What are we learning?**	**What is our evidence?**	**What does it mean for the challenge or question?**

IT'S ABOUT TIME ®
HERFF JONES EDUCATION DIVISION

84 Business Park Drive, Armonk, NY 10504
Phone (914) 273-2233 Fax (914) 273-2227
www.its-about-time.com

Publishing Team

President
Tom Laster

Director of Product Development
Barbara Zahm, Ph.D

Creative Director
John Nordland

Managing Editor
Maureen Grassi

Production/Studio Manager
Robert Schwalb

Project Development Editor
Ruta Demery

Layout
Sean Campbell

Project Manager
Sarah V. Gruber

Illustrator
Dennis Falcon

Writer
Christine Caputo

Technical Art/Photo Research
Sean Campbell
Doreen Flaherty
Michael Hortens
Marie Killoran
Louise Landry
Cora Roman
MaryBeth Schulze

Editor, Student Edition
Nomi Schwartz

Editors, Teacher's Planning Guide
Kelly Crowley
Gary Hickernell
Nomi Schwartz

Pre-press
Rich Ciotti

Equipment Kit Developers
Dana Turner
Henry J. Garcia

NOTES

NOTES

NOTES

NOTES

NOTES

NOTES

NOTES

NOTES

NOTES

NOTES